Workbook

Impuls Deutsch 2

Intercultural | Interdisciplinary | Interactive

Niko Tracksdorf
Petra Volkhausen
Birgit Jensen
Steffen Kaupp
Friedemann Weidauer

Ernst Klett Sprachen
Stuttgart

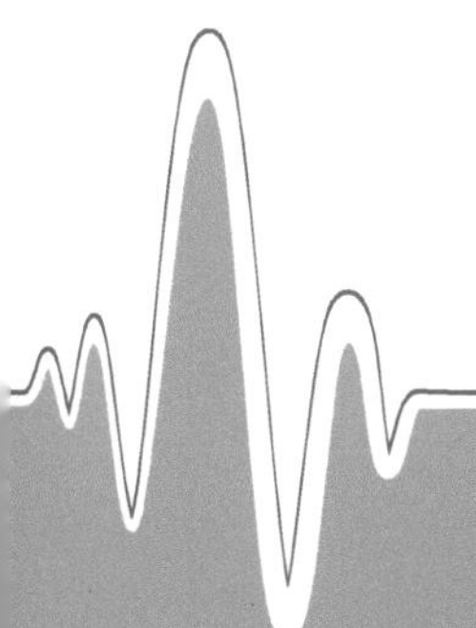

Herausgeber Niko Tracksdorf
Authors Niko Tracksdorf, Petra Volkhausen, Birgit Jensen, Steffen Kaupp, Friedemann Weidauer

Guest Authors / Focus Groups Nicole Coleman (Chapters 1–8), Kyle Frackman (Kulturpunkt: Queer Germany), Joela Jacobs (Chapters 5–7), Priscilla Layne (Chapters 4–7), Maria Reger (Chapters 1–8), Didem Uca (Chapters 5–7), Margrit Zinggeler (Chapter 3)

Consultants Lauren Brooks, Michael Byram, Stine Eckert (East-West), Katharina Häussler-Gross, Joela Jacobs (Diversity and Inclusion), Natasha Kelly (Diversity and Inclusion), Judith Keyler-Mayer (Grammar), Hartmut Rastalsky (Chapter 1), Kristina Reardon (English Language), Jennifer Redmann, Daniel Schoppen (Roller Coasters), Renae Watchman (Unit 95: Indigenous Peoples)

Phonetics Ulrike Trebesius-Bensch
Extended Reading Gabi Baier (*Gefährliches Spiel in Essen, Verschollen in Berlin*), Roland Dittrich (*Der Schützenkönig vom Chiemsee*), Cordula Schurig (*Kalt erwischt in Hamburg, Die Lerche aus Leipzig*), Stefanie Wülfing (*Böses Erwachen in Heidelberg*)

Redaktion Maria Reger (Print), Ingrid Scholz (Print, LMS)
Glossary Editors Christina Wirth, Torsten Lasse
Project Manager Rebecca Mehne
Prepress Claudia Stumpfe
Design/Layout Niko Tracksdorf
Cover Design Andreas Drabarek
Typesetting Markus Dollenbacher, Satzkasten, Stuttgart
Vocabulary Lists Isabel Choinowski, Niko Tracksdorf
LMS (blink) Niko Tracksdorf, Bolin Ai

Authors and publisher would like to thank our consultants, the many colleagues (and students) who tested *Impuls Deutsch 2* in their classrooms, and our interns, who all offered invaluable suggestions and input during the development of the book. In addition to our official consultants named above, this includes (among others) Bolin Ai, Maureen Gallagher, Norbert Hedderich, and Shawna Rambur.

The audio and video material in this book can be downloaded and played by using the Klett Augmented app.

Install and open the free Klett Augmented app. | Start *Bilderkennung* and scan the **pages with audio and video.** | Download audio and video and play immediately or save for later.

Scan this page for further components belonging to this book.

Audio and video files for download at www.klett-usa.com/impuls
Code: ImDe%S2c
To purchase the online reader of your choice, visit www.klett-usa.com/Impuls2Readers
Add code: ID2+RE50 for a 50% discount at checkout.

1. Auflage 1 4 3 2 | 2023 22 21

Printed in Germany by Elanders GmbH, Waiblingen

Workbook:
ISBN 978-3-12-**605304**-4

How to Use the Workbook

Learning a new language is certainly one of life's most rewarding experiences. Over time, your new skills will become like a set of tools that will set you apart on your career path and make travel more enjoyable. But beyond these superficial and immediate benefits, growing your competence in a foreign language will change you. You will learn to connect with new people and places—from the past and present—in deeper, more meaningful ways. You will become not merely a passive recipient of new knowledge, but you will also become able to actively engage with worlds that were previously closed to you.

Impuls Deutsch takes a unique, progressive approach to the teaching and learning of German. It is written from the stance that the best way to learn a language is to use it actively. This means that you will work with your classmates to complete meaningful, content-based tasks, designed to promote communication and critical thinking. In order to maximize the amount of time spent on active language practice, *Impuls Deutsch* introduces new grammar and vocabulary *prior* to class, freeing up valuable class time for you to work effectively with your instructor and classmates *in* class.

Accepting responsibility for your own learning is integral to your future success in learning German. You should not expect to attend a "lecture" where you will be "taught" how to speak German. You must study the material before class, and come to class prepared. This book provides you with a variety of exercises along the way, among them also drills and memorization. However, the primary goal of this book is to help you evaluate, synthesize, and apply material at a higher cognitive level, designed to make learning German engaging.

Being prepared for class will give you a sense of accomplishment and confidence, allowing you to experiment, take risks, and play with the language you are learning. This agency is key for engaging with your classmates and instructor as you figure out what works and what doesn't. You will be able to make the most of opportunities to do something with the information presented, to interact with it, and use it to complete tasks and solve problems.

This chart explains how to use the components of *Impuls Deutsch*:

Phase	When?	What?	Why?
1	Before class	LERNEN	studying, learning, preparing
2	During class	MACHEN	doing, making, performing
3	After class	ZEIGEN	showing, demonstrating, reinforcing, reflecting

Your instructor will assign specific exercises from LERNEN that will prepare you for MACHEN. Following that, you will complete the unit in ZEIGEN. For the next class, the phases start over again.

To help you stay on track between components, the numbering of exercises in LERNEN and ZEIGEN always corresponds to a specific activity in the course book MACHEN. For example:

LERNEN	MACHEN	ZEIGEN
2a, 2b, 2c	2	2d, 2e, 2f, 2g

Before starting with LERNEN, look over the corresponding unit in MACHEN and ZEIGEN to get a sense of what you are preparing for and what kinds of activities you will be involved in. Next, look over the vocabulary list for your unit (given at the start of each chapter), which is also available to you via the vocabulary training platform Quizlet.

LERNEN provides the tools to build a solid foundation for the active work you will be doing in the course book, including work with grammar, pronunciation, and vocabulary. You will need to learn and practice these structures regularly to make progress on your comprehensive language skills (speaking, listening, reading, writing). Your instructor will assign activities in ZEIGEN that will allow you to revisit and/or reflect on the material you covered in class.

We wish you all the best on your journey to continue learning German. It is exciting to have you on board as an *Impuls Deutsch* student, entering our community of learners who share in the fun and accomplishment of speaking German. Always remember that making mistakes is essential to (and a normal feature of) language learning—it's a part of risk-taking that will reward you throughout your life!

Niko Tracksdorf *Petra Volkhausen* *Birgit Jensen* *Steffen Kaupp* *Friedemann Weidauer*

TUTORIAL: GENDER-INCLUSIVE LANGUAGE

0a The Gender Star

As you have learned throughout your work with *Impuls Deutsch* so far, nouns for people are gendered in German. You get to the feminine form by adding ***-in*** to the masculine form, e.g. *der Lehrer – die Lehrer**in**, der Chef – die Chef**in***, etc.

Often, and especially in the plural forms, the masculine words are used to refer to both men and women, which has been criticized by both feminist and queer activists. Studies, in fact, show that the generic masculine word is most often associated with men. For example, when somebody says that *der Arzt* will come soon, people picture a male doctor. Language can thus reinforce patriarchal structures in society.

A longstanding practice is to spell out both words for female and male persons, e.g. *die Lehrerinnen und Lehrer*. This, however, keeps the binary of male and female alive and does not leave space for those who neither identify as male nor female. The gender star (*Lehrer*in)* creates a visual representation of the spectrum of possible gender identities.

In *Impuls Deutsch*, we use the gender star or gender-neutral nouns to refer to people. In the glossary, you will also find a gender-neutral alternative with every gendered noun that refers to people. You will not have to memorize all of these forms (choose the ones that are most relevant to you), but we recommend you consciously acknowledge them. You may also consult resources such as a gender-inclusive online dictionary, which you can find at the link for this activity at www.klett-usa.com/impuls2links. Resources like this dictionary allow you to be more creative with your language, and help you challenge gender-binary, normative language use.

Let's first stay with the gender star and then address gender-neutral nouns as well as alternatives and workarounds later.

0b Wie spricht man das? Das Gendersternchen wird als kurze Pause ausgesprochen. Zum Beispiel: Mechaniker...in oder Ärzt...innen. Sprechen Sie die Nomen mit kurzen Pausen.

Lehrer*in	Student*in	Sänger*in	Ärzt*in
Freund*innen	Professor*innen	Maler*innen	Pilot*innen

0c Grammatik entdecken I: Read the examples, and describe in English how the gender-neutral version with the gender star is formed out of the masculine and feminine forms. Also explain how you can infer the masculine and feminine forms when only given the gender star version of a noun.

Nominativ:	der Lehrer, die Lehrerin	→	der*die Lehrer*in
Akkusativ:	den Lehrer, die Lehrerin	→	den*die Lehrer*in
Dativ:	dem Lehrer, der Lehrerin	→	dem*der Lehrer*in
Nominativ:	der*die Tänzer*in	→	der Tänzer, die Tänzerin
Akkusativ:	den*die Tänzer*in	→	den Tänzer, die Tänzerin
Dativ:	dem*der Tänzer*in	→	dem Tänzer, der Tänzerin

Explain how you get from the masculine and feminine forms to the gender star version:

____

____

____

Explain how you get from the gender star version to the masculine and feminine forms:

____

____

____

0d **Das Gendersternchen: Bilden Sie die Gendersternchen-Form für die gegenderten Nomen.**

der Professor, die Professorin ___der*die Professor*in___
der Freund, die Freundin ______________________
der Direktor, die Direktorin ______________________
der Schüler, die Schülerin ______________________
der Architekt, die Architektin ______________________
der Musiker, die Musikerin ______________________
der Maler, die Malerin ______________________
der Schauspieler, die Schauspielerin ______________________
der Polizist, die Polizistin ______________________
der Präsident, die Präsidentin ______________________
der Pilot, die Pilotin ______________________
der Fotograf, die Fotografin ______________________
der Friseur, die Friseurin ______________________

0e **Grammatik entdecken II: Manchmal verlieren wir grammatische Informationen durch das Gendersternchen. Sehen Sie sich die Beispiele an und füllen Sie die Lücken aus.**

der Koch / die Köchin → der*die Köch*in

der Arzt / die Ärztin → der*die Ärzt*in

der Jude / die Jüdin → der*die Jüd*in

der Bauer / die Bäuerin → der*die Bäuer*in

Wenn die maskuline Form keinen Umlaut hat, aber die feminine Form schon, sieht man in der Gendersternchen-Variante ______________ (einen | keinen) Umlaut. Man sieht also nicht leicht, was die ______________ (maskuline | feminine) Form ist.

der Sänger / die Sängerin → der*die Sänger*in

der König / die Königin → der*die König*in

Aber nicht alle Umlaute deuten auf dieses Problem hin. Bei Sänger*in und König*in gibt es den Umlaut bei ______________ (beiden | keiner) binären Form(en).

Note: When masculine and feminine forms differ, it is inevitable that some grammatical information will be omitted. When you see the gender star form *Köch*in*, for example, you might infer that the masculine form is *der Köch*. Therefore, you should pay close attention to gender star forms with *Umlaut* and check the glossary if you are unsure about the singular masculine forms.

Maskulinum Plural	Femininum Plural	Gendersternchen Plural
die Freund**e**	die Freundin**nen**	die Freund*innen
die Lehrer	die Lehrerin**nen**	die Lehrer*innen
die Pilot**en**	die Pilotin**nen**	die Pilot*innen

Der Plural von femininen Personen ist meistens ______________ (regelmäßig | unregelmäßig). Hier hängt man normalerweise ______________ (-nen | -innen) an. Der Plural von maskulinen Personen ist ______________ (regelmäßig | unregelmäßig). Hier gibt es ______________ (verschiedene | zwei) Pluralformen. Die maskulinen Endungen ______________ (sieht man | sieht man nicht) in der Gendersternchen-Pluralform.

Note: As a basic principle, the plural gender star forms will omit the masculine plural endings. Therefore, you need to check the glossary if you are unsure about the correct endings for the masculine plural forms.

	Maskulinum	Femininum	Gender-neutral
Nom.	Wer ist der Pilot?	Wer ist die Pilot**in**?	Wer ist der*die Pilot***in**?
Akk.	Ich treffe den Pilot**en**.	Ich treffe die Pilot**in**.	Ich treffe den*die Pilot***in**.
Dat.	Ich glaube dem Pilot**en**.	Ich glaube der Pilot**in**.	Ich glaube dem*der Pilot***in**.

Wenn die ______________ (maskuline | feminine) Form zur sogenannten n-Deklination gehört (das heißt, das Nomen bekommt im Singular Akkusativ, Dativ und Genitiv eine n-Endung), dann sieht man diese Information in der Gendersternchen-Form ______________ (-- | nicht).

Note: As you know, we need to add an *-n* to the dative plural forms of nouns, e.g. *die Lehrer* (*nom.*) → *den Lehrern* (*dat.*). Since gender star forms end in *-n* anyways, you won't see this grammatical information either, e.g. *die Lehrer*innen* (*nom.*) → *den Lehrer*innen* (*dat.*).

0f Gender-Neutral Nouns and Alternatives

While the *Gendersternchen* offers a visual representation of the spectrum of gender identities, in German you can also use neutral forms that avoid gendering altogether. Some gender-neutral nouns have become very common in everyday usage. *Studierende*, for example, has widely replaced the gendered form *Student/Studentin*. There are others that follow the same pattern. Other alternatives are also common, but they don't follow this pattern, e.g. *Lehrkraft*.

In cases where no single gender-neutral noun exists, there are different ways of using gender-neutral alternatives. You can simply use a relative clause to describe what a person does. For example, *Aktivist*in* could be described as *eine Person, die politisch aktiv ist*. Similarly, *der*die Bäcker*in* is *eine Person, die beruflich Brot backt*.

To shorten things a bit, the relative clauses can also be replaced by extended adjective constructions with the present participle. (You will learn about this grammatical concept in chapter 8. For now, you can memorize these gender-neutral options when you see them in the vocabulary list or glossary.) Using this construction, *Bäcker*in* could be expressed as *eine Brot backende Person*.

0g **Was ist was? Bestimmen Sie, ob die Wörter maskulin, feminin oder gender-neutral – im Singular oder im Plural – sind?**

	m	f	gn	Sg.	Pl.
der*die Student*in			X	X	
die Arbeiterinnen					
die Gründer					
die Ingenieurinnen					
der Student					
die Jüd*innen					
die Rentnerin					
die Reporter*innen					
der Zuschauer					

	m	f	gn	Sg.	Pl.
die Künstler					
der Jude					
die politisch aktiven Personen					
die Regisseurin					
die Studierenden					
die singende Person					
der*die Veganer*in					
die protestierenden Personen					
die Protagonistin					

0h **Vor- und Nachteile von den drei Optionen. Sortieren Sie die Vor- und Nachteile zu den drei Möglichkeiten der gender-inklusiven Sprache.**

Option	Vorteil	Nachteil
1 Gendersternchen	leicht zu benutzen, weil es ein Wort für alle ist	manchmal umständlich (*cumbersome*), nicht immer präzise oder äquivalent
2 gender-neutrales Nomen	visuelle Repräsentation von non-binären Identitäten, man kann oft die maskulinen und femininen Formen erkennen	Es gibt sie nicht für alle Wörter.
3 gender-neutrale Alternative	Es gibt sie für alle Wörter.	Manchmal gehen grammatische Informationen verloren. Es ist schwieriger für non-binäre Personen, sich selbst zu benennen.

0i **Glossar-Übung: Im „English-German"-Glossar von „Impuls Deutsch 2" gibt es für alle Nomen, die Personen beschreiben, eine gender-neutrale Alternative. Suchen Sie im Glossar für die folgenden Wörter jeweils die maskuline und feminine Form sowie die gender-neutrale Alternative.**

Englisch	Maskulinum	Femininum	Gender-neutrale Form
advisor	*der Berater*	*die Beraterin*	*die beratende Person*
consumer			
participant			
liar			
boss			
owner			
employee			
producer			

0j **Wie sprechen wir über ...? Schreiben Sie die korrekten Wörter zu den Situationen. Schauen Sie im Glossar nach und checken Sie auch die korrekten Pluralformen.**

You are talking about two **professors** who identify as female. You refer to them as: *zwei* ______________________________. You identify as male and you are talking about your **Jew**ish identity. You say: *Ich bin (ein)* ______________________________. You are traveling and talk about three of your **fellow travellers**; two identify as non-binary and one as male. You refer to them as: *meine* ______________________________. You are talking about a dubbed version of a movie, and you are unsure how the **dubbing artist** identifies. You refer to them as: ______________________________. You are talking politics with a friend and you are talking about the two male **candidates**. You refer to them as: *die zwei* ______________________________. You identify as non-binary and you tell somebody that you are a **poet**. You say: *Ich bin (ein)* ______________________________. You are talking about the other **students** in your German class. There are so many that you don't know how everyone identifies. You call them ______________________________. You are going to a physics conference. You don't know whether a female, male, or non-binary **physicist** will be the keynote speaker. You refer to the person as ______________________________. You want to invite one **speaker** for a student conference. To be inclusive, you refer to the speaker as ______________________________.

Inhalts-verzeichnis

Kapitel 1: Was war da los? Ost-West-Geschichte(n)

Kapitel 2: Wer würde sich trauen? Achterbahnen ...

Kapitel 3: Wie wird das gemacht? Die Schweiz als Herstellerin ...

KAPITEL 4: WIE LEBEN WIR NACHHALTIG? KOMMUNIKATION ...

KAPITEL 5: WER SIND WIR? DEUTSCH IM PLURAL

KAPITEL 6: WIE UNTERHALTEN WIR UNS? ALTE UND NEUE MEDIEN

Kapitel 7: Wofür/Wogegen sind wir? Protest, Widerstand, Mitbestimmung

Kapitel 8: Was prägt uns? Transatlantische Beziehungen und Einflüsse

Symbols

Listen. *Impuls Deutsch 2* includes more than 150 audio files for practicing your listening and pronunciation skills. Access the files with the Klett Augmented app or visit www.klett-usa.com/impuls2resources.

Watch. Whenever you see this symbol, you will be asked to watch a video. You can do this either with the Klett Augmented app or by visiting www.klett-usa.com/impuls2resources.

Research. Whenever you see this symbol, you are asked to do online research on a given topic. We encourage you to use German versions of websites, such as wikipedia.**de** (not **.com**).

Write. You will write reflective blog entries to share your thoughts and opinions about some of the topics featured in *Impuls Deutsch 2*. If you use the blended or online bundle, you will submit your reflections via BlinkLearning (check with your instructor in case they have another submission preference).

Speak. In each chapter, you will record yourself speaking German. If you use the blended or online bundle, you will share your recordings with your instructor using BlinkLearning (check with your instructor in case they have another submission preference).

Quelle: **Authentic Texts.** A short source is quoted under each authentic text. Full text sources and copyright information can be found at the back of the book on page N-3.

Lernen
Machen
Zeigen

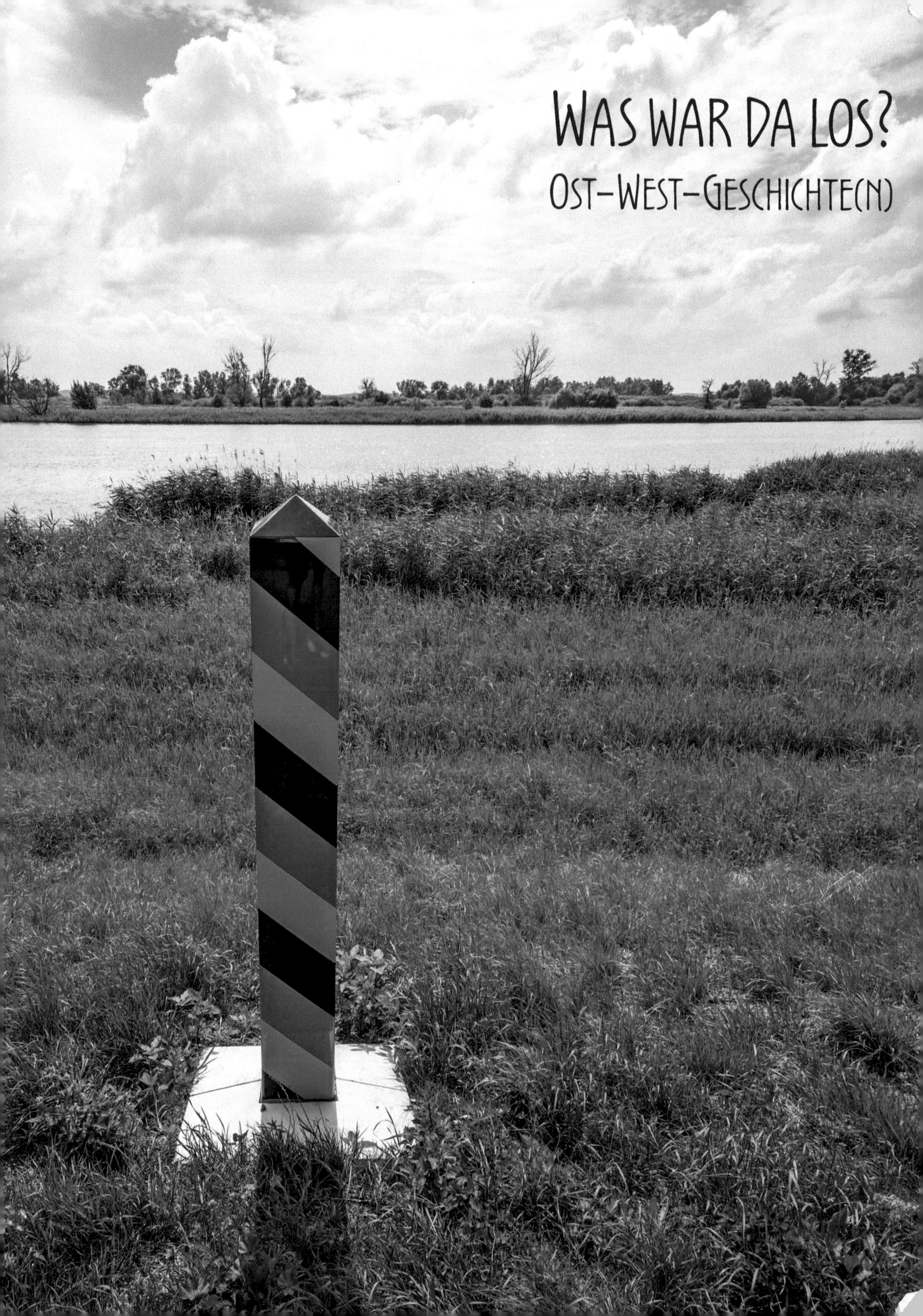

Was war da los?

Ost-West-Geschichte(n)

WORTSCHATZ

1: DEUTSCHE GESCHICHTE(N)

der Weltkrieg, ⸗e	world war
der Bau	construction
die Mauer, -n	wall (*structure made of bricks*)
die Gründung, -en	foundation, founding
die Bundesrepublik Deutschland (BRD)	Federal Republic of Germany (FRG)
die Deutsche Demokratische Republik (DDR)	German Democratic Republic (GDR)
der Aufstand, ⸗e	uprising, rebellion, revolt
die Einheit, -en	unity; unit
die Wiedervereinigung, -en	reunification
der Tag der Deutschen Einheit	German Unification Day
der Präsident, -en	president (*male*)
die Präsidentin, -nen	president (*female*)
das Staatsoberhaupt, ⸗er	head of state (*gender-neutral alternative for president*)
die Botschaft, -en	embassy; message
der Vertrag, ⸗e	contract; treaty
schließen, schloss, hat ... geschlossen	to close, shut
einen Vertrag schließen, schloss, hat ... geschlossen	to enter into an agreement / a contract
die Rede, -n	speech
eine Rede halten (hält), hielt, hat ... gehalten	to give/deliver a speech
die Grenze, -n	border; boundary
ein·tragen (trägt ... ein), trug ... ein, hat ... eingetragen	to enter (*e.g. into a list*)
erleben, erlebte, hat ... erlebt	to experience
der Bezirk, -e	district
überlegen, überlegte, hat ... überlegt	to think (about)
das Gefühl, -e	feeling
dar·stellen, stellte ... dar, hat ... dargestellt	to depict, represent

Weitere Wörter: einander (each other); **sich (*akk.*) ab·wechseln, wechselte ... ab, hat ... abgewechselt** (to take turns); **die Studierendendemonstration, -en** (student demonstration); **osteuropäisch** (Eastern European); **der Staat, -en** (state); **demonstrieren, demonstrierte, hat ... demonstriert** (to demonstrate); **der Eiserne Vorhang** (Iron Curtain); **aus·reisen, reiste ... aus, ist ... ausgereist** (to leave (a country)); **relevant (für + *akk.*)** (relevant (for)); **zu dieser Zeit** (during this time); **der Kalte Krieg** (Cold War); **die Krise, -n** (crisis); **gesichert** (secured); **die Emotion, -en** (emotion); **zeichnen, zeichnete, hat ... gezeichnet** (to draw)

3: GETEILTES BERLIN

der Pass, ⸗e	passport
bauen, baute, hat ... gebaut	to build
teilen, teilte, hat ... geteilt	to divide; share
bestehen (aus + *dat.*), bestand, hat ... bestanden	to consist (of)
einzeln	single
die Sicherheit, -en	safety, security; certainty
der Weg, -e	path
das Gebäude, -	building
dienen (zu + *dat.*), diente, hat ... gedient	to serve (as)
verhindern, verhinderte, hat ... verhindert	to prevent
sperren, sperrte, hat ... gesperrt	to block
versichern, versicherte, hat ... versichert	to ensure
warnen (vor + *dat.*), warnte, hat ... gewarnt	to warn (of)
zeigen, zeigte, hat ... gezeigt	to show
die Flucht, -en	escape
die Freiheit, -en	freedom
fliehen, floh, ist ... geflohen	to flee
verlassen (verlässt), verließ, hat ... verlassen	to leave
bleiben, blieb, ist ... geblieben	to stay
gelingen, gelang, ist ... gelungen	to succeed
an·wenden, wendete/wandte ... an, hat ... angewendet/angewandt	to apply, make use of
das Gefängnis, -se	prison
wählen, wählte, hat ... gewählt	to pick, choose; vote
regieren, regierte, hat ... regiert	to govern
die Partei, -en	party (*political*)
das Mitglied, -er	member

Weitere Wörter: bedeuten, bedeutete, hat ... bedeutet (to mean; matter); **die Leute (*pl.*)** (people); **der Zufall, ⸗e** (coincidence); **führen (zu + *dat.*), führte, hat ... geführt** (to lead (to)); **die Trennung, -en** (division; separation); **der Zaun, ⸗e** (fence); **die Sperre, -n** (barrier; blockage); **der Graben, ⸗** (trench); **die Trasse, -n** (line); **sich (*akk.*) in Gefahr begeben (begibt), begab, hat ... begeben** (to put oneself in danger); **vergleichen, verglich, hat ... verglichen** (to compare); **gehören (zu + *dat.*), gehörte, hat ... gehört** (to belong (to)); **die Meinungsfreiheit, -en** (freedom of speech/opinion); **die Pressefreiheit, -en** (freedom of press)

4: KINDHEIT IM OSTEN UND WESTEN

gründen, gründete, hat ... gegründet	to establish, found
der Verein, -e	club; association
bevor	before
während (+ *gen.*)	while, during
nach (+ *dat.*)	after
dort	there
teil·nehmen (an + *dat.*) (nimmt ... teil), nahm ... teil, hat ... teilgenommen	to participate (in)
die Behörde, -n	local authority, government office (*administration*)

trotzdem	nevertheless
Sie macht es trotzdem.	She does it nevertheless.
verhaften, verhaftete, hat ... verhaftet	to arrest
sich (*akk.*) beteiligen (an + *dat.*), beteiligte, hat ... beteiligt	to take part, participate (in)
die Gewalt	violence
treten (auf + *akk.*) (tritt), trat, ist ... getreten	to step (on)

Weitere Wörter: existieren, existierte, hat ... existiert (to exist); **verwenden, verwendete, hat ... verwendet** (to use); **heraus·finden, fand ... heraus, hat ... herausgefunden** (to find out); **der Zeitraum, ⸚e** (period, stretch of time); **die Ecke, -n** (corner); **der erste Eindruck, ⸚e** (first impression); **der Gründer, -** (founder (*male*)); **die Gründerin, -nen** (founder (*female*)); **die gründende Person, die Gründenden** (founder (*gender-neutral alternative for founder*)); **unterstellen, unterstellte, hat ... unterstellt** (to allege); **aus·bürgern, bürgerte ... aus, hat ... ausgebürgert** (to denaturalize, expatriate); **Rücksicht nehmen (auf + *akk.*) (nimmt), nahm, hat ... genommen** (to be considerate (of)); **fort·führen, führte ... fort, hat ... fortgeführt** (to continue)

5: „Zwischen uns die Mauer"

schriftlich	written, in writing
mündlich	verbal(ly), oral(ly)
verrückt	crazy
irgendwie	somehow
traurig	sad
leer	empty
endlich	finally
auf·hören, hörte ... auf, hat ... aufgehört	to stop
verlieren, verlor, hat ... verloren	to lose
hoffen, hoffte, hat ... gehofft	to hope
der Traum, ⸚e	dream
hören, hörte, hat ... gehört	to hear
sich (*akk.*) fühlen, fühlte, hat ... gefühlt	to feel
Ich fühle mich heute fantastisch!	I'm feeling fantastic today!
die Beziehung, -en	relationship
damals	back then
Damals war es schöner.	It was nicer back then.

Weitere Wörter: Zeit verlieren, verlor, hat ... verloren (to lose time); **aus·suchen, suchte ... aus, hat ... ausgesucht** (to choose); **zusammen·wachsen (wächst ... zusammen), wuchs ... zusammen, ist ... zusammengewachsen** (to grow closer); **engstehend** (close together); **hilflos** (helpless); **die Zeile, -n** (line); **aus·reichen, reichte ... aus, hat ... ausgereicht** (to last; suffice); **funktionieren, funktionierte, hat ... funktioniert** (to work; function)

7: Chancengleichheit?

die Chancengleichheit, -en	equality of opportunities
die Gleichberechtigung, -en	equal rights, equality
gleichberechtigt	having equal rights
die Bedingung, -en	condition
die Mehrheit, -en	majority
das Geschlecht, -er	sex; gender
die Meinung, -en	opinion
die Einschätzung, -en	estimate, evaluation
vermuten, vermutete, hat ... vermutet	to assume, suppose, guess
die Wirklichkeit, -en	reality
das Gesetz, -e	law
die Veränderung, -en	change
um Erlaubnis fragen, fragte, hat ... gefragt	to ask permission
verbieten, verbot, hat ... verboten	to prohibit
fortschrittlich	progressive, advanced
genauso	just the same
sich (*akk.*) kümmern (um + *akk.*), kümmerte, hat ... gekümmert	to take care (of)
sich (*akk.*) fertig machen, machte, hat ... gemacht	to get ready
dauern, dauerte, hat ... gedauert	to take, last
einen Termin aus·machen, machte ... aus, hat ... ausgemacht	to schedule an appointment
sauber machen, machte, hat ... gemacht	to clean up
begründen, begründete, hat ... begründet	to reason
kämpfen (für + *akk.*), kämpfte, hat ... gekämpft	to fight (for)

Weitere Wörter: die Kindererziehung (parenting; child education); **basieren (auf + *dat.*), basierte, hat ... basiert** (to be based (on)); **die Schwangerschaft, -en** (pregnancy); **ab·treiben, trieb ... ab, hat ... abgetrieben** (to abort); **berufstätig** (employed); **geschlechtergerecht** (gender-fair); **die geschlechtergerechte Sprache** (gender-fair language); **unverheiratet** (single, not married); **ledig** (single); **das Äquivalent, -e** (equivalent); **die Aufmerksamkeit, -en** (attention); **schaffen, schuf, hat ... geschaffen** (to create)

8: Vertrags- und Gastarbeit in der DDR und BRD

die Alliierten (*pl.*)	allies
die Wirtschaft, -en	economy
der Gastarbeiter, -	guest worker (*male*)
die Gastarbeiterin, -nen	guest worker (*female*)
die Gastarbeitskraft, ⸚e	guest worker (*gender-neutral alternative*)
auf·bauen, baute ... auf, hat ... aufgebaut	to establish; construct
genug	enough
brauchen, brauchte, hat ... gebraucht	to need
steigen, stieg, ist ... gestiegen	to rise, increase
die Heimat, -en	home (*country/region*)
zurück·gehen, ging ... zurück, ist ... zurückgegangen	to return, go back
der Rassismus	racism
die Autorin, -nen	author (*female*)

der Autor, -en	author (*male*)
die schreibende Person, die Schreibenden	author (*gender-neutral alternative*)
der Regisseur, -e	director (*male*)
die Regisseurin, -nen	director (*female*)
die Regie führende Person, die Regie führenden Personen	director (*gender-neutral alternative*)
der Roman, -e	novel
die Rezension, -en	review
empfehlen (empfiehlt), empfahl, hat ... empfohlen	to recommend

Weitere Wörter: das Abkommen, - (treaty; agreement); **ursprünglich** (original(ly), initial(ly)); **die Fremdenfeindlichkeit, -en** (xenophobia); **handeln (von + *dat.*), handelte, hat ... gehandelt** (to deal (with)); **die Webseite, -n** (website); **bevorzugen, bevorzugte, hat ... bevorzugt** (to prefer)

9: Die Wende

die Wende [hist.: Wiedervereinigung Deutschlands]	turning point [hist.: German reunification]
erlauben, erlaubte, hat ... erlaubt	to permit
die Ausreise, -n	departure
sofort	immediately
auf·machen, machte ... auf, hat ... aufgemacht	to open
offen	open
der Grenzübergang, ¨-e	border checkpoint
lassen (lässt), ließ, hat ... gelassen	to let
ungültig	invalid
rufen, rief, hat ... gerufen	to call, exclaim
das Tor, -e	gate
der Offizier, -e	officer (*male*)
die Offizierin, -nen	officer (*female*)
die Person, -en mit Offiziersrang	officer (*gender-neutral alternative*)
der Soldat, -en	soldier (*male*)
die Soldatin, -nen	soldier (*female*)
das Mitglied, -er der Streitkräfte	soldier (*gender-neutral alternative*)
die Stasi (Staatssicherheitsdienst)	Stasi (*State Security of the GDR*)
beobachten, beobachtete, hat ... beobachtet	to observe
laut	loud
leise	quiet
wieder	again
die Nationalhymne, -n	national anthem
die Verfassung, -en	constitution
die Freude, -n	joy, delight
jubeln, jubelte, hat ... gejubelt	to cheer
die Aufregung, -en	excitement
das Leiden, -	suffering
die Spannung, -en	tension

Weitere Wörter: die Entscheidung, -en (decision); **entscheiden, entschied, hat ... entschieden** (to decide); **melden, meldete, hat ... gemeldet** (to report, announce); **erfolgen, erfolgte, ist ... erfolgt** (to occur); **klettern, kletterte, ist ... geklettert** (to climb); **spazieren gehen, ging, ist ... gegangen** (to go for a walk); **tanzen, tanzte, hat ... getanzt** (to dance); **achten (auf + *akk.*), achtete, hat ... geachtet** (to pay attention (to)); **ängstlich** (afraid); **wütend** (angry); **die Beobachtung, -en** (observation)

11: Wer wir sind

die Identität, -en	identity
sich (*akk.*) identifizieren (als + *nom.*), identifizierte, hat ... identifiziert	to identify (as)
Ich identifiziere mich als Europäerin.	I identify as a (*female*) European.
die Umgebung, -en	environment, surroundings
die Gemeinschaft, -en	community
die Gesellschaft, -en	society
entwickeln, entwickelte, hat ... entwickelt	to develop
unterscheiden, unterschied, hat ... unterschieden	to differentiate
die Gegend, -en	region, area
die Erinnerung, -en	memory; reminder
die Medien (*pl.*)	media
das Unrecht	injustice
erinnern (an + *akk.*), erinnerte, hat ... erinnert	to recall, remember; remind

Weitere Wörter: die Diskriminierung, -en (discrimination); **die Befreiung, -en** (liberation); **breit** (wide, broad)

12: „Good Bye, Lenin!" und „Das Leben der Anderen"

die Komödie, -n	comedy
das Drama, Dramen	drama
dramatisch	dramatic(ally)
schlimm	severe, sad
der Schriftsteller, -	writer (*male*)
die Schriftstellerin, -nen	writer (*female*)
die schriftstellerisch tätige Person, die Schreibenden	writer (*gender-neutral alternative*)
erwarten, erwartete, hat ... erwartet	to expect
der Blick, -e	view
der Einfluss, ¨-e	influence
schützen, schützte, hat ... geschützt	to protect
überwachen, überwachte, hat ... überwacht	to surveil, observe
spionieren, spionierte, hat ... spioniert	to spy
der Nachbar, -n	neighbor (*male*)
die Nachbarin, -nen	neighbor (*female*)
die benachbarte Person, Benachbarten	neighbor (*gender-neutral alternative*)
die Nachbarschaft,-en	neighborhood
die Auswertung, -en	evaluation

Weitere Wörter: der Thriller, - (thriller); **der Eindruck, ¨-e** (impression); **der Befehl, -e** (order)

4a Temporal Prepositions: *im, am, um*

In both English and German, times are usually indicated by a preposition and a noun (in the morning, at 5 p.m., etc.).

You already know frequent forms like *im Sommer, am Montag, am Abend, um 7 Uhr.*
In spite of the similarity of the two languages, the prepositions do not line up, so they can't be translated directly. However, German is fairly consistent when it comes to temporal prepositions. It sorts them by unit or rather the "size"/duration of the unit.

larger units of time = ***im***		
such as centuries	**im** 20. Jahrhundert	*in the 20th century*
and years	**im** Jahr(e) 1945	*in the year 1945*
but:	— 1945	*in 1945*
seasons	**im** Winter	*in winter*
months	**im** Mai	*in May*
units on the day level = ***am***		
like specific dates	**am** 8. Mai	*on May 8th*
days	**am** Montag	*on Monday*
and time of day	**am** Nachmittag	*in the afternoon*
exact time of day = ***um***	**um** 12:15 Uhr	*at 12:15 p.m.*

Note: The preposition *in* (that signals larger units of time) is also used for less precise periods of time like *im Krieg, in der Nachkriegszeit, in der Kindheit, in den Ferien.*

As you know and see in some of the examples, *im* is not the actual preposition but the contraction of *in + dem = im. In* and *an* as temporal prepositions are always followed by the dative case. Since most time units are in fact masculine, most often you will see *im* and *am*. Here is what this looks like for all genders:

der Abend	an dem = **am** Abend
das 19. Jahrhundert	in dem = **im** 19. Jahrhundert
die Nacht	**in der** Nacht (no contraction)
die Ferien (*pl.*)	**in den** Ferien (no contraction)

4b Sven erzählt von seinem Sommerurlaub auf Sylt. Ergänzen Sie „im" oder „am".

____ Sommer mietet meine Familie manchmal ein Haus auf der norddeutschen Insel Sylt. Das beste Wetter gibt es ____ Juli oder ____ August. Wir waren auch ____ letzten Jahr auf Sylt. ____ August sind wir angekommen und dreißig Tage später sind wir wieder nach Hause gefahren. Wir hatten eine tolle Routine: ____ Morgen sind wir alle sehr früh aufgestanden. Wir sind mit unseren Fahrrädern an den Strand gefahren und erst ____ Nachmittag zurückgekommen. Zum Abendessen haben wir ____ Montag immer Krabben gegessen, ____ Mittwoch rote Grütze und ____ Freitag Hering. Und ____ Abend sind wir oft ins Kino gegangen oder haben Karten gespielt. Wie ist es wohl ____ Winter auf Sylt? Ist es sehr windig und kalt? Schneit es? ____ kommenden Jahr werden wir mit der Bahn nach Italien fahren. Wir haben eigentlich immer viel Familienspaß in der Urlaubszeit!

Rote Grütze, ein norddeutsches Dessert

4c When Did This Happen? How to Read the Date

In German, the full date is given in the order: **day.month.year**

While May 8, 1945 would be written in American English as 5/8/1945, in German it is written as 08.05.1945—not to be confused with August 5! As you can see, the units are divided by slashes in American English and by periods in German.

First, we will look at how to express the day on which something happened.

German dates—the specific day as well as the month—are expressed with ordinal numbers and will often be preceded by *am*, meaning "on."

Wann warst du in Berlin?	*When were you in Berlin?*
→ **Am** 21.05. (= am einundzwanzigsten Fünften)	→ *On the twenty-first of May.*

Ordinal numbers following the preposition *am* are constructed
a) by adding -*ten* for numbers under 20,
b) by adding -*sten* for 20 and above.

am 01.01.	am 1. Januar	am **ers**ten Januar
am 02.05.	am 2. Mai	am zweiten Mai
am 03.07.	am 3. Juli	am **drit**ten Juli
am 06.06.	am 6. Juni	am sechsten Juni
am 07.05.	am 7. Mai	am **sieb**ten Mai
am 21.02.	am 21. Februar	am einundzwanzigsten Februar

Note the **small deviations** when forming the ordinal numbers of **01**, **03**, and **07**.

4d

Elias (14) hat vor einem Monat in seiner Schule zu den achtziger Jahren und der deutsch-deutschen Geschichte recherchiert. Er und seine Familie besuchen Elias' Großonkel Jochen (82), der in der DDR gelebt hat. Ergänzen Sie „am" und die Ordinalzahlen im Brief.

Lieber Onkel Jochen,

ich freue mich, dass wir dich __am dritten__ (3.) Oktober in Neuruppin besuchen. Das ist natürlich der Tag der Deutschen Einheit und du kannst uns viel von der DDR erzählen. Ich möchte gerne wissen, wo du __dreizehnten__ (13.) August 1961 warst, als man begann, die Berliner Mauer zu bauen. Hat man mit dir darüber gesprochen? Ich weiß, dass Tante Irmtraud __neunundzwanzigsten__ (29.) Juli 1961 in den Westen geflüchtet ist. Hast du deine Schwester sehr vermisst? Hast du sie wirklich erst __neunten__ (9.) November 1989 wiedergesehen? Das ist so eine lange Zeit! Onkel Jochen, kennst du die Rockmusiker David Bowie und Bruce Springsteen? Mama war __sechsten__ (6.) Juni 1987 in Westberlin, als David Bowie direkt an der Mauer sang. Mama erzählte, dass auch die Bowie-Fans im Osten dieses Konzert hörten und es wilde Randale in Ostberlin gab. Eine Woche später, __zwolften__ (12.) Juni 1987, sagte der US-amerikanische Präsident Ronald Reagan zum sowjetischen Generalsekretär Michail Gorbatschow: „Mr. Gorbachev, tear down this Wall!" Ein Jahr danach gab Bruce Springsteen __neunzehnten__ (19.) Juli 1988 ein Konzert in Ostberlin. Bruce im Osten! Gut, dass wir erst __einsundzwanzigsten__ (21.) Oktober von Neuruppin nach Hause fahren. So kannst du uns viel über dein Leben im Osten erzählen. Ich bin super gespannt!

Liebe Grüße und bis bald
dein Großneffe Elias in Stuttgart
(Besuch uns doch auch mal!)

Neuruppin ist eine kleine Stadt im östlichen Bundesland Brandenburg.

4e When Did This Happen? How to Read the Year

Now let's add how to read the year.

As in English, if the year is 2000 and later you just read it as a normal number, all in one word.

2019	zweitausendneunzehn	*two thousand nineteen*

Again like in English, if the year is between 1100 and 1999 the reading follows a different pattern, using *hundert*:

1848	achtzehnhundertachtundvierzig	*eighteen hundred forty eight*
1989	neunzehnhundertneunundachtzig	*nineteen hundred eighty nine*

Remember that the number of the year in German (unlike in English) is NOT preceded by any preposition:

Der Krieg war **1945** zu Ende.	*The war ended in 1945.*
Die Mauer ist **1989** gefallen.	*The wall came down (fell) in 1989.*
1963 hat John F. Kennedy Berlin besucht.	*In 1963, John F. Kennedy visited Berlin.*

You may add the phrase *im Jahr …* to avoid that pitfall. Though quite common in written German, it is rather uncommon in the spoken language.

Im Jahr 1963 hat John F. Kennedy Berlin besucht.	*In 1963, John F. Kennedy visited Berlin.*

4f Daten rund um die Berliner Mauer. Präposition oder nicht? Korrigieren Sie die Jahresangaben, wie im Beispiel.

Beispiel: ~~In~~ 1960 gab es noch keine Mauer in Berlin.

In 1960:
Circa 200.000 Menschen flüchteten aus der DDR. 150.000 von ihnen flohen im Jahr 1960 von Ostberlin nach Westberlin, denn da gab es eine offene Grenze.

Juni bis August 1961:
Immer mehr Menschen flüchteten in 1961 aus dem Ostsektor nach Westberlin. Zwischen Januar und Juli in 1961 waren es fast 135.000. 50 % von diesen Geflüchteten waren junge Leute unter 25 Jahren. Im Juli 1961 gab es die meisten Geflüchteten seit Juni 1953. Besonders im Jahr 1961 hatten die DDR-Politiker*innen Angst vor einer Wirtschaftskrise, weil viele Facharbeiter*innen und Akademiker*innen flohen.

In 1989:
Am 8. März in 1989 wollte Winfried Freudenberg (32 Jahre alt) mit einem selbstgebastelten Heißluftballon nach Westberlin fliegen. Der Ballon stürzte ab und Freudenberg starb. Er war das letzte Todesopfer – nur acht Monate, bevor die Mauer fiel.

1961–1989:
390 Menschen starben an der Grenze oder beim Grenzübergang. 18 DDR-Bürger*innen starben in 1962. Ungefähr 5.000 Leute konnten fliehen. 57 Menschen flohen in 1964 durch einen Tunnel unter der Berliner Mauer (der Tunnel heißt jetzt „Tunnel 57"). Manchmal wollten ganze Familien fliehen. Im Jahr 1988 paddelte die Familie Kostbade (Mutter, Vater und zwei Kinder) in einem Gummiboot in den Westen.

Manchmal gingen Geflüchtete auch wieder in den Osten zurück, weil sie vom Westen desillusioniert waren.

2: OST-WEST-PERSPEKTIVEN ZUM 17.06.1953°

 **Reflektieren: Die DDR und die BRD im Kontext. Lesen Sie den Text und reflektieren Sie über eine der beiden Fragen.**

The Cold War was basically an ideological tug of war between the West (the U.S. and its allies) and the East (the Soviet Union and its allies). Both sides interpreted events very differently, which influenced the way they talked about them and how they set policies. Let me give you a few examples that have to do with the two German states, the Federal Republic of Germany (FRG = West) and the German Democratic Republic (GDR = East).

The FRG assumed that it was the only legitimate successor state of the German Empire, which meant the West-German government didn't recognize the GDR as a country until 1972. It also resulted in a policy called *Alleinvertretungsanspruch*, which means that the FRG thought it was the only legitimate representation of all Germans. Based on this claim, East Germans could get a FRG passport if they applied for one in West Germany or at a West German embassy. While the border between East and West Germany was secured quickly after the founding of both states, West Berlin became a backdoor into West Germany. Though the city of Berlin was entirely on GDR territory, the West part of the city was under the FRG's administration. So East Germans could walk into the Western part of the city and apply for a West German passport there. This is one of the reasons that the GDR would eventually build a wall to stop migration and the brain drain they experienced because of it. The fact that the FRG didn't recognize the GDR as a country could also be seen in common parlance because the GDR was often called the Soviet Zone to underscore the fact that it was a Soviet occupied part of Germany rather than its own sovereign state. This policy only changed in the 1970s under Chancellor Willy Brandt, who began diplomatic relations with the GDR in order to find a way for West and East Germans to visit each other.

The GDR also saw the FRG as a successor state—but of the Third Reich. As a successor state of Hitler's Germany, the FRG was often called "fascist" in East German news. In fact, denazification in the West was not complete, as many administrative positions were held by those who had also been in these positions during the Third Reich. In the 1960s, this led to student protests in the West. Students challenged the older generation about their involvement in Nazi crimes, which was the beginning of a process of coming to terms with the past that is still ongoing. In the East, because the GDR saw itself as socialist and thereby automatically resistant to Nazi Germany, neither denazification nor coming to terms with the past happened. The Berlin Wall would become known as the "anti-fascist protective barrier" (*Antifaschistischer Schutzwall*), trying to paint it not as a way of keeping people in but rather of keeping West German fascists out.

Similarly, the event that you will learn about in MACHEN was interpreted very differently. Here are a few pieces of background information. The GDR's economic system was a planned economy, which means that the state estimates the needs of the consumers and plans what and how much needs to be produced. In contrast, a capitalist economy is ruled by supply and demand, and the state interferes very little (the West German system of *Soziale Marktwirtschaft*, social market economy, is a capitalist system in which the state interferes to provide a social safety net). When the East German government changed its economic plan in June 1953 and increased the quota that workers then had to achieve, East German workers protested. These protests spread throughout the GDR and were interpreted by the West as a political uprising. At the same time, the East maintained that the West had paid people to provoke and to instigate these protests to undermine the East German government. How the event, one of the most important of German post-war history, was commemorated or talked about in both parts of Germany differed widely.

Have you learned about the Cold War in school? If so, what did you learn? Do you think there is a perspective that you didn't learn about?

or

What do you know about Russia? How is Russia represented in the news media, in history classes, or political science courses? Do you think there may be a perspective that you are not hearing?

12a *Präteritum:* Overview

We have already learned two grammatical tenses for describing things that happened in the past in German:

> ***Perfekt***, which you already know and which we will review later in this chapter,
> and
> ***Präteritum***, of which you already know the forms for *haben* (→ *hatte*) and *sein* (→ *war*) and for the modal verbs (→ *konnte, wollte, musste, durfte, sollte*).

Unlike in English and its similar looking past tenses Present Perfect and Simple Past, there is no distinction in the meaning of these two tenses; the difference lies in the context and situation they are used:

> The ***Perfekt*** (also called the conversational past) is commonly used in speaking and informal writing (e.g. emails).
> The ***Präteritum*** (also described as the narrative past) is preferred most of the time in print and formal speaking (like the news on TV) and is less common in everyday speech.

You may remember that the *Perfekt* is expressed by two verbs: an auxiliary/helping verb (*haben* or *sein*) and a past participle. The *Präteritum*, in contrast, is expressed with a single verb (similar to the simple past in English). How German verbs form the *Präteritum* differs:

> **Weak verbs** carry a ***t*** as the marker for *Präteritum*, followed by the *Präteritum* endings ***-e, -est, -e, -en, -et, -en***.
> There is no vowel change.
>
> **Strong verbs** will signal the *Präteritum* by a vowel change.
> The typical personal endings for strong verbs are: ***--, -st, --, -en, -et, -en***.
>
> **Mixed verbs** mark the *Präteritum* by adding ***t*** (like weak verbs) plus a vowel change (like strong verbs) followed by the *Präteritum* endings: ***-e, -est, -e, -en, -et, -en***.

Since you were already introduced to the *Präteritum* forms of the most frequent verbs (*haben, sein*, and the modal verbs), we will look at these again to get an idea of some patterns.

	haben	**können**	**sein**
ich	hat**te**	konn**te**	war--
du	hat**test**	konn**test**	war**st**
er/es/sie	hat**te**	konn**te**	war--
wir	hat**ten**	konn**ten**	war**en**
ihr	hat**tet**	konn**tet**	war**t**
sie/Sie	hat**ten**	konn**ten**	war**en**
	weak	mixed	strong

The verb *sein* on the right side has changed such that it doesn't show any resemblance to the infinitive form *sein* at all (compare in English to be → was). Fortunately, this is an exception.

Remember the modal verbs with an umlaut work like this: *müssen* → *ich mus**ste**, dürfen* → *ich dur**fte***.

The verbs *wollen* and *sollen* work like weak verbs; there is no vowel change: *wollen* → *ich woll**te**, sollen* → *ich soll**te***.

12b **Grammatik entdecken: Lesen Sie den Text über Familie Holzapfel und markieren Sie alle konjugierten Verben. Schreiben Sie dann die Verben in die Tabelle mit ihren Infinitiven. Zum Schluss ergänzen Sie die Regel.**

Familie Holzapfel lebte in Ostberlin. Weil die DDR die Mauer baute, wollte die Familie das Land verlassen. Sie hatte einen Plan: Herr Holzapfel kaufte ein langes Seil. Mit diesem Seil wollte die Familie von einem Gebäude im Osten in den Westen kommen. Herr Holzapfel arbeitete in dem Gebäude. Deshalb hatte er Zugang (*access*) zum Gebäude. Aber er sagte seiner Familie, dass sie ihn erst spät am Abend dort treffen sollte. Funktionierte der Plan? Mehr über diese Geschichte und wie sie endete, erfahren Sie in ZEIGEN.

Verbform	Infinitiv	Verbform	Infinitiv
lebte	leben		

Die Infinitivform besteht aus dem Verbstamm plus der Endung ______.

Die konjugierte Verbform im Präteritum besteht aus dem Verbstamm plus dem Buchstaben ______ und Verbendung.

Wenn ein Verbstamm auf den Buchstaben ______ oder ______ endet, dann gibt es ein extra ______ vor dem -t.

12c *Präteritum*: Weak Verbs

For now, let's concentrate on **weak verbs**, which comprise the majority of German verbs. When you compare the verbs *bauen* and *arbeiten* in their *Präsens* and *Präteritum* forms, you will find different personal endings.

	Präsens	Präteritum	Präsens	Präteritum
ich	bau**e**	bau**te**	arbeit**e**	arbeite**te**
du	bau**st**	bau**test**	arbeit**est**	arbeite**test**
er/es/sie	bau**t**	bau**te**	arbeit**et**	arbeite**te**
wir	bau**en**	bau**ten**	arbeit**en**	arbeite**ten**
ihr	bau**t**	bau**tet**	arbeit**et**	arbeite**tet**
sie/Sie	bau**en**	bau**ten**	arbeit**en**	arbeite**ten**

The general rule is to add the *Präteritum* marker ***t*** to the verb stem followed by the *Präteritum* endings (**-e, -est, -e, -en, -et, -en**) as shown above. When the stem ends in ***-t*** or ***-d***, the *Präteritum* marker has to include an e before the ***t***.

12d **Der Tunnel 57. In diesem Text gibt es viele schwache Verben und Modalverben im Präteritum. Aber sie sind alle verschwunden. Können Sie sie wieder in die korrekten Positionen bringen? Schreiben Sie die Verben aus dem Kasten in die Lücken.**

plante | führte | arbeitete | wohnte | konnte | bauten | flüchtete | endete

Wolfgang Fuchs ______________ in der ostdeutschen Stadt Jena. Im Jahr 1957 ______________ er nach Westberlin, wo er als Optiker ______________ . Im Jahr 1964, als er 25 Jahre alt war, ______________ er einen Tunnel, damit er Freund*innen aus der DDR helfen ______________ . Er und etwa 30 Freund*innen ______________ diesen Tunnel. Er war 145 Meter lang, ______________ unter der Berliner Mauer durch und ______________ in einem Toilettenhaus in der Strelitzer Straße.

zeigte | krabbelten | wollten | alarmierte | kontaktierten | konnten | verhinderte | sperrte

Als der Tunnel fertig war, ______________ Fluchthelfer*innen die 120 DDR-Bürger*innen, die fliehen ______________ . 57 Menschen ______________ durch den Tunnel auf Händen und Füßen in die Freiheit. Leider ______________ ein Spion die Stasi und ______________ den Stasi-Mitarbeiter*innen, wo der Tunnel begann. Natürlich ______________ man den Tunnel sofort. Das ______________, dass die restlichen 67 Menschen auch fliehen ______________ .

12e **Gefährliche Grenzen. Unten sehen Sie Bilder von bekannten Grenzen in der Welt. Welche (er)kennen Sie?**

- China
- Mittelmeer
- Mexiko-USA
- Zypern (Nikosia)
- Republik Irland-Nordirland
- Indien-Pakistan
- Israel-Westjordanland
- Nordkorea-Südkorea

12f **Wählen Sie eine Grenze (z. B. von Aktivität 12e), recherchieren Sie einige Informationen darüber und halten Sie Ihre Ergebnisse schriftlich fest.**

Recherche

____

____

____

____

13a *Präteritum*: Strong Verbs

Strong verbs have a different way of signaling the *Präteritum* than weak verbs. Instead of adding the past tense marker ***t*** (weak and mixed verbs), strong verbs change the stem vowel, followed by a different set of personal endings: ***--, -st, --, -en, -t, -en***.

	Präsens	**Präteritum**	**Präsens**	**Präteritum**
ich	fahr**e**	fuhr	flieh**e**	floh
du	fähr**st**	fuhr**st**	flieh**st**	floh**st**
er/es/sie	fähr**t**	fuhr	flieh**t**	floh
wir	fahr**en**	fuhr**en**	flieh**en**	floh**en**
ihr	fahr**t**	fuhr**t**	flieh**t**	floh**t**
sie/Sie	fahr**en**	fuhr**en**	flieh**en**	floh**en**

Some common and high frequency strong verbs are:

essen	→ aß	beginnen	→ begann	fliegen	→ flog
sehen	→ sah	schwimmen	→ schwamm	fliehen	→ floh
helfen	→ half	trinken	→ trank	schlafen	→ schlief
nehmen	→ nahm	springen	→ sprang	lassen	→ ließ
sprechen	→ sprach	fahren	→ fuhr	gehen	→ ging
kommen	→ kam	schreiben	→ schrieb	liegen	→ lag

This list is, of course, not complete, but it already shows some patterns behind vowel changes, which we will discuss in detail below. We recommend learning strong verbs with their *Präteritum* and past participle forms. There are fewer strong than weak verbs out there. Still, their *Präteritum* forms are highly frequent. In a written text, the vowel change sometimes makes it hard to guess which verb is "hiding" in the form you are reading. Once you recognize a certain pattern behind the vowel changes, it will be much easier to memorize them.

13b **Wer floh wie? Ergänzen Sie die passenden Verben im Präteritum. Achten Sie dabei auf die richtige Konjugation.**

springen | fahren | mitnehmen

Der Soldat Konrad Schumann ____________ am 15. August 1961 über den Stacheldraht in Ostberlin. Aus Liebe ____________ Heinz Meixner seine Freundin und ihre Mutter in einem kleinen Auto (ohne Dach und mit wenig Luft in den Reifen) über den Checkpoint Charlie ____________. Im September 1964 ____________ elf Kinder und drei Erwachsene in einem Lastkraftwagen über die Grenze.

fliehen | fliegen | lassen | schwimmen

Ein Arzt ____________ 1971 von Rostock nach Dänemark. Im Jahr 1975 ____________ sich zwei Freunde mit einer Luftmatratze über die Elbe treiben (sich treiben lassen = *to drift*). Am 16. September 1979 ____________ zwei Familien mit einem Heißluftballon in den Westen. Holger Bethke ____________ mit einer Zip-Leine in die Freiheit.

13c *Präteritum*: Mixed Verbs

Mixed verbs—as the name tells us already—signal the *Präteritum* in two ways:
The verbs undergo a vowel change (like strong verbs), and in addition, they add the ***t*** as a *Präteritum* marker (like weak verbs). The endings follow the weak verb pattern: ***-e, -est, -e, -en, -et, -en***.

	Präsens	Präteritum	Präsens	Präteritum
ich	renn**e**	rann**te**	denk**e**	dach**te**
du	renn**st**	rann**test**	denk**st**	dach**test**
er/es/sie	renn**t**	rann**te**	denk**t**	dach**te**
wir	renn**en**	rann**ten**	denk**en**	dach**ten**
ihr	renn**t**	rann**tet**	denk**t**	dach**tet**
sie/Sie	renn**en**	rann**ten**	denk**en**	dach**ten**

Mixed verbs include:

Some modal verbs		**Other frequent verbs**			
können	konn**te**	bringen	brach**te**	kennen	kann**te**
müssen	muss**te**	denken	dach**te**	rennen	rann**te**
dürfen	durf**te**	wissen	wuss**te**	brennen	brann**te**
mögen	moch**te**			nennen	nann**te**

13d Wie heißen die gemischten Verben im Präteritum?

brennen: ______________________

bringen: ______________________

denken: ______________________

dürfen: ______________________

kennen: ______________________

können: ______________________

mögen: ______________________

müssen: ______________________

nennen: ______________________

rennen: ______________________

senden: ______________________

wenden: ______________________

wissen: ______________________

mochte   brachte   sandte   rannte   wandte
durfte   dachte
kannte   musste
brannte   wusste
nannte   konnte

4: Kindheit im Osten und Westen

14a Review: *Perfekt*

The *Perfekt*, also called the conversational past, is mostly used in oral contexts. It is a composed form, consisting of an auxiliary/helping verb (*haben* or *sein*) and the past participle form.

	helping verb		**past participle**	
Ich	**habe**	in Westberlin	gelebt.	*I lived in West Berlin.*
Du	**bist**	oft nach Ostberlin	gefahren.	*You went to East Berlin often.*
Wir	**haben**	in Berlin	geheiratet.	*We got married in Berlin.*

Element 1, the **helping verb**, is conjugated and takes the second position.
Element 2, the **past participle,** takes the last position in the main clause.

The helping verb: *sein* or *haben*?

You might remember that most verbs form the *Perfekt* with the helping verb *haben*, while only a small group requires *sein*. The ground rules are:

- Verbs with *sein* are never reflexive;
- they don't have accusative or dative objects;
- they usually describe a change of location (*gehen, fahren*) or change of condition (*aufwachen, schmelzen*);
- they include the high frequency verbs *sein, werden, bleiben.*

The past participle

The past participle comes in different shapes. Most past participles start with the prefix *ge*-:
lernen → gelernt, arbeiten → gearbeitet, laufen → gelaufen, lesen → gelesen

Exceptions are verbs that already have a non-separable prefix or that end in *-ieren*:
besuchen → besucht, erzählen → erzählt, vergessen → vergessen, studieren → studiert

Past participles of separable verbs incorporate the *-ge*-:
abholen → abgeholt, aufstehen → aufgestanden, mitbringen → mitgebracht

Past participles of weak verbs add a ***-t*** to the verb stem (or an ***-et*** when the stem ends in a *-d* or *-t*):
kaufen → gekauf**t**, arbeiten → gearbeit**et**

Past participles of strong verbs end with an ***-en***, and they often have a vowel change in the stem:
singen → gesung**en**, nehmen → genomm**en**, schreiben → geschrieb**en**

Past participles of mixed verbs end with a ***-t*** (like weak verbs), but also have a vowel change (like strong verbs):
bringen → gebrach**t**, kennen → gekann**t**, wissen → gewuss**t**

How to study the past participle:
We recommend learning each (strong or mixed) verb with their *Präteritum* form and their past participle.

gehen	ging	gegangen
fahren (fährt)	fuhr	gefahren
singen	sang	gesungen
liegen	lag	gelegen
kommen	kam	gekommen

14b **Was sagt Hänschen (Perfekt) und was schreibt Hans (Präteritum)?**

Hänschen sagt: *Ich habe gut geschlafen.* (gut schlafen)
und Hans schreibt: *Ich schlief gut.*

Hänschen sagt: ______________________ (viel essen)
und Hans schreibt: ______________________

Hänschen sagt: ______________________ (Früchtetee trinken)
und Hans schreibt: ______________________

Hänschen sagt: ______________________ (im Gras liegen)
und Hans schreibt: ______________________

Hänschen sagt: ______________________ (einen Text schreiben)
und Hans schreibt: ______________________

Hänschen sagt: ______________________ (nach der Schule heimgehen)
und Hans schreibt: ______________________

Hänschen sagt: ______________________ (von der Schule kommen)
und Hans schreibt: ______________________

14c **Organisierte Jugend. Beantworten Sie die Fragen.**

Welche Jugendorganisationen kennen Sie? Machen Sie eine Liste.

____

____

Waren Sie selbst in einer Jugendorganisation? Wenn ja, in welcher? Was hat Ihnen gefallen und/oder nicht so gut gefallen? Wenn nein, gab es einen Grund?

____

____

____

Stellen Sie sich vor, Sie gründen Ihre eigene Organisation oder einen eigenen Verein für Jugendliche: Welches Thema hat der Verein? Für wen ist er? Für welches Alter? Was machen Sie in dem Verein? Machen Sie sich Notizen dazu und bringen Sie diese mit in den Kurs.

____

____

____

14d **Organisierte Jugend: Seid bereit! Freundschaft! Lesen Sie die Informationen über die zwei DDR-Jugendorganisationen und vergleichen Sie sie mit den Jugendorganisationen aus Ihrer Liste in Aktivität 14c. Was ist anders, was ist gleich?**

____

____

____

____

____

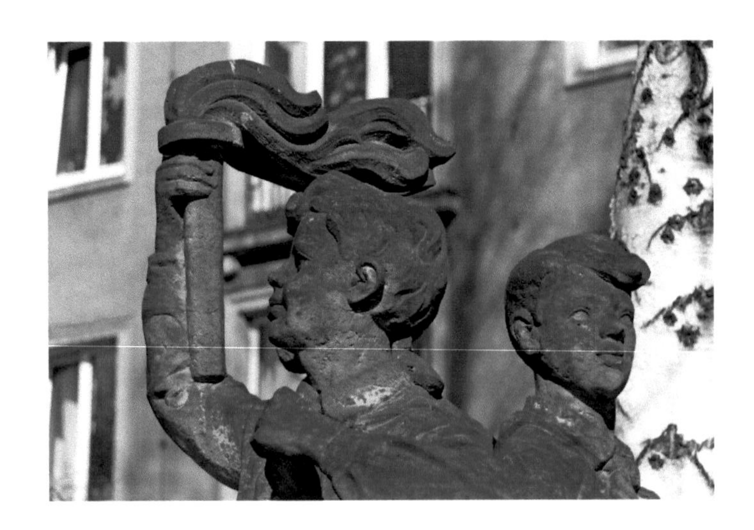

Die Pionierorganisation Ernst Thälmann

Alter:	1.–4. Grundschulklasse (Junge Pioniere = JP) 4.–7. Klasse (Thälmann Pioniere = TP)
Uniform:	blauer Rock / blaue Hose, weiße Bluse, blaues Käppchen blaues Halstuch (JP) rotes Halstuch (TP)
Gruß:	„Für Frieden und Sozialismus: Seid bereit!" „Immer bereit!"
Aktivitäten:	basteln, Aktionen zur Solidarität mit anderen Ländern, Altglas und Altpapier sammeln, malen, töpfern, älteren Menschen helfen
Wöchentlich:	Fahnenappell
Ferienlager:	18 Tage umsonst, manchmal mit Kindern aus kommunistischen Parteien des Westens

Die Freie Deutsche Jugend

Alter:	ab der 7. Klasse bis zum Ende der Ausbildung
Uniform:	blaues Hemd mit Aufnäher (*patch*)
Gruß:	„FDJler: Freundschaft!" „Freundschaft!"
Aktivitäten:	landesweit z. B. die Weltfestspiele, Chöre, Theater, Treffen mit Organisationen aus anderen sozialistischen Ländern, Hilfe bei der Ernte (*harvest*) und bei Bauprojekten
Zeitung:	Junge Welt
Auch:	militärische und politische Ausbildung
Nächster Schritt:	Eintritt in die SED

14e Temporal Clauses: *wenn/als, bevor, während*

Temporal subordinate clauses allow us to talk about two or more independent actions that happened before, after, or parallel to each other. Specific conjunctions indicate the order of events.

We already learned the subordinating conjunctions ***wenn*** and ***als***. Both of them mean "when" in English but are different from each other in German.

Wenn can be used in all tenses and indicates repeated events in the past and present tense.

Ich habe gute Erinnerungen, **wenn** ich an meine Zeit bei der FDJ denke.	*I have good memories* ***when*** *thinking back to my time with the FDJ.*
Ich war immer glücklich, **wenn** ich mit meiner FDJ-Gruppe ins Zeltlager fuhr.	*I was always happy* ***when*** *I went camping with my FDJ group.*

Wenn can also be used for conditional sentences with the meaning of "if."

Wenn ich dich finde, kann ich dich gerne besuchen.	***If*** *I find you, I can visit you.*

Als is reserved for one-time events that happened in the past.

Als ich 17 Jahre alt war, machten wir sogar eine Reise nach Polen.	***When*** *I was 17 years old,* *we even went on a trip to Poland.*

Bevor (before) and ***während*** (while) are our new conjunctions.

Während ich im Zeltlager war, fuhren meine Freund*innen zum Ernteeinsatz.	***While*** *I was camping,* *my friends went to do harvest service.*
Bevor ich ins Zeltlager fuhr, war ich sehr aufgeregt.	***Before*** *going to tent camp, I was pretty excited.*

Remember the different <u>verb placement</u> for main and subordinate clauses: The verb in main clauses is in second position (and in last if there are two parts to the verb). Subordinate clauses start with the conjunction and end with the verb.

Wir <u>sprechen</u> oft über unsere Zeit bei der FDJ, **wenn** ich meine Jugendfreund*innen <u>treffe</u>.	*We often speak about our time at the FDJ* ***when*** *I meet my childhood friends.*

When the subordinate clause comes first, it counts as the first position of the main clause, so the main clause will start with the verb:

Wenn ich meine Jugendfreund*innen <u>treffe</u>, <u>sprechen</u> wir oft über unsere Zeit bei der FDJ.	***When*** *I meet my childhood friends,* *we often speak about our time at the FDJ.*

14f **Früher und heute: „wenn“ oder „als“? Ergänzen Sie.**

________ ich klein war, bin ich nicht gerne in die Schule gegangen. Aber jetzt freue ich mich, ________ ich vormittags zur Uni fahre.

________ ich heute meine Hausaufgaben mache, verstehe ich, dass ich üben muss. Ich wollte aber nie Hausaufgaben machen, ________ ich noch klein war.

Ich habe immer die Wahrheit gesagt, ________ ich sechs Jahre alt war. ________ ich sechzehn Jahre alt wurde, habe ich fast nie die Wahrheit gesagt. Und ________ ich jetzt die Wahrheit sagen soll, weiß ich nicht mehr, was ich sagen darf.

Ich habe als Kind oft geweint, ________ ich etwas Trauriges gesehen habe. Jetzt weine ich nur, ________ ich einen Film ohne Happy-End sehe.

________ ich noch kein Geld verdienen musste, habe ich nicht viel gebraucht. Und ________ ich jetzt Geld in der Tasche habe, ist es nie genug.

15a **Hier ist eine Liste mit einer Auswahl an fiktiven und realen Kinderheld*innen und Idolen von Personen, die in den 70ern und 80ern Kinder waren. Suchen Sie sich eine*n fiktive*n Held*in und eine*n reale*n Held*in aus. Finden Sie online Informationen und machen Sie sich Notizen. Präsentieren Sie im Kurs.**

Recherche

Fiktive Held*innen/Idole
Pittiplatsch
Pippi Langstrumpf
Lolek und Bolek
Biene Maja
He-Man
Wickie
Meister Nadelöhr
Jim Knopf
Frau Puppendoktor Pille
Die drei ???
Ellen Tiedtke
Willi Schwabes Rumpelkammer
Mila Superstar
Das Sandmännchen

Reale Held*innen/Idole
Adolf Hennecke
Alice Schwarzer
Albert Einstein
Joachim Streich
Martin Luther King
Regine Hildebrandt
Walentina Tereschkowa
Steffi Graf
Gustav-Adolf „Täve“ Schur
Frida Hockauf
John F. Kennedy
Karl Marx
Katarina Witt
Beate Klarsfeld

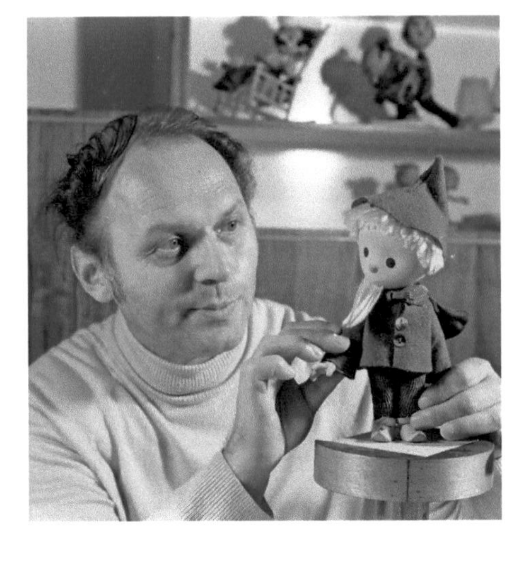

15b **Zugehört: Folge 2 – Fernsehgeschichten. Die beiden Professorinnen sprechen darüber, was sie sich gerne als Kind im Fernsehen angeschaut haben. Hören Sie zu und wählen Sie aus: Über welche Serien spricht Nicole Coleman, über welche Stine Eckert und über welche sprechen beide?**

Kindheit / vor der Wende				Jugend / nach der Wende			
„Sandmännchen“	NC	SE	beide	„Knight Rider“	NC	SE	beide
„Augsburger Puppenkiste“	NC	SE	beide	„A-Team“	NC	SE	beide
„Achim und Kunibert“	NC	SE	beide	„Baywatch“	NC	SE	beide
„Mach mit, mach's nach …“	NC	SE	beide	„Dallas“	NC	SE	beide
„Spuk im Hochhaus“	NC	SE	beide	„Blossom“	NC	SE	beide
„Sesamstraße“	NC	SE	beide	„GZSZ“	NC	SE	beide
„Disney Club“	NC	SE	beide	„Unter uns“	NC	SE	beide
„Tigerentenclub“	NC	SE	beide	„Verbotene Liebe“	NC	SE	beide

5: „Zwischen uns die Mauer"

17a **Trennung in Wörtern: Eine Vokabel-Mindmap. Welche Wörter (Nomen, Verben, Adjektive) zum Thema „Trennung, Teilung, Getrenntsein" kennen Sie? Erstellen Sie eine Mindmap mit den Wörtern. Gruppieren Sie die Wörter, die verwandt sind, z. B. „vermissen" und „Sehnsucht". Finden Sie in einem Wörterbuch mindestens drei neue Wörter.**

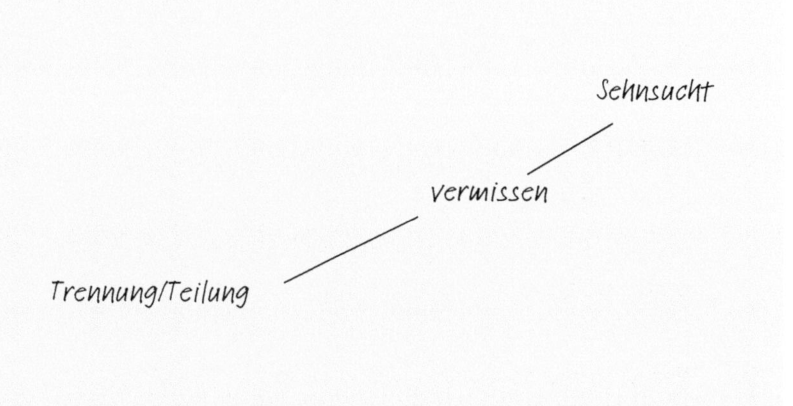

18a **„Zwischen uns die Mauer": Der Hintergrund. Sie hören jetzt Hintergrundinformationen zum Buch. Hören Sie gut zu und markieren Sie, ob die Aussagen richtig oder falsch sind.**

richtig	falsch	
		Der Regenbogen auf den Briefen erinnert an das Wetter in der DDR.
		Die Person liest die Briefe, um sich an die Vergangenheit zu erinnern.
		Die Briefe kommen aus dem Jahr 1961, als die Mauer gebaut wurde.
		Damals hat die Person nicht geglaubt, dass die Mauer jemals fallen wird.

18b **„Zwischen uns die Mauer": Klappentext. Lesen Sie den Klappentext, also den Text auf der Rückseite vom Buch, und markieren Sie die Wörter, die für das Textverständnis wichtig sind. Wenn Sie die Wörter nicht kennen, suchen Sie sie im Wörterbuch. Markieren Sie, ob die Aussagen richtig oder falsch sind.**

Bevor Katja ihren Freund besuchen kann, muss sie durch eine strenge Pass- und Personenkontrolle, ihr Gepäck wird durchsucht, nicht erlaubte Bücher werden konfisziert. Ihr Freund kann sie niemals besuchen. Er wohnt in Berlin, Hauptstadt der DDR. Der autobiografische Roman erzählt von den großen Schwierigkeiten einer Liebe und macht die Absurditäten des geteilten Deutschlands und des eingemauerten Ostberlins deutlich.

Quelle: Katja Hildebrand, „Zwischen uns die Mauer", Thienemann-Esslinger Verlag (gekürzt und vereinfacht)

richtig	falsch	
		Katja besucht ihren Freund oft in Ostberlin, weil es einfach ist, dorthin zu reisen.
		Jede zweite Woche kommt Katjas Freund zu Katja zu Besuch.
		Der Roman ist komplett fiktiv.
		Der Roman erzählt von den Konsequenzen der Mauer für Menschen, die durch sie getrennt waren.

18c **„Zwischen uns die Mauer“: Katja und Markus. Die Hauptfiguren im Roman heißen Katja und Markus. Unten sehen Sie in Stichworten einige Hintergrundinformationen zu den beiden und zur Geschichte. Schreiben Sie mit diesen Informationen einen kurzen Text. Wer ist Katja? Wo wohnt sie? Wer ist Markus? Wo wohnt er? Wo haben sich die beiden getroffen? Wie kommunizieren sie miteinander? Welche Probleme haben sie?**

Katja	Alter:	16 Jahre
	Wohnort:	Kleinstadt in Westdeutschland
Markus	Alter:	17 Jahre
	Wohnort:	Ostberlin
Informationen	Kennenlernort:	deutsch-deutsche Jugendbegegnung in Berlin
	Probleme:	Leben in unterschiedlichen Ländern, Grenzkontrollen, keine Reisefreiheit für Markus, Markus und Katja können sich nicht sehen, Liebe auf Distanz
	Kommunikation:	Briefe, Telefon

18d **„Zwischen uns die Mauer“: Lesen I. Sie lesen jetzt den Beginn eines Briefes von Katja an Markus. Lesen Sie den Text und beantworten Sie die Fragen auf der nächsten Seite in Stichworten.**

16. November 1984

Hallo, lieber Markus!

Auf der Karte siehst du'n Stückchen von dem Ort, in dem ich wohne. Ein verschlafenes Nest hinter den sieben Bergen bei den sieben Zwergen. Aber die Idylle auf dem Bild ist in echt nicht so idyllisch …

Vielen Dank für deine beiden Briefe! Komisch: Samstag und Sonntag und gestern, als sie angekommen sind, hab ich's vorher gespürt. Ging mit dem Gefühl nach Haus, dass Post von dir da ist – und wirklich. Vielleicht findest du das komisch, aber ich finde es toll. […]

Und um mal wieder zur realistischen Gegenwart (frier!) zu kommen: Hier ist's zurzeit ganz lustig. Nichts ist mehr normal. Nach einer langen depressiven Phase (Ohnmachtsgefühle wegen der Weltsituation, Sinnlosigkeit von allem …) ging's auf einmal nur noch ab. Jonas und ich haben uns getrennt. […] Mensch, du. Ich lieb dich. Irgendwie unheimlich doll. Und möchte noch so viel mit dir machen.

Ich freue mich schon auf deinen nächsten Brief!
Tschau
Katja

Quelle: Katja Hildebrand, „Zwischen uns die Mauer“, Thienemann-Esslinger Verlag (gekürzt und vereinfacht)

Fragen:

Was schickt Katja Markus in ihrem Brief? Was sagt sie darüber?

Wie hat sich Katja an den Tagen gefühlt, bevor die Briefe kamen?

6: Ampelmann – Eine Ost-West-Geschichte°

21a **Verkehrspsychologie: Wie können Verkehrsregeln effektiv kommuniziert werden? Machen Sie sich Gedanken und Notizen zu den folgenden Fragen.**

Welche Verkehrsregeln kennen Sie?

Welche dieser Regeln befolgen (*obey*) Sie gerne? Welche nicht? Warum?

Wie kann man Verkehrszeichen und -schilder designen, damit Menschen sie gern befolgen? (Farbe, Text, Zahlen, Bilder ... ?) Welche Elemente sollte ein effektives Verkehrsschild für Sie haben?

7: CHANCENGLEICHHEIT?

24a **Füllen Sie für drei Personen in Ihrem Haushalt (z. B. für Sie, Ihre Mutter, Ihren Vater, Ihren Stiefvater, Ihre Großmutter …) die Tabelle aus: Wer arbeitete in Ihrer Kindheit wie viele Stunden pro Woche? Beantworten Sie dann die Fragen.**

	Claude			
Erwerbstätigkeit	40 Std. (Lehrer)			
putzen	2 Std.			
waschen und bügeln	0 Std.			
Geschirr spülen	2 Std.			
einkaufen	1 Std.			
kochen	3 Std.			
Gartenarbeit/Haustiere	2 Std.			
handwerkliche Arbeiten	2 Std.			
administrative Arbeiten	1 Std.			
Kinder versorgen (baden, vorlesen, zum Sport fahren etc.)	3 Std.			
Summe in Stunden:	56 Std.			

Wie viele Stunden Hausarbeit gab es jede Woche ungefähr? ______________________

Rechnen Sie die Anteile aus: Wer machte wie viel Prozent der Hausarbeit und Kinderbetreuung?

____

Wer arbeitete insgesamt am meisten? ______________________

Denken Sie, dass diese Verteilung fair und für alle gut war? Warum (nicht)?

____

____

in, an, and *um*

With the prepositions *in, an,* and *um* we already learned how to express when something happens.

Wann fährst du nach Deutschland?	→ **im** Sommer, **im** Juli, **in der** Nacht
Wann gehst du zum Zahnarzt?	→ **am** Montag, **am** 5. (fünften) September, **am** Vormittag
Wann kommst du nach Hause?	→ **um** 11:30 Uhr (elf Uhr dreißig / halb zwölf)

vor and *nach*

You can add to this concept by pointing out times that happened or are happening before or after a specific event.

vor dem Zweiten Weltkrieg	*before World War II*
nach meinem Geburtstag	*after my birthday*

Vor is also used to indicate how much time passed since an event in the past. Compare it to "ago" in English, but pay attention to the different position in the sentence, as *vor* is a preposition, while "ago" is not.

Ich war **vor** drei Jahren in Berlin.	*I was in Berlin three years ago.*

As you can see, the preposition *vor* and *nach* are followed by dative forms (as most temporal prepositions).

von … bis

For questions that ask how long something took, you can either indicate start and end point (from … until = *von … bis*), or the duration of the event (… minutes/hours/days).

Die Show ging **von** acht **bis** neun.	*The show went from eight till nine.*
Ich war **vom** zweiten **bis** (zum) neunten Juli in Leipzig.	*I was in Leipzig from July 2 to July 9.*

seit

If the endpoint is not yet defined or if something has been going on up until now, the English language uses the preposition "since." For intervals, you would use the preposition "for," no matter whether these intervals are ongoing or happened in the past (I worked for the company for three months, from January to April 2001). Furthermore, the English language uses the proposition "in" to indicate an unfinished action or state that has started in the past. In German, it's much easier, since all of these expressions of time just use one preposition: *seit (+ dat.).*

Ich lebe **seit** dem 3. (dritten) Oktober in Bremen.	*I've been living in Bremen since October 3rd.*
Ich arbeite hier **seit** drei Jahren.	*I've been working here for three years.*
Ich bin **seit** mehreren Tagen nicht zu Hause gewesen.	*I haven't been home in several days.*

without *seit*

There is the option in German to not use *seit* + dative, and instead use the accusative without any preposition at all. You can use this for both past and present events:

Ich arbeite hier drei Jahre.	*I've been working here for three years.*
Ich bin mehrere Tage nicht zu Hause gewesen.	*I haven't been home in several days.*
Ich habe den ganzen Tag geschlafen.	*I've slept (for) the entire day.*

Let's summarize and compare the use of *seit*:

German			English
seit + dative	**seit** dem fünften Januar	**since** January fifth	since
seit + dative	**seit** einem Monat	**for** one month	for
no prep./acc.	einen Monat	**for** one month	for
seit + dative	**seit** Monaten	**in** months	in

25b **Frauen im Osten – überarbeitet und extrem effizient! Wählen Sie die richtige Präposition.**

__Von__ (Von | ~~Seit~~) 1949 (Beginn der DDR) bis 1989 (Ende der DDR) war das sozialistische Frauenideal: 40 Stunden Arbeit in der Woche, kontinuierliche Weiterbildung im Beruf, politische Aktivität, Haushalt, Mutter und Ehefrau. __Seit__ (Am | Seit) 1949 waren Frauen laut Verfassung (*constitution*) gleichberechtigt. __Nach__ (Um | Nach) dem Hitlerfaschismus sollte die Frauenrolle nicht mehr nur Hausfrau und Mutter sein. Die DDR brauchte __Nach__ (nach | bis) dem Krieg und der Flucht von vielen Facharbeiter*innen mehr Leute in der Produktion, also sollten alle Frauen arbeiten.

__Am__ (Von | Am) 9. April 1968 sagte ein neues DDR-Gesetz, dass Arbeiten eine Pflicht (*duty*) für jede*n arbeitsfähige*n Bürger*in war. __In__ (---- | In) 1950 waren 40 % aller berufstätigen Menschen Frauen; ________ (---- | in) 1986 waren es 49,1 %. Die meisten Kinder gingen in die Krippe oder in den Kindergarten. Immer noch sieht man Unterschiede zwischen Ost und West. So hatten __im__ (vor | im) Jahr 2016 60,6 % aller Kinder in den östlichen Bundesländern einen Platz in Krippen und Horten im Vergleich zu 36,1 % im Westen.

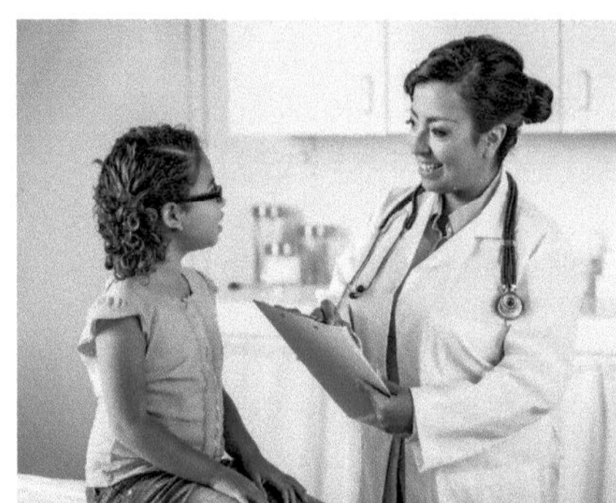

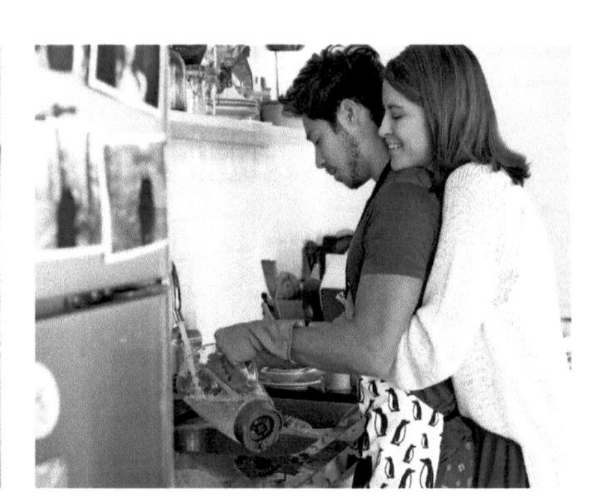

25c **Frauen im Westen – eine langwierige Emanzipation. Welche Präposition passt am besten? Es gibt mehrere Möglichkeiten.**

am | bis | im | nach | seit | ab | um | von | vor

__________ 1949 bestimmt die Verfassung, dass Frauen in der BRD gleichberechtigt sind. Aber Frauen durften legal nur erwerbstätig (*employed*) sein, wenn sie auch die Arbeit im Haus gut machten und der Ehemann die Arbeit außerhalb des Hauses erlaubte. Die westdeutsche Gesellschaft ist also schon __________ Anfang der BRD patriarchalisch. Durch die Limitierung ihrer Arbeitsmöglichkeiten blieben viele Frauen zu Hause. Dadurch gab es __________ zum Jahr 1971 nicht viele Kindergärten. Das war ein großes Problem für berufstätige Frauen. Das soziale Ideal der BRD __________ 1957 __________ 1977 war, dass Frauen sich als Mutter, Ehefrau und Hausfrau sahen. Erst __________ dem Reformjahr 1977 durften Frauen arbeiten, ohne ihre Ehemänner zu fragen. __________ dem Jahr 1968 gab es in der BRD keinen gesetzlichen Mutterschutz für berufstätige Frauen. __________ 1977 gehörte das Gehalt (*salary*) einer Frau ihr und nicht automatisch ihrem Mann. Aber erst __________ 1994 förderte (*promoted*) der Staat aktiv die Gleichberechtigung von Frauen. Von allen Frauen in der BRD waren 50 % __________ Jahr 1986 berufstätig.

25d **Frauen in der BRD und der DDR. 1969 berichtete die westdeutsche Wochenzeitschrift Der Spiegel (vergleichbar mit The Economist oder Time Magazine) über Frauen in der DDR. Der Artikel nannte Zahlen zur politischen und wirtschaftlichen Teilhabe (*participation*) von Frauen. Lesen Sie den Ausschnitt und kreuzen Sie unten an.**

In der DDR sind rund 34 Prozent der Richter[1] (*judges*) Frauen. In Westdeutschland sind es sechs Prozent.
Mehr noch: In der Volkskammer, dem DDR-Parlament mit 500 Abgeordneten, sitzen 153 Frauen – im Bundestag (518 Abgeordnete), dem Bonner Parlament, zur Zeit 41.
Das SED-Politbüro ließ 22 Frauen in sein Zentralkomitee wählen (zur Zeit 177 Mitglieder und Kandidaten) – in den Vorständen aller drei Bundestagsparteien Westdeutschlands sitzen zehn Frauen.
In 1.172 von 9.021 DDR-Städten und -Gemeinden gibt es Bürgermeisterinnen (*female mayors*) – in acht Ländern der Bundesrepublik mit 14.869 Städten und Gemeinden amtieren dagegen nur zwölf weibliche Bürgermeister[1].
70 Prozent der Lehrer[1] an den polytechnischen Oberschulen (*similar to high schools*) und 31,5 Prozent der Ärzte[1] sind weiblich.

Häufiger als in westlichen Ländern haben DDR-Frauen traditionelle Männerberufe ergriffen. [...] So stellen Frauen rund zwei Drittel der im Handel (*trade*) und im Post- und Fernmeldewesen (*telecommunications*) Beschäftigten (*employees*), fast jeden zweiten LPG-Bauern[1] (*farmer*), 41 Prozent von Arbeitern[1] und Angestellten[1] in der Industrie sowie zwölf Prozent im Bau (*construction*) dar. 80 Prozent von den Lehrlingen (*trainees*) in der Datenverarbeitung (*data processing*), 60 Prozent in der chemischen Industrie und fast 50 Prozent der angehenden Fernmeldemechaniker[1] (*telecommunications maintenance and repairs*) gehören zum weiblichen Geschlecht.

Quelle: DER SPIEGEL (vereinfacht)

[1] Notice that the author of this West German article from the 1960s uses the generic masculine forms for all professions. We will talk about the gendering of the German language and its consequences in this unit as well.

richtig	falsch	
		In der BRD waren mehr Frauen als Männer Richter*innen.
		Die DDR hatte mehr weibliche Parlamentarier*innen als die BRD.
		In der DDR gab es mehr weibliche als männliche Ärzt*innen.
		Nur ein Drittel der Angestellten im Handel in der DDR waren Männer.
		Datenverarbeitung war in der DDR ein komplett männlicher Beruf.
		Es gab in der DDR mehr weibliche als männliche Lehrlinge in der chemischen Industrie.

25e **Lesen Sie den Ausschnitt noch einmal und vergleichen Sie dann Frauen in der BRD und der DDR. Schreiben Sie mindestens fünf Sätze.**

____

____

____

25f **Zugehört: Folge 3 – Frauengeschichten. Hören Sie Geschichten über die Mütter und Großmütter der beiden Frauen. Lesen Sie die Statements und entscheiden Sie: richtig oder falsch?**

richtig	falsch	
		Stine Eckerts Mutter hat viel gearbeitet und war nur kurz zu Hause, nachdem Stine geboren worden war.
		Ihre Mutter hat gearbeitet, seit sie 20 Jahre alt war.
		Nicole Colemans Mutter hat studiert und danach immer gearbeitet.
		In Westdeutschland kamen Kinder mit 3 Jahren in den Kindergarten.
		In Ostdeutschland war es die Norm, dass Männer und Frauen arbeiteten.
		Es war leicht für Frauen in der DDR, Arbeit und Kinder unter einen Hut zu bringen.
		Nicole Colemans Oma hat den Haushalt gemacht und gearbeitet.
		Stine Eckerts Oma hat in einer Käsefabrik gearbeitet.
		Im Osten gab und gibt es viele Kinderkrippen/Kindergärten, im Westen nicht.

8: Vertrags- und Gastarbeit in der DDR und BRD

27a *Ablaut* Patterns

As you have learned before, **strong verbs** will display a stem vowel change in their *Präteritum* form and most of the time also in the past participle. Often, these verbs also change their stem vowel for the second and third person singular in the present tense. This variation of vowels is called *Ablaut*, and you can observe this phenomenon in all languages with Germanic origins, including English. Fortunately, verbs do not change their vowels wildly all over the place. There are actually some basic patterns which will help you with memorizing most strong verbs.

And some even overlap with English like:	we sing	we sang	we have sung
which looks like this in German:	*wir singen*	*wir sangen*	*wir haben gesungen*

Verbs with stem vowel *'a'*

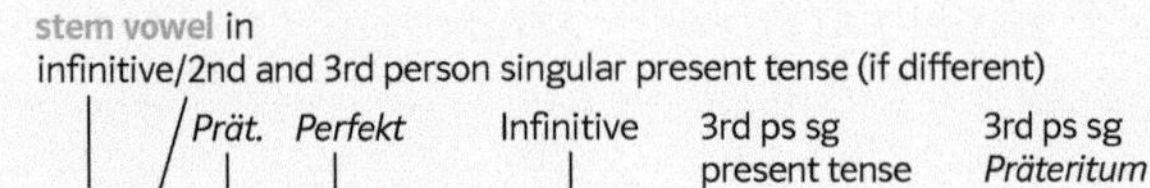

	Infinitive / 3rd ps sg present tense	3rd ps sg *Präteritum*	past participle	Read the following tables like this. These verbs are also in the groups:
a/ä – i(e) – a:	schlafen / schläft	schlief	geschlafen	fallen, fangen, halten, lassen
a/ä – u – a:	fahren / fährt	fuhr	gefahren	laden, schlagen, tragen, waschen

Verbs with stem vowel *'e'*

e/i(e) – a – e:	essen / isst	aß	gegessen	geben, lesen, messen, sehen
e/i(e) – a – o:	sprechen / spricht	sprach	gesprochen	helfen, nehmen, brechen, empfehlen

Verbs with stem vowel 'i'

i(e) – a – e:	bitten	bat	gebeten	liegen, sitzen
i – a – o:	beginnen	begann	begonnen	gewinnen, schwimmen
i – a – u:	binden	band	gebunden	finden, singen, sinken, springen, trinken
i(e) – o – o:	fliegen	flog	geflogen	fliehen, bieten, schießen, verlieren

Verbs with stem vowel *'ei'*

ei – i(e) – i(e):	schreiben	schrieb	geschrieben	bleiben, steigen, leihen, entscheiden

Irregular verbs

Some verbs will not fit into these patterns, so they can be considered irregular. These you will need to memorize individually. But since they are so few and so frequent, you will soon be able to recognize and use them.

gehen	ging	gegangen
heißen	hieß	geheißen
kommen	kam	gekommen

27b **Ein Wochenendtrip nach Berlin. Luke besuchte seine Schwester in Berlin. Hier sehen Sie Sätze aus einem Brief, den er seinen Großeltern nach dem Besuch schrieb. Ergänzen Sie die Sätze mit der richtigen Verbform im Präteritum.**

Letzten Samstag ___war___ ich bei Ayla in Berlin. (sein)

Ich ____________ gegen Mittag los und ____________ um halb zwei an. (fahren; kommen)

Als erstes ____________ wir Kaffee und ____________ über alles Mögliche. (trinken; sprechen)

Danach ____________ wir die Straßenbahn zur Museumsinsel, wo wir eine neue Ausstellung über islamische Kulturen ____________. (nehmen; besuchen)

Am Samstag ____________ ich mit Ayla und ihrer Freundin Corinna auf einen Flohmarkt. (gehen)

Ayla ____________ eine antike Kommode, die sie unbedingt haben ____________. (finden; wollen)

Corinna ____________, den Preis herunterzuhandeln (*negotiate down*). (versuchen)

Am Ende ____________ der Händler die Kommode für die Hälfte vom Preis! (verkaufen)

Am Abend ____________ wir auf einem Festival, wo es gute Musik und leckeres Essen ____________. (sein; geben)

Am Sonntag ____________ ich Ayla, die Kommode vom Keller in ihre Wohnung zu tragen. (helfen)

Dann ____________ wir einen Film und am späten Nachmittag ____________ ich schon wieder nach Hause fahren. (sehen; müssen)

27c **Textvorbereitung: Lesen Sie den Text in Aktivität 27 in MACHEN. Sie müssen nicht alles verstehen. Ihr Ziel ist, einen globalen Überblick zu bekommen. Schreiben Sie für jeden Absatz (*paragraph*) einen Titel, der das Thema beschreibt. Sie dürfen pro Absatz nur drei Wörter im Wörterbuch suchen. Notieren Sie sich hier die drei Wörter mit den Übersetzungen.**

Absatz 1: Titel ____________________

Wörter: ____________ ____________

____________ ____________

____________ ____________

Absatz 2: Titel ____________________

Wörter: ____________ ____________

____________ ____________

____________ ____________

Absatz 3: Titel ____________________

Wörter: ____________ ____________

____________ ____________

____________ ____________

Absatz 4: Titel ____________________

Wörter: ____________ ____________

____________ ____________

____________ ____________

28a MaTHEMAtik: Percentages

Der Prozentsatz (*percentage rate*) p % gibt den Teil (*part*) von einem Grundwert (*basic value*) G an.

Zum Beispiel: Wenn etwas 100 Euro kostet, dann ist G = 100. Oder wenn es um die Bevölkerung in Deutschland geht, dann ist G = 82.790.000 (Stand aus dem Jahr 2017).

Wenn es auf ein Produkt 30 % Rabatt (*discount*) gibt, dann ist **p % = 30 %.** Man kann auch stattdessen die Prozentzahl (p) schreiben, dann lässt man das Prozentzeichen (%) weg: **p = 30.**

Ein Prozent ist $\frac{1}{100}$ (also ein Hundertstel). Das ist die Formel:

$p\,\% = \frac{p}{100}$ das heißt $12\,\% = \frac{12}{100} = 0{,}12$

Wie rechnet man jetzt damit?

Beispiel 1: **Prozentzahl (p)** berechnen $p = \frac{W \cdot 100}{G}$

Beispiel: Wie viel sind 3 von 12? 3 von 12 sind 25 % $p = \frac{3 \cdot 100}{12} = 25$

Beispiel 2: **Prozentwert (W)** berechnen $W = \frac{p \cdot G}{100}$

gleiche Zahlen wie oben: 25 % von 12 sind 3. $W = \frac{25 \cdot 12}{100} = 3$

Beispiel 3: **Grundwert (G)** berechnen $G = \frac{W \cdot 100}{p}$

gleiche Zahlen wie oben: Der Grundwert beträgt 12. $G = \frac{3 \cdot 100}{12} = 12$

28b Prozentzahlen, Grundwerte und Anteile. Lesen Sie den Text und ergänzen Sie unten die Zahlen.

Die BRD lud in der Zeit ihres Wirtschaftswunders ausländische Männer (später auch Frauen) als Gastarbeiter*innen ein. In der DDR hießen diese ausländischen Arbeitskräfte Vertragsarbeiter*innen. Im Jahr 1966 gab es ca. 3.500 Vertragsarbeiter*innen in der DDR. 1989 waren es 59.000 Menschen aus Vietnam, 15.100 aus Mosambik, 8.300 aus Kuba, 1.300 aus Angola und 900 aus China.

Was war der Grundwert von Vertragsarbeiter*innen in der DDR im Jahr 1989? ______

Wie viel Prozent der Vertragsarbeiter*innen im Jahr 1989 waren aus Asien? ______

Insgesamt lebten 1989 16.450.000 Menschen in der DDR. Was war der Anteil von Vertragsarbeiter*innen?

______

Beim Zensus 1987 gab es 61.077.000 Menschen in der BRD. Davon lebten 2.013.000 in Westberlin. In Ostberlin lebten 1.284.500 Menschen.

Was war 1987 der Grundwert von Berliner*innen (Ost und West)? ______

Wie viel Prozent von Bewohner*innen der BRD lebten in Westberlin? ______

Wie viel Prozent von Berliner*innen lebten in Ostberlin? ______

27,6 Millionen Menschen in der BRD waren berufstätig. In der DDR waren 9,3 Millionen Menschen berufstätig. Was war der Anteil der arbeitenden Bevölkerung in der DDR? ______

30a **Grammatik entdecken: Das Plusquamperfekt oder die Vorvergangenheit. Lesen Sie den Text und markieren Sie alle Verben.**

Als sie in Dresden war, besuchte Sanne auch das Konservatorium, wo sie vor 30 Jahren Musik studiert hatte. Sie erinnerte sich an so viele kleine und große Dinge. Nach einer Stunde nahm sie ein Taxi zum Bahnhof. Früher war sie den kurzen Weg immer zu Fuß gegangen. Ihr Zug zurück nach Berlin ging um 14 Uhr.

The episode is written in the *Präteritum* for the most part. But some phrases are not in chronological order. They are marked by a different tense, the *Plusquamperfekt*, which we also call *Vorvergangenheit*, so something that happened "before" the past, meaning before something else that happened in the past.

Schreiben Sie den kurzen Text noch einmal. Schreiben Sie links alle Sätze im Präteritum. Die anderen Sätze schreiben Sie rechts (unter Plusquamperfekt).

Präteritum	Plusquamperfekt
Als sie in Dresden war,	
besuchte Sanne auch das Konservatorium,	wo sie vor 30 Jahren Musik studiert hatte.
______________________	
______________________	______________________
______________________	

The sentences on the left are basically what happened on the day that is narrated. The sentences on the right are retrospective, referring to a time about 30 years earlier. Do you recognize the pattern on the right from an English tense? Which one? ______________________

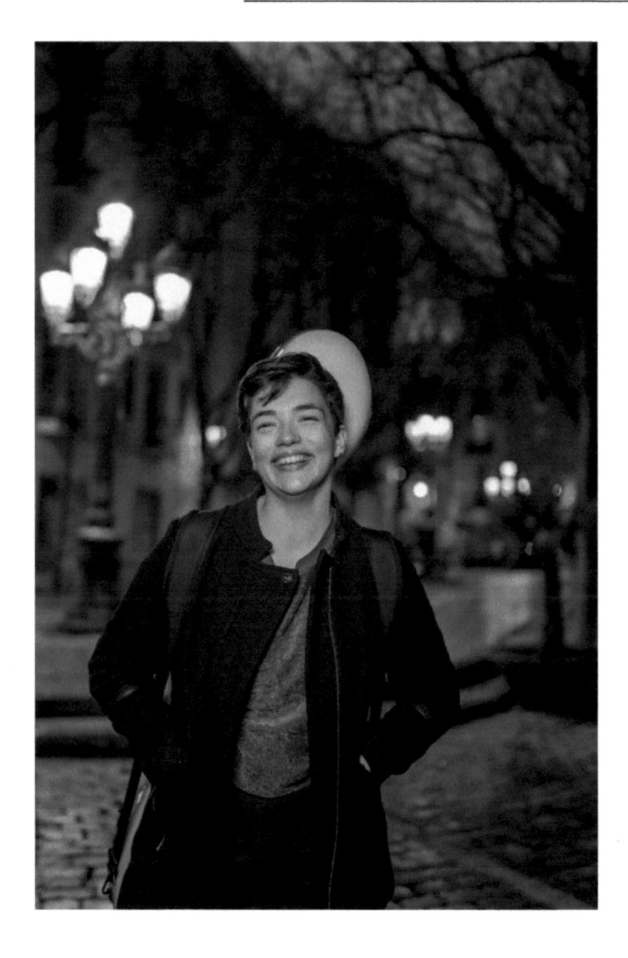

30b *Plusquamperfekt*

When communicating something that happened in the past, Germans usually choose a "base time" according to the content and social context. For reports and stories that happened in the past, German speakers tend to use the *Perfekt* in spoken language and *Präteritum* for formal and written texts.

When you tell a story or give a report, most of the times the text will unfold chronologically: You start at the beginning and then go step by step in the order things happened until you come to the end.

Sometimes, however, the sequence of events is interrupted by information that happened outside of a given chronology, such as things that happened before the story even began. These inserts are marked by an additional tense, the *Plusquamperfekt* (in English Past Perfect), which is also called *Vorvergangenheit*, meaning "before the past."

The *Plusquamperfekt* looks a lot like the *Perfekt*. It consists of a auxiliary/helping verb in the second position of a sentence (either *sein* or *haben* depending on the verb) and a **past participle** at the end of the sentence. The nice thing is that you already know all the parts! You know the past participle from *Perfekt* and the version of the auxiliary verb from *Präteritum*.

Perfekt				**Plusquamperfekt**			
Sanne	hat	Musik	**studiert.**	Sanne	hatte	Musik	**studiert.**
Sanne	ist	zu Fuß	**gegangen.**	Sanne	war	zu Fuß	**gegangen.**

You will notice that
- the **past participle** at the end of the sentence remains unchanged.
- the *Hilfsverb* (*haben* or *sein*) in the left column (*Perfekt*) is in the *Präsens*.
- the *Hilfsverb* (*haben* or *sein*) in the right column (*Plusquamperfekt*) is in the *Präteritum*.

How does the Plusquamperfekt fit into the other tenses?
Whether you present your story conversationally (*Perfekt*) or in a written text (*Präteritum*):
The *Plusquamperfekt* is a useful tool when you want to point out that a piece of information in your story or report happened before the other events that you are narrating.

Spoken/Informal (*Perfekt + Plusquamperfekt*):

Die Offiziere haben einige Leute über die Grenze **gelassen**, aber sie hatten „ungültig" in den Pass **gestempelt**.

The officers let some people cross the border, but they had stamped the passport invalid.

Written/Formal: (*Präteritum + Plusquamperfekt*):

Die Offiziere **ließen** einige Leute über die Grenze, aber sie hatten „ungültig" in den Pass **gestempelt**.

The officers let some people cross the border, but they had stamped the passport invalid.

30c Vom Perfekt zum Plusquamperfekt. Schreiben Sie die Perfektsätze ins Plusquamperfekt um.

Die DDR-Regierung hat Quoten für die Produktion von Autos bestimmt.

____

Bundeskanzler Helmut Kohl hat energisch für eine Vereinigung von West- und Ostdeutschland gekämpft.

____

Im Osten und im Westen hat es viele Jugendorganisationen gegeben.

____

Am 9. November 1989 sind viele Menschen zur Berliner Mauer gegangen, um zu protestieren.

____

30d Temporal Clauses: *nachdem*

The last subordinating conjunction we will learn for temporal clauses is ***nachdem*** (after). It is used to express two actions, one already finished and the other one following. This means that they happen successively and therefore on two different temporal planes.

Event 1	happened before	Event 2

The other temporal clauses with *wenn*, *als*, *bevor*, or *während* usually have the same tense in both parts of the sentence. Because of the different temporal planes, the subordinate clause with ***nachdem***, however, will have a different tense than the main clause.

The subordinate clause with ***nachdem*** will be in *Perfekt*, when the main clause is in the present tense.

Nachdem Anna ihre Hausaufgaben gemacht hat,
übt sie Klavier.

After Anna does her homework,
she practices the piano.

The subordinate clause with ***nachdem*** will be in *Plusquamperfekt*, when the main clause is in *Perfekt* or *Präteritum*.

Nachdem Anna ihre Hausaufgaben gemacht hatte,
hat sie Klavier geübt.

After Anna did her homework,
she practiced the piano.

Anna übte Klavier,
nachdem sie ihre Hausaufgaben gemacht hatte.

Anna practiced the piano,
after she did her homework.

30e

Mein Tag. Was haben Sie gestern gemacht? Schreiben Sie fünf Aktivitäten und die entsprechenden Uhrzeiten auf.

Beispiel: Ich bin um 7 Uhr aufgestanden. Ich habe um 8 Uhr gefrühstückt.

1. ______________________
2. ______________________
3. ______________________
4. ______________________
5. ______________________

Jetzt verbinden Sie die Aktivitäten, indem Sie eine Reihe erstellen. Benutzen Sie das Plusquamperfekt und „nachdem" für einen Satz und das Perfekt für den anderen Satz. Also ...

Satz 1: „nachdem" und Plusquamperfekt + Satz 2: im Perfekt ODER
Satz 1: im Perfekt + Satz 2: „nachdem" und Plusquamperfekt

Beispiel: Ich habe um 8 Uhr gefrühstückt, nachdem ich um 7 Uhr aufgestanden war.
Nachdem ich um 8 Uhr gefrühstückt hatte, habe ich ...

1. + 2. ______________________

2. + 3. ______________________

3. + 4. ______________________

4. + 5. ______________________

30f **Der Mauerfall und die Wiedervereinigung im Kontext I. Lesen Sie den Text und sortieren Sie die Informationen. Was ist international und was ist in der DDR passiert?**

Nachdem Michail Gorbatschow 1985 in der Sowjetunion an die Macht gekommen war, begann er einen Reformkurs (Glasnost und Perestroika). Die Öffnung, die er propagierte, galt auch für die osteuropäischen Staaten. Dadurch konnte es in Osteuropa in allen Ländern zu Reformen kommen. Viele dieser Länder begannen einen Transformationsprozess zur Demokratie. In der DDR weckte dies Hoffnung, aber der DDR-Generalsekretär Erich Honecker lehnte Glasnost und Perestroika ab (*reject*).

Anders in Ungarn: Ungarn ließ schon im August 1989 DDR-Bürger*innen in den Westen reisen. Nachdem am 11.09.1989 Ungarn die Grenze zu Österreich ganz geöffnet hatte, reisten innerhalb von drei Tagen 15.000 DDR-Bürger*innen in den Westen aus.

Und auch in Tschechien bewegte sich etwas. Nachdem im Sommer 1989 viele DDR-Bürger*innen in die westdeutsche Botschaft in Prag geflüchtet waren, verkündete (*declare*) am 30.09.1989 der BRD-Außenminister Hans-Dietrich Genscher, dass sie in die BRD ausreisen durften. 4.000 DDR-Bürger*innen reisten mit dem Zug durch die DDR in die BRD.

Gleichzeitig versammelten (*gather*) sich immer mehr und mehr Menschen in der DDR bei den sogenannten „Montagsdemonstrationen". Seit 1981 hatten sich Menschen bereits zu Friedensgebeten (*prayer for peace*) getroffen. Am 04.09.1989 nach einem Treffen in der Leipziger Nikolaikirche blieben 1.000 Menschen vor der Kirche versammelt und demonstrierten. Sie hatten Angst vor der Polizei, aber jeden Montag kamen mehr Menschen dazu. Am 09.10.1989 waren es schon 70.000 Menschen in Leipzig. Es gab auch Demonstrationen in anderen ostdeutschen Städten. Die Demonstrant*innen riefen „Wir sind das Volk!" und wollten demokratische Reformen und Reisefreiheit. Am 16.10. demonstrierten 120.000 Menschen in Leipzig, am 23.10. circa 250.000 und am 30.10. dann schon an die 300.000.

Die SED ließ Menschen verhaften, aber sie reagierte nicht mit militärischer Gewalt. Nachdem die Partei Anfang Oktober noch den 40. Jahrestag der DDR gefeiert hatte, musste Honecker am 18.10. zurücktreten (*resign*). Sein Nachfolger (*successor*) Egon Krenz kündigte Reformen an. Doch dann kam der 9. November 1989.

International	National
______________	______________
______________	______________
______________	______________
______________	______________
______________	______________

30g **Der Mauerfall und die Wiedervereinigung im Kontext II. Kreuzen Sie die richtige Antwort an.**

Was machte Michail Gorbatschow, nachdem er an die Macht gekommen war?
- X Er führte Reformen ein.
- ☐ Er begann eine Transformation zur Demokratie.

Warum hatten die DDR-Bürger*innen wenig Hoffnung auf mehr Demokratie?
- ☐ Sie hatten ein sozialistisches Land gewollt.
- ☐ Ihr Staatschef war gegen Reformen gewesen.

Warum reisten Menschen aus der DDR im August 1989 nach Ungarn?
- ☐ Sie hatten Urlaubspläne für Ungarn gemacht.
- ☐ Ungarn hatte die Grenze nach Österreich geöffnet.

Warum durften DDR-Bürger*innen aus Tschechien nach Westdeutschland reisen?
- ☐ Sie waren in die westdeutsche Botschaft in Prag geflüchtet.
- ☐ Sie hatten mit der BRD telefoniert.

Wie war es zu den Montagsdemonstrationen gekommen?
- ☐ Immer weniger Demonstrant*innen versammelten sich.
- ☐ Immer mehr Demonstrant*innen versammelten sich.

Wie zeigten die DDR-Bürger*innen ihre Solidarität miteinander?
- ☐ Sie riefen „Wir sind das Volk!"
- ☐ Sie sangen „Wir sind das Volk!"

32a **In dieser Aktivität lernen Sie die Personen der Video-Ecken in Impuls Deutsch 2 kennen: Jan, Marie, Nardos, Lorenz, Charlotte, Mahdi, Li und Jana. Schauen Sie sich das Video an. Zu welchen Personen passen die Aussagen?**

Ich bin im Iran aufgewachsen.	Marie	Lorenz	Mahdi	Jana
Ich bin Schüler*in an einem Gymnasium.	Jan	Nardos	Charlotte	Mahdi
Ich habe in Köln gewohnt.	Lorenz	Charlotte	Mahdi	Jana
Ich interessiere mich für Pflanzen und Bäume.	Marie	Nardos	Lorenz	Jana
Ich komme aus Tschechien.	Marie	Nardos	Li	Jana
Ich lese gerne.	Marie	Nardos	Lorenz	Charlotte
Ich mache Akrobatik im Zirkus.	Jan	Lorenz	Mahdi	Li
Ich reise gern.	Lorenz	Mahdi	Li	Jana
Ich spiele gern Fußball.	Lorenz	Charlotte	Mahdi	Li
Ich spiele ein Instrument.	Marie	Nardos	Charlotte	Li
Ich studiere Elektrotechnik.	Jan	Marie	Charlotte	Li
Ich studiere Kulturanthropologie.	Nardos	Lorenz	Charlotte	Li
Ich tanze gern.	Jan	Nardos	Lorenz	Jana
Ich wohne momentan in Stuttgart.	Jan	Mahdi	Li	Jana

10: Einheit?°

34a **Peggy Piesche. Ergänzen Sie die temporalen Konjunktionen und Präpositionen in Peggy Piesches Biografie.**

Peggy Piesche ist heute eine der wichtigsten Stimmen für Schwarze Frauen und für LGBTQ+ Menschen in Deutschland. Sie wurde 1968 in Arnstadt in der DDR geboren. _______________ (Während | Wenn) sie Deutsch und Russisch auf Lehramt studierte, verbrachte sie ein Semester in Smolensk, in der Sowjetunion. _______________ (Nachdem | Bevor) die Mauer gefallen war, zog sie nach Tübingen und machte dort ihren Magister in Literatur, Geschichte und Philosophie. Die nächsten Jahre verbrachte Piesche als Dozentin an den Universitäten Bonn und Bochum. Sie hatte auch noch andere Lehraufträge in den Niederlanden, in Deutschland und auch in den USA. _______ (In | Von) 2004 _______ (bis | zu) 2007 koordinierte sie das Projekt „Black European Studies", das sich mit Schwarzer Kultur in Europa beschäftigte. _________ (Vor | Seit) 2017 unterrichtet Piesche nicht mehr. Sie arbeitete erst in einem Institut für Feminismus der Heinrich-Böll-Stiftung, das der Partei Bündnis 90/Die Grünen nahe steht. _________ (Im | Seit) November 2019 ist sie Referentin für Diversität, Intersektionalität und Dekolonialität bei der Bundeszentrale für politische Bildung in Bonn. Auch _________ (wenn | bevor) sie diese Arbeit machte, war Piesche politisch aktiv gewesen. ___________ (Seit | Nach) 1990 engagiert sie sich in der Schwarzen feministischen Bewegung in Deutschland und weltweit. Piesche hat viele Bücher geschrieben, in denen es unter anderem um Rassismus geht und vor allem ihre Erfahrungen als Schwarze Frau in der DDR. Neben ihrer ostdeutschen und Schwarzen ist auch ihre lesbische Identität wichtig für ihren Aktivismus. Sie kritisiert zum Beispiel die deutsche Schwulen- und Lesbenszene, in der PoC und trans* Menschen nicht genug repräsentiert sind.

34b **Jetzt lesen Sie einen kurzen Abschnitt aus einem Artikel von Deutschlandfunk Kultur. Lesen Sie den Text und markieren Sie Informationen, die Sie wichtig finden.**

Peggy Piesche sagt, dass der anfängliche Optimismus nicht lange hielt. Für Schwarze und People of Color wurde der öffentliche Raum relativ schnell gefährlich, erklärt sie. Das neue konstruierte „Wir" der Gesellschaft hat nicht-weiße Menschen ausgeschlossen. Das weiße Ostdeutschland wollte sich mit dem weißen Westdeutschland sehr schnell verbinden, sagt sie: „Da wurde aus ‚Wir sind das Volk' ‚wir sind ein Volk' und ‚Deutschland den Deutschen', ‚Ausländer raus', und das ging sehr schnell."

Quelle: deutschlandfunkkultur.de © Azadê Peşmen (vereinfacht)

34c **Normalerweise beantworten Sie immer Fragen zu Texten. Aber jetzt schreiben Sie über den Text in Aktivität 34a selbst drei Fragen, die Sie mit Informationen aus dem Text beantworten können.**

Frage 1: ____________________

Frage 2: ____________________

Frage 3: ____________________

34d **Wählen Sie nun eine Ihrer Fragen aus Aktivität 34c und beantworten Sie sie.**

____

____

____

35a **May Ayim. Recherchieren Sie einige Informationen über das Leben und das Werk von May Ayim und schreiben Sie drei Sätze.**

Recherche

____

____

____

____

____

11: WER WIR SIND

36a **Ich bin ich. Stellen Sie einen Timer auf drei Minuten und schreiben Sie so viele Sätze über sich selbst wie möglich. Beginnen Sie jeden Satz mit „Ich bin ...".**

Beispiel: Ich bin eine Frau.

____

____

____

____

____

Aussprache: Rhythmus

37a **Hören Sie die verschiedenen Rhythmen und lesen Sie mit.**

O	Oo	oO	Ooo	oOo
Nacht	**Mor**gen	Ter**min**	**Vor**mittag	Ka**len**der
Jahr	**Mo**nat	Be**ginn**	**Fei**ertag	Ge**burts**tag

Hören Sie die verschiedenen Rhythmen noch einmal und klopfen Sie mit.
Klopfen Sie mit einem Finger und leise für eine unbetonte Silbe, mit der Faust und laut für eine betonte Silbe. Das heißt: Für „Nacht" klopfen Sie einmal mit der Faust, für „Morgen" klopfen Sie einmal laut mit der Faust und einmal leise mit einem Finger.

Sprechen Sie die Wörter aus der Tabelle.

37b **Hören Sie die Rhythmen und lesen Sie mit.**

Mauer
Krieg
Jahrhundert
Deutschland
Berlin
Datum
Geschichte
Staat
Tag
Arbeiter
Volksaufstand
Wirtschaft
Grenze
Rebellion
Politik

Hören Sie die Rhythmen noch einmal und klopfen Sie mit.

Schreiben Sie die Wörter in die Tabelle und sprechen Sie sie dann.

O	Oo	oO	Ooo	ooO	oOo

37c **Zugehört: Folge 5 – Sprachgeschichten. Die beiden Frauen vergleichen Wörter. Welche Wörter drücken die beiden unterschiedlich aus? Kreuzen Sie die Wörter an, die Sie hören.**

Viertel nach sechs / Viertel sieben

dusseln

ne?/gell?/gelle?

Necessaire/Kulturbeutel/Waschtasche

Kartoffeln/Erdäpfel

Köbes/Kneipenwirt

Fernseher/Glotze

tschö/tschüss/tschüssi

Plastik/Plaste

Hähnchen/Broiler

Döskopp

Keks/Plätzchen

lummern

hallo/hallöle/hi

Tüte/Sackerl

Apfelgriebsch/Apfelbutz

fimschig

schwätzen

38a Sentence Structure: Time Before Place

Now that you have learned how to express when something happened or how long it lasted, you will want to know where to put this information in the sentence.
The German language is like a big box of bricks that can be assembled in many ways. This makes it creative and flexible, but there are some rules to stick to when building your sentences. There are only two non-negotiable positions: the second position and the last position (the last position is not always filled), which are reserved for verbs, or for parts of verbs (prefixes of separable verbs). Between these fix points, in the so-called "middle field," there can be many elements that also have to follow certain rules. As you know, the subject is often in the first position, or—when the first position is filled by another element—it will normally stand directly after the verb in the third position.

First Position	Second Position (conjugated verb)	Middle Field (3, 4, 5 ... L-1)	Last Position (verb 2)
Ich (→ *subject*)	habe	gestern das Buch	gelesen.
Gestern	habe	ich (→*subject*) das Buch	gelesen.
Sie (→ *subject*)	möchte	nächsten Sommer nach Italien	fahren.
Im Sommer	möchte	sie (→ *subject*) nach Italien	fahren.

Temporal information tends to be at the beginning of the sentence. You will often find it in the first position or in the middle field, shortly after the verb. Locations tend to be placed at the end of the middle field, shortly before the last position (held by the second verb). For now: Remember time before place.

First Position	Verb	Time	Other Info	Place	Verb 2
Die Jugendlichen	wollten	gestern	gerne	ins Schwimmbad	gehen.
Wir	fahren	nächstes Jahr	mit Peter	in den Urlaub.	
Die Student*innen	haben	am Montag		in der Mensa	gegessen.
Dort[1]	gab es	an dem Tag	Schnitzel.		

[1] *Dort* (there) often takes the first position and also tends to come early in the middle field: *Es gab dort an dem Tag ...*

38b Sortieren Sie die Satzteile und bauen Sie Sätze, die den Regeln oben folgen.

ins Kino / gegangen / wir / sind / letzte Woche / .

Letzte Woche sind wir ins Kino gegangen. / Wir sind letzte Woche ins Kino gegangen.

dort / wir / den neuesten Film mit Daniel Brühl / gesehen / haben / .

____

haben / ihn / wir / gefunden / ganz gut / .

____

meine Freundin / danach / wollte / gehen / in ein Café / .

____

noch zwei Stunden / haben / gesessen und gequatscht / wir / in dem Café / .

____

38c **Zeit vor Ort! Beantworten Sie die folgenden Fragen in ganzen Sätzen. Jeder Satz soll eine Zeitangabe und eine Ortsangabe haben.**

Was haben Sie am Wochenende gemacht?

*Ich war am Wochenende mit Freund*innen im Kino. ODER: Am Wochenende war ich mit Freund*innen im Kino.*

Wo wollen Sie in fünf Jahren wohnen?

In welcher Stadt haben Sie als Kind gewohnt?

Wann sind Sie zuletzt mit dem Zug gefahren?

Wo waren Sie letzten Sommer?

Wo haben Sie gestern zu Mittag gegessen?

38d **Textvorbereitung: Lesen Sie den Text in Aktivität 38 in MACHEN und finden Sie die Passagen im Text für die englischen Aussagen unten.**

We all did similar things in our free time. There also were not many differences on a social level.

Soon we will celebrate the thirtieth anniversary of the fall of the wall. Will the "liberation" of the East Germans take center stage again during those celebrations?

But many East Germans cannot identify with this memory.

The GDR was not only a dictatorship.

12: „Good Bye, Lenin!" und „Das Leben der Anderen"

39a **Was passt zusammen? Welche Wörter beschreiben diese Genres am besten? Ordnen Sie zu.**

Genre	Beschreibung
___ Thriller	a) entspannend, lustig, humorvoll, fröhlich, parodistisch
___ Komödie	b) mysteriös, detektivisch, aufregend, rätselhaft
___ Dokumentarfilm	c) futuristisch, post-apokalyptisch, innovativ, übernatürlich
___ Actionfilm	d) (politisch/sozial/subjektiv) problematisch, realistisch, emotional
___ Sci-Fi	e) objektiv, wissenschaftlich, informativ, journalistisch
___ Krimi	f) angsterregend, verwirrend, labyrinthisch, spannend
_d_ Drama	g) gruselig, unheimlich, dämonisch, schockierend
___ Horror	h) spektakulär, stimulierend, physisch akrobatisch, explosiv, aktiv

40a **Im folgenden Text lernen Sie etwas über den Schauspieler Ulrich Mühe. Ergänzen Sie die Verben in der korrekten Präteritumsform.**

Ulrich Mühe, mit vollem Namen Friedrich Hans Ulrich Mühe, _wurde_ (werden) 1953 in Grimma in der Nähe von Leipzig geboren. Er ___________ (sein) ein bekannter, deutscher Film- und Theater-schauspieler. Im Film „Das Leben der Anderen" ___________ (spielen) er die Hauptrolle, nämlich den Stasi-Agenten Gerd Wiesler.

Von 1975 bis 1979 ___________ (studieren) Mühe Schauspiel an der Theaterhochschule Hans Otto in Leipzig. 1983 ___________ (werden) er Ensemblemitglied am Deutschen Theater in Berlin, wo er erste große Rollen ___________ (spielen), zum Beispiel Hamlet. Im selben Jahr ___________ (beginnen) Mühe seine Arbeit als Film- und Fernsehschauspieler. Für seine Leistung im Film „Das Leben der Anderen" ___________ (bekommen) er 2006 den Deutschen Filmpreis sowie den Europäischen Filmpreis als bester Darsteller.

2007 ___________ (sterben) Ulrich Mühe an Krebs, nur wenige Monate nachdem „Das Leben der Anderen" einen Oscar erhalten ___________ (haben).

Wer würde sich trauen?

Achterbahnen und anderer Nervenkitzel

14: AUF DEM VOLKSFEST

das Volksfest, -e	fair, funfair
die Achterbahn, -en	roller coaster
das Karussell, -s/-e	carousel
das Riesenrad, ⸚er	Ferris wheel
würde (+ *inf.*)	would
fahren (mit + *dat.*) (fährt), fuhr, ist ... gefahren	to ride (*a roller coaster / dark ride / ghost train*)
die Angst, ⸚e	fear
Angst haben (vor + *dat.*) (hat), hatte, hat ... gehabt	to be afraid (of)
lieber	rather (*preference*)
der Schausteller, -	show traveller, fairground person (*male*)
die Schaustellerin, -nen	show traveller, fairground person (*female*)
der*die Schaustellende, -n	people operating a showman/fairground business (*gender-neutral workaround for show traveller*)
kurzfristig	short-term; last-minute
sich (*dat.*) leisten, leistete, hat ... geleistet	to afford; to treat oneself (to)
das Fahrgeschäft, -e	fun ride (*business*)
verdienen, verdiente, hat ... verdient	to earn; deserve
ersetzen, ersetzte, hat ... ersetzt	to replace, substitute
auf·bauen, baute ... auf, hat ... aufgebaut	to construct, establish
ab·bauen, baute ... ab, hat ... abgebaut	to dismantle, take apart
sich (*akk.*) trauen, traute, hat ... getraut	to dare, have the courage to do
die Ware, -n	goods, merchandise
ein·steigen, stieg ... ein, ist ... eingestiegen	to step in, get in
genießen, genoss, hat ... genossen	to enjoy
suchen, suchte, hat ... gesucht	to look for, search
die Eintrittskarte, -n	ticket (*admission*)
sorgen (für + *akk.*), sorgte, hat ... gesorgt	to take care (of)
um·setzen, setzte ... um, hat ... umgesetzt	to implement

Weitere Wörter: das Dosenwerfen (can knockdown (*game*)); **die Geisterbahn, -en** (ghost train (*amusement ride*)); **das Kettenkarussell, -s/-e** (swing carousel, chairoplane); **die Schaustellerei, -en** (showmanship); **in der Nähe (von + *dat.*)** (in the vicinity (of)); **Spaß machen, machte, hat ... gemacht** (to be fun); **der Autoscooter, -** (bumper car ride); **die Schießbude, -n** (shooting gallery (*at a fair*)); **die gebrannten Mandeln (*pl.*)** (candied/roasted almonds)

16: FREIZEITPARKS

der Freizeitpark, -s	amusement park
dort	there
das Thema, Themen	theme, topic
die Bewertung, -en	evaluation
verändern, veränderte, hat ... verändert	to alter, change
vermitteln, vermittelte, hat ... vermittelt	to convey; mediate
sich (*akk.*) identifizieren (mit + *dat.*), identifizierte, hat ... identifiziert	to identify (with)
der Vorschlag, ⸚e	suggestion
entwerfen (entwirft), entwarf, hat ... entworfen	to design, draft
besonders	particular(ly), (e)special(ly)
weiter·gehen, ging ... weiter, ist ... weitergegangen	to continue; keep going
Das stimmt!	That is true!
auf jeden Fall	definitely
nass	wet

Weitere Wörter: drehen, drehte, hat ... gedreht (to turn); **An deiner Stelle würde ich ...** (If I were you, I would ...); **die Gästezahl, -en** (attendance, number of guests); **überhaupt nicht** (not at all); **die Themenwelt, -en** (theme world (*in amusement park*)); **stereotypisch** (stereotypical); **der Kulturberater, -** (advisor/consultant for culture (*male*)); **die Kulturberaterin, -nen** (advisor/consultant for culture (*female*)); **die kulturell beratende Person, die kulturell beratenden Personen** (advisor/consultant for culture (*gender-neutral alternative*))

17: PARKS IN IHRER NACHBARSCHAFT

die Umgebung, -en	surroundings, environment
vor·schlagen (schlägt ... vor), schlug ... vor, hat ... vorgeschlagen	to suggest, propose
der Bürger, -	citizen (*male*)
die Bürgerin, -nen	citizen (*female*)
der Mitmensch, -en	fellow human being (*gender-neutral workaround for citizen*)
zusammen·fassen, fasste ... zusammen, hat ... zusammengefasst	to summarize
Haupt-	main
der Hauptgewinn, -e	main prize, jackpot
die Erweiterung, -en	expansion, extension
die Forderung, -en	demand
die Bitte, -n	request, appeal
der Wunsch, ⸚e	wish
der Gedanke, -n	thought
wenn ... doch	if only
Wenn es doch nur Sommer wäre.	If only it was summer.

der Wald, ¨er	forest, woods
schützen, schützte, hat … geschützt	to protect
die Störung, -en	disturbance
der Lärm	noise

Weitere Wörter: das Bürgerbegehren, - (citizen's initiative); **das Bürger*innenbegehren, -** (citizen's initiative (*gender-neutral alternative*)); **der Umweltminister, -** (minister of the environment (*male*)); **die Umweltministerin, -nen** (minister of the environment (*female*)); **höflich** (polite(ly)); **zwischen den Zeilen lesen** (to read between the lines); **irreal** (unrealistic); **die Ruhe** (quiet, calm); **unterschreiben, unterschrieb, hat … unterschrieben** (to sign)

19: Achterbahn – Made in D-A-CH-L

der Hersteller, -	manufacturer, producer (*male*)
die Herstellerin, -nen	manufacturer, producer (*female*)
die herstellende Person, die herstellenden Personen	manufacturer, producer (*gender-neutral alternative*)
der Ingenieur, -e	engineer (*male*)
die Ingenieurin, -nen	engineer (*female*)
die Fachperson für Ingenieurwesen, das Fachpersonal für Ingenieurwesen	engineer (*gender-neutral alternative*)
die Ehre, -n	honor
berechnen, berechnete, hat … berechnet	to calculate
die Geschwindigkeit, -en	speed
auf·geben (gibt … auf), gab … auf, hat … aufgegeben	to give up
der Auftrag, ¨e	order; task, assignment
der Erfolg, -e	success
entwickeln, entwickelte, hat … entwickelt	to develop
ein·führen, führte … ein, hat … eingeführt	to introduce
das Ereignis, -se	event
rückwärts	backwards
passieren, passierte, ist … passiert	to happen
das Unternehmen, -	business, company
erfolgreich	successful
bekannt (für + *akk.*)	known (for)
schnell	fast
hoch (höher, am höchsten)	high

Weitere Wörter: der Stahl, ¨e (steel); **die Innovation, -en** (innovation); **der Looping, -s** (looping); **der Ursprung, ¨e** (origin, root); **der Rekord, -e** (record)

20: Schwerelos – Physik der Achterbahn

schwer	heavy
schwerelos	weightless
die Kraft, ¨e	force; strength
die Schwerkraft, ¨e	gravity, gravitational force
die Fliehkraft, ¨e	centrifugal force
wirken, wirkte, hat … gewirkt	to act, have an effect
Die Kraft wirkt auf den Körper.	The force acts on the body.
das Gesetz, -e	law; principle
das Prinzip, -ien	principle
die Formel, -n	formula
die Klammer, -n	parenthesis
die Wurzel, -n	root
hoch	to the power of; high
ein Fünftel	one fifth
ein Zweiunddreißigstel	one thirty-second
das Tal, ¨er	valley
der Hügel, -	hill
der Wagen, -	car, vehicle
die Beschleunigung, -en	acceleration
das Ergebnis, -se	result; outcome

Weitere Wörter: die Zentrifugalkraft, ¨e (centrifugal force); **die Lageenergie, -n** (position energy); **die Bewegungsenergie, -n** (kinetic energy, motional energy)

21: Design und Gestaltung

das Design, -s	design
die Gestaltung, -en	style (*design*); layout
steil	steep
die Kurve, -n	curve, turn (*bend*)
die Schiene, -n	rail
stehend	standing
die Schraube, -n	vertical spin; screw
die Höhe, -n	height
das Holz, ¨er	wood
die Länge, -n	length
die Kapazität, -en	capacity
die Behinderung, -en	disability, handicap
barrierefrei	accessible (*for people with impairments/disabilities*)
zugänglich	accessible
an·sprechen (spricht … an), sprach … an, hat … angesprochen	to address; approach
der Aufzug, ¨e	elevator
die Schlange, -n	line; snake
an·stehen, stand … an, hat … angestanden	to queue
sich (*akk.*) aus·ruhen, ruhte … aus, hat … ausgeruht	to rest
krass	stark, blatant, rad
unterhaltsam	entertaining
der Schatten, -	shade, shadow
behandeln, behandelte, hat … behandelt	to treat

Weitere Wörter: das Schild, -er (sign); **taub** (deaf); **liegend** (lying, prone); **der Korkenzieher, -** (cork-screw); **sitzend** (seated, sitting); **der Rollstuhl, ¨e** (wheelchair); **die Rampe, -n** (ramp); **die Auffahrt, -en** (ascent; ramp); **die Barrierefreiheit, -en** (accessibility (*for people with impairments/disabilities*)); **die Zugänglichkeit, -en** (accessibility); **sich drehend** (rotating); **der Rückzugsort, -e** (retreat; haven)

23: Hobbys und Berufe für Adrenalin-Junkies

der Extremsport	extreme sports
der Arbeitsplatz, ⸚e	job; workplace
das Vorbild, -er	role model
die Gelegenheit, -en	opportunity, chance
aus·probieren, probierte … aus, hat … ausprobiert	to try (out)
der Turm, ⸚e	tower
klettern, kletterte, ist … geklettert	to climb
atemberaubend	breathtaking
mutig	brave, courageous
traurig	sad
leben, lebte, hat … gelebt	to live
lebendig	lively, alive
zittern, zitterte, hat … gezittert	to shiver, shake
die Höhenangst, ⸚e	vertigo, fear of heights
ein·stufen, stufte … ein, hat … eingestuft	to rank

Weitere Wörter: der Fensterputzer, - (window cleaner (*male*)); **die Fensterputzerin, -nen** (window cleaner (*female*)); **die Fensterreinigungskraft, ⸚e** (window cleaner (*gender-neutral alternative*)); **sterben (stirbt), starb, ist … gestorben** (to die, pass away); **der Tod, -e** (death); **der Angsthase, -n** (fraidy cat, timid person); **die Phobie, -n** (phobia); **das Unglück, -e** (disaster; misfortune)

24: Angst – Psyche und Körper

die Psyche, -n	psyche
der Körper, -	body
die Gefahr, -en	danger
das Gefühl, -e	feeling, sense
fühlen, fühlte, hat … gefühlt	to feel; sense
weh·tun, tat … weh, hat … wehgetan	to hurt, ache
schwitzen, schwitzte, hat … geschwitzt	to sweat
weinen, weinte, hat … geweint	to cry
lachen, lachte, hat … gelacht	to laugh
atmen, atmete, hat … geatmet	to breathe
sich (*akk.*) erschrecken (vor + *dat.*), erschreckte, hat … erschreckt (*ugs.*)	to be frightened (by)
die Flucht, -en	escape, flight
reagieren, reagierte, hat … reagiert	to react
plötzlich	suddenly, all of a sudden
dringend	urgent(ly)
die Ausrede, -n	excuse

Weitere Wörter: Mir stockt der Atem! (It takes my breath away!); **mit·fahren (fährt … mit), fuhr … mit, ist … mitgefahren** (to go with, ride along); **glänzend** (shiny); **tränen, tränte, hat … geträint** (to tear, water (*of eyes*)); **der Einbrecher, -** (burglar, intruder (*male*)); **die Einbrecherin, -nen** (burglar, intruder (*female*)); **die einbrechende Person, die einbrechenden Personen** (burglar, intruder (*gender-neutral alternative*)); **stottern, stotterte, hat … gestottert** (to stammer, stutter); **die Starre** (rigidity, stiffness)

25: Das Leben ist eine Achterbahn

der Höhepunkt, -e	climax; peak; summit
der Tiefpunkt, -e	low; anticlimax
bergauf	uphill
bergab	downhill
der Plan, ⸚e	plan
die Stimmung, -en	mood; atmosphere
die Erwartung, -en	expectation
erwarten, erwartete, hat … erwartet	to expect
der Eindruck, ⸚e	impression
ab·stürzen, stürzte … ab, ist … abgestürzt	to crash; fall (*from a great height*)
gelähmt	paralyzed
die Gesundheit	health
die Erschöpfung, -en	exhaustion
die Erkrankung, -en	disease, illness
heraus·kommen (aus + *dat.*), kam … heraus, ist … herausgekommen	to get out; be published
häufig	common(ly); frequent(ly)
schaffen, schaffte, hat … geschafft	to accomplish
allein(e)	alone
die Ursache, -n	cause, reason

Weitere Wörter: das Auf und Ab (the up and down); **die Strophe, -n** (stanza); **wie verrückt** (like crazy, how crazy); **heutzutage** (nowadays); **die Hilfe, -n** (help); **nutzlos** (useless)

14: Auf dem Volksfest

43a Subjunctive II: Expressing What You'd Like to Do With *würde*

To express an activity that you would like to do (but are actually not going to do), you can use the German pattern *würde gern* plus an infinitive verb:

Ich würde gern ein Eis essen. *I would like to eat an ice cream.*

If you compare this activity to a more attractive one you say *würde lieber* plus an infinitive verb:

Susi würde lieber einen Eiskaffee[1] trinken. *Susi would rather drink an ice cream coffee.*

As you can see, the auxiliary verb *würde* is in the second position in main clauses, and the infinitive verb is in the last position.

The verb *würde* is in the so-called subjunctive II (in German: *Konjunktiv II*). When you look at the table below, you will see that the *Präteritum* and the subjunctive II forms of this verb are only distinguished by the *Umlaut*.

	Präsens	**Präteritum**	**Konjunktiv II**
ich	werde	wurde	würde
du	wirst	wurdest	würdest
er/es/sie	wird	wurde	würde
wir	werden	wurden	würden
ihr	werdet	wurdet	würdet
sie/Sie	werden	wurden	würden

Note: All verbs have a subjunctive II form, but they are quite uncommon in speech and increasingly also in written texts. Therefore, we will not practice producing them. However, since they are still present in literary texts, we will show you what they look like so that you can recognize them.

Weak verbs in subjunctive II look like their *Präteritum* form. Context can tell you whether the verb is in *Präteritum* or *Konjunktiv II*.

Strong and mixed verbs add an *Umlaut* to their *Präteritum* form as you just saw with *wurde* plus the typical **subjunctive II endings** (an *Umlaut* can only be added to *a*, *o*, and *u*!). E.g.

ich ging (*Präteritum*) – ich ging**e** (*Konjunktiv II*)
ich kam (*Präteritum*) – ich käm**e** (*Konjunktiv II*)
ich fuhr (*Präteritum*) – ich führ**e** (*Konjunktiv II*)

[1] *Eiskaffee* in Germany is usually coffee with ice cream. If you only know iced coffee with ice cubes, you will never go back!

43b Was würdest du lieber ... ? Zwei Optionen. Beantworten Sie die Fragen.

Würdest du lieber ...

Schokolade oder Chips essen? ______________________

nach Russland oder Spanien reisen? ______________________

einen Horrorfilm oder eine Komödie sehen? ______________________

in einer Großstadt oder auf dem Land leben? ______________________

43c What is a Grammatical Mood?

In addition to all the verb tenses we studied already, there is another category: **moods**. German distinguishes among three.

Indikativ	Susi isst Zuckerwatte.	*Susi is eating cotton candy.*
Imperativ	Susi, iss nicht so viel Zuckerwatte!	*Susi, don't eat so much cotton candy!*
Konjunktiv	Susi würde gern Zuckerwatte essen.	*Susi would like to eat cotton candy.*

Indikativ:
The indicative is used for all factual statements and is used in all tenses that we have studied already.

Susi besuchte letztes Jahr das Oktoberfest. — *Susi visited the Oktoberfest last year.*
Susi isst gern Zuckerwatte. — *Susi likes to eat cotton candy.*

Imperativ:
The imperative is used to express direct commands. It doesn't have any tenses, but it comes in three forms (for *du/ihr/Sie*). Normally you put an exclamation mark at the end of the sentence.

Kauf mir gebrannte Mandeln! (du) — *Buy me candied almonds! (you)*
Lauft nicht so schnell! (ihr) — *Don't walk so fast! (you plural)*
Rufen Sie mich an! (Sie) — *Call me! (formal you)*

Except in certain contexts (e.g. military) or circumstances (like emergencies) or purposes (instructions), the imperative form might be perceived as blunt. In order to soften it, you can use the word *bitte* or add the modal particles ***mal***, ***doch***, or a combined ***doch mal***.

Bitte, kauf mir **mal** gebrannte Mandeln! — *Please buy me some candied almonds!*
Lauft **doch** nicht so schnell, bitte! — *Don't walk so fast please!*
Rufen Sie mich **doch mal** an, bitte! — *Call me please!*

Konjunktiv:
There are actually two kinds of subjunctives. For now, we will focus on subjunctive II (in German: *Konjunktiv II*). It is used to express hypothetical or imaginary events, possibilities, counterfactual statements, wishes; in short: **something unreal**.

We just studied the subjunctive II with *würde* plus infinitive. In *Impuls Deutsch 1* (Chapter 8), you studied the subjunctive II forms of the auxiliary verbs *wäre* and *hätte*, and the modal verbs *müsste*, *könnte*, *dürfte*, and *sollte*. Our old friend *möchte* is actually the subjunctive II form of *mögen*.

Susi würde jeden Tag Zuckerwatte essen. — *Susi would eat cotton candy every day.*
Ich wäre jetzt gern auf dem Oktoberfest. — *I would like to be at the Oktoberfest now.*
Ich hätte Angst auf der Achterbahn. — *I would be scared on the roller coaster.*
Du solltest auf deine Handtasche aufpassen. — *You should keep an eye on your purse.*

The subjunctive II (*Konjunktiv II)* can also express events that depend on a condition that hasn't been realized yet. In other languages, there is often a separate mood called the conditional.

Wenn ich nicht so viel Angst hätte,
würde ich mit der Achterbahn fahren.
If I wasn't so scared,
I would ride the roller coaster.

In many other languages, this would be equivalent to the subjunctive.

43d **Die Bungee-Kugel: Was sagt die Rekommandeurin (*fair barker*)? Sortieren Sie ihre Sätze in die drei Kategorien.**

a) ~~Wir brauchen noch eine Person für die nächste Fahrt!~~
b) Ihr jungen Frauen da, wie wäre es mit euch?
c) Nein? Habt ihr Angst?
d) Steigt ein und lasst euch fallen!
e) Leute, wer von euch könnte noch mitfahren?
f) Ich hätte gerne noch einen Mitfahrer für diese mutige Dame hier.
g) Und jetzt haben wir einen mutigen Mann gefunden!
h) Steigen Sie ein und genießen Sie die Fahrt!

Indikativ: a ______________________

Imperativ: ______________________

Konjunktiv: ______________________

Aussprache: Das Ü

43e **Hören und Sprechen: Hören Sie die Bildung vom Laut „ü" und sprechen Sie nach.**

Das „ü" liegt in der Mitte zwischen „i" und „u". Denken Sie an ein „i", wenn Sie ein „ü" sprechen. Die Zunge ist wie beim „i" und die Lippen wie beim „u".

i → ü ← u

43f **Hören und Sprechen: Hören Sie die Namen und sprechen Sie sie nach.**

Kiehn	Kühn	Kuhn	Kinnemann	Künnemann	Kunnemann
Griener	Grüner	Gruner	Hirtner	Hürtner	Hurtner

43g **Sie hören jetzt immer nur zwei von den drei Namen oben. Was hören Sie nicht? Kreuzen Sie an.**

Hören Sie die Namen noch einmal. Welche Akzentvokale sind lang (= --), welche kurz (= ●)? Markieren Sie.

43h **Hören und Sprechen: Hören Sie die Wortpaare und sprechen Sie sie dann nach.**

Buch - Bücher	Frucht - Früchte	Gruß - Grüße	Brust - Brüste
Mund - Münder	Wunsch - Wünsche	Fuß - Füße	Tuch - Tücher

43i **Wörter mit „ü". Fallen Ihnen Wörter mit „ü" in den folgenden Kategorien ein? Schreiben Sie sie auf.**

Farben: ______________________

Körperteile: ______________________

Essen: ______________________

eine Jahreszeit: ______________________

Kleidung: ______________________

43j **Ruth und Jan fahren mit ihren Kindern Denise, Sebastian und Leni zum Nürnberger Volksfest. Kreisen Sie ein: Sind die Sätze im Indikativ (IN), Imperativ (IM) oder Konjunktiv (KO)?**

Ruth:	Jan, da ist noch ein Parkplatz frei!	((IN) | IM | KO)
Leni:	Vati, park nicht so weit weg vom Volksfest!	(IN | IM | KO)
	Ich möchte später nicht so lange zum Auto zurücklaufen.	(IN | IM | KO)
Sebastian:	Du planst wohl, ganz viel Zuckerwatte zu essen?	(IN | IM | KO)
Leni:	Genau! Und gebrannte Mandeln, eine Schokobanane und ein Lebkuchenherz!	
Jan:	Puh, da hätte ich Bauchschmerzen …	(IN | IM | KO)
Denise:	Ich auch. Leni, wäre es nicht besser, wenn du gesünder essen würdest?	(IN | IM | KO)
Ruth:	Sie wird bald lernen, was gut für sie ist. Nicht wahr, Leni?	(IN | IM | KO)
Leni:	Ja, Mutti. Aber noch nicht heute!	

44a **Ein Ausflug mit Freund*innen. Sie sind mit Freund*innen in Nordrhein-Westfalen und suchen eine Kirmes (so heißen viele Volksfeste in NRW) in Ihrer Nähe aus. Wählen Sie jeweils eine Option aus.**

nach Oberhausen | nach Düsseldorf | nach Herne fahren

Wir würden nach Herne fahren.

mit dem Taxi | mit der Bahn | mit dem Auto fahren

____

um 11 Uhr | um 16 Uhr | um 20 Uhr ankommen

____

zum Gottesdienst | zum Rainbow Monday | zur Ladies Night | zum Feuerwerk | zum Karaoke gehen

____

eine Bratwurst | ein Softeis | gebratene Champignons essen ______________________________

bis 22 Uhr | bis Mitternacht auf dem Volksfest bleiben ______________________________

ein paar Fahrgeschäfte | keine Fahrgeschäfte besuchen ______________________________

ein Gruppen-Selfie | kein Gruppen-Selfie machen ______________________________

am nächsten Tag die Kirmes wieder besuchen | lange schlafen und heimfahren ______________________________

____

Was noch? Schreiben Sie eine eigene Idee auf. ______________________________

44b **Auf einem deutschen Volksfest. Hier sehen Sie Bilder von Snacks, die für ein deutsches Volksfest typisch sind. Ordnen Sie zu.**

1 2  3  4

5 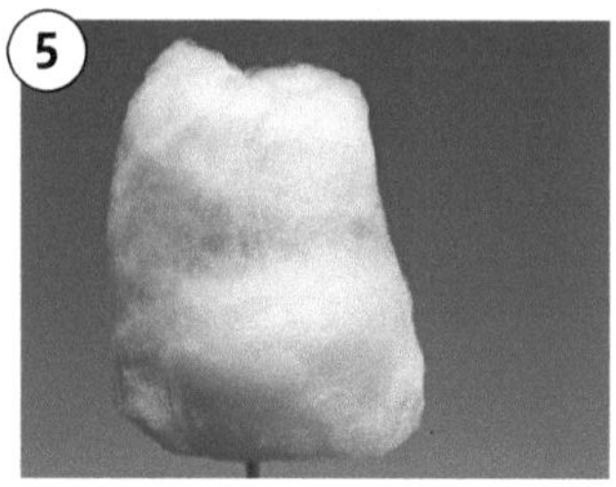 6  7  8

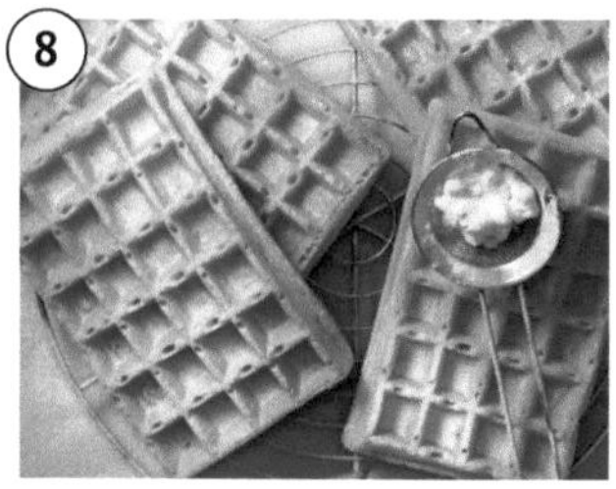

Zuckerwatte	gebrannte Mandeln	Pommes	Salzgurken
kandierte Äpfel	Waffeln	Bratwurst	gebratene Champignons

Ergänzen Sie für die Sätze die richtige Form von „würde".

Meine Mutter ______________ gern eine Waffel essen.

Meine Freund*innen ______________ lieber gebratene Champignons essen.

Wie viele kandierte Äpfel ______________ du essen?

______________ ihr gern eine Salzgurke essen?

Was würden Sie auf einem deutschen Volksfest essen?

____

____

15: Oktoberfest – damals und heute°

47a **Oktoberfest? Machen Sie eine Liste mit allen Dingen, die Sie mit dem Oktoberfest assoziieren.**

____

____

____

____

____

Warum assoziieren Sie diese Dinge mit dem Oktoberfest? Woher haben Sie diese Informationen?

____

____

49a **O'zapft is! Stellen Sie sich vor, dass Sie zum ersten Mal aufs Oktoberfest gehen. Wie würden Sie sich darauf vorbereiten? Was würden Sie dort tun? Beantworten Sie die folgenden Fragen in jeweils 2–3 Sätzen.**

Welche Informationen über das Oktoberfest würden Sie vor Ihrem Besuch sammeln?

____

____

Outfit: Was würden Sie tragen?

____

____

Was würden Sie auf dem Oktoberfest essen und trinken?

____

____

Was würden Sie noch auf dem Oktoberfest machen?

____

____

16: Freizeitparks

51a **Jana, Maria, Li, Charlotte, Jan, Nardos und Lorenz erzählen, welche Freizeitparks sie schon besucht haben. Schauen Sie sich das Video an und schreiben Sie für jeden Park, wie viele Personen ihn nennen.**

- Allgäu Skyline Park (DE)
- Belantis Leipzig (DE)
- Beto Carrero World (BR)
- Disneyland Paris (FR)
- Disneyland Park (US)
- Erlebnispark Tripsdrill (DE)
- Europa-Park (DE)
- Filmpark Babelsberg (DE)
- Hansa-Park (DE)
- Happy Valley (CN)
- Heide Park (DE)
- IMG Worlds of Adventure (AE)
- Legoland Deutschland (DE)
- Movie Park Germany (DE)
- Phantasialand (DE)
- Playmobil FunPark (DE)
- PortAventura (ES)
- Ravensburger Spieleland (DE)
- SeaWorld San Diego (US)
- Six Flags Fiesta Texas (US)
- Universal Studio Florida (US)

51b **Meine Erfahrungen mit Freizeitparks. In MACHEN werden Sie und die anderen Kursteilnehmer*innen über Ihre Erfahrungen mit Freizeitparks sprechen. Damit Sie gut vorbereitet sind, gibt es hier ein kleines Brainstorming. Machen Sie sich zu den folgenden Fragen ein paar Notizen.**

In welchen Freizeitparks waren Sie schon?

____

____

Hatten diese Parks ein bestimmtes Thema oder gab es verschiedene Themenwelten?

____

____

Welcher Park oder welche Parks hat/haben Ihnen besonders gut gefallen?

____

Welcher Park oder welche Parks hat/haben Ihnen weniger gut gefallen?

____

Welche Freizeitparkattraktionen mögen Sie besonders und welche mögen Sie überhaupt nicht?

____

Gehen Sie gern in Freizeitparks? Warum (nicht)?

____

____

53a Review: The Subjunctive II Forms of Modal Verbs

In *Impuls Deutsch 1* (Chapter 8), you learned the subjunctive II (*Konjunktiv II*) forms of the modal verbs: *müssen* → *müsste* (would have to), *können* → *könnte* (could, might), *sollen* → *sollte* (should), and *dürfen* → *dürfte* (would be allowed to).

These forms are also very useful when you want to make polite and cautious suggestions (like "You might want to buy the larger shirt") instead of using an imperative (like: "Buy the larger shirt!"), which might come across as a little blunt and rude.

In a sentence, modal verbs in the subjunctive II mood behave just like in the indicative, in that the conjugated modal verb gets paired with an infinitive of another verb at the end of the sentence:

Ich könnte ein autonomes Auto kaufen.	*I could buy a self-driving car.*

These kinds of gentle suggestions often come with the modal particle ***mal*** (normally reserved for—guess what—the imperative!).

Ihr könntet **mal** in die Geisterbahn gehen.	*You could go on the ghost train.*
Du solltest **mal** auf deine Handtasche aufpassen.	*You should keep an eye on your purse.*
Wir müssten **mal** unseren Heimweg planen.	*We would have to plan our trip back home.*
Die Achterbahn dürfte nicht schneller sein.	*The roller coaster should not be allowed to be/go faster.*

53b Was meinen Sie? Welches Modalverb im Konjunktiv II passt hier am besten: „sollte", „könnte" oder „müsste"? Vergessen Sie nicht, die Verben korrekt zu konjugieren.

Mein Freund Helge isst oft fünf Bratwurstbrötchen im Freizeitpark. Ich finde, das ___sollte___ er nicht machen.

Wir fahren immer zum Freizeitpark in Brühl. Das nächste Mal ____________ wir den Heide-Park in Soltau besuchen.

Meine Schwester mag den Freefalltower im Seregenti-Park Hodenhagen. Sie sagt, ich ____________ das auch mal ausprobieren.

Ravensburger Spieleland

Ich habe meinen Freundinnen Inge und Karen gestern gesagt, dass sie ihren Kindern bald das Legoland in Günzburg zeigen ____________. Es ist echt super für kleine Lego-Baumeister*innen!

Unser Nachbar Maximilian sitzt im Rollstuhl und findet den Freizeitpark Efteling in den Niederlanden fantastisch, weil der Park sehr rollstuhlgerecht ist. Ich finde, man ____________ die Freizeitparks in Deutschland auch zugänglicher für Menschen mit Behinderungen designen.

Kati, ich weiß, du liebst Brettspiele. Du ____________ mal mit mir ins Ravensburger Spieleland nach Meckenbeuren fahren. Da kann man Spiele in XXL entdecken.

53c The Subjunctive II for Suggestions With *würde*

The subjunctive II (*Konjunktiv II*) with würde + infinitive is a very good tool when you want to signal your approval or disapproval of an action:

Ich würde meine amerikanischen Freund*innen nicht in einen Wild West-Themenpark mitnehmen.	*I would not take my American friends to a Wild West theme park.*
Ich würde in den USA keinen deutschen Themenpark besuchen.	*I would not visit a German theme park in the U.S.*

This pattern also works when you want to give a suggestion to another person how you would proceed in a certain situation. This way of making suggestions is an alternative to using modal verbs in the subjunctive II.

Ich würde nicht am Sonntag in den Themenpark gehen.	*I would not go to the theme park on Sunday.*
Ich würde eher am Mittwoch oder Donnerstag gehen.	*I would rather go on Wednesday or Thursday.*

Often a suggestion starts with or includes the phrase *An deiner Stelle ...*

An deiner Stelle würde ich am Mittwoch in den Park gehen.	*If I were you (literally: in your place), I would go to the park on Wednesday.*
Ich würde an deiner Stelle nicht am Sonntag in den Park gehen.	*If I were you, I wouldn't go to the park on Sunday.*

53d Ratschläge: An deiner/ihrer/seiner/eurer Stelle würde ich ... ! Wählen Sie das korrekte Possessivpronomen und vervollständigen Sie die Sätze.

Katharina kommt jeden Tag zu spät zum Unterricht.

An ihrer Stelle würde ich einen zweiten Wecker stellen.

Morgen ist unser Gruppenprojekt fällig *(due)* und wir haben noch nichts dafür gemacht!

__________ würde ich beim nächsten Projekt früher anfangen.

Mesut fragt, ob ich morgen mit ihm ins Kino gehe. Aber ich treffe mich morgen schon mit Lara! Was soll ich tun?

__________ würde ich Mesut fragen, ob er übermorgen Zeit hat.

Paul hat seit zwei Wochen eine furchtbare Erkältung.

__________ würde ich endlich zum Arzt gehen.

Die Studierenden wissen nicht, welches Buch sie für den Kurs brauchen.

__________ würde ich einfach auf den Lehrplan schauen.

53e Xenia hat Probleme und holt sich Ratschläge von ihren Freund*innen. Rekonstruieren Sie durch Xenias Reaktionen, was ihre Freund*innen ihr raten. Lesen Sie zuerst für jede Situation alle Sätze. Beginnen Sie dann Ihre Ratschläge mit „An deiner Stelle würde ich ...“ oder „Du solltest/könntest ...“.

Beispiel:

Xenia: Meine Mitbewohner sind so laut, ich kann keine Hausaufgaben machen.

Nicole: *An deiner Stelle würde ich in die Bibliothek gehen.*

Xenia: Aber die Bibliothek ist doch so weit weg.

Nicole: *Du könntest vielleicht mit deinen Mitbewohnern sprechen.*

Xenia: Ich habe schon versucht, mit meinen Mitbewohnern zu sprechen, aber sie nehmen mich nicht ernst.

Situation 1:

Xenia: Bei meinem Auto ist der Motor kaputt.

Nicole: ______________________________

Xenia: Ich habe aber kein Geld für die Reparatur.

Nicole: ______________________________

Xenia: Ich habe keine Zeit, neben dem Studium zu arbeiten.

Nicole: ______________________________

Xenia: Meine Eltern nach Geld fragen? Das wäre mir peinlich.

Situation 2:

Xenia: Ich habe Streit mit meiner Freundin.

Nils: ______________________________

Xenia: Auf meine SMS reagiert sie nicht.

Nils: ______________________________

Xenia: Direkt zu ihrer Wohnung gehen? Und wenn sie gerade keine Zeit hat?

Nils: ______________________________

Xenia: Einen Brief schreiben ... Aber da muss ich ja ewig auf die Antwort warten.

Nils: ______________________________

Xenia: Eine nette E-Mail? Das könnte funktionieren.

Situation 3:

Xenia: Unser Nachbar wirft immer seinen Restmüll in die blaue Tonne.

Lea: ______________________________

Xenia: Er hört mir nie zu und geht immer gleich weiter.

Lea: ______________________________

Xenia: Wenn alle Nachbar*innen einen Brief schreiben, fühlt er sich doch als Außenseiter (*outsider*).

Lea: ______________________________

Xenia: Du hast Recht. Ich werde die Hausbesitzerin darüber informieren.

17: Parks in ihrer Nachbarschaft

56a Subjunctive II for Polite Requests

Politeness is always a good approach in any language, especially when you want something from another person and when you request or ask for things or services. The subjunctive II (*Konjunktiv II)* is a fine instrument to express courteousness and good manners in situations when a blunt imperative might not be appropriate. It also sounds so much more cultivated and eloquent!
Instead of giving out an order at a shop or restaurant with a straightforward imperative or declaration, you might want to mellow your request with an elegant formula including a subjunctive II.

impolite/neutral	**more polite**	
Ich will ein Schnitzel.	Ich möchte gern ein Schnitzel.	*I would like a Schnitzel.*
Ich nehme ein Schnitzel.[1]	Ich hätte gern ein Schnitzel.	*I would like a Schnitzel.*
Bringen Sie mir ein Schnitzel!	Könnte ich ein Schnitzel haben?	*Could I have a Schnitzel?*

[1] This is a neutral and common way of ordering food.

In other situations and interactions, the subjunctive II will also give you a wider range of wording your request more personably and politely.

impolite	**polite**	
Gib mir deine Adresse!	Würdest du mir deine Adresse geben?	*Would you give me your address?*
	Könntest du mir deine Adresse geben?	*Could you give me your address?*
	Dürfte ich deine Adresse haben?	*Might I have your address?*

56b

Marion und Saras Mitbewohner*innen sind sauer, denn sie wollen eine bessere Kommunikation in der Wohngemeinschaft. Sie hängen diese Notiz an den Kühlschrank:

Liebe Mitbewohner*innen! Bitte lasst uns höflicher sein!

Nein!	**Ja!**
Macht das Licht aus!	Könntet ihr bitte das Licht ausmachen?
Putzen wir endlich das Bad!	
Gebt mir Geld!	
Koch besseres Essen!	
Seien wir nett zueinander!	
Trompetet nicht in der Wohnung!	

56c

Ärger in der Wohngemeinschaft! Marion und Sara haben heute keine Lust, höflich zu sein. Was sollten sie sagen und was sagen sie wirklich?

Sie sollten sagen ...	**Aber sie sagen ...**
Würdet ihr bitte alles recyceln?	Recycelt alles!
Könntet ihr abends bitte leiser sprechen?	
Würdest du bitte deine Schuhe ausziehen?	
Könnten wir morgen einkaufen gehen?	
Würdet ihr bitte die Tür schließen?	
Könntest du mir bitte meine Jacke zurückgeben?	

56d **Ein feines Restaurant im Freizeitpark: Wie kann man das höflich sagen? Wählen Sie das passende Verb. (Mehrere Optionen sind möglich.)**

dürften | könnten | würden | hätten | möchten

Gast: Könnten oder Würden Sie mir bitte ein Gericht empfehlen?

Kellner: __________________ Sie lieber ein vegetarisches Gericht oder Fleisch?

Gast: Ich esse nur Fisch. Und ich __________________ gern eine Suppe.

Kellner: Da __________________ ich Ihnen die Büsumer Krabbensuppe anbieten.

Gast: Das klingt wunderbar. Ich ______________ auch gerne ein Glas Mineralwasser.

Kellner: Selbstverständlich. Unser Restaurant __________________ seine Gäste verwöhnen (*to pamper*). Sie bekommen ein Dessert gratis.

Gast: Vielen Dank!

57a Subjunctive II for Irreal Wishes

In an imperfect world like ours, there is much to wish for. Some of our desires can be expressed by saying something like …

Ich hätte gerne ein großes Schokoladeneis.	*I would like a big chocolate ice cream.*
Ich wünsche mir ein neues iPhone zum Geburtstag.	*I wish for a new iPhone for my birthday.*

Sometimes, however, you might want to express a wish with a very small likelihood of being fulfilled. It might be out of the listeners' power to grant your wish, the wish might be actually more like a dream ("world peace"), or it might be simply over the top ("a million euros to spend on *Zuckerwatte*"). Still, it is completely acceptable to utter a wish like that, and the subjunctive II is the perfect tool to mark the wish as an irreal one.

These wish sentences come in two unusual structures:

The first one looks like a subordinate clause (*Nebensatz*), starting with the subordinating conjunction ***wenn*** and the verb in subjunctive II at the end of the sentence. The big differences are that there is no main clause, that the modal particle ***doch*** or ***nur*** has to be inserted, and that you need an exclamation mark at the end.

Wenn ich **nur** kein Examen schreiben müsste!	*If only I didn't have to take an exam!*
Wenn ich **doch** auf meine Mutter gehört hätte!	*If only I had listened to my mother!*

The second structure resembles an imperative since the sentence starts with the verb in subjunctive II. You will also have to mark the sentence with the modal particle ***doch*** or ***nur***, and add an exclamation mark.

Hätte ich **doch** genug Geld für die Reise!	*If only I had enough money for the trip!*
Wäre ich **nur** zu Hause geblieben!	*If only I had stayed home!*

57b **Mareks Wünsche. Marek träumt von einem besseren Leben. Was wünscht er sich?**

Meine Eltern sind schon alt … Ach, wenn meine Eltern doch nur nicht *so alt wären*!

Ich habe keinen Job … Ach, wenn ich doch ________________!

Meine Freund*innen spielen zu viel „Fortnite" … Ach, wenn sie doch ________________!

Meine Oma gibt mir kein Geld … Ach, wenn sie mir doch ________________!

Ich schlafe nicht genug … Ach, wenn ich doch ________________!

Wir reisen so selten … Ach, wenn wir doch ________________!

18: „Penny Pepper: Alarm auf der Achterbahn"°

58a **Kriminalgeschichten, im Deutschen auch Krimis genannt, haben als Genre oft eine ähnliche Struktur. Hier sehen Sie sich die typische Struktur von Krimis in der westlichen Literaturtradition an. Erstellen Sie zuerst Ihr Krimi-Glossar mit einem Wörterbuch. Bringen Sie dann die Elemente unten in die richtige Reihenfolge (1–7).**

Deutsch	Englisch	Deutsch	Englisch
die Bestrafung	________	die Ordnung	________
die Verhaftung	________	die Sicherheit	________
der*die Schuldige	________	unschuldig	________
die Lösung	________	der*die Verdächtige	________
die Tat / das Verbrechen	________	die Fährte	________
die Wiederherstellung	________	die Hypothese	________

____ Bestrafung/Verhaftung des*der Schuldigen

____ Detektiv*in ermittelt

____ überraschende Lösung

____ rätselhafte(s) Tat/Verbrechen

____ Wiederherstellung der Ordnung/Sicherheit

____ unschuldige*r Hauptverdächtige*r

____ falsche Fährte/Hypothesen

58b **Welche Kriminalgeschichten kennen Sie? Wählen Sie bis zu drei Krimis. Welche Elemente aus 58a haben Ihre Krimis? Welche nicht? Schreiben Sie „ja" oder „nein" in die Tabelle.**

Element Nummer	Krimi 1: ________	Krimi 2: ________	Krimi 3: ________
1			
2			
3			
4			
5			
6			
7			

58c **Lesen Sie gern Kriminalgeschichten? Warum (nicht)? Welche Elemente muss eine gute Kriminalgeschichte für Sie haben? Schreiben Sie 2–3 Sätze und benutzen Sie „weil"-Konstruktionen.**

59a **„Penny Pepper: Alarm auf der Achterbahn". In MACHEN lesen Sie einen Teil von Ulrike Rylances Buch. Aber wer ist die Autorin? Lesen Sie die Kurzbiografie und beantworten Sie die Fragen dazu.**

Ulrike Rylance kommt ursprünglich aus Jena. Sie wohnte ein paar Jahre lang in Leipzig und in London und heute lebt sie mit ihrer Familie in Seattle, USA. Sie arbeitet als freiberufliche Autorin. Rylance studierte Anglistik und Germanistik in Leipzig und London. Als Studentin arbeitete sie auch als Assistant Teacher in Wales und Manchester. Nachdem sie ihr Studium abgeschlossen hatte, blieb sie zuerst in London und arbeitete dort als Deutschlehrerin für Kinder und Erwachsene. 2010 veröffentlichte sie ihren ersten Jugendroman und seitdem hat sie weitere Kinder- und Jugendbücher geschrieben. Sie schreibt auch unter den Pseudonymen Ulrike Herwig (Unterhaltungsromane für Erwachsene), Caro Martini (Frauenromane mit „Magic Twist") und Carly Wilson (High School-Serie „Myriad High"). Rylances „Penny Pepper"-Bücher sind eine Serie von Kriminalgeschichten für Kinder und Jugendliche.

In welchen Ländern hat Ulrike Rylance schon gewohnt (inklusive ihres jetzigen Wohnortes)?

Wo und was studierte Ulrike Rylance und was war ihr Job als Studentin?

Was hat sie nach ihrem Studium zuerst gemacht?

Wann hat sie ihr erstes Buch publiziert?

Zu welchen Genres gehören ihre Bücher?

59b **Penny Pepper und ihre Freundinnen. Im Buch erlebt Penny viele Abenteuer mit ihren Freundinnen Ida, Marie, Flora und dem Hund Dschastin. Aber wir erfahren nicht viele persönliche Details über die Personen. Seien Sie kreativ: Schauen Sie sich das Foto der vier Freundinnen an. Schreiben Sie dann für jede Person eine fiktive Minibiografie. Wie alt ist die Person? Wo wohnt sie? Was sind ihre Hobbys? Etc. Schreiben Sie ca. zwei Sätze pro Person.**

Penny:

____

____

Marie:

____

____

Ida:

____

____

Flora:

____

____

60a **Textvorbereitung: Gehen Sie durch den Text in Aktivität 60 in MACHEN. Markieren Sie alle Wörter, die Sie nicht kennen. Entscheiden Sie: Welche fünf Wörter sind davon am wichtigsten? Finden Sie für diese Wörter die englische Übersetzung in einem Wörterbuch.**

Wort 1: ____________________ Englische Übersetzung: ____________________

Wort 2: ____________________ Englische Übersetzung: ____________________

Wort 3: ____________________ Englische Übersetzung: ____________________

Wort 4: ____________________ Englische Übersetzung: ____________________

Wort 5: ____________________ Englische Übersetzung: ____________________

19: Achterbahn – Made in D-A-CH-L

62a **Sie haben schon über Ihre Erfahrungen in Freizeitparks gesprochen und auch etwas über deutsche Freizeitparks gelernt. Kommen wir nun zum Thema „Achterbahn". Beantworten Sie die folgenden Fragen.**

Welche Freizeitparks gibt es in Ihrer Nähe?

____

____

Gibt es in diesen Parks auch Achterbahnen?

Wenn ja, sind Sie schon damit gefahren? Wie war es?

____

____

Was ist Ihre Lieblingsachterbahn? Warum ist diese Bahn so toll? Wie oft sind Sie schon damit gefahren?

____

In welchem Park befindet sich Ihre Lieblingsachterbahn?

____

Kennen Sie eine Achterbahn, mit der Sie nicht fahren möchten? Welche ist das? Und warum?

____

62b **Wo spricht man noch mal Deutsch? Die meisten Achterbahnen kommen aus der D-A-CH-L-Region, also aus Deutschland, Österreich, der Schweiz oder Liechtenstein. Das sind natürlich Länder, in denen man Deutsch spricht. Aber in welchen anderen Ländern spricht man noch Deutsch? Lesen Sie den Text. Markieren Sie dann in drei verschiedenen Farben a) alle deutschsprachigen Länder, b) Länder, in denen Deutsch eine Amts- oder Minderheitensprache ist, und c) Länder oder Gemeinden, wo man noch Deutsch oder deutsche Varianten spricht.**

Überall auf der Welt sprechen Menschen Deutsch. Für ca. 100 Millionen Menschen ist Deutsch Mutter- oder Zweitsprache. Und knapp 80 Millionen sprechen Deutsch als Fremdsprache! Zu den deutschsprachigen Ländern gehören außer Deutschland noch Österreich und Liechtenstein. Zusätzlich hat Deutsch in mehreren Ländern den Status einer Amtssprache oder gilt offiziell als Minderheitensprache (Schweiz, Belgien, Dänemark, Italien – Südtirol und Vatikanstadt –, Luxemburg, Polen, Slowakei, Rumänien, Tschechische Republik, Ungarn und Russland).

Aber auch außerhalb des europäischen Kontinents ist die deutsche Sprache präsent. So wird Deutsch zum Beispiel in Brasilien von über einer Million Menschen gesprochen. Und auch in Mexiko oder Australien gibt es deutschsprachige Gemeinden, weil viele Deutsche in der ersten Hälfte des 20. Jahrhunderts ausgewandert sind.

Auch in Afrika spricht man Deutsch. Im afrikanischen Namibia ist es für etwa 20.000 Menschen Muttersprache und gehört zu den elf Nationalsprachen. Der Grund hierfür ist allerdings Deutschlands Kolonialgeschichte. Bis 1915 gab es in Namibia die Kolonie Deutsch-Südwestafrika. Von 1904 bis 1908 verübten die deutschen Kolonialmächte dort einen Genozid an den Herero und Nama.

In den USA gibt es Regionen bzw. Gemeinden, in denen man Varianten des Deutschen spricht. Bestimmt haben Sie schon mal etwas vom *Pennsylvania Dutch* (oder Pennsylvaniadeutsch) gehört. Es waren deutsche Siedler*innen aus der Pfalz, die ihren Dialekt vor dreihundert Jahren in die Staaten mitgebracht haben. Ein anderes Beispiel ist Plautdietsch, eine Variante des Niederdeutschen. Es kam im 16. Jahrhundert mit den Mennonit*innen in die USA. Nur sehr wenige amerikanische Mennonit*innen sprechen heute noch Plautdietsch, z. B. in Oklahoma und Kansas.

63a Subjunctive II in the Past

The subjunctive II can be used for unreal statements in the present time, but sometimes you also want to express something that might, would, or should have happened in the past. Thus we have to look at the **past tense** of **the subjunctive II**. Fortunately, there is only one structure to learn.

Let's construct a real event in the past and its logical consequences in the indicative mood:

real event		real consequences
Ich war krank.	⇒	Ich ging nicht auf die Kirmes.
	⇒	Ich musste im Bett bleiben.

And now let's speculate with the subjunctive II (*Konjunktiv II*) what would have happened in the past if I had not been sick, which is the subjunctive II in the past tense:

- the subjunctive II forms of *haben* or *sein* as the auxiliary verbs in the second position of the sentence,
- and a past participle in the last position of the sentence.

Ich hätte die Kirmes besucht. — *I would have visited the fairground.*
Ich hätte ein Kilo Zuckerwatte gegessen. — *I would have eaten a kilo of cotton candy.*
Ich wäre mit der Achterbahn gefahren. — *I would have ridden the roller coaster.*
Ich wäre den ganzen Abend dort geblieben. — *I would have stayed the whole night.*

As you can see, **subjunctive II** in the **past tense** can be formulated in two ways:
with *hätte* + participle
with *wäre* + participle

When we add the **modal verbs** to the mix, we always have
- the conjugated form of *hätte* in the second position,
- the infinitive of the original verb + **the infinitive of the modal verb** at the end of the sentence.

- Ich hätte auch mit der Geisterbahn fahren **können**. — *I could have ridden the ghost train as well.*
- Ich hätte nicht im Bett bleiben **müssen**. — *I would not have had to stay in bed.*
- Ich hätte nicht so viel Cola trinken **sollen**. — *I shouldn't have drunk so much Coke.*

As you can see, **subjunctive II** in the **past tense with modal verbs** is formed as follows:
with *hätte*
+ infinitive (original verb)
+ **infinitive (modal verb)**

63b Setzen Sie die Hilfsverben in den Konjunktiv II der Vergangenheit.

Plusquamperfekt	Konjunktiv II der Vergangenheit
war geflogen	*wäre* geflogen
hatte gearbeitet	________ gearbeitet
hatte gegessen	________ gegessen
war gekommen	________ gekommen
hatte geschrieben	________ geschrieben
war gewesen	________ gewesen

63c **Leider konnte Mimi gestern nicht auf das Volksfest gehen, weil sie zu viel zu tun hatte. Was denkt sie? Setzen Sie das fehlende Hilfsverb im Konjunktiv II ein.**

______________ ich doch nur Zeit für das Volksfest gehabt!

Ich ______________ ganz viel Zuckerwatte gegessen …

Ich ______________ dreimal mit der Achterbahn gefahren!

Meine Freund*innen und ich ______________ andere Leute von der Uni getroffen.

Wir ______________ zum Bierzelt gegangen.

Dort ______________ wir viel gelacht und gesungen.

Harry ______________ mit mir Geisterbahn gefahren.

63d **Klaas denkt an letztes Jahr. Er hat so viele Fehler gemacht! Was hätte er besser machen können? Benutzen Sie den Konjunktiv II der Vergangenheit mit Modalverben.**

Konjunktiv II der Vergangenheit	**Konjunktiv II der Vergangenheit mit Modalverb**	
hätte mehr Briefe geschrieben (*would have written*)	Er hätte mehr Briefe schreiben können. (*could have written*)	(können)
hätte Pläne entwickelt (*would have developed*)	______________ (*should have developed*)	(sollen)
hätte mehr gearbeitet (*would have worked*)	______________ (*would have wanted to work*)	(wollen)
hätte weniger Schoko gegessen (*would have eaten*)	______________ (*would have been allowed to eat*)	(dürfen)
hätte Hilfe bekommen (*would have received*)	______________ (*would have had to receive*)	(müssen)
hätte mehr Leute kennengelernt (*would have gotten to know*)	______________ (*could have gotten to know*)	(können)
hätte Komplimente gemacht (*would have made*)	______________ (*should have made*)	(sollen)
wäre öfter zu Mutter gekommen (*would have come*)	______________ (*would have wanted to come*)	(wollen)
wäre optimistischer geworden (*would have become*)	______________ (*would have been allowed to become*)	(dürfen)
wäre nicht nach Las Vegas geflogen (*would have flown*)	______________ (*would have had to fly*)	(müssen)
wäre netter zu allen gewesen (*would have been*)	______________ (*could have been*)	(können)

20: Schwerelos – Physik der Achterbahn

67a **Lesen Sie den Text.**

Das Aktionsprinzip, auch 2. Newtonsches Gesetz genannt, trägt den Namen des bekannten Physikers Isaac Newton. Es besagt, dass die Beschleunigung direkt proportional zur Kraft und indirekt proportional zur Masse des Körpers ist. Die Schwerkraft bewirkt auf der Erde, dass alle Körper nach „unten", das bedeutet in Richtung Erdmittelpunkt fallen, solange sie nicht daran gehindert werden. Die Fliehkraft ist die zentrifugale Kraft, die bei Dreh- und Kreisbewegungen eines Körpers auftritt. Die Lageenergie ist die potentielle Energie eines Körpers, wenn er aus einer bestimmten Höhe herunterfällt. Die kinetische Energie ist die Energie, die ein Körper aufgrund seiner Bewegung hat. Sie wird auch Bewegungsenergie genannt.

Ordnen Sie mithilfe des Textes (ohne Wörterbuch!) den deutschen Begriffen die englischen Übersetzungen zu.

a) das Aktionsprinzip — *Newton's second law of motion*
b) die Schwerkraft — *gravity*
c) die Fliehkraft — *centrifugal force*
d) die Lageenergie — *potential energy*
e) die Bewegungsenergie — *kinetic energy*

67b **Ordnen Sie zu.**

a) Kraft = Masse • Beschleunigung — $E = m \cdot g \cdot h$
b) Gravitation auf der Erde = 9,81 Meter/Sekunde^2 — $g = 9{,}81\ m/s^2$
c) Zentrifugalkraft = Masse • Geschwindigkeit^2/Radius — $F = m \cdot a$
d) potentielle Energie = Masse • Gravitation • Höhe — $F = m \cdot v^2/r$
e) kinetische Energie = ½ • Masse • Geschwindigkeit^2 — $a = v^2/r$
f) Zentrifugalbeschleunigung = Geschwindigkeit^2/Radius — $P = m \cdot a \cdot v \cdot y$
g) Leistung = Masse • Beschleunigung • Geschwindigkeit • Wirkungsgrad — $E = ½ \cdot m \cdot v^2$

67c **Rechnen Sie und wählen Sie die korrekte Lösung aus.**

Ein Körper mit einer Masse m = 120 kg wird mit einer Beschleunigung von a = 45 m/s^2 beschleunigt. Wie groß ist die Kraft?

5.200 N — 5.400 N — 5.600 N — 5.800 N

Wir schleudern eine Masse von 4 kg mit einer Geschwindigkeit von 20 m/s auf einer Kreisbahn mit einem Radius von 0,80 m. Wie groß ist die wirkende Zentrifugalkraft?

1.000 N — 1.500 N — 2.000 N — 2.500 N

Wie viel potentielle Energie verliert ein 40,77 kg schweres Mädchen beim Sprung von einem 5 m hohen Turm?

2.000 MJ — 2.500 MJ — 3.000 MJ — 3.500 MJ

21: Design und Gestaltung

70a Review: Adjective Endings

Adjectives in both German and English serve to describe, characterize, or clarify a noun. In both languages, adjectives are typically placed before a noun (= attributive adjectives, those that aren't known as predicative adjectives).

Die Achterbahn ist schnell.	*The roller coaster is fast. (= predicative adjective)*
Ich fahre mit einer **schnellen** Achterbahn.	*I am riding a fast roller coaster.*
Die **schnelle** Achterbahn ist klasse!	*The fast roller coaster is awesome!*
Schnelle Achterbahnen sind besser.	*Fast roller coasters are better.*

In English, we do not change adjective endings based on the noun being described. German adjectives, however, change endings based on gender, case, number of the noun, and the article used/not used.

There are several methods for learning adjective endings, including the memorization of tables of adjective endings based on gender, number, case, and article word. The following method avoids such rote memorization by **asking four questions about the article preceding the ADJECTIVE and the noun it is referring to:**

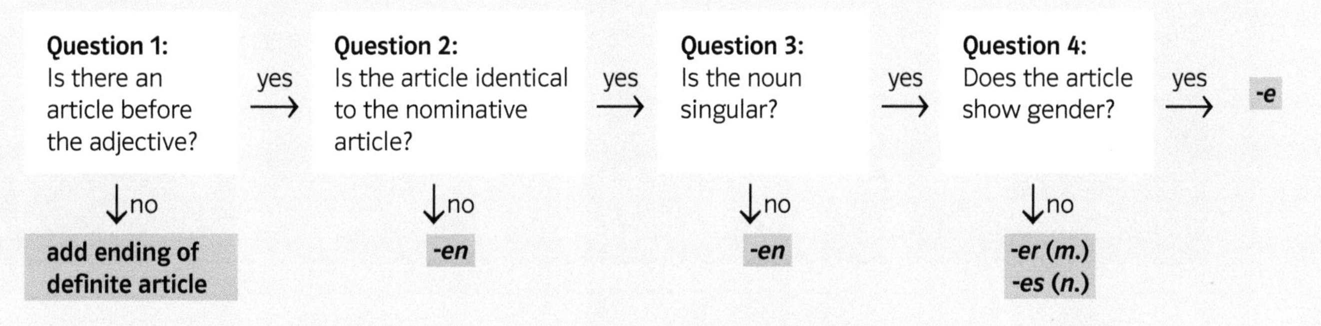

70b Wie heißt die richtige Adjektivendung? Tipp: Lesen Sie noch einmal Frage 1 der Flowchart.

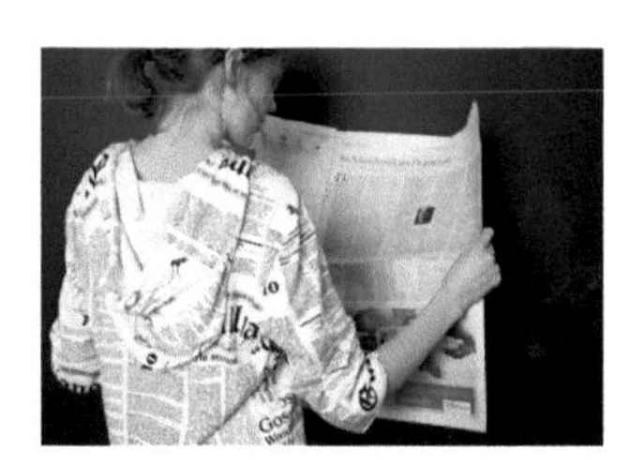

Gigantisch____ Achterbahn (*f.*) im Freizeitpark geplant!

Neu____ Naturpark (*m.*) in Aachen jetzt geöffnet

Profitabl____ Fahrgeschäft (*n.*) zu verkaufen

Groß____ Rummel (*m.*) in Aischingen erwartet

Lustig____ Besucher*innen (*pl.*) im Spielepark: 500 Kinder aus Litauen kommen zu Besuch

70c Wie heißt die richtige Adjektivendung? Tipp: Lesen Sie noch einmal Frage 2 der Flowchart.

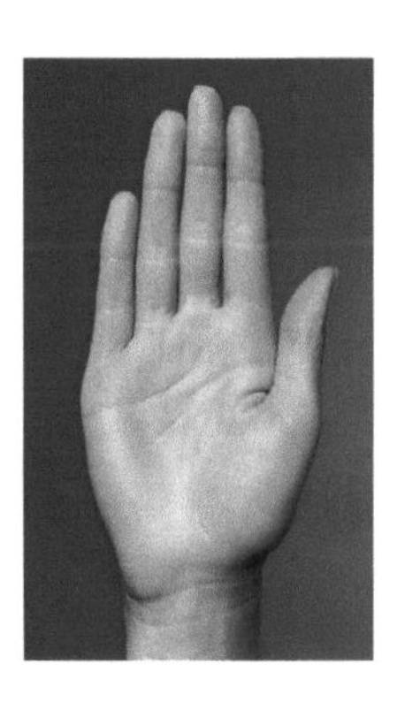

Penny Pepper besuchte eine fahrend____ Wahrsagerin (*f.*), Madame Cherie.

Madame Cherie sah nur eine ziemlich kurz____ Kopflinie (*f.*) in Pennys Hand.

Aber das passt nicht. Denn Penny hat einen sehr hoh____ Intelligenzquotienten (*m.*).

Mit ihrem scharf____ Intellekt (*m.*) hat Penny schon viele Kriminalfälle gelöst.

Die lang____ Sonnen(glücks)linie (*f.*) in Pennys Hand hat Madame Cherie auch falsch interpretiert.

Pennys Geldbörse wurde aus ihrem klein____ Rucksack (*m.*) gestohlen – also hatte Penny kein Glück.

70d **Auf der Achterbahn. Hier lernen Sie, welche Arten von Achterbahnen es gibt. Lesen Sie die acht Beschreibungen und finden Sie das passende Bild dazu.**

Sitting Coaster
Die Wagen fahren, ganz klassisch, auf der Schiene und die Mitfahrenden sitzen.
Bild Nr. ________

Stand up Coaster
Auch hier fahren die Wagen auf der Schiene, aber die Mitfahrenden stehen.
Bild Nr. ________

Inverted Coaster
Die Wagen hängen unter der Schiene und die Beine baumeln frei herunter.
Bild Nr. ________

Flying Coaster
Die Mitfahrenden liegen in den Wagen und fahren, mit dem Kopf voraus, entweder auf dem Bauch oder dem Rücken.
Bild Nr. ________

Suspended Coaster
Das Fahrgestell hängt unter der Schiene und kann frei hin und her schwingen. Deshalb gibt es keine Überkopffiguren.
Bild Nr. ________

Floorless Coaster
Die Wagen fahren auf (oder neben) der Schiene, aber sie haben keinen Boden.
Bild Nr. ________

Spinning Coaster
Der Wagen dreht sich (kontrolliert oder unkontrolliert) 360 Grad im Kreis.
Bild Nr. ________

Wing Coaster
Die Mitfahrenden sitzen zu zweit rechts und links von der Schiene. Das Fahrgestell hat keinen Boden.
Bild Nr. ________

70e **Auf der Achterbahn. Hier sehen Sie sechs typische Elemente einer Achterbahn. Schreiben Sie das richtige Wort unter die Bilder.**

____

____

____

____

____

____

die Kurve
der Looping
die Abfahrt
der Airtime-Hügel
die Auffahrt
der Korkenzieher

71a Review: Comparative and Superlative

Comparative
A > B oder
A < B

adjective +er **als**

Meine Limonade schmeckt frischer **als** deine. — *My lemonade tastes fresher than yours.*
Sind Saftschorlen beliebter **als** Limonaden? — *Are juice spritzers more[1] popular than lemonades?*

Comparative
A = B

(genau)so adjective **wie**

Der Luftballon ist **so** teuer **wie** die Rose. — *The balloon is as expensive as the rose.*
Der Luftballon fliegt **genauso** hoch **wie** der Vogel. — *The balloon flies just as high as the bird.*

Superlative
A > B, C, . . .
A < B, C, . . .

am adjective +sten[2]

Walzertanzen ist einfacher als Polka, aber Discofox ist **am** einfachsten. — *Dancing the waltz is easier than the polka, but the disco fox is the easiest.*

Sie sagt, dass Polka **am** traditionellsten[3] ist. — *She says that the polka is the most traditional.*

[1] Unlike English, German does not use the word ***mehr*** (more) to form the comparative of multisyllabic adjectives.
[2] In the superlative, adjectives ending in **-t**, **-d**, or a vowel add an e before **-sten**: *intelligent* → ***am** intelligent**e**sten*
[3] Note that the superlative is used as a predicative adjective here. If you use it as an attributive adjective, the *am* is dropped: *Der traditionell**ste** Tanz ist die Polka.*

Adjektiv	**A = B**	**A > B** oder **A < B**	**A > B, C, . . .** oder **A < B, C, . . .**	
schnell	**so** schnell **wie**	schneller **als**	am schnellsten	*fast*
langsam	**so** langsam **wie**	langsamer **als**	am langsamsten	*slow*
groß	**so** groß **wie**	größer **als**	am größten	*large or tall*
klein	**so** klein **wie**	kleiner **als**	am kleinsten	*small or short*
hoch	**so** hoch **wie**	höher **als**	am höchsten	*high/tall*
gut	**so** gut **wie**	besser **als**	am besten	*good*
schlecht	**so** schlecht **wie**	schlechter **als**	am schlechtesten	*bad*
gern	**so** gern **wie**	lieber **als**	am liebsten	*to like/to prefer*

71b Benutzen Sie den Link auf www.klett-usa.com/impuls2links und vergleichen Sie die drei Achterbahnen.

Recherche

Achterbahnen: „Formula Rossa" (Abu Dhabi), „Kingda Ka" (New Jersey), „Steel Dragon" 2000 (Japan)

schnell: „Formula Rossa" ist schneller als „Kingda Ka". „Kingda Ka" ist schneller als „Steel Dragon 2000".
„Formula Rossa" ist am schnellsten.

hoch: ______________________________

____

lang: ______________________________

____

gut: ______________________________

____

71c **Was wissen Sie über Holzachterbahnen? Suchen Sie online nach den Antworten.**

Recherche

Weltweit gibt es ______________ Holzachterbahnen.

0–50 100–200 300–400

Die erste Holzachterbahn wurde ________ gebaut.

1817 1885 1910

1999 baute man die erste moderne Holzachterbahn in Deutschland. Bis 2004 hieß sie „Wild Wild West".

Heute heißt sie ______________.

„Racoon" „Outlaw" „Bandit"

Die höchste je gebaute Holzachterbahn hieß „Son of Beast" im Kings Island Park (Ohio). Sie war _____ Meter hoch.

15 37 64

„Son of Beast" war mit ________ km/h auch die schnellste Holzachterbahn der Welt.

100 126 145

72a **Freizeitparks barrierefrei. In einem Freizeitpark können viele Dinge zu einem Problem werden, wenn man die Bedürfnisse (*needs*) von Menschen mit Behinderungen oder von Neuro-Minderheiten ignoriert. Für welche Menschengruppen sind welche Probleme besonders problematisch? Ordnen Sie zu.**

Menschen, die nicht gut laufen können	Menschen, die im Rollstuhl sitzen
schwere Türen zum Selberöffnen	
Menschen, die nicht gut sehen können	**Menschen, die blind sind**
Menschen, die taub sind	**Menschen mit Autismus**

Broschüren mit kleiner Schrift
~~schwere Türen zum Selberöffnen~~
keine Ruheräume
wenige oder keine Aufzüge (*elevators*)
Schilder ohne Brailleschrift
keine Rampen
Informationen, die man nur hören kann
Wege, die sehr uneben sind
Begleit- oder Assistenzhunde dürfen nicht in den Park
Toiletten, die nur für Leute konzipiert sind, die gehen können
schlechte Beleuchtung (*lighting*) auf Gehwegen
alle Gäst*innen müssen lange in der Schlange warten

22: Geprüfte Sicherheit°

73a MaTHEMAtik: Probability, Proportions, Big Numbers

Wahrscheinlichkeiten

In order to express the probability of something to happen (like winning the lottery), English uses the preposition "in" to say "one in a million." In German, ***zu*** is used to express the same meaning.

You write …	You say …	Meaning
1:1.000.000	eins **zu** einer Million	*one in a million*
1:10.000	eins **zu** zehntausend	*one in ten thousand*
2:120	zwei **zu** einhundertzwanzig	*one in one hundred and twenty*

Die Wahrscheinlichkeit, im Lotto zu gewinnen, ist eins **zu** fünf Millionen.

The chance of winning the lottery is one in five million.

Proportionen

While German and English differ in their expression of probabilities, they are very similar when it comes to expressing the frequency of events. In English, we can say something happens multiple times "per week." The German equivalent is ***pro*** *Woche*.

You write …	You say …	Meaning
3/Tag	drei (Mal) / dreimal **pro** Tag	*three (times) per day*
5/Woche	fünf (Mal) / fünfmal **pro** Woche	*five (times) per week*
7/Jahr	sieben (Mal) / siebenmal **pro** Jahr	*seven (times) per year*

Note: In German, the word *Mal/-mal* is inserted in order to answer the question "How often / How many times?" Without the *Mal/-mal*, you are replying to the question "How many?"

Wie oft gehst du in den Freizeitpark?
→ Dreimal pro Jahr.

How often do you go to the theme park?
→ Three times per year.

Wie viele Bücher liest du durchschnittlich?
→ Zwei pro Monat.

How many books do you read on average?
→ Two per month.

Große Zahlen lesen

When it comes to saying large numbers in German, there are, generally speaking, two ways of doing that. For example, 1.350.000 can either be read as *1,35 Millionen* (*eins Komma drei fünf Millionen*) or as *eine Million dreihundertfünfzigtausend.*

73b Wahrscheinlichkeiten. Füllen Sie die Lücken aus.

Schreiben:		Sprechen:
1:150.000	→	eins zu einer einshundert fünfzig tausend
1:1.250.000	→	eins zu einer Million zweihundertfünfzigtausend
3:8	→	drei zu acht
3:17.500	→	drei zu siebzehntausend fünf hundert
2:125	→	~~zw~~ zwei zu eins hundert fünfund zwanzig
4:39,003	→	vier zu dreiundneunzigtausenddrei

73c **Proportionen. Wie oft und wie viel? Schreiben Sie ganze Sätze, wie in den Beispielen.**

Tom – ins Kino gehen (3/Monat)

Tom geht dreimal pro Monat ins Kino.

Nadja – Bücher lesen (20/Jahr)

Nadja liest zwanzig Bücher pro Jahr.

Hiko – mit der Familie telefonieren (2/Woche)

____

Juri – in den Urlaub fahren (3/Jahr)

____

Sara – Kurse haben (5/Woche)

____

Nizam – Stunden schlafen (6/Nacht)

____

76a **Was ist der TÜV? In diesem Text lernen Sie etwas über den TÜV und warum es ihn gibt. Ergänzen Sie die Sätze unten rechts mit Wörtern und Formulierungen aus dem Text.**

TÜV. Diese oft gebrauchte Abkürzung steht für „Technischer Überwachungsverein". Der TÜV hat die Aufgabe, technische Geräte auf ihre Sicherheit hin zu untersuchen, zu überprüfen und für die Benutzung freizugeben.

Autobesitzer*innen wissen, dass sie alle zwei Jahre mit ihrem Fahrzeug eine Werkstatt des TÜVs besuchen müssen. Die Ingenieur*innen in der Werkstatt kontrollieren die Bremsen, die Lenkung und alle anderen Autoteile, die für eine sichere Fahrt wichtig sind.

Sehr viele Geräte und Anlagen, denen wir in unserem täglichen Leben begegnen, werden vom TÜV geprüft, bevor man sie in Betrieb nehmen kann. Dazu gehören zum Beispiel Aufzüge, Kraftwerke, Einrichtungen für die Sicherheit am Arbeitsplatz oder für den Strahlen- und Umweltschutz.

Aber auch bei großen Kirmesbetrieben müssen Karussells, Riesenräder und Achterbahnen erst vom TÜV geprüft werden, ehe sich die Besucher*innen darauf vergnügen können.

Der erste deutsche Technische Überwachungsverein wurde 1866 im Zeitalter der Industrialisierung gegründet. Damals hatte es immer wieder Unfälle mit explodierenden Dampfmaschinen gegeben. Deshalb war eine Sicherheitsüberprüfung notwendig geworden.

Quelle: HanisauLand (vereinfacht)

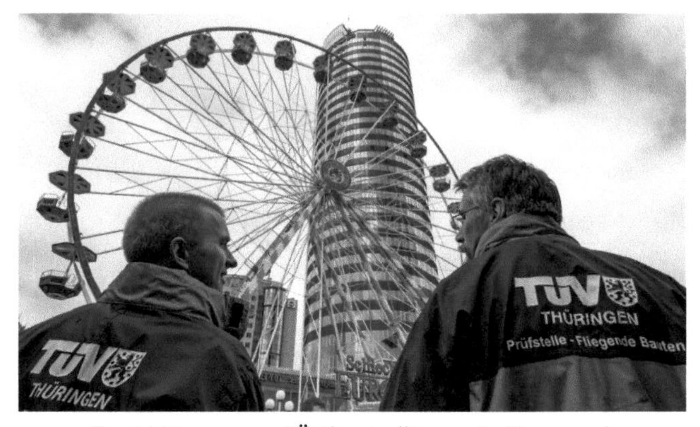

Zwei Männer vom TÜV kontrollieren ein Riesenrad.

Den TÜV gibt es seit dem Jahr ______. Gegründet wurde er, weil immer wieder Dinge, wie zum Beispiel ____________________, explodierten. Deshalb brauchte man jemanden, der diese Konstruktionen auf ihre ____________________ hin überprüfte.
Heute kontrolliert der TÜV immer noch viele Dinge aus unserem ____________________ Leben. Menschen, die ein Auto besitzen, müssen ihr Fahrzeug alle ____________________ in eine ____________________ des TÜVs bringen. Auch auf Volksfesten und Kirmessen ist der TÜV aktiv. Hier überprüft er die Sicherheit von Karussells, Achterbahnen und ____________________.
Wenn der TÜV sagt, dass ein Gerät oder eine Anlage nicht sicher ist, dann darf man es/sie nicht ______ ____________________ nehmen.

23: Hobbys und Berufe für Adrenalin-Junkies

77a Review: *warum* and *weil*

In English, questions starting with "why" are inevitably linked to answers beginning with "because":
Why is Maria going home? She's going home because she's tired.

German works the same way using *warum* and *weil*:
Warum geht Maria nach Hause? Sie geht nach Hause, weil sie müde ist.

1. Main clause: usual word order (conjugated verb in second position)

   Ich **habe** viel Arbeit. — *I have a lot of work.*

2. Main clause: usual word order (verb second), Subordinate clause: conjugated verb at end of clause

   Ich **gehe** nicht tanzen, weil ich viel Arbeit **habe**. — *I'm not going dancing because I have a lot of work.*

3. Subordinate clause: conjugated verb at end of clause, Main clause: usual word order (verb second)

   Weil ich viel Arbeit **habe, gehe** ich nicht tanzen. — *Because I have a lot of work, I'm not going dancing.*

   Note: Here, the entire subordinate *weil*-clause fills the first position, with *gehe* in second position.

Note: Always use a main clause with a subordinate clause (with ***weil***) in writing. In oral conversations, you can leave out the main clause, primarily because the information is already given in the question itself and does not need to be repeated:

Warum gehst du nicht tanzen? → Weil ich viel Arbeit **habe.** (verb still at end of clause)

77b Warum macht Familie Angsthase das nicht?

Warum fährt Volker Angsthase nicht gerne mit einem Aufzug? Er hat Angst, dass der Aufzug stecken bleibt.

Weil er hat Angst hat, dass der Aufzug stecken bleibt.

Warum geht Liliane Angsthase bei Gewitter ins Bett? Sie will keinen Donner hören.

Liliane geht bei Gewittir ins Bett, weil will Keinen Donner Hören

Warum hält die kleine Angelika Angsthase immer ihren Teddybären? Er gibt ihr Sicherheit.

Warum nehmen Herr und Frau Angsthase kein Taxi? Sie glauben, Taxis haben mehr Unfälle.

Warum will Marco Angsthase kein Hotelzimmer im 10. Stock? Er hat Höhenangst.

Warum mag Ulli Angsthase keine großen Partys? Er findet laute Gespräche schrecklich.

77c **Ich mag Abenteuer! Invertieren Sie die Sätze, wie im Beispiel.**

Ich fahre Ski, weil ich den Wind um meine Ohren mag.

Weil ich den Wind um meine Ohren mag, fahre ich Ski.

Ich mag Tiefseetauchen, weil ich dann vielleicht einen Hai sehe.

___

Ich surfe im Pazifik, weil die Wellen so hoch sind.

___

Ich fahre Rennautos, weil ich meine Angst kontrollieren möchte.

___

Ich klettere ohne Seile, weil man da freier ist.

___

Ich mache kein Train-Surfing, weil das verboten ist.

___

77d **Welche Extremsportler*innen kennen Sie in Ihrem Land? Was machen diese Sportler*innen? Finden Sie das extrem? Warum (nicht)? Schreiben Sie über zwei Extremsportler*innen und benutzen Sie „weil"-Sätze.**

Beispiel:

Megan Nick ist eine Freestyle-Skifahrerin. Sie macht gefährliche Sprünge (jumps) mit Skiern.
Ich finde das extrem, weil ich selbst nicht Skifahren kann.

Sportler*in 1:

___

___

Sportler*in 2:

___

___

79a **Phobien. Unten sehen Sie eine Liste mit Fachbegriffen für Phobien, die aus dem Griechischen stammen. Finden Sie die passende deutsche Definition. Schreiben Sie auch auf, was die Fachbegriffe auf Englisch heißen.**

Klaustrophobie *f*
claustrophobia

Octophobie
___

Coulrophobie
___

Arachnophobie
___

Canophobie
___

Altophobie
___

Hemaphobie
___

Decidophobie
___

a) Angst vor Blut
b) Angst vor Clowns
c) Angst vor Spinnen
d) Angst vor Hunden
e) Angst vor der Zahl Acht
f) Angst vor engen Räumen
g) Angst, Entscheidungen zu treffen
h) Angst vor Höhen

79b **Kein Job für mich! Stellen Sie sich vor, Sie haben die Ängste, die unten im Kasten stehen. Welchen Job oder Beruf könnten Sie mit diesen Ängsten nicht ausüben? Folgen Sie dem Beispiel und schreiben Sie fünf Sätze.**

Ich könnte nicht im Tierheim / als Hundesitter arbeiten, weil ich Angst vor Hunden habe.

______

______

______

______

~~Angst vor Hunden~~	eine Spinnenphobie
Höhenangst	Angst vor Menschenmassen
Angst vor Feuer	eine Clownphobie
Angst vor kleinen oder engen Räumen	Angst vor Spritzen

24: Angst – Psyche und Körper

81a **Wie heißen diese Körperteile? Schreiben Sie den Artikel und die Pluralform dazu.**

81b Körperliche Reaktionen. Wählen Sie das passende Verb aus dem Kasten. Achten Sie auf die korrekte Verbendung.

weinen | stottern | atmen | ~~schwitzen~~ | zittern | lachen | schlecht sein (+ *dat.*)

Tamir hat Fieber. Er schwitzt __________ stark.

Serena hat einen Witz[1] gehört und __________.

Ira ist furchtbar kalt. Er __________.

Ling ist gerannt, und jetzt __________ sie schnell.

Peter sieht ein Foto von seinem neugeborenen Enkel und __________.

Luis ist sehr nervös, weil er ein Referat halten muss. Er __________ und ihm __________ auch ein bisschen __________.

[1] der Witz – *joke*

82a Konjunktiv II: Conditional Sentences With *wenn*

Conditional sentences describe an action that will only take place under certain conditions. The condition is expressed in a subordinate clause starting with the subordinating conjunction wenn and ending with the verb. Since conditional structures start with the subordinate clause (*Nebensatz*) most of the time, the main clause (*Hauptsatz*) will follow up with the **verb** in the second position, e.g. directly after the comma.

Wenn es morgen **regnet**,	*If it rains tomorrow,*
gehe ich nicht auf die Kirmes.	*I won't go to the fairground.*

The condition can be a **real/factual** situation or a **hypothetical** one.

Reality/Fact: We assume that once the condition can be fulfilled (*Nebensatz*), the conclusion (*Hauptsatz*) can be fulfilled, too. We use the present tense, indicative mood in both parts. In English, we also use the present tense here.

Nebensatz	Hauptsatz	
Wenn ich Zeit **habe**,	**gehe** ich mit dir auf die Kirmes.	*If I have time, I will go to the fairground with you.*

Irreality/Contrary to fact: Since the condition (*Nebensatz*) is hypothetical and there is reasonable doubt that it can be fulfilled, the conclusion (*Hauptsatz*) is most likely not going to happen, either. This means we are expressing what would happen but is not actually happening. In English, we use "would" for the main clauses of these sentences. In English, we cannot use "would" in the if-clauses; in German, however, we will use the subjunctive II in both clauses.

Nebensatz	Hauptsatz	
Wenn ich Zeit hätte[1],	würde ich mit dir auf die Kirmes **gehen**.	*If I had time, I would go to the fairground with you.*
Wenn ich mich gut **fühlen** würde,	würde ich mit dir auf die Kirmes **gehen**.	*If I felt good, I would go to the fairground with you.*

Irreality in the past: We describe a condition that was not fulfilled in the past, but we still speculate about a possible consequence. In both clauses, we use the subjunctive II / past tense (with *hätte* and *wäre* + **past participle**). As above, in English, we only use "would" (plus present perfect) in the main clause; in the if-clause, however, we would use past perfect without "would."

Nebensatz	Hauptsatz	
Wenn ich Zeit **gehabt** hätte,	wäre ich mit dir auf die Kirmes **gegangen**.	*If I had had time, I would have gone to the fairground with you.*

[1] Remember that for *sein*, *haben*, and the modal verbs, we use the direct subjunctive II forms. For all other verbs, use *würde* + infinitive.

82b **Wählen Sie die passenden Verben.**

Fakt: Monika hat übermorgen keine Zeit. Morgen hat sie aber Zeit.

gehen | gehst | komme | habe (x2) | hätte | würde

Elisa: Monika, ________________ du übermorgen mit mir in den Movie Park?

Monika: Übermorgen ________________ ich keine Zeit. Wenn ich Zeit ________________, ________________ ich mit dir in den Park ________________. Kannst du vielleicht morgen? Wenn ich morgen Zeit ________________, ________________ ich gerne mit.

Fakt: Kim war letzte Woche krank. Morgen hat xier[1] viel Arbeit.

bist | wäre | gewesen wäre | habe | hätte | komme | kommst (x2) | kommen (x2) | gekommen | würde

Uschi: Kim, warum ________________ du letzte Woche nicht zum Judo ________________? ________________ du denn gar nicht mehr?

Kim: Wenn ich letzte Woche gesund ________________, ________________ ich natürlich ________________.

Uschi: ________________ du denn morgen zum Judo?

Kim: Nein, leider nicht. ________________ ich weniger Arbeit, ________________ ich zum Judo ________________. So funktioniert das aber leider nicht. Wenn ich nächste Woche weniger Arbeit ________________, ________________ ich wieder regelmäßig.

[1] Kim benutzt gender-neutrale Pronomen.

82c **Was fühlen Sie: Angst oder Freude? Welche Verben sind hier richtig und welche Reaktionen wählen Sie?**

Wenn ich eine Boa Constrictor …	☐ sehe,	☐ sehen würde,
würde ich …	☐ weglaufen.	☐ sie mitnehmen.
Wenn man mich …	☐ kidnappen würde,	☐ kidnappt,
würde ich …	☐ laut lachen.	☐ um Hilfe rufen.
Wenn ich zu viele Hausaufgaben …	☐ bekommen würde,	☐ bekomme,
würde ich …	☐ sie machen.	☐ protestieren.
Wenn es über meinem Haus …	☐ blitzen würde,	☐ blitzt,
würde ich …	☐ ins Bett krabbeln.	☐ aus dem Fenster sehen.
Wenn ich ein Monster …	☐ treffe,	☐ treffen würde,
würde ich …	☐ schnell weglaufen.	☐ ihm die Hand schütteln.

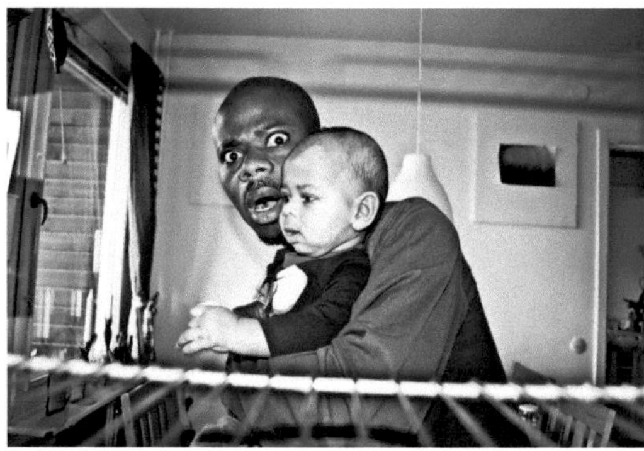

82d Was passiert bei einer gefahrvollen Situation in unserem Körper? Hören Sie das Gespräch zwischen Mutter und Sohn und beantworten Sie die Fragen.

Schritt 1: Was passiert? *Es gibt einen Adrenalinkick.*

Warum passiert das? *Der Körper muss schneller arbeiten.*

Schritt 2: Was passiert? ______

Warum passiert das? ______

Schritt 3: Was passiert? ______

Warum passiert das? ______

Schritt 4: Was passiert? ______

Warum passiert das? ______

Schritt 5: Was passiert? ______

Warum passiert das? ______

82e Was passiert, wenn unser Körper auf eine akute Gefahr reagieren muss? Nehmen Sie die Infos aus Aktivität 82d und schreiben Sie „wenn"-Sätze.

Schritt 1: *Wenn der Körper schneller arbeiten muss, gibt es einen Adrenalinkick.*

Schritt 2: ______

Schritt 3: ______

Schritt 4: ______

Schritt 5: ______

25: Das Leben ist eine Achterbahn

85a **Was würde passieren, wenn ... ? Verbinden Sie die Satzteile mit einer logischen Aussage.**

Wenn ich jeden Tag Sport treiben würde, ______

Wenn meine Freund*innen weniger Geld für Videospiele ausgeben würden, ______

Wenn wir nach Deutschland fliegen würden, ______

Wenn ihr mehr Zeit hättet, __b__

Wenn wir noch mehr Energie sparen würden, ______

Falls du mich am Wochenende besuchen solltest, ______

Falls ich in der Lotterie gewinnen sollte, ______

Wenn es billiger wäre, nach Europa zu fliegen, ______

Wenn meine Mutter mein Zimmer sehen würde, ______

Wenn Sie mich morgen anrufen könnten, ______

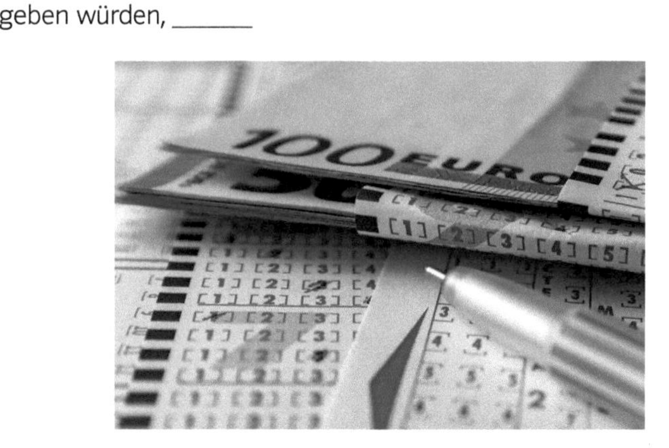

a) ... würde ich dem Roten Kreuz Geld spenden.
b) ... würden wir uns öfter sehen.
c) ... wäre es natürlich besser für die Umwelt.
d) ... würden Sonja und Majid durch ganz Österreich reisen.
e) ... wäre ich athletischer.
f) ... müsste ich die Information für Sie gefunden haben.
g) ... könnten wir öfter zusammen ins Kino gehen.
h) ... wäre sie ziemlich unglücklich über meine Unordnung.
i) ... würden wir die coole Burg Eltz besichtigen.
j) ... könnte ich dir meinen neuen Hybridwagen zeigen.

85b **Letztes Jahr hat Karim leider keine Initiative gezeigt. Schreiben Sie, was er jetzt anders machen würde.**

Er hat nicht im Ausland studiert. *Heute würde er im Ausland studieren.*

Letztes Jahr hat er nicht alle Hausaufgaben gemacht. ______

Er hat nicht mit seinen Professor*innen gesprochen. ______

Er hat kein Geld für einen Urlaub gespart. ______

Sein Freund Pietro und er sind nicht nach Mailand gereist. ______

Sie haben im Sommer auch nicht gearbeitet. ______

86a **Finden Sie im Internet den Text zu Cluesos Lied „Achterbahn“ und lesen Sie ihn. Schreiben Sie nun in die erste Sprechblase 20 Wörter (Nomen, Verben, Adjektive), die Sie schon kennen. Sammeln Sie in der zweiten Sprechblase acht Wörter, die Sie noch nicht kennen. Finden Sie für diese Wörter die englische Übersetzung.**

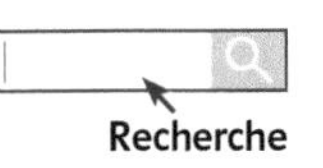

Wörter, die ich kenne | **neue Wörter**

88a **Textvorbereitung: Vom Manager zum Obdachlosen. Die folgenden Übungen helfen Ihnen, in MACHEN über den Text zu sprechen. Lesen Sie zuerst in MACHEN das Interview in Aktivität 88.**

Markieren Sie im Interview die Sätze, in denen Sie etwas über Karl Völkers Leben vor dem Burnout erfahren.

Markieren Sie die Stellen, in denen Völker über sein Leben als Obdachloser spricht. Benutzen Sie dafür eine andere Farbe.

Markieren Sie in einer dritten Farbe den Abschnitt, in dem Völker sagt, wie er aus seiner Situation herausgefunden hat.

Umkreisen Sie die Nomen und Adjektive, mit denen Völker sein Burnout beschreibt. Wenn nötig, schauen Sie sich die englische Bedeutung an.

Wie wird das gemacht?

Die Schweiz als Herstellerin von Qualitätsprodukten

WORTSCHATZ

28: GESCHICHTE(N) DER SCHWEIZ

die Szene, -n	scene
der Hut, -̈e	hat
der Pfeil, -e	dart; arrow
der Jäger, -	huntsman
die Jägerin, -nen	huntswoman
die jagende Person, die Jagenden	hunter (*gender-neutral alternative*)
schießen, schoss, hat ... geschossen	to shoot
befestigen, befestigte, hat ... befestigt	to attach
verstecken, versteckte, hat ... versteckt	to hide
töten, tötete, hat ... getötet	to kill
die Bedrohung, -en	threat
die Entscheidung, -en	decision
treffen (trifft), traf, hat ... getroffen	to hit; meet
Er hat das Ziel getroffen.	He hit the target.
Er hat eine Entscheidung getroffen.	He made a decision.
ehrlich	honest
die Macht, -̈e	power
der Mut	courage
die Organisation, -en	organization
der Grundsatz, -̈e	principle, tenet
der Begriff, -e	term
zu·stimmen, stimmte ... zu, hat ... zugestimmt	to agree
existieren, existierte, hat ... existiert	to exist
verhandeln, verhandelte, hat ... verhandelt	to negotiate, debate
unterschreiben, unterschrieb, hat ... unterschrieben	to sign
versprechen (verspricht), versprach, hat ... versprochen	to promise
kritisieren, kritisierte, hat ... kritisiert	to criticize

Weitere Wörter: der Verteidigungsbund, -̈e (defense organization, defense association); **die Neutralität, -en** (non-alignment (*pol.*); neutrality); **das Frauenstimmrecht, -e** (women's suffrage, voting rights for women); **der Mythos, Mythen** (myth); **bekannt vor·kommen, kam ... vor, ist ... vorgekommen** (to look familiar); **der Kaiser, -** (emperor); **die Kaiserin, -nen** (empress); **das Staatsoberhaupt, -̈er im Kaisertum** (head of an empire (*gender-neutral workaround for emperor/empress*)); **das Dorf, -̈er** (village); **berühmt** (famous, well-known); **grüßen, grüßte, hat ... gegrüßt** (to greet); **die Konsequenz, -en** (consequence); **der Kongress, -e** (congress); **bewaffnet** (armed); **der Konflikt, -e** (conflict); **Teil sein (von + *dat.*) (ist), war, ist ... gewesen** (to be part (of), participate (in)); **protestieren, protestierte, hat ... protestiert** (to protest)

29: GLOBALES GENF – AUF DER SUCHE NACH FORTSCHRITT

die Wissenschaft, -en	science
wissenschaftlich	scientific
die Forschung, -en	research
die Aussage, -n	statement
der Zustand, -̈e	condition, state
versuchen, versuchte, hat ... versucht	to try
der Urknall	big bang
der/das Teil, -e	part
das Teilchen, -	particle
der Beschleuniger, -	accelerator; catalyst
der Strahl, -en	beam (*e.g. of light*)
die Tiefe, -n	depth
besuchen, besuchte, hat ... besucht	to visit
beachten, beachtete, hat ... beachtet	to pay attention to
begegnen, begegnete, ist ... begegnet	to encounter
vergeben (an + *akk.*) (vergibt), vergab, hat ... vergeben	to allocate (to)
der Abschluss, -̈e	degree
öffentlich	public
ähnlich	similar

Weitere Wörter: der Ort, -e (place; location; site); **die Kernforschung, -en** (nuclear research); **analysieren, analysierte, hat ... analysiert** (to analyze); **der Physiker, -** (physicist (*male*)); **die Physikerin, -nen** (physicist (*female*)); **die Fachperson für Physik, das Fachpersonal für Physik** (physicist (*gender-neutral alternative*)); **die Kollision, -en** (collision); **der Sensor, -en** (sensor); **interpretieren, interpretierte, hat ... interpretiert** (to interpret); **besichtigen, besichtigte, hat ... besichtigt** (to visit (*e.g. tourist attraction*)); **der Baustein, -e** (module, component; building brick); **die Wasserfontäne, -n** (water fountain); **das Wappen, -** (emblem, coat of arms); **kollidieren, kollidierte, ist ... kollidiert** (to collide, clash)

31: DAS FILMFESTIVAL IN LOCARNO

der Schauspieler, -	actor
die Schauspielerin, -nen	actress
der*die Darstellende, -n	performer in film/theater (*gender-neutral alternative for actor/actress*)
unterschiedlich	different
jdn. (*akk.*) zum Lachen bringen, brachte, hat ... gebracht	to make somebody laugh
informieren, informierte, hat ... informiert	to inform

jdn. (*akk.*) zum Nachdenken bringen, brachte, hat ... gebracht	to make somebody think, reflect
ästhetisch ansprechend	aesthetically pleasant
die Möglichkeit, -en	possibility; opportunity
aus·zeichnen, zeichnete ... aus, hat ... ausgezeichnet	to award a prize (to somebody); honor
tatsächlich	real(ly), actual(ly)
möglich	possible
halten (hält), hielt, hat ... gehalten	to stop (*e.g. train, bus*); hold
(das) Hochdeutsch(e)	High German, standard German

Weitere Wörter: sinnvoll (useful, reasonable); **entführen, entführte, hat ... entführt** (to abduct, kidnap); **relevant** (relevant); **die heutige Zeit** (today's time); **spannend** (exciting, suspenseful)

32: Demokratie – Mit oder ohne Frauen?

die Bevölkerung, -en	population
die Bundesverfassung, -en	federal constitution
das Stimmrecht, -e	right to vote
die Abstimmung, -en	referendum, voting
die Volksabstimmung, -en	national referendum
Aufmerksamkeit erregen, erregte, hat ... erregt	to attract attention
ein·schränken, schränkte ... ein, hat ... eingeschränkt	to restrict, limit
später	later
erst	only; first
bekannt (für + *akk.*)	known (for)
die Wirkung, -en	impression, effect
bewirken, bewirkte, hat ... bewirkt	to cause, effect
das Plakat, -e	poster
die Rolle, -n	role
repräsentieren, repräsentierte, hat ... repräsentiert	to represent
überzeugend	convincing
beeinflussen, beeinflusste, hat ... beeinflusst	to influence
verhelfen (zu + *dat.*) (verhilft), verhalf, hat ... verholfen	to help provide
der Inhalt, -e	content

Weitere Wörter: das politische System (political system); **die Provokation, -en** (provocation); **die Kampagne, -n** (campaign); **der Föderalismus** (federalism); **unterstützen, unterstützte, hat ... unterstützt** (to support)

33: Pharmazentrum Basel

das Zentrum, Zentren	center, centrum
die Krankheit, -en	disease, illness
der Verlauf, ¨-e	process; course
im Verlauf der Krankheit	over the course of the disease
der Schmerz, -en	pain
der Kopfschmerz, -en	headache
der Bauchschmerz, -en	stomachache
das Fieber, -	fever
husten, hustete, hat ... gehustet	to cough
das Medikament, -e	drug, medication
das Arzneimittel, -	drug, medication
die Medizin	medicine
die Tablette, -n	pill (*e.g. painkiller*)
homöopathisch	homeopathic
allopathisch	allopathic
die Globuli (*pl.*)	small pellets (*med.*)
kontrollieren, kontrollierte, hat ... kontrolliert	to control
erforschen, erforschte, hat ... erforscht	to research, explore
vertrauen, vertraute, hat ... vertraut	to trust
untersuchen, untersuchte, hat ... untersucht	to examine, analyze
benutzen, benutzte, hat ... benutzt	to use
aus·bilden, bildete ... aus, hat ... ausgebildet	to train, educate
die Firma, Firmen	company, firm
das Jahrzehnt, -e	decade
der Markt, ¨-e	market
der Experte, -n	expert (*male*)
die Expertin, -nen	expert (*female*)
die Fachperson, die Fachleute	expert (*gender-neutral alternative*)

Weitere Wörter: sammeln, sammelte, hat ... gesammelt (to collect); **aus·geben (gibt ... aus), gab ... aus, hat ... ausgegeben** (to spend (*money*)); **der Wirkstoff, -e** (active agent/ingredient (*med.*)); **die Infektion, -en** (infection); **die Homöopathie** (homeopathy)

35: Schweizer Käse

das Loch, ¨-er	hole
die Käserei, -en	cheesery, dairy (*for making cheese*)
melken (milkt/melkt), molk/melkte, hat ... gemolken/gemelkt	to milk
die Vielfalt	variety, multiplicity
die Sorte, -n	kind, type
der Geschmack, ¨-e	taste; flavor
würzig	aromatic, tangy (*spicy*)
nussig	nutty
der Farbstoff, -e	coloring, dye
der Konservierungsstoff, -e	preservative
das Merkmal, -e	feature, trait, characteristic
der Schritt, -e	step
die Flüssigkeit, -en	liquid, fluid
die Temperatur, -en	temperature
die Bearbeitung, -en	treatment, handling; edit
die Reifezeit, -en	ripening time
zu·geben (gibt ... zu), gab ... zu, hat ... zugegeben	to add; admit
zerschneiden, zerschnitt, hat ... zerschnitten	to cut (up)

enthalten (enthält), enthielt, hat ... enthalten	to contain, include
auf·nehmen (nimmt ... auf), nahm ... auf, hat ... aufgenommen	to absorb; admit (*e.g. in school*); incorporate
lagern, lagerte, hat ... gelagert	to store
pflegen, pflegte, hat ... gepflegt	to take care of
ein·reiben, rieb ... ein, hat ... eingerieben	to rub (in), slather (*e.g. with a lotion*)
sparen, sparte, hat ... gespart	to save (*e.g. money, energy, resources*)

Weitere Wörter: die Kuh, ¨-e (cow); **beliebt** (popular); **schmecken (+ *dat.*), schmeckte, hat ... geschmeckt** (to taste); **rühren, rührte, hat ... gerührt** (to stir); **erwärmen, erwärmte, hat ... erwärmt** (to warm (up), heat); **die Masse, -n** (bulk, mass); **hart** (firm; hard); **der Hartkäse, -** (hard cheese); **weich** (soft); **der Weichkäse, -** (soft cheese); **das Kraut, ¨-er** (herb)

36: Formvollendete Schokolade

die Schokolade, -n	chocolate
naschen, naschte, hat ... genascht	to nibble, eat sweet things
der Kakao, -s	cocoa
der Anbau	growing, cultivation, farming
an·bauen, baute ... an, hat ... angebaut	to grow, cultivate
ernten, erntete, hat ... geerntet	to harvest, pick
verwenden, verwendete, hat ... verwendet	to use
die Schachtel, -n	box (*e.g. of chocolates*), cardboard box
die Praline, -n	chocolate candy
die Lagerung, -en	storage
das Erlebnis, -se	experience (*event, occasion*), adventure
die Geometrie, -n	geometry
dreiseitig	trigonal
eckig	angular
das Dreieck, -e	triangle
viereckig	quadrangular, quadrilateral
rechteckig	rectangular
das Rechteck, -e	rectangle
der Quader, -	cuboid
quadratisch	square
das Quadrat, -e	square
der Würfel, -	cube; die
der Kegel, -	cone
spitz	pointed, sharp
die Kugel, -n	sphere
kugelig	spherical
ringförmig	circular, annular, ring-like, ring-shaped
eng	narrow
flach	flat, plane
zackig	jagged, pronged

Weitere Wörter: der Konsum (consumption); **rund** (round, circular); **der Bezug, ¨-e** (connection, reference); **das Trapez, -e** (trapezoid)

37: Die vielsprachige Schweiz

(das) Schweizerdeutsch(e)	Swiss German
die Gemeinde, -n	municipality
die Fremdsprache, -n	foreign language
der Schriftverkehr	correspondence
die Regel, -n	rule, norm, regulation
eigen-	own
der Laut, -e	sound
klingen, klang, hat ... geklungen	to sound
ab·weichen (von + *dat.*), wich ... ab, ist ... abgewichen	to deviate (from)
helfen (+ *dat.*) (hilft), half, hat ... geholfen	to help
an·bieten, bot ... an, hat ... angeboten	to offer
Wert legen (auf + *akk.*), legte, hat ... gelegt	to put emphasis (on), value
spätestens	at the latest
zusätzlich	additional(ly)

Weitere Wörter: die Mundart, -en (dialect); **die Landessprache, -n** (national language); **das Schuljahr, -e** (school year); **der Schulhof, ¨-e** (schoolyard, playground (*at school*))

39: Produziert auf Rätoromanisch

(das) Rätoromanisch(e)	Romansh
die Gemeinsamkeit, -en	similarity, commonality
die Minderheit, -en	minority
bedrohen, bedrohte, hat ... bedroht	to threaten
bedroht	threatened, endangered
ernsthaft	serious(ly)
das Aussterben	extinction
aus·sterben (stirbt ... aus), starb ... aus, ist ... ausgestorben	to become extinct
überraschen, überraschte, hat ... überrascht	to surprise
retten (vor + *dat.*), rettete, hat ... gerettet	to protect (from)
überzeugen, überzeugte, hat ... überzeugt	to convince
verstehen, verstand, hat ... verstanden	to understand
die Atmosphäre, -n	atmosphere
der Chef, -s	boss (*male*)
die Chefin, -nen	boss (*female*)
der*die Vorgesetzte, -n	boss (*gender-neutral alternative*)

Weitere Wörter: produzieren, produzierte, hat ... produziert (to produce); **die Amtssprache, -n** (official language, administrative language); **der Stil, -e** (style); **der Nachteil, -e** (disadvantage); **die Grundschule, -n** (elementary school)

27: (Produkt-)Geografie der Schweiz°

90a **Was assoziieren Sie mit der Schweiz? Machen Sie eine Liste. Wenn Sie es wissen, schreiben Sie auch auf, wo die Schweiz liegt oder an welche Länder die Schweiz grenzt.**

91a **Review: The Four Cardinal Directions (Himmelsrichtungen)**

When talking about the location of cities, countries, and other places, it is important to know the four cardinal directions, which are known in German as: *Himmelsrichtungen* ("sky directions"):

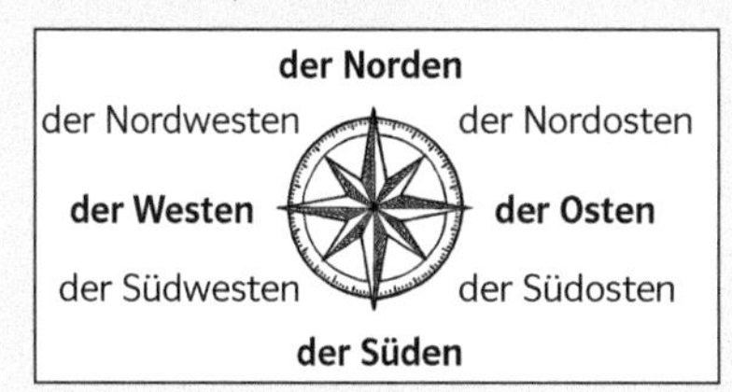

Meine Mutter wohnt **im Norden**.	*My mother lives in the north.*
Der Zug fährt **von Süden nach Norden**.	*The train goes from south to north.*
Zürich ist **im Norden** der Schweiz.	*Zurich is in the north of Switzerland.*
Bayern liegt **in Süddeutschland**.	*Bavaria is located in Southern Germany.*

If you want to say something is to the north/east/southwest/etc. of something else, you can use the following adjectives with the preposition ***von*** (+ *dat.*):

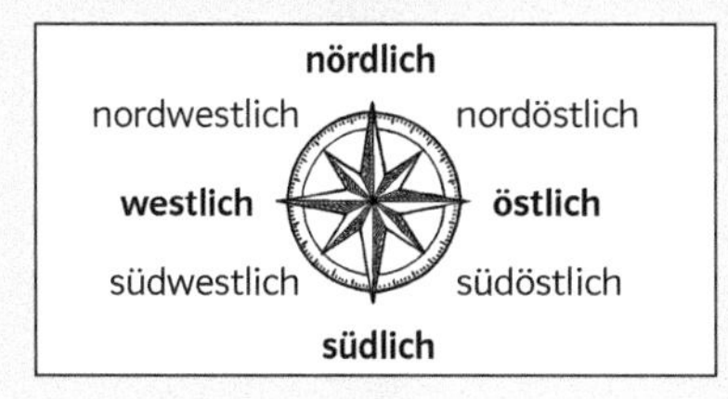

Die Bibliothek liegt **nördlich von der** Mensa.	*The library is located north of the dining hall.*
Die Mensa liegt **westlich von dem / vom** Stadion.	*The dining hall is located west of the stadium.*
Österreich liegt **südlich von** Deutschland.	*Austria is located south of Germany.*
Deutschland ist **nördlich von der** Schweiz.	*Germany is north of Switzerland.*

91b **Wo liegt die Schweiz in Europa und der Welt? Die Schweiz liegt ...**

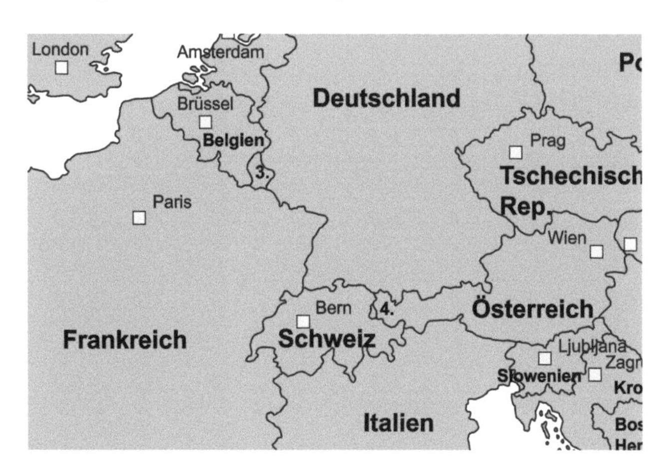

südöstlich von England
________ von Belgien
________ von Italien
________ von Österreich
________ von den USA

3. Luxemburg
4. Liechtenstein

28: Geschichte(n) der Schweiz

94a What is a Grammatical Voice?

Like English, German has both an active and a passive voice. So far, we have only used the active voice, in which a subject of the sentence (the **agent**) acts upon or interacts with an object (in German most likely in the accusative form).

Swatch stellt 1.500 Uhren pro Tag her.	***Swatch*** *produces 1,500 watches per day.*
Arbeitskräfte rösten Bohnen in der Fabrik.	***Workers*** *roast beans in the factory.*
Schweizer Käse essen **Menschen** überall.	*Everywhere* ***people*** *eat Swiss cheese.*

In English and German, you can also express these facts from a different angle by using the so-called passive voice. In passive sentences, the emphasis shifts to the process and action itself. The former object is now the subject of the sentence and will receive the action. The sentence may or may not include the **agent**, depending on the context and whether the **agent** is known and relevant or not. You may have heard the helpful rule that if you can add "by zombies" to a sentence, it is written in the passive voice. In the following examples, the **agents** are a little less creepy:

1.500 Uhren werden pro Tag (**von Swatch**) hergestellt.	1,500 watches *are produced (**by Swatch**) per day.*
Bohnen werden (**von Arbeitskräften**) in der Fabrik geröstet.	*Beans are being roasted (**by workers**) in the factory.*
Schweizer Käse wird überall (**von Menschen**) gegessen.	*Swiss cheese is eaten (**by people**) everywhere.*

94b Welcher der beiden Sätze ist jeweils im Passiv? Markieren Sie.

Passiv

- ☐ Toblerone was invented by two Swiss men.
- ☐ Two Swiss men invented Toblerone.

- ☐ The founding of Switzerland was in 1291.
- ☐ Switzerland was founded in 1291.

Passiv

- ☐ "Wilhelm Tell" was written by Friedrich Schiller.
- ☐ Friedrich Schiller wrote "Wilhelm Tell."

- ☐ People around the world enjoy Swiss cheese.
- ☐ Swiss cheese is enjoyed around the world.

94c Fakten über die Schweiz. Entscheiden Sie, ob der Satz im Aktiv oder Passiv ist. Schreiben Sie dann die englische Übersetzung.

Die Schweizer Theodor Tobler und Emil Baumann haben die leckere Toblerone erfunden.

____

Am 12. September 1848 wurde die Schweiz als moderner Bundesstaat gegründet.

____

In der Schweiz werden vier offizielle Sprachen gesprochen.

____

Die meisten Schweizer*innen sprechen mindestens zwei Sprachen, manche sogar mehr.

____

94d **Analysieren Sie: Look back at the passive voice sentences in activities 94b and 94c in German and English. What similarities are there in how passive voice is formed in both languages? Are there any noticeable differences? Reflect on these questions in either English or German.**

____

____

____

____

____

____

____

____

29: Globales Genf – Auf der Suche nach Fortschritt

97a **Die Stadt Genf: Wo, wer, was? Recherchieren Sie online und lösen Sie die Aufgaben in Stichworten.**

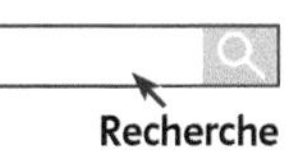

Recherche

Wo in der Schweiz liegt Genf?

____

Wie viele Einwohner*innen hat Genf?

____

Wie viele von diesen Einwohner*innen sind Ausländer*innen?

____

Wie groß ist Genf? ____

Genf gibt es in der Schweiz zweimal: die Stadt und den ____________________.

Finden Sie zwei oder drei kulturelle Sehenswürdigkeiten in Genf (z.B. Museen, Konzerthäuser …).

____

Finden Sie 2–3 Firmen, die es in Genf gibt.

____

Recherchieren Sie, welches Essen typisch für Genf ist. Finden Sie dann 3–4 Genfer Restaurants, die Sie gern besuchen würden, um diese Speisen zu essen.

____

____

97b **Genfer Sehenswürdigkeiten im Detail. Wählen Sie zwei Attraktionen, die Sie bei einem Besuch in Genf gerne besichtigen würden. Ergänzen Sie die Steckbriefe.**

Attraktion Nr. 1: ______	Attraktion Nr. 2: ______
Wo in Genf ist das? ______	Wo in Genf ist das? ______
Was kann man dort machen? ______	Was kann man dort machen? ______
Was kann man da sehen, besuchen oder besichtigen? ______	Was kann man da sehen, besuchen oder besichtigen? ______
Warum gefällt Ihnen diese Attraktion so gut? ______	Warum gefällt Ihnen diese Attraktion so gut? ______

98a How to Build a Sentence in the Passive Voice

So far, we have mostly learned and used sentences in the active voice in which a person, thing, or concept, the so-called "agent" is performing an action (the verb). In many cases, this action is done to another person or thing. Sentences in the **active voice** basically follow the structure subject → verb → (accusative) object.

Die Arbeitskräfte prüfen täglich den Kakao. — *The workers check the cocoa daily.*

We will now look at sentences in the **passive voice** which focus less on the agent but instead more on the action or process itself.

Der Kakao wird täglich (von den Arbeitskräften) geprüft. — *The cocoa is checked daily (by the workers).*

As you see, we are using the same elements but assign them different roles, positions, and forms.

	Active Voice	**Passive Voice**	
1. verb (active form):	prüfen	**wird geprüft**	verb (passive form): *werden + Partizip II*
2. accusative object	**den** Kakao	**der** Kakao	subject
3. subject	**die** Arbeitskräfte	**von den** Arbeitskräfte**n**	prepositional phrase with *von* (+ *dat.*)
4. other elements	täglich	täglich	stay unchanged

1. The sentence shifts the focus away from the workers' action (checking) to what is being done to the *Kakao* (being checked). The verb *prüfen* is split up into *wird* (as the conjugated form of the auxiliary verb *werden*) and in a past participle form *geprüft*.
2. Since the *Kakao* is now the grammatical subject, its form is changed from accusative *den Kakao* to nominative *der Kakao*.
3. The *Arbeitskräfte*, as the former agent of the active sentence, can be mentioned in the passive sentence as a prepositional phrase with *von* (+ *dat.*) *von den Arbeitskräften*, but the sentence would be grammatically complete without them.
4. All other elements can be integrated again without change.

And now let's put the sentences together again.

Active:	**Die** Arbeitskräfte	**prüfen**	täglich	**den** Kakao.	
Passive:	**Der** Kakao	**wird**	täglich	**von den** Arbeitskräfte**n**	**geprüft**.

98b Schreiben Sie die Sätze vom Aktiv in das Passiv oder vom Passiv in das Aktiv um.

Aktiv	Passiv
Der Käser produziert den Käse.	*Der Käse wird vom Käser produziert.*
______________________	Die Uhren werden von IWC entwickelt.
Die Familie isst das Käse-Fondue.	______________________
Roche stellt Medikamente und medizinische Geräte her.	______________________
______________________ ______________________	Vier Landessprachen werden von den Schweizer*innen gesprochen.

98c The Tenses in the Passive Voice

Both voices, the active and the passive voice, exist in all tenses (present, past, future) and moods (*Indikativ* and *Konjunktiv*). We will introduce all tenses here, but only practice the **present tense** in this unit. In unit 31, we will also work with the ***Präteritum***. The other tenses are only listed to give you an overview.

Forming them is quite easy. All you need to know are the different tenses of the verb **werden**.
The participle of the main verb remains unchanged.

Präsens	Der Käse wird produziert.	*The cheese is being produced.*
Präteritum	Der Käse wurde produziert.	*The cheese was produced.*
Perfekt	Der Käse ist produziert worden.	*The cheese has been produced.*
Plusquamperfekt	Der Käse war produziert worden.	*The cheese had been produced.*
Futur	Der Käse wird produziert werden.	*The cheese will be produced.*

As you can see,

- *werden* forms the *Perfekt* with the auxiliary verb *sein*.
- the *Partizip II* of *werden* is *worden*[1] in the passive voice. ([1] *worden* does not have a prefix in the passive voice)
- *Partizip II* produziert remains unchanged in all tenses.

98d Eine Reise nach Genf. Beantworten Sie die Fragen.

Aktivsatz: **Man findet die Statuen im Parc des Bastions.**

Was ist das Objekt im Aktivsatz? *die Statuen*

Was ist das Partizip II vom Verb im Aktivsatz? *gefunden*

Was ist der neue Passivsatz? *Die Statuen werden im Parc des Bastions gefunden.*

Aktivsatz: **Man besucht Genf oft im Sommer.**

Was ist das Objekt im Aktivsatz? ______________________

Was ist das Partizip II vom Verb im Aktivsatz? ______________________

Was ist der neue Passivsatz? ______________________

Aktivsatz: **Man isst den besten Pflaumenkuchen am Genfer Bettag.**

Was ist das Objekt im Aktivsatz? ______________________

Was ist das Partizip II vom Verb im Aktivsatz? ______________________

Was ist der neue Passivsatz? ______________________

Aktivsatz: **Man kauft Luxusprodukte am besten im Balexert.**

Was ist das Objekt im Aktivsatz? ______________________

Was ist das Partizip II vom Verb im Aktivsatz? ______________________

Was ist der neue Passivsatz? ______________________

Aktivsatz: **Man sieht den Reformator John Calvin am Denkmal gegenüber der Genfer Universität.**

Was ist das Objekt im Aktivsatz? ______________________

Was ist das Partizip II vom Verb im Aktivsatz? ______________________

Was ist der neue Passivsatz? ______________________

98e **Textvorbereitung: Finden Sie jeweils die richtige Definition für diese acht Wörter. Wenn Sie sich nicht sicher sind, schlagen Sie zuerst die englische Bedeutung nach.**

die Teilchen (*pl.*) ______

beschleunigen ______

der Umfang ______

die Forschung ______

der Strahl ______

der Zustand ______

der Urknall ______

a) der Beginn des Universums

b) wissenschaftliches Arbeiten

c) sehr kleine Körper, Partikel

d) von einer Lichtquelle in gerader Linie ausgehendes Licht; ein sich geradlinig bewegender Strom materieller Partikel

e) Situation, momentane Lage

f) (bei einem Kreis) die Länge der Linie, die den Kreis begrenzt

g) schneller werden (lassen)

30: Wie werden Schweizer Uhren hergestellt?°

102a **Das Innenleben einer Uhr. Hier lernen Sie, aus welchen Einzelteilen eine Uhr besteht. Lesen Sie alle Wörter laut vor. Benutzen Sie ein Online-Wörterbuch mit Audioclips, wenn Sie sich bei der Aussprache unsicher sind.**

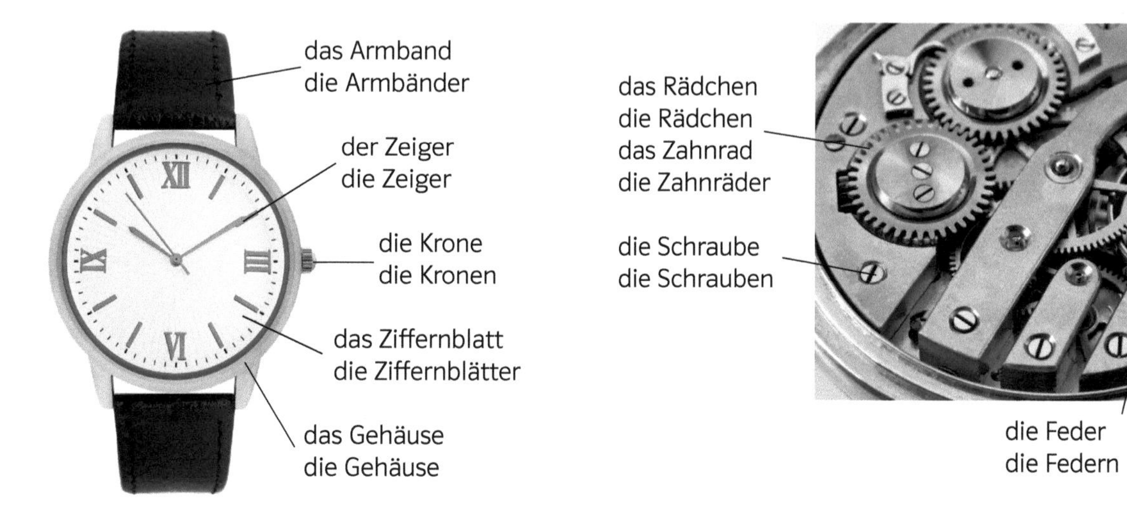

102b **Ergänzen Sie die folgenden Sätze mit den richtigen Wörtern von Aktivität 102a.**

Die ______________________ einer Uhr sagen dir, wie spät es ist.

Im Inneren der Uhr drehen sich viele ______________________.

Auf dem ______________________ gibt es meistens Striche und Zahlen, damit man die Zeit ablesen kann.

Die ______________________ halten die Einzelteile im Inneren einer Uhr fest zusammen.

Wenn deine Uhr vor- oder nachgeht, kannst du die ______________________ benutzen, um die Zeit zu korrigieren.

103a **Sprichwörter (*proverbs*). Finden Sie mindestens vier Sprichwörter zum Thema „Zeit". Die Sprichwörter können auf Deutsch oder Englisch sein oder aus einer anderen Sprache stammen.**

Recherche

Zeit heilt alle Wunden. (Time heals all wounds.)

____

____

____

____

____

____

____

____

31: Das Filmfestival in Locarno

104a The Passive Voice in *Präteritum*

Forming the passive voice in the ***Präteritum*** requires only one more step than in the present tense since the only part that needs to be changed is the verb ***werden***. So all you need to know are the *Präteritum* forms of ***werden*** → ***wurde***.

ich	wurd**e**	gefragt
du	wurd**est**	gefragt
er/es/sie	wurd**e**	gefragt
wir	wurd**en**	gefragt
ihr	wurd**et**	gefragt
sie/Sie	wurd**en**	gefragt

Präsens:	Die Uhr **wird** repariert.	*The watch is being repaired.*
Präteritum:	Die Uhr wurd**e** repariert.	*The watch was repaired.*

105a Das Filmfestival von Locarno. Die folgenden Sätze sollen im Passiv Präteritum stehen. Ergänzen Sie deshalb die korrekte Form von „werden" im Präteritum.

Beispiel: Ich wurde in der Schweiz geboren.

Das Filmfestival von Locarno wurde 1946 ins Leben gerufen.

Ungefähr 130 Filme wurde 2019 auf diesem Festival gezeigt.

Lili Hinstin wurde 2018 zur künstlerischen Leiterin des Festivals ernannt.

1968 wurde zum ersten Mal der Goldene Leopard für den besten Film vergeben.

wurdest du schon mal mit einem Preis ausgezeichnet?

107a Fakten zum Film. Die folgenden Sätze geben Ihnen Informationen über den Film „Die göttliche Ordnung". Bringen Sie die Wörter in die richtige Reihenfolge und setzen Sie den Infinitiv in das Partizip II.

wurde / veröffentlichen / Der Film / 2017

Der Film wurde 2017 veröffentlicht.

in der Schweiz / Er / drehen / wurde

Er wurde in der Schweiz drehen

Das Drehbuch / von Petra Volpe / wurde / schreiben

Das Drehbuch wurde von Petra Volpe schreiben.

von der Berlinerin Marie Leuenberger / spielen / wurde / Die Hauptrolle

Die Hauptrolle wurde von der Berlinerin Marie Leuenberger spielen

positiv bewerten / wurde / von den meisten Kritiker*innen / Der Film

Der Film wurde von den meisten Kritikerinnen positiv bewerten

32: Demokratie – Mit oder ohne Frauen?

108a **Hier finden Sie fünf Begriffe, die repräsentativ für das politische System der Schweiz sind. Finden Sie die passende Definition. Wenn nötig, schlagen Sie zuerst die Bedeutung der Begriffe nach.**

die Neutralität d

die direkte Demokratie b

die Volksabstimmung e

der Föderalismus a

die Bundesverfassung c

a) Auch die Kantone und Gemeinden (*municipalities*) haben politische Verantwortung. Regionale Probleme sollen von Menschen gelöst werden, die diese Probleme am besten verstehen.

b) Das Volk darf selber über Sachfragen und Gesetze abstimmen (*vote*).

c) Das ist der wichtigste Gesetzestext der Schweiz.

d) Die Schweiz beteiligt sich nicht (*doesn't partake in*) an bewaffneten Konflikten zwischen anderen Staaten.

e) Das ist ein Instrument der direkten Demokratie. Alle Bürger*innen, die wählen dürfen, stimmen über eine wichtige Frage ab. Die einfache Mehrheit (*majority*) entscheidet.

108b **Das Frauenstimmrecht in der Schweiz. In der Schweiz dürfen Frauen erst seit 1971 wählen. Warum so spät? Finden Sie zwei Gründe. Beginnen Sie Ihre Recherche auf Englisch. Lesen Sie dann auch deutsche Artikel und notieren Sie Ihre Ergebnisse auf Deutsch.**

Recherche

Grund 1:

Teile der Schweiz hatten ein direkte Demokratie, die aus Männern bestanden.

Grund 2:

Das Wahlrecht war an den Militärdienst geknüpft. Nur Männer durften dienen.

109a **Der Frauenstreik. Im Juni 2019 haben Schweizer Frauen für gerechte Bezahlung, mehr Respekt für ihre Arbeit und gegen Sexismus am Arbeitsplatz protestiert. Lernen Sie hier mehr über den Streik. Setzen Sie die Sätze ins Passiv Präteritum: Ergänzen Sie dafür die korrekte Form von „werden" und das Partizip II.**

Der Frauenstreik _wurde_ am 14. Juni 2019 _durchgeführt_. (durchführen)

Tausende Fahnen ______________ für den Streik ____________________. (drucken)

„Lohn. Zeit. Respekt." ______________ zum offiziellen Slogan des Streiks ____________________. (wählen)

Über den Streik ______________ in der internationalen Presse ____________________. (schreiben)

Viele Fotos von streikenden Frauen ______________ in den sozialen Medien ____________________. (hochladen)

109b **Das Passiv im Präteritum. Übersetzen Sie die folgenden Sätze ins Englische.**

Der erste Frauenstreik in der Schweiz wurde 1991 organisiert.

____

Hunderttausende Frauen wurden bei Protestaktionen gesehen.

____

Der Gleichstellungsartikel in der Schweizer Verfassung wurde immer noch nicht umgesetzt. Deshalb wurde gestreikt.

____

____

Die Frauen wurden von vielen Männern unterstützt.

____

33: Pharmazentrum Basel

111a Passive Voice and Modal Verbs

The good news: modal verbs themselves do not have a passive voice.
However, the infinitive verb following a modal verb might have one. This construction becomes quite clear when you reflect on how a sentence with a modal verb is built in the **active voice**:

- The modal verb is in the second position,
- and the other verb in the infinitive form will be at the last position of the sentence.

	II		L	
Meister Eder	kann	heute die Uhr	reparieren.	*Master Eder can repair the watch today.*

This concept stays the same in a **passive sentence**:

- The modal verb is in the second position and will indicate the sentence's tense,
- but in the last position there will be an infinitive passive.

So, what is an infinitive passive?

- the infinitive of the verb *werden*
- preceded by the *Partizip II* of the other verb → repariert werden.

	II		L	
Die Uhr	kann	heute (von Meister Eder)	repariert werden.	*The watch can be repaired today.*

To put a sentence into the different tenses, all you have to know are the tenses of the modal verb since the infinitive passive will stay unchanged in all tenses.

Präsens	Die Uhr kann heute repariert werden.	*The watch can be repaired today.*
Präteritum	Die Uhr konnte heute repariert werden.	*The watch could be repaired today.*
Perfekt	Die Uhr hat heute repariert werden können.	*The watch could be repaired today.*

111b Wann passiert(e) das? Fügen Sie ein passendes Modalverb im richtigen Tempus ein.

Präsens:	Heute ___können___ die Bücher gelesen werden.
Präteritum:	Gestern ______________ die Bücher gelesen werden.
Perfekt:	Heute Morgen ______________ die Bücher gelesen werden ______________.

Präsens:	Heute ______________ der Brief geschrieben werden.
Präteritum:	Gestern ______________ der Brief geschrieben werden.
Perfekt:	Heute Morgen ______________ der Brief geschrieben werden ______________.

111c **Krank – was tun? Elena ist Krankenschwester in einem Basler Krankenhaus. Heute hat sie Besuch von Viko (11 Jahre alt), der später Krankenpfleger werden möchte. Was sagt Elena?**

Schlaflosigkeit

Viko: Was macht man, wenn die Patientin nicht schlafen kann?

Elena: Dann _muss das Licht ausgemacht werden._

(das Licht ausmachen / müssen)

Erbrechen

Viko: Was macht man, wenn die Patientin sich erbricht?

Elena: Dann ______________________________

(etwas Wasser geben / dürfen)

Husten

Viko: Was macht man, wenn der Patient sehr stark hustet?

Elena: Dann ______________________________

(eine Tasse Tee mit Honig trinken / können)

Halsschmerzen

Viko: Was macht man, wenn der Patient schlimme Halsschmerzen hat?

Elena: Dann ______________________________

(ein Medikament einnehmen / sollen)

112a **Was kann man in Basel machen? Was kann in Basel gemacht werden? Finden Sie in einer kurzen Online-Recherche heraus, was man in der Stadt Basel machen kann, soll oder muss. Welche Sehenswürdigkeiten gibt es? Welche Basler Spezialitäten entdecken Sie? Formulieren Sie vier Sätze im Aktiv mit „man". Setzen Sie diese Sätze dann ins Passiv.**

Recherche

Beispiel: Man kann das historische Rathaus besuchen. → Das historische Rathaus kann besucht werden.

____
____
____
____
____
____

114a **Was ist Homöopathie? Machen Sie eine Online-Recherche und sammeln Sie so viele Informationen wie möglich. Was sind die Prinzipien dieser Lehre?**

Recherche

____
____
____
____
____

34: LÄRMVERSCHMUTZUNG IN TRANSKULTURELLER PERSPEKTIVE°

115a **Lärmquellen im Alltag. Welche Lärmquellen gibt es in Ihrem Alltag? Erstellen Sie drei kurze Listen.**

Zu Hause

Wecker (A)

Im Straßenverkehr

Auf dem Campus

Studierende in der Mensa (A)

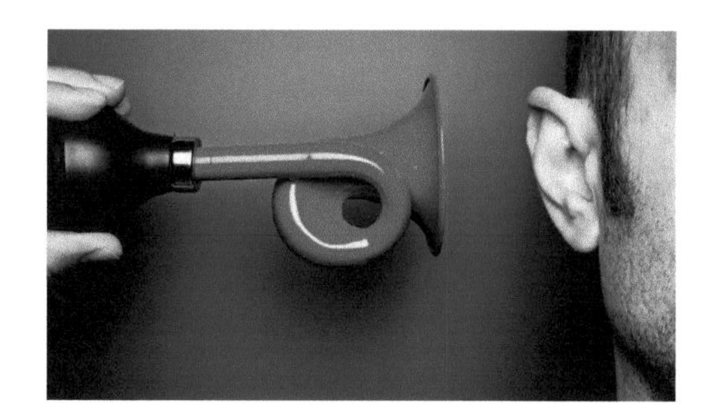

Welche von diesen Lärmquellen sind für Sie akzeptabel? Welche finden Sie störend? Schreiben Sie hinter jede Lärmquelle entweder „A" (für akzeptabel) oder „S" (für störend).

115b **Zu laut! Wir sind auf einem Rockkonzert in Hamburg, um die Explodierenden Köpfe zu hören. Das ist unsere Lieblingsband. Wie könnte man das anders sagen? Benutzen Sie das Passiv mit Modalverben.**

Wir müssen Ohrstöpsel (*ear plugs*) mitbringen.

Ohrstöpsel müssen mitgebracht werden.

Die Stadt soll die Nachbar*innen in den Straßen vor dem Konzert warnen.

____

Man darf die Explodierenden Köpfe nicht zu laut hören!

____

Ihr könnt eure Autos nicht zum Konzert mitbringen.

____

Ihr müsst die U-Bahn nehmen.

____

117a **Textvorbereitung I: Wie kann Lärm reguliert werden? In MACHEN (Aktivität 117) gibt es einen Text über Lärmregulierung in der Schweiz. Lesen Sie den Text. Machen Sie dann eine Liste mit fünf Wörtern, die Ihnen unbekannt sind. Schlagen Sie für diese Wörter die englische Übersetzung nach.**

Wort 1: ____________ Englisch: ____________

Wort 2: ____________ Englisch: ____________

Wort 3: ____________ Englisch: ____________

Wort 4: ____________ Englisch: ____________

Wort 5: ____________ Englisch: ____________

117b **Textvorbereitung II: Ordnen Sie die folgenden Aussagen den korrespondieren Sätzen im Text von MACHEN (Aktivität 117) zu.**

The Swiss noise control act was issued in the eighties.

____

The noise control act defines the noise level which must not be exceeded in different types of buildings.

____

Regulating noise became a public issue in Switzerland in the seventies.

____

Buildings at the planning stage may only be constructed if they meet the standard defined in the noise control act.

____

35: Schweizer Käse

119a **Käse: Lecker oder nein, danke? Essen Sie gern Käse? Wenn ja, machen Sie eine Liste mit den Käsesorten, die Sie gerne essen und schreiben Sie Eigenschaften auf, die den Käse beschreiben. Wenn nein, erklären Sie warum.**

Käsesorte	Eigenschaften
Schweizerkäse	leicht, schmacklos
Mascarpone	leicht,
monterey Jack	lecker, umami
gouda	bohnenkraut

Ich mag keinen Käse, weil ...

____

____

____

____

____

119b **Schweizer Käse: Eine kleine Geschichte. Lesen Sie diesen Text zur Geschichte des Schweizer Käses und schreiben Sie für jeden Abschnitt unbekannte/neue Wörter unten in die Zeilen.**

Die Käseherstellung hat eine lange Tradition in der Schweiz, die bis zum 19. Jahrhundert ein Agrarland war. Käse wurde auf den Bauernhöfen von den Käser*innen hergestellt, bevor die Käserei eine Industrie wurde. Seit dem 15. Jahrhundert wird Lab (ein Enzym) bei der Herstellung von Käse verwendet. Durch Lab wird der Käse härter und länger haltbar (*long-lasting*) gemacht. Im Sommer werden viele Kühe auf die Alm geführt. Dort muss der*die Senner*in die Kühe melken und den Alpkäse herstellen. Die Kühe werden für den Alpaufzug (*cattle drive*) und den Alpabzug im Herbst mit Blumen dekoriert und sie tragen große Kuhglocken (*cowbells*). Es ist immer ein Volksfest mit Musik, Tanzen und Jodeln.

Neue Wörter: ______________________________

In der Schweiz werden etwa 700 Käsesorten hergestellt. Jede Region hat ihre eigenen geheimen Rezepte für die Produktion. Der Emmentaler Käse mit den großen Löchern ist weltbekannt. Die Käseherstellung ist eine Kunst und Schweizer Käser*innen sind hochqualifiziert. Qualitätskäse wird nur mit der besten Milch hergestellt. Die Qualität der Milch ist unter anderem von der Tierart, dem Futter, der Tierhaltung und dem Klima abhängig. Nur gesunde und glückliche Kühe produzieren keimarme Milch, nachdem sie ein Kalb geboren haben. Dann werden die Kühe zweimal pro Tag gemolken; früher von Hand, heute mit einer Melkmaschine.

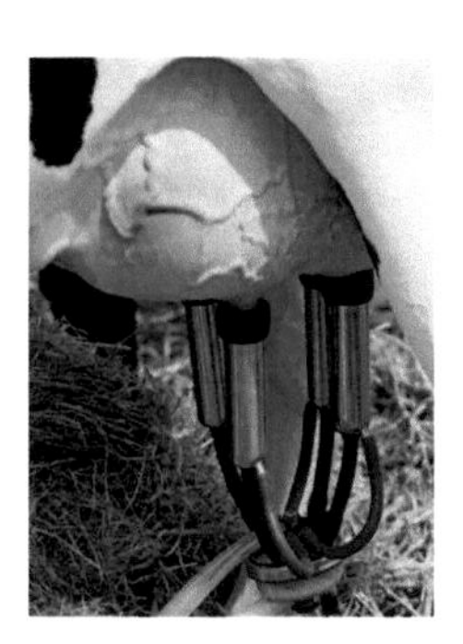

Neue Wörter: ______________________________

Die Milch wird in sehr sauberen Behältern in eine Käserei transportiert und hier zu Käse verarbeitet. Dann muss der Käse ruhen und mehrere Monate reifen. Man braucht ungefähr 10 Liter Milch für ein Kilo Käse. Zusatzstoffe wie Konservierungs- und Farbstoffe oder gentechnologisch veränderte Mittel sind im ganzen Land seit 2002 verboten. Zuerst wird die Milch intensiv im Labor getestet. Die Zellzahl gibt Auskunft über die Gesundheit der Kühe, die Keimzahl über die Milchhygiene, Hemmstoffe (*inhibitors*) über mögliche Antibiotikareste im Tier und der Gefrierpunkt, ob Wasser in die Milch gegossen wurde. Viele Speisen werden mit Käse zubereitet. Ein Nationalgericht in der Schweiz ist Fondue. Auch Raclette ist sehr beliebt.

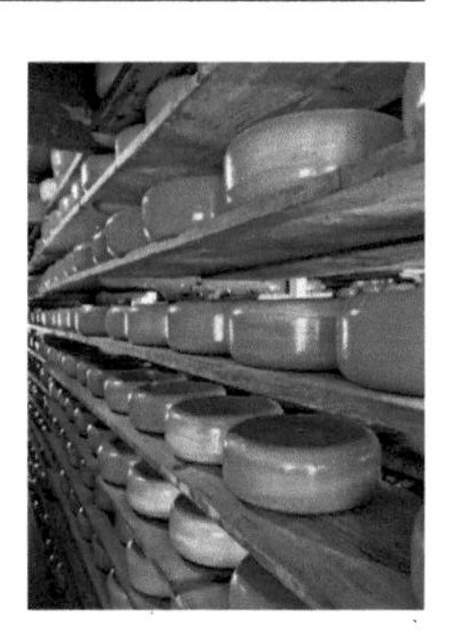

Neue Wörter: ______________________________

119c **Lesen Sie die drei Abschnitte in Aktivität 119b noch einmal und ordnen Sie dann die korrekten Antworten den Fragen zu.**

a) Wie wird der Käse härter und haltbarer gemacht? Was wird dafür benutzt?

b) Was ist der Alpaufzug? Und wie wird er gefeiert?

c) Welche Faktoren sind wichtig für die Qualität der Milch?

d) Werden Kühe heute anders als früher gemolken? Was sind die Unterschiede?

e) Wie wird die Qualität der Milch kontrolliert?

____ Senner*innen bringen die Kühe auf die Alm. Die Kühe werden mit Blumen dekoriert und sie tragen Kuhglocken.

____ Die Milch wird im Labor getestet. Man bekommt so Informationen über die Gesundheit der Kühe, die Milchhygiene und mögliche Antibiotikareste im Tier.

_a_ Durch Lab wird der Käse haltbarer gemacht.

____ Die wichtigsten Faktoren für die Qualität der Milch sind die Tierart, das Futter, die Tierhaltung und das Klima.

____ Heute werden die Kühe mit einer Maschine gemolken, früher wurden sie von Hand gemolken.

119d Grammatik entdecken: Hier sehen Sie drei Sätze aus dem Text, die im Passiv sind. Markieren Sie in jedem Passivsatz das Agens (*by whom something is being done*). Füllen Sie danach die Lücken aus.

Satz 1: Die Kühe werden für den Alpaufzug (und den Alpabzug im Herbst) von den Senner*innen mit Blumen geschmückt und sie tragen große Kuhglocken.

Satz 2: Hüttenkäse wurde auf den Bauernhöfen von den Käser*innen hergestellt.

Satz 3: Durch Lab wird der Käse härter und länger haltbar gemacht.

If the agent is one or multiple person(s) or an animal, then the preposition ______________ is used. If the agent is something inanimate, then the preposition ______________ is used.

119e How to Deal With "the Agent"

As mentioned before, one of the reasons to use the passive voice is that you do not have to name an agent. The agent can be omitted for several reasons. For instance, when the agent is not specific, as with "everyone," "one," "people." One option to express this in German would be to use the impersonal pronoun *man* for this case—or you use the passive voice.

Man isst Schweizer Käse auf der ganzen Welt.	*One eats Swiss cheese all over the world.*
Auf der ganzen Welt wird Schweizer Käse gegessen.	*Swiss cheese is eaten all over the world.*

Sometimes, you do not know "who did it" …

Mein Fahrrad wurde gestohlen.	*My bycicle was stolen.*

Sometimes, you do know "who did it," but intentionally do not want to say it (for instance, to not expose someone).

Fehler wurden gemacht.	*Mistakes were made.*

When you describe procedures, especially in technical contexts, "who did it" is redundant or simply irrelevant.

Die Kakaobohnen werden in einer Mühle zerrieben.	*The cocoa beans are ground in a mill.*

The majority of passive sentences do not show an agent. Thus, the appearance of an agent normally means that it is relevant information in the context. Sometimes the passive voice is even used to put emphasis on the agent.

Die Conchiermethode wird heute auch **von anderen Firmen** angewandt.	*The conching method is being used* ***by other companies*** *as well nowadays.*

Now, when you do want to mention the agent, you might have to consider that not all "agents" are active to the same degree. Sometimes the grammatical agents are means or instruments rather than the initiator or the driving force. In English, the agent in a passive sentence is mostly described by the preposition "by."

The Lindt "Goldhase" was rescued from the pool	**by Susi.**
	by a spectacular stunt.

In German, you have to differentiate: the preposition *von* (+ *dat.*) is used for **direct agents** that cause the action of the sentence. For **indirect agents** you need a different prepositions: *durch* (+ *acc.*).

Der Lindt „Goldhase" wurde	**von Susi**[1]	aus dem Pool gerettet.
	durch einen spektakulären Stunt	

[1] Der Goldhase wurde anschließend von Susi gegessen.

120a **Käsekultur international: Welche Länder oder Kulturen sind bekannt für ihren Käse? Machen Sie eine Liste.**

Spielt Käse in Ihrer Heimat/Kultur eine wichtige Rolle? Zu welchen Anlässen (*occasions*) wird Käse gegessen? Welche Käsesorten werden gegessen? Wo wird Käse normalerweise gekauft? Gibt es Gerichte, bei denen Käse die „Hauptrolle" spielt, wie zum Beispiel bei *mac and cheese* aus den USA oder Käsefondue aus den Westalpen? Benutzen Sie in Ihren Antworten so oft wie möglich das Passiv.

36: Formvollendete Schokolade

122a **Schweizer Qualitätsschokolade. Lesen Sie den Text und formulieren Sie Fragen und Antworten im Passiv.**

Wer kennt sie nicht? Die dreieckige Toblerone aus der Schweiz oder die zartschmelzenden (*melt-in-your-mouth*) Produkte von Lindt sind weltbekannt und haben einen exzellenten Ruf. Das Geschäft mit dem braunen Gold in der Schweiz boomt. 2018 wurden 138.153 Tonnen ins Ausland exportiert und der Umsatz stieg um 6,0 % auf 991 Mio. Franken. Dieser Erfolg basiert auf der hohen Qualität von Rohstoffen und innovativen, technischen Prozessen bei der Herstellung. Nur wenn die Schokolade vollständig in der Schweiz aus Kakaobohnen, Kakaobutter, Zucker, Milchpulver und natürlichen Aromen „conchiert" worden ist, darf sie als „Schweizer Schokolade" bezeichnet werden.

Die Schweizer*innen waren schon früh erfinderisch, um das Produkt zu verbessern und zu vermarkten. Daniel Peter etwa fand nach vielen Versuchen 1875 einen Weg, dem Kakao Milchpulver hinzuzufügen, und erfand die Milchschokolade. 1879 revolutionierte Rodolphe Lindt die Schokoladenherstellung mit der Erfindung der Conchiermaschine (Conche). Durch den Prozess des „Conchierens" wird die Schokoladenmasse so lange gerührt, bis die charakteristische, samtige (*velvet*) Textur entsteht.

Die allerersten, die kakaohaltige Produkte konsumierten, waren die Maya. Ihre „Schokolade" war flüssig. Sie wurde ungesüßt und oft mit Gewürzen wie Vanille oder Pfeffer getrunken. Für den Kakaobaum gab es in Mittelamerika die optimalen klimatischen Bedingungen. Heutzutage wird der meiste Kakao in Westafrika (Elfenbeinküste, Ghana, Nigeria), aber auch in Südostasien (Indonesien) und Lateinamerika (Brasilien, Ecuador) angebaut. Die ersten Verarbeitungsschritte finden vor Ort statt, bevor die Bohnen zur Weiterverarbeitung mit Schiffen nach Europa und Nordamerika transportiert werden. Nachdem die Kakaofrüchte mit Macheten geerntet wurden, müssen die Bohnen vor dem Transport noch fermentiert und getrocknet werden.

Dass die Schweizer*innen von ihrem Produkt überzeugt sind, zeigt sich auch daran, dass sie selbst ziemlich viel davon essen. Etwa 11 kg Kakao- und Schokoladenprodukte pro Person und Jahr werden durchschnittlich konsumiert, so viel wie sonst nur in Deutschland. In den USA sind es ca. 5 kg. Schokolade wird weltweit immer beliebter und es werden neue Produkte entdeckt und hergestellt. Kennen Sie z. B. schon pinke oder blonde Schokolade?

Frage	Antwort
Welche Zutaten werden für Schokolade verwendet?	______________________________
______________________________	138.153 Tonnen wurden 2018 ins Ausland exportiert.
Von wem wurde die Milchschokolade erfunden?	______________________________
______________________________	In der Conchiermaschine wird die Masse gerührt.
Wie wurde Kakao bei den Maya konsumiert?	______________________________
______________________________	Der meiste Kakao wird in Westafrika angebaut.
Wie werden die Kakaofrüchte geerntet?	______________________________
______________________________	Es werden etwa 11 kg pro Person konsumiert.

Und bei Ihnen? Antworten Sie auf die Fragen in ganzen Sätzen.

Wie viel Schokolade wird bei Ihnen zu Hause gegessen? ______________________________

Welche Schokoladen- und Kakaoprodukte werden besonders gerne in Ihrem Land konsumiert? ______________________________

____

Stellen Sie jetzt Ihre eigene Frage zum Thema „Schokolade" und beantworten Sie sie. Ihre Sätze können im Passiv oder Aktiv stehen.

____

____

124a **Wortschatz Geometrie I. Ordnen Sie den Flächen und Körpern die richtige Bezeichnung zu.**

das dreiseitige Prisma, die dreiseitigen Prismen | das Dreieck, -e | der Kreis, -e | das Trapez, -e |
das Parallelogramm, -e | das Rechteck, -e | die Kugel, -n | das sechsseitige Prisma, die sechsseitigen Prismen |
der Würfel, - | die Pyramide, -n | die Ellipse, -n | der Quader, - | der Zylinder, - | das Quadrat, -e | der Kegel, -

124b **Wortschatz Geometrie II. Sortieren Sie die Adjektive nach den Kategorien.**

dreieckig | zylinderförmig | rund | rechteckig | quadratisch | sechseckig | würfelförmig | herzförmig | elliptisch | spitz | kugelförmig | rhombisch | ~~ringförmig~~ | oval | viereckig | kugelig | halbkreisförmig

-eckig	-förmig	-isch	andere
dreieckig	*ringförmig*	quadratisch	rund
rechteckig	zylinderförmig	elliptisch	spitz
sechseckig	würfelförmig	rhombisch	oval
viereckig	herzförmig		kugelig
~~kugelig~~	kugelförmig		
	halbkreisförmig		

124c **Wie viele? Identifizieren Sie die Formen und zählen Sie, wie viele Sie von jeder Kategorie sehen.**

Ich sehe und zähle ______ *Dreiecke,* ______ *Ringe,* ______

______

______

______

______

______

124d **Gestalten Sie ein Haus, indem Sie jeweils ein Adjektiv auswählen. Vergessen Sie die Adjektivendungen nicht, wenn das Adjektiv attributiv gebraucht wird.**

Das ______ (klein | berühmt | würfelförmig) Haus steht vor einem ______ (hoch | steil | spitz) Berg an einer ______ (lang | eng | kurvig) Straße.
Es hat eine ______ (rechteckig | quadratisch | rund) Tür mit ______ (halbkreisförmig | grün | golden) Klinke (*handle*). (*dat. f.*)
Alle dreizehn Fenster sind ______ (dreieckig | sternförmig | oval), ______ (herzförmig | achteckige | kugelig) Fenster (*pl.*) gab es leider nicht.
Auf dem ______ (pyramidenförmig | flach | elliptisch) Dach sitzt ein ______ (klein | rot | dick) Eichhörnchen mit ______ (kugelrund | mandelförmig | viereckig) Augen. (*dat. pl.*)

124e **Geometrie im Alltag. Ordnen Sie den geometrischen Körpern aus dem Alltag die richtige Bezeichnung zu.**

- ___ die Pyramide
- ___ das dreiseitige Prisma
- ___ der Quader
- *1* die Kugel
- ___ der Kegel
- ___ der Zylinder
- ___ der Würfel
- ___ das sechsseitige Prisma

1

2

3

4

5
6

7

8

124f **Beschreiben Sie für drei geometrische Körper, aus welchen Flächen sie bestehen.**

Die vierseitige Pyramide besteht aus einem Quadrat als Grundfläche und vier Dreiecken.

125a The Impersonal Passive

Like in English, most verbs that require a direct object (the so-called transitive verbs) can be easily converted into passive voice, since the direct object of the active sentence (in German, the accusative object) will then be eligible to serve as the subject of the **passive sentence.**

		II			L
Active	Die Arbeitskräfte	prüfen	täglich	den Kakao.	
Passive	Der Kakao	wird	täglich	von den Arbeitskräften	geprüft.

The passive voice is used very often to direct the attention away from the agent towards the action itself. For this purpose, the use of the passive voice can be extended to intransitive verbs. These are verbs without a direct object (like *schlafen, gehen, arbeiten*).

So, where does the subject in the passive sentence come from when there is no accusative object available in the active sentence? The answer is very practical: when there is no subject, we have to make a "dummy subject," and this will be the pronoun ***es*** by default. The construction is called **impersonal passive.**

		II			L
Active	Man	arbeitet	am Sonntag nicht.		
Passive	**Es**	wird	am Sonntag	nicht	gearbeitet.

The dummy subject ***es***, however, is only visible in the first position. When the first position is filled by another element, ***es*** will not appear on the surface of the sentence anymore. But it will still be the ruling grammatical subject and will, thus, determine the verb form.

		II			L
Active	Man	arbeitet	am Sonntag nicht.		
Passive	**Es**	wird	am Sonntag	nicht	gearbeitet.
	Am Sonntag	wird	~~es~~	nicht	gearbeitet.

Typical examples for the impersonal passive might be **commands,** when you don't want to address a specific receiver or when you want to describe activities in a general way.

Hier wird nicht geraucht!	*Smoking is not allowed here.* *(Literally: It is not being smoked here.)*
In diesem Kurs wird viel gelesen.	*In this course, there is a lot of reading.* *(Literally: In this course, it is being read a lot.)*

125b **Eine Woche zum Entspannen. Bilden Sie Sätze im unpersönlichen Passiv. Für jeden Satz gibt es zwei Versionen: einmal ohne und einmal mit „es“, wie im Beispiel.**

am Montag im Café relaxen: *Am Montag wird im Café relaxt. & Es wird am Montag im Café relaxt.*

dienstags mit Freund*innen frühstücken: ______________________

am Mittwoch den ganzen Tag lesen: ______________________

donnerstags im See baden: ______________________

am Freitag malen: ______________________

samstags endlich mal ausschlafen: ______________________

am Sonntag Yoga machen: ______________________

37: Die vielsprachige Schweiz

126a **Punkt versus Komma. Im ersten Buch von „Impuls Deutsch“ haben Sie bereits gelernt, dass man im Deutschen und im Englischen Zahlen anders schreibt. Erinnern Sie sich noch daran? Ergänzen Sie die Tabelle.**

	Deutsch	Englisch
1/2	*0,5*	*0.5*
1/4		
eintausend + 1/4		
zwanzigtausend		
eine Million		

127a **Was wird an diesen Orten gemacht? Schreiben Sie kurze Sätze im Passiv, wie im Beispiel.**

in Locarno / Filme auszeichnen: *In Locarno werden Filme ausgezeichnet.*

an der Uni / studieren: ______________________

auf dem Volksfest / mit der Achterbahn fahren: ______________________

im Krankenhaus / operieren: ______________________

in Genf / forschen: ______________________

beim Stammtisch / über Politik diskutieren: ______________________

127b **Was passiert auf Lottis Party im Schweizer Lausanne? Etwas UNgenauer und dramatischer, bitte! Schreiben Sie die Sätze im unpersönlichen Passiv.**

Lieder werden gesungen. *Es wird gesungen.*

Wein wird getrunken. ______________________

Spiele werden gespielt. ______________________

Rock ’n’ Roll wird getanzt. ______________________

Geschichten werden erzählt. ______________________

Bratwurst und Salat werden gegessen. ______________________

Alle werden fotografiert. ______________________

128a **Schweizerdeutsch: Ein kleines Wörterbuch. Die Tabelle enthält Wörter und Sätze auf Schweizerdeutsch (auch als „Schwyzerdütsch" bekannt). Wissen Sie, was das auf Hochdeutsch heißt? Schreiben Sie.**

Schweizerdeutsch	Hochdeutsch
Grüezi!	*Hallo!*
Guete Morge!	
Wie gaht's dir?	
Mir gaht's guet, danke!	
Chönnte Sie mir hälfe?	
Ich wohne i de Schwiz.	
Wo isch dia nöchst U-Bahn Station?	
Möchtisch mit miar en Kaffi go trinka?	

AUSSPRACHE: DEUTSCH IN D-A-CH-L

128b **Deutsch klingt anders. Hören Sie die Wörter in den folgenden Varianten und kreuzen Sie an.**

Bundesdeutsch	Österreichisches Deutsch			Schweizer Standarddeutsch		
beim Abendessen	klingt ...	anders	gleich	klingt ...	anders	gleich
reden	klingt ...	anders	gleich	klingt ...	anders	gleich
Sonne	klingt ...	anders	gleich	klingt ...	anders	gleich
Haus	klingt ...	anders	gleich	klingt ...	anders	gleich
Häuser	klingt ...	anders	gleich	klingt ...	anders	gleich
bei der Post	klingt ...	anders	gleich	klingt ...	anders	gleich
die Katze im Garten	klingt ...	anders	gleich	klingt ...	anders	gleich
der Tipp	klingt ...	anders	gleich	klingt ...	anders	gleich
richtig	klingt ...	anders	gleich	klingt ...	anders	gleich

128c **Hören Sie die Wörter und markieren Sie den Akzent. Kreuzen Sie dann an, ob er anders oder gleich ist.**

Bundesdeutsch	Österreichisches Deutsch			Schweizer Standarddeutsch		
Büro	Büro	anders	gleich	Büro	anders	gleich
Journalist	Journalist	anders	gleich	Journalist	anders	gleich
Balkon	Balkon	anders	gleich	Balkon	anders	gleich
Kopie	Kopie	anders	gleich	Kopie	anders	gleich
ADAC	ADAC	anders	gleich	ADAC	anders	gleich
DVD	DVD	anders	gleich	DVD	anders	gleich
VW	VW	anders	gleich	VW	anders	gleich

128d Hören und Sprechen: Hören Sie ein Gedicht dreimal und kreuzen Sie an, welche Variante Sie hören (Deutschland = D, Österreich = A, Schweiz = CH). Lesen Sie dann das Gedicht.

Vortrag 1:	D	A	CH
Vortrag 2:	D	A	CH
Vortrag 3:	D	A	CH

Es war eine Mutter, die hatte vier Kinder, den Frühling,
den Sommer, den Herbst und den Winter.
Der Frühling bringt Blumen, der Sommer den Klee,
der Herbst, der bringt Trauben, der Winter den Schnee.

38: Produktmarketing in vier Sprachen°

129a **Die Welt der Werbung. Die meisten Firmen geben viel Geld für gutes Marketing aus, damit möglichst viele Menschen ihre Produkte kaufen. Neben der Verpackung sind Slogans besonders wichtig. Doch was macht einen guten Slogan aus?**

Jeden Tag sehen oder hören Sie Werbeslogans. Welche Slogans fallen Ihnen spontan ein?

I'm loving it. ________________

________________ ________________

________________ ________________

Was denken Sie: Welche Eigenschaften hat ein guter Werbeslogan? Welchen Effekt sollte er haben?

____

____

Haben die Slogans, die Sie oben aufgeschrieben haben, diese Eigenschaften?

____

____

129b **Hier sehen Sie zehn deutsche Werbeslogans. Wählen Sie aus dieser Liste Ihre Top 3 und sagen Sie, warum Ihnen diese Slogans gut gefallen.**

a) Das Auto. (*Volkswagen*)
b) Wir lieben Lebensmittel. (*Edeka*, Supermarkt)
c) Haribo macht Kinder froh und Erwachsene ebenso. (*Haribo*)
d) Always trocken. Always sauber. Und mit Sicherheit ein gutes Gefühl. (*Always*, Damenbinden)
e) Die Bahn kommt. (*Deutsche Bahn*)
f) 3...2...1...meins! (*Ebay*)
g) There's no better way to fly. (*Lufthansa*)
h) Der gesunde Start in den Tag. (*Hohes C*, Orangensaft)
i) We love to entertain you. (*Pro7*, Fernsehsender)
j) Alles Müller, oder was? (*Müller*, Milchprodukte)

Platz 1: *Der Slogan von* ________________ *gefällt mir, weil* ________________

Platz 2: ________________

Platz 3: ________________

Gefallen Ihnen die englischen Slogans oder der Slogan, der Deutsch und Englisch kombiniert? Warum (nicht)?

____

____

39: Produziert auf Rätoromanisch

131a **Rätoromanisch. Lesen Sie den Text und entscheiden Sie, ob die Aussagen unten richtig oder falsch sind.**

Rätoromanisch ist eine Sprache, die eigentlich Bündnerromanisch heißt, weil sie nur im Schweizer Kanton Graubünden gesprochen wird.

Graubünden hat knapp 200.000 Einwohner*innen. Ungefähr die Hälfte von ihnen kann Rätoromanisch verstehen, aber für weniger als 40.000 ist es die Hauptsprache. Trotzdem ist Rätoromanisch neben Deutsch, Französisch und Italienisch eine der vier offiziellen Landessprachen in der Schweiz.

Wichtig zu wissen ist, dass es nicht *das* Rätoromanische gibt, sondern fünf Mundarten (= Dialekte): Sursilvan, Sutsilvan, Surmiran, Putér und Vallader. Und jeder dieser fünf Dialekte hat sogar eine Schriftsprache. Es kann also passieren, dass zwei Menschen, die Bündnerromanisch sprechen, sich nicht ohne Probleme verstehen können!

In den Grundschulen in Graubünden sprechen die Kinder zunächst ihre Mundart. Ab der 4. Klasse lernen sie Deutsch als Fremdsprache. Später findet der Unterricht dann nur auf Deutsch statt.

Weil immer weniger Menschen in Graubünden Rätoromanisch sprechen, glauben Wissenschaftler*innen, dass die Sprache in einigen Jahrzehnten ausgestorben sein könnte. Um das zu verhindern, soll es zum Beispiel mehr zweisprachige Kindergärten und Grundschulen in deutschsprachigen Regionen geben.

Auch an Universitäten würden Expert*innen gerne Seminare in Rätoromanisch sehen. Ob das aber Realität wird, ist schwer zu sagen.

Davos in Graubünden, auf Rätoromanisch „Tavau"
Die Stadt ist international bekannt, weil hier jedes Jahr im Januar das Weltwirtschaftsforum (WEF) stattfindet.

richtig falsch

- Circa 100.000 Menschen in Graubünden können Rätoromanisch verstehen.
- In der Schweiz hat Rätoromanisch denselben offiziellen Status wie Deutsch, Französisch und Italienisch.
- Rätoromanisch ist keine homogene Sprache, denn es gibt verschiedene regionale Varietäten.
- Kinder in Graubünden sprechen von Beginn an Rätoromanisch und Deutsch.
- Rätoromanisch wird in der Schweiz immer populärer.

132a **Rätoromanisch unter der Lupe. In Aktivität 131a haben Sie etwas über das Rätoromanische gelernt. Aber wie sieht diese Sprache aus und wie hört sie sich an? Finden Sie im Internet ein rätoromanisch-deutsches Wörterbuch (z. B. von Glosbe). Schauen Sie die rätoromanische Übersetzung der folgenden Wörter nach. Übersetzen Sie dann noch drei weitere deutsche Wörter Ihrer Wahl. Für die meisten Wörter werden Sie mehr als eine Übersetzung finden – schreiben Sie in diesem Fall mindestens zwei auf. Gibt es Parallelen zum Deutschen oder zu anderen Sprachen, die Sie kennen?**

Recherche

Deutsch	Rätoromanisch
Berg	*muntogna, culm*
Haus	
Katze	
Apfel	
Großmutter	
______________	
______________	
______________	

132b **Suchen Sie online nach mindestens zwei Videos zum Thema „Rätoromanisch für Anfänger". Können Sie etwas verstehen? Machen Sie sich ein paar Notizen und sagen Sie dann, wie das Rätoromanische für Sie klingt.**

Recherche

____

____

____

____

132c **Rund um die Sprachen der Welt! Formulieren Sie diese Passivsätze im Aktiv.**

In der ganzen Welt werden circa 6.500 Sprachen in 195 Ländern gesprochen.

In der ganzen Welt spricht man circa 6.500 Sprachen in 195 Ländern.

In Papua-Neuguinea wird von den Einwohner*innen in 850 verschiedenen Sprachen kommuniziert.

____

Wenn eine Sprache von den Menschen nur für offizielle Zwecke (*purposes*) benutzt wird, ist das die Amtssprache.

____

In einigen Ländern wird eine Minderheitensprache nur von kleinen Gruppen gesprochen.

____

In anderen Ländern wird eine Minderheitensprache von der dominanten Sprache bedroht.

____

Ein aussterbender Dialekt wird nicht mehr von jungen Leuten gelernt.

____

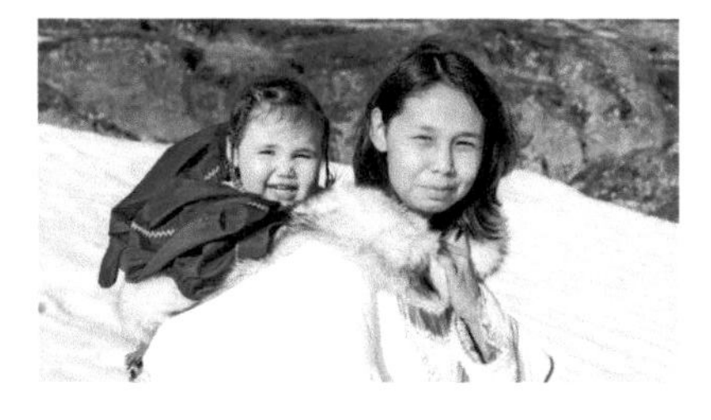

133a **Der rätoromanische Rundfunksender Radiotelevisiun Svizra Rumantscha. Welche Form von „werden" brauchen wir hier?**

RTR (Radiotelevisiun Svizra Rumantscha) ___wurde___ 1926 gegründet.

In den RTR-Sendungen ________________ nur Rätoromanisch gesprochen.

Seit über neunzig Jahren ________________ rätoromanische Sprecher*innen in der ganzen Schweiz durch den RTR unterhalten.

Die erste Fernsehsendung in rätoromanischer Sprache ________________ 1963 gezeigt.

Ab 1997 ________________ RTR auch im Internet als Website präsent. (Achtung: Dieser Satz steht im Aktiv.)

Im Jahr 2013 ________________ rätoromanische Sprecher*innen interviewt und zwei Drittel gaben an, RTR zu hören und zu sehen.

Wie leben wir nachhaltig?

Kommunikation für die Zukunft unseres Planeten

Wortschatz

41: Was ist Nachhaltigkeit?

die Nachhaltigkeit	sustainability
nachhaltig	sustainable
spürbar	noticeable, perceptible
das Bedürfnis, -se	need; desire
der Nachweis, -e	proof, evidence
die Lebensbedingung, -en	living conditions
der Ursprung, ⸚e	origin
ökologisch	ecological
ökonomisch	economic(al), economically
weltweit	worldwide
vergleichbar	comparable
der Handel	trade, commerce
die Beschäftigung, -en	employment; (pre-)occupation
die Natur, -en	nature
der Rohstoff, -e	raw material; natural resource; commodity (*stock*)
der Klimaschutz	climate protection
das Verhalten	behavior
die Verantwortung	responsibility
die Umwelt	environment
statt (+ *gen.*)	instead of
die Mode, -n	fashion
möglichst	preferably; as possible
möglichst schnell	as fast as possible
ändern, änderte, hat ... geändert	to change
sichern, sicherte, hat ... gesichert	to ensure, secure
regeln, regelte, hat ... geregelt	to take care of

Weitere Wörter: die Vermarktung, -en (marketing; commercialization); **das Ökosystem, -e** (ecosystem, ecological system); **nachwachsend (*Rohstoffe*)** (renewable (*raw materials*)); **ethisch** (ethical(ly)); **auf natürliche Weise** (naturally); **der Schadstoff, -e** (pollutant, harmful/toxic substance); **der Konsument, -en** (consumer (*male*)); **die Konsumentin, -nen** (consumer (*female*)); **die konsumierende Person, die Konsumierenden** (consumer (*gender-neutral alternative*)); **recyceln, recycelte, hat ... recycelt** (to recycle), **der Unfall, ⸚e** (accident)

43: Ich in der Umwelt

der Fußabdruck, ⸚e	footprint
die Erde, -n	earth, globe
die Ressource, -n	resource
die Auswirkung, -en	repercussion
leiden (unter + *dat.*), litt, hat ... gelitten	to suffer (from)
Ich leide unter den Auswirkungen.	I'm suffering from the repercussions.
die Verschwendung, -en	waste, wastefulness
verringern, verringerte, hat ... verringert	to lower, reduce, decrease
die Botschaft, -en	message; embassy
der Anteil, -e	amount, share, portion
die Emission, -en	emission
der Platz, ⸚e	space; place

Weitere Wörter: konsumieren, konsumierte, hat ... konsumiert (to consume); **die Hälfte, -n** (half); **das Futter** (feed, food (*e.g. for animals*))

44: „Die Wolke"

die Wolke, -n	cloud
der Notfall, ⸚e	emergency
die Gefahr, -en	danger
das Kernkraftwerk, -e	nuclear power plant
die Katastrophe, -n	catastrophe
sich (*akk.*) erinnern (an + *akk.*), erinnerte, hat ... erinnert	to remember
Ich erinnere mich an die Katastrophe.	I remember the catastrophe.
betreffen (betrifft), betraf, hat ... betroffen	to affect, concern
mit·nehmen (nimmt ... mit), nahm ... mit, hat ... mitgenommen	to take along; give sb. a ride
die Stimmung, -en	atmosphere, sentiment
sich (*akk.*) ändern, änderte, hat ... geändert	to change
die Änderung, -en	change
die Darstellung, -en	depiction
die Kernenergie, -n	nuclear power
der Rauch	smoke

Weitere Wörter: der Alarm, -e (alert); **die Atomkraft** (nuclear power); **die Atomenergie** (nuclear energy); **radioaktiv** (radioactive(ly))

45: Umweltbewegungen

die Bewegung, -en	movement
der Bau, -ten	construction (*building*)
sicher	safe; secure; sure
wirtschaftlich	economic(al), economically
der Ausbau	expansion
die Steigerung, -en	increase
die Bevölkerung, -en	population
die Unterstützung, -en	support
bundesweit	nationwide [*referring to a federation*]
gewaltsam	violent
das Wahlplakat, -e	election poster
die Umweltbewegung, -en	environmental movement
aktuell	recent, current
spalten, spaltete, hat ... gespalten/gespaltet	to divide, split
ein Ziel verfolgen, verfolgte, hat ... verfolgt	to pursue a goal

Weitere Wörter: prognostizieren, prognostizierte, hat ... prognostiziert (to predict, forecast); **der Energiebedarf** (energy needs); **der Atomkraftgegner, -** (opponent of nuclear power (*male*)); **die Atomkraftgegnerin, -nen** (opponent of nuclear power (*female*)); **die Person, -en gegen Atomkraft** (opponent of nuclear power (*gender-neutral alternative*)); **die Räumung, -en** (eviction, evacuation)

47: Deutschland, grünes Vorbild?

die Stiftung, -en	foundation; institution; charity
sinken, sank, ist ... gesunken	to decrease; sink
derzeit	currently, at present
das Gericht, -e	court; dish
enthalten (enthält), enthielt, hat ... enthalten	to contain, comprise, include
die Menge, -n	amount, quantity
das Angebot, -e	offer; quote; proposal
die Untersuchung, -en	study; examination
die Debatte, -n	debate
verbrauchen, verbrauchte, hat ... verbraucht	to use, consume
senken, senkte, hat ... gesenkt	to reduce, lower
Wir senken den Verbrauch.	We reduce the usage.
höchstens	at the most
das Recht, -e	right
verursachen, verursachte, hat ... verursacht	to cause
zwingen, zwang, hat ... gezwungen	to force
zufrieden (mit + *dat.*)	content, happy (with)
der CO_2-Ausstoß	CO_2 emissions

Weitere Wörter: der Verbrauch (consumption); **rasen, raste, ist ... gerast** (to speed; rush); **der Stau, -s** (traffic jam)

48: Kommunikation

die Nachricht, -en	message; news
die Ampel, -n	traffic light
der Empfänger, -	recipient (*male*)
die Empfängerin, -nen	recipient (*female*)
die empfangende Person, die Empfangenden	recipient (*gender-neutral alternative*)
empfangen (empfängt), empfing, hat ... empfangen	to receive
der Sachinhalt, -e	factual content
es eilig haben (hat), hatte, hat ... gehabt	to be in a hurry
der Termin, -e	appointment
die Selbstaussage, -n	self-statement
die Reaktion, -en	reaction
die Beziehung, -en	relationship, relation
das Verständigungsproblem, -e	communication problem
das Missverständnis, -se	misunderstanding

Weitere Wörter: spät (late); **der Plan, ¨-e** (plan; map; schedule); **der Sprecher, -** (speaker (*male*)); **die Sprecherin, -nen** (speaker (*female*)); **das Sprachrohr, die Sprechenden** (speaker (*gender-neutral alternative*)); **der Appell, -e** (appeal; plea); **liefern, lieferte, hat ... geliefert** (to provide; supply; deliver)

49: Was bewegt zu nachhaltigem Handeln?

jdn. (*akk.*) bewegen (zu + *dat.*), bewegte, hat ... bewegt	to bring sb. to do something
das Handeln	action
die Gewohnheit, -en	habit; custom
der Rat, ¨-e	council
zurück·kommen, kam ... zurück, ist ... zurückgekommen	to return, come back
die Anzeige, -n	advertisement
die Dienstleistung, -en	service
wegen (+ *gen.*)	because of
während (+ *gen.*)	during
trotz (+ *gen.*)	in spite of

Weitere Wörter: moralisch (moral(ly)); **die Verbindung, -en** (connection, link); **bewerben (bewirbt), bewarb, hat ... beworben** (to advertise, promote); **das Umweltbewusstsein** (environmental awareness); **brennen, brannte, hat ... gebrannt** (to burn)

41: Was ist Nachhaltigkeit?

137a Review: Relative Clauses

Relative clauses are a practical and creative way to pack additional information into a sentence:

The student **who** is taking German courses is a chemistry major.

Relative clauses are usually placed after the noun which they specify, describe, modify, explain, and decorate (here: after "the student"). A **relative pronoun** at the beginning of the relative clause creates a link to the noun that is being described (here: "who"). Here are some example sentences in German where some additional information was added with the help of relative clauses:

Deutsch ist eine Sprache. Deutsch ist eine Sprache, **die** leicht zu lernen **ist**.	*German is a language.* *German is a language **that** is easy to learn.*
Mein Freund Leo wird bald nach Berlin fliegen. Mein Freund Leo, **der** an der Uni Deutsch **studiert**, wird bald nach Berlin fliegen.	*My friend Leo will fly to Berlin soon.* *My friend Leo **who** studies German at university will fly to Berlin soon.*
Es gibt viele Vokabeln. Es gibt viele Vokabeln, **die** Leo nicht **kennt**.	*There is a lot of vocab.* *There is a lot of vocab ___ Leo doesn't know.*

As you can see, relative clauses also exist in English:
In English, "which" and "that" are the most common relative pronouns, and for references to people, the relative pronoun "who" is used. In English, the relative pronoun is also sometimes omitted.

In German, the relative pronouns for people and things will be forms of *der, das,* and *die*.
Relative pronouns will—like articles—reflect the grammatical gender, number, and case of the noun they refer to.

You might have noticed that in German, the relative clause is a subordinate clause (*Nebensatz*) with the **conjugated verb** placed in the last position. This subordinate clause is clearly marked with a comma in the beginning, and—when it is inserted—with another comma at the end.

Er hat ein Wörterbuch, **das** zu groß und zu schwer für seinen Koffer **ist**.	*He owns a dictionary* ***that** is too big and too heavy for his suitcase.*

Sometimes, it is necessary to put a preposition in front of the relative pronoun; we will look into the specifics later.

Aber er hat eine App gekauft, mit **der** er schnell eine Übersetzung finden **kann**.	*But he bought an app with **which** he can find a translation quickly.*

Sometimes, a verb can sneak between the noun and the referring relative clause (here: *besuchen*).

Er will in Berlin einen Sprachkurs besuchen, **den** ein Freund ihm empfohlen **hat**.	*He wants to attend a language class* *___ a friend has recommended to him.*

137b Review: The Nominative Case

You have been using the nominative case since you started learning German—maybe without knowing this term. "Nominative" is the name for the basic form of articles, nouns, and pronouns as they are listed in a dictionary: *der Student, das Wetter, die Schule, ich, du, er, es, sie*, etc.

The nominative form (or the nominative case) is used when the noun (and its article) or the pronoun is the subject of the sentence. In the active voice, the subject of a sentence is the person or thing that is doing the action indicated by the verb.

Der Student kauft ein Wörterbuch. — *The student is buying a dictionary.*

In the sentence above, "the student" acts as the subject of the sentence. He is the one doing the action (= buying) to the dictionary. *Der Student* consequently is in the nominative form.

In the following table, you will see that you already know the nominative case. All you need to know for now is that the nominative form is ONE out of four forms for nouns (and their articles) and for pronouns. The other three forms are accusative, dative, and genitive, which we will tackle in detail later.

DEFINITE ARTICLES	Nominative	Accusative	Dative	Genitive
masculine	der Abfall	**den** Abfall	**dem** Abfall	**des** Abfall**s**
neuter	das Klima	**das** Klima	**dem** Klima	**des** Klima**s**
feminine	die Industrie	**die** Industrie	**der** Industrie	**der** Industrie
plural	die Vorschläge	**die** Vorschläge	**den** Vorschläge**n**	**der** Vorschläge

In addition to marking the subject of a sentence, the nominative often follows the verb ***sein*** (to be). The verb "to be" acts like an equal sign (my friend = med student). The same is true for the verb ***werden*** (to become) and ***bleiben*** (to stay).

Meine Freundin Anna **ist** Medizinstudentin. — *My friend Anna is a med student.*

Sie **wird** eine gute Ärztin. — *She will become a great doctor.*

Und sie **bleibt** hoffentlich meine beste Freundin. — *And hopefully she will remain my best friend.*

137c Setzen Sie die passenden bestimmten Artikel (der, das, die), Demonstrativartikel (dieser, dieses, diese) Personalpronomen (er, es, sie) oder unbestimmten Artikel (ein, eine) im Nominativ ein.

Mein Lieblingspullover ist ___ein___ Pullover von H&M. ___Das___ Pullover ist blau und hat weiße Streifen. ___Das___ Pullover ist sehr modern und schick, aber ___es___ ist nicht besonders nachhaltig, weil ___die___ Fast Fashion ist.

Fairkauf ist ___eine___ neues Geschäft in Berlin. ___Die___ Geschäft hat nur lokale Lieferanten. ___Es___ ist im Zentrum der Stadt, was sehr praktisch ist. Fairkauf ist ___eine___ tolles Geschäft!

___Die___ neue Politikerin in der Stadt Essen hat schon in ihrem ersten Monat begonnen, sich für Nachhaltigkeit einzusetzen. ___Sie___ war schon als Studentin bekannt für ihre Umweltaktionen. Jetzt plant ____________, viele ihrer Ideen stadtweit umzusetzen. ___Die___ Politikerin wird noch in die Geschichte der Stadt eingehen!

137d Review: Relative Clauses and Pronouns in the Nominative

Relative clauses are a practical and creative way to add additional information to nouns by specifying them with another sentence in tow. Theoretically, each noun in a sentence can be "decorated" by a relative clause. For now, however, we will only insert one relative clause into a main clause (*Hauptsatz*).

Look at the nouns of the following sets of sentences. We can elaborate on each of the nouns in the first sentence with another sentence that also mentions the noun or refers to it with a pronoun.

Mein Freund Leo studiert in Bonn. Leo (er) ist ehrgeizig.	*My friend Leo studies in Bonn.* *Leo (he) is ambitious.*
Ich finde die Sprachschule zu teuer. Sie liegt am Stadtrand.	*I find the language school too expensive.* *It is situated on the outskirts.*
In Wien gibt es auch ein Sprachprogramm. Das Sprachprogramm in Wien ist billiger.	*There is a language program in Vienna, too.* *The language program in Vienna is cheaper.*
Dort finden die Kurse an der TU statt. Sie dauern vier Wochen.	*There, the courses take place at the Technical University.* *They last four weeks.*

We will now change the additional information (second sentence) into relative clauses in order to insert them into the main clause (first sentence). Let's have a look at the first set of example sentences from above:

The relative clause will be located after the noun to be specified:

Mein Freund Leo [ ] studiert in Bonn. Leo (er) **ist** ehrgeizig.	*My friend Leo studies in Bonn.* *Leo (he) is ambitious.*

We already know that the relative clause is a *Nebensatz*, so the **verb** will go to the end.

Mein Freund Leo [ ] studiert in Bonn. Leo (er) ist ehrgeizig **ist**.	*My friend Leo studies in Bonn.* *Leo (he) is ambitious.*

Now, it's time to choose the appropriate **relative pronoun**. In English, these relative pronouns are "who," "that," "which," "whose," "where," and "when." Choosing the relative pronoun in German is fairly simple. We have to decide what role the described noun plays in the additional sentence and what features it has: number, grammatical gender, case. When you look at the additional sentence in the example above, you will see that the noun is in the nominative case. The relative pronouns for the nominative are ***der***, ***das***, ***die***, ***die***, exactly the same as the definite articles:

RELATIVE PRONOUNS	Nominative	Accusative	Dative	Genitive
masculine	Abfall, **der**	Abfall, **den**	Abfall, **dem**	Abfall, **dessen**
neuter	Klima, **das**	Klima, **das**	Klima, **dem**	Klima, **dessen**
feminine	Industrie, **die**	Industrie, **die**	Industrie, **der**	Industrie, **deren**
plural	Vorschläge, **die**	Vorschläge, **die**	Vorschläge, **denen**	Vorschläge, **deren**

Since Leo is masculine, the relative pronoun is ***der***. The relative clause will be initiated by a relative pronoun:

Mein Freund Leo [ ] studiert in Bonn. ~~Leo (er)~~ **der** ehrgeizig **ist**.	*My friend Leo studies in Bonn.* *~~Leo (he)~~* ***who*** *is ambitious.*

Finally, let's insert the relative clause into the space we marked earlier, right after the noun it specifies:

Mein Freund Leo, **der** ehrgeizig **ist**, studiert in Bonn. *My friend Leo,* ***who*** *is ambitious, studies in Bonn.*

Now you can do the same with the other sets of sentences from the examples above.

137e **Benutzen Sie die Anweisung in der Grammatik 137d, um die anderen Beispielsätze aus der Grammatik zu kombinieren.**

Ich finde <u>die Sprachschule</u> zu teuer. <u>Sie</u> liegt am Stadtrand.	*I find the language school too expensive.* *It is situated in the outskirts.*

Nach welchem Wort im ersten Satz kommt der Relativsatz? Sprachschule

Schreiben Sie den zweiten Satz neu, mit dem Verb am Ende: sie am Stadtrand liegt

Ersetzen Sie das (Pro)Nomen durch das Relativpronomen: die am Stadtrand liegt

Setzen Sie den fertigen Relativsatz in den Hauptsatz ein:

Ich finde die Sprachschule, die am Stadtrand liegt, zu teuer.

In Wien gibt es auch <u>ein Sprachprogramm</u>. <u>Das Sprachprogramm</u> in Wien ist billiger.	*In Vienna there is a language program, too.* *The language program in Vienna is cheaper.*

Nach welchem Wort im ersten Satz kommt der Relativsatz? Sprachprogramm

Schreiben Sie den zweiten Satz neu, mit dem Verb am Ende: ein [illegible] billiger ist

Ersetzen Sie das (Pro)Nomen durch das Relativpronomen: das [illegible] billiger ist

Setzen Sie den fertigen Relativsatz in den Hauptsatz ein:

In Wien gibt es auch ein Sprachprogramm, das billiger ist.

Dort finden <u>die Kurse</u> an der TU statt. <u>Sie</u> dauern vier Wochen.	*There, the courses take place at the Technical University.* *They last four weeks.*

Nach welchem Wort im ersten Satz kommt der Relativsatz? Kurse

Schreiben Sie den zweiten Satz neu, mit dem Verb am Ende: die vier Wochen dauern

Ersetzen Sie das (Pro)Nomen durch das Relativpronomen: Sie vier Wochen dauern

Setzen Sie den fertigen Relativsatz in den Hauptsatz ein:

Dort finden die Kurse an der TU statt, sie vier Wochen dauern

137f **Benutzen Sie Relativsätze, um alle Zusatzinformationen in den Hauptsatz zu integrieren. Vergessen Sie nicht, das Komma zu setzen, wo nötig.**

Hauptsatz:	Der Lieferant spricht mit der Ladenbesitzerin, um Waren günstiger anzubieten.
Zusatzinformationen:	Der Lieferant (*m.*) hat seinen Hauptsitz in Berlin. Die Ladenbesitzerin (*f.*) bietet saisonale und lokale Produkte an. Die Waren (*pl.*) haben keine Verpackung.

Hauptsatz:	Abfallreduktion, fairer Handel und das Recht auf Gesundheit sind sehr verschiedene Aspekte von Nachhaltigkeit.
Zusatzinformationen:	Abfallreduktion (*f.*) ist ein Element ökologischer Nachhaltigkeit. Fairer Handel (*m.*) gehört zur ökonomischen Nachhaltigkeit. Das Recht (*n.*) auf Gesundheit ist Teil der sozialen Nachhaltigkeit.

137g **Ordnen Sie zu. Tipp: Sortieren Sie zuerst die möglichen Antworten. Wo sind die femininen Relativpronomen, wo die maskulinen und wo die Relativpronomen im Plural?**

Eine Person (*f.*), ___die gerne im Wald spazieren geht___, ist ein*e Naturliebhaber*in.

Jemand (*m.*), ___der Plastik vermeidet___, handelt umweltbewusst.

Alle (*pl.*), ___die sich informieren___, können mit rationalen Argumenten diskutieren.

Eine Person, ______________________, zeigt Verantwortung gegenüber der nächsten Generation.

Das ist jemand, ______________________, denn er lebt nachhaltig.

Alle, ______________________, reduzieren ihren Abfall.

Eine Person, ______________________, kauft viele regionale Produkte.

Jemand, ______________________, sichert Naturressourcen für die Menschen in der Zukunft.

Alle, ______________________, wollen Chancengleichheit für alle Menschen auf der Welt.

Das ist eine Person, ______________________, weil sie Produkte aus dem fairen Handel kauft.

Jemand, ______________________, schützt das Klima.

Alle, ______________________, wollen ihnen bessere Lebensbedingungen sichern .

der die Naturressourcen erhalten will	die Glas und Papier recyceln	der ein Elektroauto fährt
die Ökonomie und Ökologie verbindet	die andere Menschen respektieren	die ihre Enkelkinder lieben
die Transport-Emissionen vermeiden will	die so nachhaltig wie möglich lebt	der nachhaltig konsumiert

137h **Esther und ihr Vater Geert sprechen über Nachhaltigkeit. Ergänzen Sie die Sätze mit dem passenden Relativpronomen.**

Esther: Papa, nächste Woche lernen wir in der Schule etwas über Nachhaltigkeit. Was ist das eigentlich?

Geert: Nachhaltigkeit ist ein Prinzip, ___das___ uns hilft, Luft und Wasser auch für deine Kinder zu erhalten.

Esther: Bin ich nachhaltig, wenn ich recycle?

Geert: Genau. Alle, __________ recyceln, verstehen, dass Plastik, Glas und Papier Ressourcen sind.

Esther: Sind nur Menschen nachhaltig?

Geert: Nein, ganze Länder können nachhaltig werden. Ein nachhaltiges Land ist ein Staat, __________ Gesetze macht, damit seine Bürger und Bürgerinnen die Umwelt und die Ressourcen schützen.

Esther: Und was passiert mit den Menschen, __________ nicht auf diese Gesetze achten?

Geert: Eine Person, __________ nicht recycelt, wenn sie muss, handelt unethisch. Das bedeutet, sie handelt falsch.

Esther: Was kann ich machen, um ethisch zu handeln?

Geert: Du bist ein Mädchen, __________ schon sehr viel für die Umwelt macht. Und du bist in der Generation, __________ etwas gegen Umweltverschmutzung und Klimawandel tun wird. Wir brauchen eure Ideen, __________ unserer Erde helfen können!

138a **Bestandsaufnahme: Wie viele T-Shirts haben Sie? Wo wurden sie hergestellt? Wie viele davon waren eher günstig oder eher teuer?**

Kleidungsstück	Material	Herkunftsland	Transport	Preis
T-Shirt 1	Baumwolle	Malaysia	weit	echt billig
T-Shirt 2				

138b **Schreiben Sie mehr über Ihre Bestandsaufnahme aus Aktivität 138a.**

Beschreiben Sie Ihr Lieblings-T-Shirt: Wie sieht es aus? Wie alt ist es? Wie oft tragen Sie es? Warum ist es Ihr Lieblings-T-Shirt?

___

___

Worauf achten Sie, wenn Sie T-Shirts kaufen? Was ist Ihr wichtigstes Kriterium (z. B. Preis, Qualität oder Modetrends)? Warum?

___

___

Ist Nachhaltigkeit hier auch ein Kriterium für Sie? Warum (nicht)?

___

___

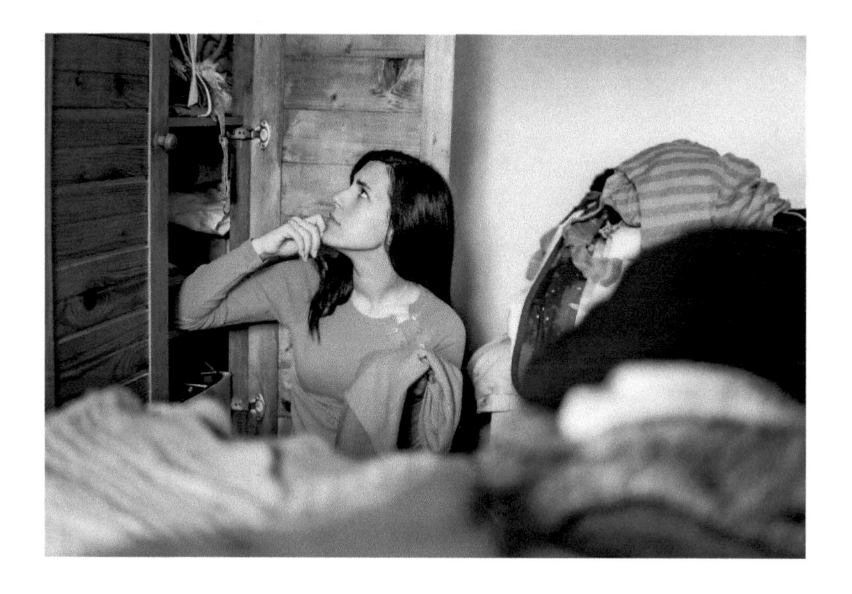

42: KLIMAWANDEL °

139a **Was ist Klimawandel? Schlagen Sie zuerst die fettgedruckten Wörter nach. Lesen Sie dann den Text und beantworten Sie die Fragen in Stichpunkten. Benutzen Sie dafür Ihre eigenen Worte.**

Wissenschaftler*innen sprechen heute von Klimawandel, wenn sich die **durchschnittliche** Temperatur der Erde um nur wenige Grad erhöht. Vor allem der Mensch **trägt** zum Klimawandel **bei**. Einige Gründe sind z. B. die Masse an Fabriken, Autos und Flugzeugen, die umweltschädliches CO_2 produzieren; unsere Kleidung und unser Essen reisen weite Strecken über Land, Wasser oder in der Luft; Tiere aus der Massentierhaltung, vor allem Kühe, stoßen viel Methan in die Atmosphäre aus; je mehr der Regenwald abgeholzt wird, desto weniger Bäume gibt es, die CO_2 wieder in Sauerstoff **umwandeln** können.

Schon jetzt können wir die Folgen des Klimawandels beobachten. Immer öfter gibt es Naturkatastrophen, z. B. Überschwemmungen, extreme Sturmfronten und **Hitzewellen**. In einigen Regionen Afrikas wird der Anbau von Getreide oder Gemüse immer schwieriger, weil es so heiß ist und Trinkwasser **knapp** wird. Der Lebensraum von Menschen und Tieren verkleinert sich, während **Wüstengebiete** immer größer werden.

Die Erwärmung der Erde um vier Grad wäre katastrophal. Die Meere würden um einen halben Meter **steigen**, weil das Eis an den Polen schmelzen würde. Tiere, wie der Eisbär, hätten keinen Platz zum Leben mehr. Viele Korallenriffe würden sterben. Der Anstieg des Meeresspiegels hätte auch für den Menschen schlimme Folgen: Städte an den Küsten wie Shanghai, Tokio oder Hamburg müssten **umgesiedelt** werden, weil sie überschwemmt werden würden. In wärmeren Regionen, wie z. B. in großen Teilen Afrikas, könnten Menschen nicht mehr leben.

Einige Menschen denken, dass der heutige Klimawandel kein wirkliches Problem ist, weil sich das Klima der Erde schon immer geändert hat. Das stimmt. Aber in der Vergangenheit haben sich diese Veränderungen über Millionen von Jahren entwickelt. Der Klimawandel, wie wir ihn heute sehen, hat **sich** innerhalb von nur ungefähr hundert Jahren **ergeben**.

Wie wird Klimawandel heute definiert?

____

____

Welche von Menschen verursachten Gründe für den Klimawandel gibt es?

____

____

____

Welche Folgen hat der Klimawandel für viele Menschen in Afrika?

____

____

Wie würde sich die Situation noch mehr verschlimmern, wenn sich die Erde um durchschnittlich vier Grad erwärmen würde?

____

____

Warum ist das Argument, dass der Klimawandel kein wirkliches Problem ist, nicht haltbar?

____

____

140a **Tiere im Klimastress: Vokabelarbeit. Welches Wort passt in die Lücke?**

Kohlenstoffdioxid | Küken | Kreislauf | füttern | Sauerstoff | Teufelskreis | Gewässer
ersticken | Nahrung | Zugvögel | Wärme | Mangel | ansteigen | Treibhauseffekt

Ein natürlicher ____________ sieht so aus: Wasser wird über dem Meer zu Wolken, aus den Wolken regnet es, der Regen fällt in die Flüsse, die Flüsse fließen ins Meer. Aber in einem ____________ ist es egal, was getan wird: Alles hat schlechte Konsequenzen!
Seen, Flüsse und Meere sind ____________ . Wenn sie wärmer werden, sterben die Fische. Dann gibt es nicht genug ____________ für die Tiere, die Fische fressen.
Insekten brauchen Pflanzen und Wasser. Wenn die Temperaturen im Süden zu sehr ____________ , gibt es einen akuten ____________ an Pflanzen und Wasser für die Insekten und sie sterben.
Alle Vögel legen Eier; ihre Babys heißen ____________ . Wenn Vögel im Winter in wärmere Regionen ziehen, sind sie ____________ . Wenn diese Vögel in den zu heißen Süden fliegen, finden sie keine Insekten mehr. Ohne Insekten können Elternvögel ihre Jungtiere nicht mehr ____________ .
In der Luft gibt es etwa 21% ____________ und 78% Stickstoff. Ohne Luft ____________ Menschen und Tiere. Smog hat zu viel ____________ . Dieses Gas sammelt sich in der Atmosphäre und verhindert, dass ____________ von der Erde abgeht. So kommt es zu einem ____________ für alles, was auf unserem Planeten lebt.

141a **Wir leben da: Vokabelarbeit. Finden Sie die englische Übersetzung für die folgenden Wörter. Benutzen Sie ein Online-Wörterbuch mit Audioclips und hören Sie, wie die Vokabeln ausgesprochen werden. Sprechen Sie die Wörter laut nach.**

versinken ____________________ beschädigen ____________________
der Friedhof ____________________ unfruchtbar ____________________
verschlucken ____________________ überschwemmen ____________________
unaufhaltsam ____________________ umsiedeln ____________________

142a **Der Klimawandel und seine Folgen. Welche konkreten Folgen könnte der Klimawandel für unseren Alltag haben? Arbeiten Sie mit „könnt-“ und „müsst-“.**

Es gibt immer weniger Fische in den Meeren.
Fisch könnte immer teurer werden.

Viele Regionen werden in der Zukunft unter Wasser liegen.
____

Dieselben Städte werden immer wieder durch Hurrikane oder Feuer bedroht.
____

Durch die steigende Erderwärmung kommen Tropenkrankheiten nach Südeuropa.
____

Es gibt immer weniger Insekten.
____

43: Ich in der Umwelt

143a Review: The Accusative Case

The accusative is a case used with nouns, articles, and pronouns that differs from the nominative form we have looked at before. This difference for nouns and their articles is very simple and very small since it only affects masculine nouns.

DEFINITE ARTICLES	Nominative	Accusative	Dative	Genitive
masculine	**der** Abfall	den Abfall	**dem** Abfall	**des** Abfall**s**
neuter	**das** Klima	das Klima	**dem** Klima	**des** Klima**s**
feminine	**die** Industrie	die Industrie	**der** Industrie	**der** Industrie
plural	**die** Vorschläge	die Vorschläge	**den** Vorschläge**n**	**der** Vorschläge

The masculine article ***der*** changes to *den* (and all other masculine articles will end with an *-en* as well, such as *einen, keinen, meinen*).

And this is how the accusative functions:

1. The accusative form of a noun or pronoun marks direct objects in a sentence. The subject does the action, and the object receives the action.

   Leo belegt den Sprachkurs. — *Leo is taking the language course.*

Leo is the subject; he is doing something ("taking"). *Sprachkurs* is the element that receives the action (being "verbed," here "being taken"). As you can see, the direct object is marked with an accusative form *den Sprachkurs*. The English language does not add markers to nouns in the role of an object. But you can normally recognize the direct object anyway—by its position (most times after the verb). And in many cases, the content or the context will tell you who does what to whom. In other words, it will tell you who/what the subject is and who/what the object is: "The student reads the novel" versus "The novel reads the student."

Direct objects in German are often called *Akkusativobjekt*. These accusative objects are highly frequent; actually most German verbs (called "transitive verbs") will require a direct object that will consequently be marked as such with an accusative form.

2. Some **prepositions** require the following noun (and its article) or the following pronoun to be in the accusative form. The most important and frequent ones are ***bis***, ***durch***, ***für***, ***gegen***, ***ohne***, and ***um***.

   Leo arbeitet viel **für** den Sprachkurs. — *Leo works a lot for the language course.*
   Ohne seinen Computer könnte er die Arbeit nicht machen. — *Without his computer he couldn't do the work.*
   Nach dem Kurs geht er **durch** den Park. — *After class he walks through the park.*

3. Time information (frequency and duration) is marked with the accusative case as long as there is no preposition.

   Leo ist **ein**en Monat in Bonn. — *Leo is in Bonn for a month.*
   Er geht **jed**en Tag zum Deutschkurs. — *He goes to the German course every day.*
   Er bleibt den ganzen Morgen dort. — *He is staying for the whole month.*

4. Measurements are also given in the accusative form.

   Der Tisch ist **ein**en Meter hoch. — *The table is one meter high.*
   Der Stift kostet **ein**en Euro. — *The pen costs a euro.*
   Der Campus ist **ein**en Kilometer entfernt. — *The campus is one kilometer away.*

143b **Unsere Aktion kann helfen! Die Schulklasse 10a in Füssingen plant ein Umweltprojekt mit ihrem Biologielehrer, Herrn Doerr. Setzen Sie die passenden bestimmten Artikel (den, das, die), Demonstrativartikel (diesen, dieses, diese), Personalpronomen (ihn, es, sie) oder unbestimmten Artikel (einen, ein, eine) im Akkusativ ein.**

Herr Doerr: Also, wir brauchen ___die___ Botschaft für unsere Aktion.

Marlen: Ich finde, dass wir uns für ___die___ Botschaft etwas Dramatisches ausdenken sollten.

Tim: Ich finde ___einen___ dramatische Botschaft nicht so gut, weil dann Emotionen im Vordergrund sind.

Marlen: Das kann aber doch auch gut sein. Schau dir mal ___diesen___ Botschaft hier an. Klar, die ist sehr emotional, aber auch effektiv.

Mine: Okay, wir können ja ___einen___ dramatische Botschaft haben, aber ___deinen___ muss auch zum Thema passen. Was ist denn unser Thema?

Marlen: Wir müssen ___ein___ Thema finden, für das sich alle hier an der Schule interessieren.

Tim: Ich glaube, dass viele sich für ___dein___ Thema „mein ökologischer Fußabdruck" interessieren. Auch die Schulzeitung hat schon über ___ein___ Thema berichtet. ___Es___ ist sehr aktuell.

Mine: Ja, das stimmt, denn wir haben ja alle ___den___ ökologischen Fußabdruck. Und ___den___ Fußabdruck kann für jede Person individuell berechnet werden. Da es so individuell ist, kann auch unsere Aktion ganz individuell jede Person ansprechen.

143c Review: Relative Clauses and Pronouns in the Accusative

We will now look at relative clauses that are initiated by **relative pronouns** in the accusative form. These sentences and pronouns will be used when the matching element in the second sentence (additional information) is in the accusative case.

Mein Freund Leo studiert in Bonn. Du kennst ihn auch.	*My friend Leo is studying in Bonn.* *You also know him.*
Ich finde die Sprachschule zu teuer. Leo hat sie beschrieben.	*I find the language school too expensive.* *Leo has described it.*
In Wien gibt es auch ein Sprachprogramm. Sonja und Elsa besuchen es.	*There is a language program in Vienna, too.* *Sonja and Elsa are attending it.*
Dort finden die Kurse an der TU statt. Viele Lehrer*innen empfehlen die Kurse.	*There, the courses take place at the Technical University.* *Many teachers recommend the courses.*

We will now integrate the additional information from the second sentence into the main sentence (first sentence), by changing it into a relative clause.

Mein Freund Leo studiert in Bonn. Du kennst ihn auch.	*My friend Leo is studying in Bonn.* *You also know him.*

You already know where to put the additional information (after *mein Freund Leo*) and that the verb will be at the end of the relative clause, as seen before.

When you pick the appropriate relative pronoun to initiate the relative clause, please note that in the additional information (second sentence) our matching word is not the subject but the **accusative object** (*ihn*). Our connecting relative pronoun will now have to be in the accusative case, too.

RELATIVE PRONOUNS	Nominative	Accusative	Dative	Genitive
masculine	Abfall, **der**	Abfall, den	Abfall, **dem**	Abfall, **dessen**
neuter	Klima, **das**	Klima, das	Klima, **dem**	Klima, **dessen**
feminine	Industrie, **die**	Industrie, die	Industrie, **der**	Industrie, **deren**
plural	Vorschläge, **die**	Vorschläge, die	Vorschläge, **denen**	Vorschläge, **deren**

The relative pronoun in the accusative case (*den*) will start the relative clause, followed by the subject. The verb in the relative clause (***kennst***) will be at the end.

Mein Freund Leo [ ] studiert in Bonn. — *My friend Leo is studying in Bonn.*
den du kennst ~~ihn~~ auch **kennst**. — *whom you also know ~~him~~.*

Let's insert the relative clause into the space we marked, right after the noun it specifies:

Mein Freund Leo, den du auch **kennst**, studiert in Bonn. — *My friend Leo whom you also know, is studying in Bonn.*

Now, before moving to the next activity, you can do the same with the other sets of sentences from the examples above.

143d **Benutzen Sie Relativsätze, um alle Zusatzinformationen in den Hauptsatz zu integrieren.**

Hauptsatz: Das Bio-Restaurant ändert Speisen, weil Lebensmittelverschwendung verringert werden soll.

Zusatzinformationen: Wir besuchen das Bio-Restaurant (*n.*) oft.
Es bietet die Speisen (*pl.*) täglich an.
Es gibt Lebensmittelverschwendung (*f.*) auch da.

___

___

___

Hauptsatz: In diesem Öko-Laden gibt es jetzt aus Naturfasern einen modernen Schal.

Zusatzinformationen: In unserer Stadt gibt es jetzt einen Öko-Laden (*m.*).
Meine Freundin findet den Schal (*m.*) modisch.
Wir können die Naturfasern (*pl.*) kompostieren.

___

___

___

143e **Unser ökologischer Fußabdruck. Welche Relativpronomen im Akkusativ passen hier?**

Unser ökologischer Fußabdruck ist die biologisch produktive Fläche (*area*) auf der Erde (*f.*), ________ wir für unseren Lebenskomfort brauchen.

Ein Leben mit viel Konsum von Rohstoffen hinterlässt einen großen Fußabdruck (*m.*), ________ wir verkleinern müssen.

Das Fleisch und die Wurst (*pl.*), ________ wir essen, vergrößern unseren ökologischen Fußabdruck.

Wir reduzieren unseren Fußabdruck, wenn wir Bio-Produkte (*pl.*) kaufen, ________ in unserer Region angebaut werden.

Jeder Kilometer (*m.*), ________ wir mit Auto oder Flugzeug zurücklegen, vergrößert unseren ökologischen Fußabdruck.

Wenn wir Dinge (*pl.*) kaufen, ________ andere schon einmal gebraucht haben, konsumieren wir weniger Ressourcen, als wenn wir nagelneue Produkte kaufen.

Auch in deinem Land (*n.*), ________ du als Mitbürger*in gut kennst, hat fast jede Person einen zu großen Fußabdruck.

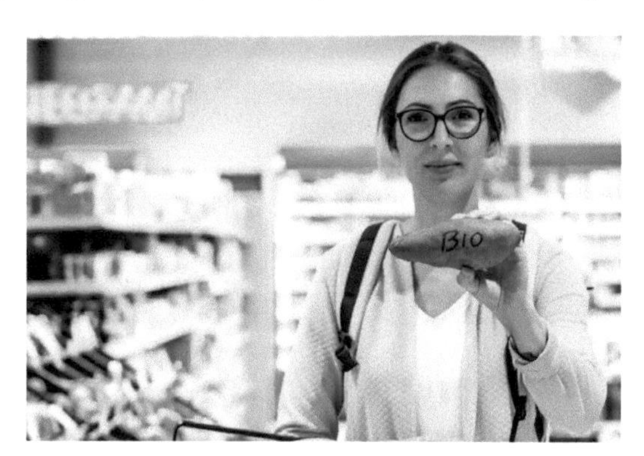

143f **Mein ökologischer Fußabdruck. Gehen Sie auf die Webseite, die Sie für diese Aktivität unter www.klett-usa.com/impuls2links finden, und berechnen Sie Ihren Fußabdruck. Bringen Sie die Ergebnisseite (PDF auf der letzten Seite) in den Kurs mit.**

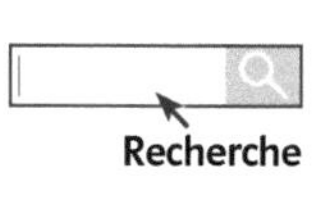

144a **Klimawandel und Ernährung. Schlagen Sie die Übersetzung für die fett gedruckten Wörter nach, wenn Sie die Wörter nicht kennen. Lesen Sie dann den Text und beantworten Sie die Fragen in Stichpunkten.**

Zwischen dem Klimawandel und unserer **Ernährung** gibt es einen direkten Zusammenhang. Die Produktion von Lebensmitteln verbraucht wertvolle Ressourcen: Wasser, Land, Strom. Außerdem entstehen bei jedem Schritt der Produktionskette **Treibhausgase**, kurz THG, die zur Erderwärmung beitragen und die Gesundheit aller Lebewesen **bedrohen**.
Der hohe Fleischkonsum vieler Nationen, auch der Deutschen, ist das größte Problem. Man braucht enorm viel Soja, das zu Futter für die Tiere verarbeitet wird – mehr als 70 Prozent des weltweiten Sojaanbaus geht in die Futterindustrie. Dafür werden riesige Regenwaldflächen abgeholzt und der Lebensraum vieler Tierarten zerstört. Oft wird Soja auch als Monokultur angebaut. Das bedeutet, dass keine anderen Pflanzen auf diesen Feldern wachsen und so die Erde mit der Zeit weniger fruchtbar (*fertile*) wird, weil ihr jedes Jahr die gleichen **Nährstoffe** entzogen werden. Die biologische Balance kommt aus dem **Gleichgewicht**, sodass die Pflanzen zum Beispiel schneller krank werden können.
Durch die Verdauung (*digestion*) von Kühen gelangt außerdem eine große Menge des Treibhausgases Methan in die Atmosphäre. Lachgas, auch ein THG, wird hingegen freigesetzt, wenn Landwirt*innen ihre Felder mit **Stickstoffdünger** düngen. Durch die Produktion, Lieferung und Lagerung von Fleischprodukten entsteht wiederum Kohlendioxid, CO_2.
Ein weiteres Problem ist, dass wir viel zu viele Lebensmittel **wegschmeißen**. Wir kaufen zu viel und das Essen wird schlecht, weil es zu lange im Kühlschrank liegt. Oder wir werfen Lebensmittel in den Abfall, weil sie nicht mehr ganz frisch aussehen, obwohl wir sie trotzdem noch essen könnten. Wir **verschwenden** Ressourcen und verursachen (*cause*) den Ausstoß, das heißt die Emission, von noch mehr THG.

Um einfacher über die Emission von allen THGs sprechen zu können, arbeiten Wissenschaftler*innen mit sogenannten CO_2-Äquivalenten. Das heißt, die emittierten **Mengen** spezifischer THGs werden in äquivalente CO_2-**Werte** konvertiert. CO_2-Äquivalente beschreiben das Treibhauspotenzial, also wie sehr diese Emissionen die Erderwärmung verstärken können. In Deutschland liegt der Ausstoß an CO_2-Äquivalenten durch die Ernährung mit Fleisch momentan bei ca. 1,7 t pro Person pro Jahr. Laut einer Studie von 2012 könnten die Deutschen durch eine gesündere Ernährung und weniger Verschwendung 67 Mio. t CO_2-Äquivalente einsparen. Dazu würden etwa 4 Mio. ha Land „frei" werden, die nachhaltiger genutzt werden könnten.
Was bedeutet aber „gesünder" in diesem Kontext? Idealerweise sollten Menschen, die Fleisch essen, ihren Fleischkonsum auf ein Minimum reduzieren. Stattdessen sollten sie viel mehr Gemüse essen. Denn Gemüse ist nicht nur gesund, sondern es werden auch weniger Ressourcen beim **Anbau** verbraucht. Und es ist ratsam, saisonales und regionales Gemüse und Obst zu kaufen, damit kürzere Distanzen für den Transport zurückgelegt werden. Wenn möglich, sollten die Menschen Biofleisch kaufen, weil der ökologische **Landbau** umweltfreundlicher ist.
„Gesünder" heißt also nachhaltiger – für die Menschen, das Klima und den ganzen Planeten.

Was machen Treibhausgase? ______________________________

Warum ist die Fleischproduktion so problematisch für das Klima? Nennen Sie zwei Beispiele.

____

____

Was ist ein anderes Wort für „Emission"? (siehe Abschnitt 4) ______________________________

Was können Menschen tun, um den weltweiten CO_2-Ausstoß zu verringern? Nennen Sie drei Beispiele.

____

____

____

144b n-Declension

Unlike German articles, nouns don't change dramatically when they are in different cases. So far, we have only added plural endings (*der Fußabdruck – die Fußabdrücke*), including the additional *-n* for marking the dative plural (*mit den Fußabdrücke**n***).

However, there is a small group of masculine nouns with a feature called "n-declension." The nouns in this group all have a plural form that ends in *-n* or *-en*. For this special group, the ending *-n* or *-en* is also required when the case changes from the original nominative form to the accusative, the dative, and the genitive. Highly frequent and typical examples are *der Mensch, der Student, der Präsident, der Nachbar, der Bär.*

Please compare the chart below to see the difference between the standard declension of masculine nouns (called "s-declension") and masculine nouns following the n-declension:

	s-declension	n-declension
singular		
nominative	der Fußabdruck	der Planet_
accusative	den Fußabdruck	den Planeten
dative	dem Fußabdruck	dem Planeten
genitive	des Fußabdruck**s**	des Planeten
plural		
nominative	die Fußabdrücke	die Planet**en**
accusative	die Fußabdrücke	die Planet**en**
dative	den Fußabdrücke**n**	den Planet**en**
genitive	der Fußabdrücke	der Planet**en**

144c Nouns With n-Declension in *Impuls Deutsch*

A significant number of the masculine nouns with n-declension are foreign words, imported from Latin or Greek. You can recognize them by their typical endings: ***-ant***,***-ent***,***-ist***, ***-at***, ***-loge***, ***-goge***, ***-soph***, and ***-aut***. All of these form the plural with *-en*.

-ant	der Praktik**ant**	die Praktikanten	*the intern (male)*
	der Demonstr**ant**	die Demonstranten	*the demonstrator (male)*
-ent	der Stud**ent**	die Studenten	*the student (male)*
	der Assist**ent**	die Assistenten	*the assistant (male)*
	der Präsid**ent**	die Präsidenten	*the president (male)*
-ist	der Poliz**ist**	die Polizisten	*the policeman*
	der Tour**ist**	die Touristen	*the tourist (male)*
-at	der Autom**at**	die Automaten	*the (vending) machine*
	der Sold**at**	die Soldaten	*the soldier (male)*
-loge	der Bio**loge**	die Biologen	*the biologist (male)*
-goge	der Päda**goge**	die Pädagogen	*the pedagogue (male)*
-soph	der Philo**soph**	die Philosophen	*the philosopher (male)*
-aut	der Astron**aut**	die Astronauten	*the astronaut (male)*

There are also masculine nouns with mostly German origin that belong to the group with n-declension. Very often these nouns end with an ***-e***, and the plural form is *-en*. Frequent examples in this group include:

persons	der Neff**e**	die Neffen	*the nephew*
	der Kund**e**	die Kunden	*the client (male)*
	der Jung**e**	die Jungen	*the boy*
	der Erb**e**	die Erben	*the heir (male)*
	der Zeug**e**	die Zeugen	*the witness (male)*
	der Kolleg**e**	de Kollegen	*the colleague (male)*
	der Bot**e**	die Boten	*the messenger (male)*
nationalities	der Deutsch**e**	die Deutschen	*the German man*
	der Türk**e**	die Türken	*the Turkish man*
	der Franzos**e**	die Franzosen	*the Frenchman*
	der Tschech**e**	die Tschechen	*the Czech man*
	der Chines**e**	die Chinesen	*the Chinese man*
	der Dän**e**	die Dänen	*the Danish man*
	der Russ**e**	die Russen	*the Russian man*
animals	der Has**e**	die Hasen	*the hare*
	der Rab**e**	die Raben	*the raven*
	der Löw**e**	die Löwen	*the lion*

Unfortunately, some words are not recognizable by their ending. These have to be learned by heart:

	der Mensch	die Menschen	*the human*
	der Bauer	die Bauern	*the farmer (male)*
	der Nachbar	die Nachbarn	*the neighbor (male)*
	der Kamerad	die Kameraden	*the companion (male)*
	der Bär	die Bären	*the bear*
	der Prinz	die Prinzen	*the prince*
	der Held	die Helden	*the hero*

144d **Ein Gespräch auf dem Wochenmarkt. Welche Nomen brauchen eine n-Endung? (Vergessen Sie nicht, dass es die n-Deklination nur bei bestimmten maskulinen Nomen und nur im Akkusativ, Dativ und Genitiv gibt.)**

Frau Herder: Guten Morgen, Herr Nachbar___. Ich habe Sie schon lange nicht mehr gesehen.

Herr Bianchi: Ja, Frau Herder, Ihren Nachbar_n_ können Sie nur sehen, wenn er in der Stadt ist. Ich war in Italien.

Frau Herder: Italien im Frühling – wie schön! Da möchte ich auch mal Tourist___ sein. Sind Sie geflogen?

Herr Bianchi: Nein, das tut unserem Planet___ nicht gut. Ich bin mit dem Zug gefahren.

Frau Herder: Übrigens, gestern wollte mein Kollege___ wissen, ob Sie sein Elektrofahrrad kaufen wollen.

Herr Bianchi: Oh ja, sagen Sie bitte Ihrem Kollege___, dass ich an seinem E-Bike sehr interessiert bin.

Frau Herder: Auf Wiedersehen, Herr Bianchi. Ich kaufe noch schnell Äpfel bei diesem Bauer___ da. Er hat die besten.

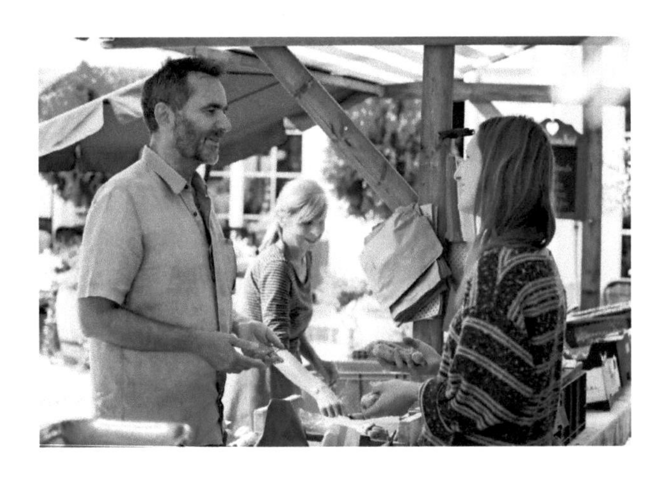

145a INFO Review: Talking About Charts and Tables

Statistics, graphics, and other figures can provide interesting insights. The phrases below introduce you to some important words and phrases that you can use to describe charts and tables.

die Daten	*data/information*	gibt (geben) Auskunft über …	*gives information about …*
das Diagramm	*diagram*	stellt (stellen) … dar.	*portrays/depicts …*
die Grafik	*graphic/chart*	zeigt (zeigen) … / zeigt, dass …	*shows … / shows that …*
das Schaubild	*chart/graph/diagram/figure*	vergleicht (vergleichen) …	*compares …*
die Statistik	*statistic*		
die Tabelle	*table/chart/spreadsheet*		

in den Daten im Diagramm in der Grafik im Schaubild in der Statistik in der Tabelle	geht es um …	*is about …*

Beispiele:
Die Statistik gibt Auskunft über den Fleischkonsum in Österreich.
Das Schaubild zeigt die Einwohnerzahlen von Wien und Graz.
Die Tabelle vergleicht den Wasserverbrauch von Italien und der Schweiz.

145b **Wie viel Wasser steckt in unseren Lebensmitteln? Ergänzen Sie die Sätze mit den Redemitteln aus dem Info-Kasten in 145a.**

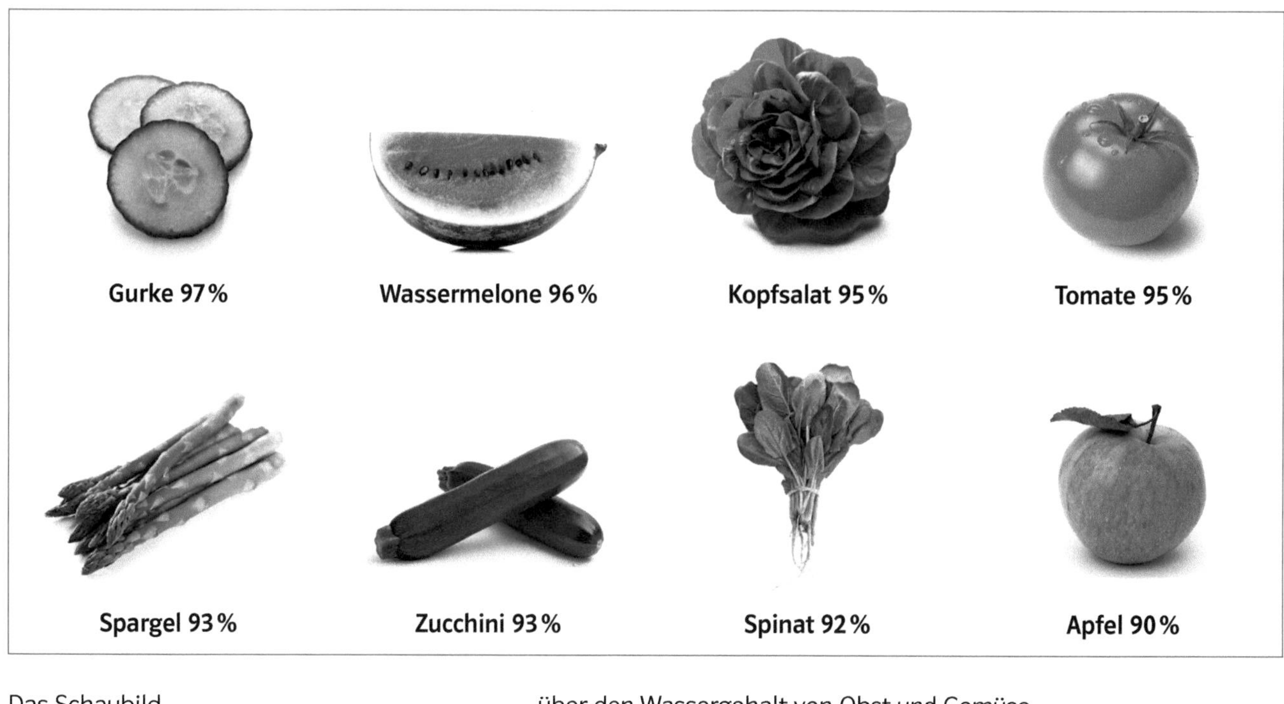

Das Schaubild ______________________ über den Wassergehalt von Obst und Gemüse.

______________ Grafik geht ______________ den Wassergehalt von Obst und Gemüse.

Die Grafik ________________ den Wassergehalt von Obst und Gemüse.

Die Grafik ________________, dass Gurken den höchsten Wassergehalt haben.

Das Schaubild ________________ den Wassergehalt von Obst und Gemüse ________________.

44: „Die Wolke"

146a **In dieser Einheit lesen Sie einen Ausschnitt aus einem Buch, das „Die Wolke" heißt. Was assoziieren Sie mit dem Wort „Wolke"? Notieren Sie sich sowohl positive als auch negative Assoziationen.**

Positive Assoziationen	Negative Assoziationen
Himmel	*Gewitter*

146b **Wählen Sie aus der Tabelle aus Aktivität 146a jeweils zwei positive und zwei negative Assoziationen und schreiben Sie damit jeweils einen Satz. Der Satz soll Ihre Assoziation im Detail erklären. Nutzen Sie die folgenden Strukturen:**

Wenn ich an eine Wolke denke, dann denke ich an … , weil …
Wenn ich an eine Wolke denke, dann dann fühle ich mich … , weil …

Wenn ich an eine Wolke denke, dann fühle ich mich traurig, weil Wolken mich an schlechtes Wetter erinnern.

147a Review: The Dative Case

The dative is another case used with nouns, articles, and pronouns. In the dative case ALL articles (and sometimes even the nouns) change their original form.

DEFINITE ARTICLES	Nominative	Accusative	Dative	Genitive
masculine	**der** Abfall	**den** Abfall	dem Abfall	**des** Abfall**s**
neuter	**das** Klima	**das** Klima	dem Klima	**des** Klima**s**
feminine	**die** Industrie	**die** Industrie	der Industrie	**der** Industrie
plural	**die** Vorschläge	**die** Vorschläge	den Vorschlägen	**der** Vorschläge

Please note that in the plural of the dative case, both the article and the noun are marked with an additional *-n*.

The dative case—like the accusative case—has several functions.

1. The dative case marks indirect objects. We already talked about the subject of a sentence (in the nominative case, doing the action) and the direct object (marked with accusative forms, receiving the action).

   Leo liest einen Bericht. — *Leo is reading a report.*

   Some verbs, however, require an additional object. So in addition to the subject and the direct object, there can be an indirect object in the sentence. This would be a noun (with its article) or a pronoun in the sentence to whom the action is directed. To distinguish the indirect object from the subject and from the direct object, it will be marked with the dative forms.

   Leo liest seinem Freund Tim einen Bericht vor. — *Leo is reading a report to his friend Tim.*

   In this sentence, *Leo* is the subject; he is doing the action (reading). *Bericht* is the element that receives the action (being read), so it is the direct object. It is marked with an accusative form. The *Freund* is the person to whom the action is directed, so his role in the sentence is the indirect object. The indirect object can be the recipient or "beneficiary" of an action. Whether this action is good or bad for the indirect object doesn't matter; it has to be marked with a dative form anyway.

2. Some **verbs**, however, can only connect to dative objects, even if there is no accusative object in the sentence like ***helfen, gehören, gefallen***, and ***zuhören***.

   Leo **hilft** seinem Freund Tim oft. — *Leo often helps his friend Tim.*

3. As seen with the accusative case, the dative case is also required for a noun (and its pronoun) or for a pronoun after certain **prepositions**: ***aus, außer, bei, mit, nach, seit, von***, and ***zu***.

   Tim isst **bei** seiner Oma zu Abend. — *Tim has dinner at his grandmother's.*

147b **Felix und Katja haben „Die Wolke" nicht gelesen, erinnern sich aber an den Film. Lesen Sie die Beschreibung und setzen Sie die passenden bestimmten Artikel (dem, der, den), Demonstrativartikel (diesem, dieser, diesen) Personalpronomen (ihm, ihr, ihnen) oder unbestimmten Artikel (einem, einer) im Dativ ein.**

Was passiert mit menschlichen Beziehungen bei ____________ atomaren Katastrophe? Mit ____________ Frage beschäftigt sich der Film „Die Wolke". In ____________ Film wird ____________ atomaren Unfall (*dat.*) eine romantische Liebesbeziehung gegenübergestellt. Mit ____________ Beziehung von Janna-Berta und Elmar entwickelt sich auch der Film in eine dramatische Richtung. Wird es ____________ möglich sein, bis zum Ende des Films zusammenzubleiben? Was wird ____________ Paar in dieser schwierigen Situation helfen? Wird ____________ die Liebe Kraft geben? All diese Fragen werden in ____________ Film beantwortet. Obwohl es ein sehr düsterer Film ist, wird bei ____________ Darstellung auch auf das ästhetisch Schöne geachtet. ____________ ästhetischen Darstellung verdankt der Film auch seine schönen Momente.

148a **Bevor Sie in MACHEN einen Ausschnitt aus „Die Wolke" lesen, lernen Sie hier die wichtigsten Personen der Geschichte kennen. Hören Sie gut zu und füllen Sie die Lücken aus.**

Janna-Berta ist eine 14-jährige junge ____________ und die Protagonistin des Buchs. Sie lebt in dem kleinen ____________ Schlitz und geht dort zur Schule. Sie hat zwei jüngere ____________, Uli und Kai, und lebt gemeinsam mit ihren Geschwistern, Eltern und den ____________, Oma Berta und Opa Hans-Georg, in einem Haus. Janna-Berta ist ____________ und verantwortungsbewusst.

Uli ist Janna-Bertas achtjähriger ____________. Nach dem atomaren ____________ muss er gemeinsam mit Janna-Berta fliehen. Er ist noch zu jung, um die ____________ wirklich zu verstehen.

Lars geht auf dieselbe ____________ wie Janna-Berta, aber er ist schon etwas älter und kann schon ____________ fahren. Nach dem ABC-Alarm nimmt er Janna-Berta mit zu ihrem ____________ nach Schlitz.

Oma Berta und Opa Hans-Georg sind Janna-Bertas Großeltern väterlicherseits. Sie ____________ in demselben Haus wie Janna-Berta. Während des Super-GAUs sind sie im ____________ und wissen nicht, wie schlimm die ____________ ist.

Elmar ist ein ____________ von Janna-Berta. Sie gingen früher einmal in dieselbe ____________ und treffen sich nach dem Super-GAU in Hamburg. Obwohl Janna-Berta ihn eigentlich nicht mag, kommen sie sich näher und werden irgendwann ____________.

148b **Lesen Sie den Text in Aktivität 148a noch einmal. Ordnen Sie dann die Beschreibungen den richtigen Personen zu.**

a) Janna-Berta
b) Uli
c) Elmar
d) Lars
e) Oma Berta / Opa Hans-Georg

___ Janna-Berta und diese Person treffen sich in Hamburg.
___ Diese Personen sind während des Unfalls nicht zu Hause, sondern im Urlaub.
_a_ Diese verantwortungsbewusste Person hat zwei Brüder.
___ Diese Person und Janna-Berta entwickeln romantische Gefühle füreinander.
___ Diese Person kann Auto fahren und kennt Janna-Berta aus der Schule.
___ Sie ist die 14-jährige Protagonistin des Buchs.
___ Diese Person hat zwei Geschwister, einen Bruder und eine Schwester.
___ Diese Person versteht die Gefahr des atomaren Unfalls nicht.

148c Review: Relative Clauses and Pronouns in the Dative

The next group of relative clauses are the ones initiated by relative pronouns in the dative case. These sentences will be used when the matching element in the second sentence is in the dative case.

Ken trainiert jeden Tag im Fitnessstudio. Diese Boxhandschuhe gehören ihm.	*Ken works out at the gym daily.* *These boxing gloves belong to him.*
Seine Freundin Kim geht lieber zum Yoga. Die Boxhandschuhe passen ihr nicht.	*His girlfriend Kim prefers to go to yoga.* *The boxing gloves don't fit her.*
Ken hat endlich ein Hobby gefunden. Er widmet dem Hobby seine ganze Kraft.	*Finally, Ken found a hobby.* *He dedicates all his energy to it.*
Im Boxsport gibt es viele Regeln. Ken muss den Regeln genau folgen.	*In boxing, there are many rules.* *Ken has to follow them exactly.*

We will now integrate the additional information from the second sentence into the main sentence (first sentence), by changing it into a relative clause.

Ken trainiert jeden Tag im Fitnessstudio. Diese Boxhandschuhe gehören ihm.	*Ken works out at the gym daily.* *These boxing gloves belong to him.*

The additional information in the second sentence is being added to the noun in the first sentence (*Ken*—here, a name or proper noun). The matching word in the second sentence is *ihm*. You already know to put the relative clause with additional information after *Ken*, and we will put the verb at the end of the relative clause, as seen before. When you pick the appropriate relative pronoun to initiate the relative clause, please note that in the additional information (second sentence) our matching word is in the dative case (*ihm*). Our connecting relative pronoun will now have to be in the dative case, too → ***dem***.

RELATIVE PRONOUNS	Nominative	Accusative	Dative	Genitive
masculine	Abfall, **der**	Abfall, **den**	Abfall, **dem**	Abfall, **dessen**
neuter	Klima, **das**	Klima, **das**	Klima, **dem**	Klima, **dessen**
feminine	Industrie, **die**	Industrie, **die**	Industrie, **der**	Industrie, **deren**
plural	Vorschläge, **die**	Vorschläge, **die**	Vorschläge, **denen**	Vorschläge, **deren**

The relative pronoun in the dative case (*dem*) will start the relative clause, followed by the subject (*diese Boxhandschuhe*). The verb of the relative clause (***gehören***) will be at the end.

Ken [ ] trainiert jeden Tag im Fitnessstudio. dem diese Boxhandschuhe **gehören** ~~ihm~~.	*Ken works out at the gym daily.* *to whom these boxing gloves belong ~~to him~~.*

Let's insert the relative clause into the space we marked, right after the noun it specifies:

Ken, dem diese Boxhandschuhe **gehören**, trainiert jeden Tag im Fitnessstudio.	*Ken, to whom these boxing gloves belong,* *works out at the gym daily.*

Now, before moving to the next activity, you can do the same with the other sets of sentences from the examples above.

148d **Benutzen Sie Relativsätze, um alle Zusatzinformationen in den Hauptsatz zu integrieren.**

Hauptsatz: Der Roman „Die Wolke" handelt von einem Reaktorunfall und seinen Folgen für die Protagonistin Janna-Berta.

Zusatzinformationen: Der Regisseur Gregor Schnitzler hat den Roman „Die Wolke" (*m.*) verfilmt.
Der Reaktorunfall (*m.*) ereignet sich in Westdeutschland.
Die Leser*innen folgen der Protagonistin Janna-Berta (*f.*) gespannt.

___

___

___

Hauptsatz: In dem Film zeigt der Regisseur zuerst die Panik und fokussiert sich dann auf die Beziehung zwischen den beiden Hauptcharakteren.

Zusatzinformationen: Der Film (*m.*) basiert auf Gudrun Pausewangs Roman „Die Wolke".
Die Menschen verspüren Panik (*f.*).
Den beiden Hauptcharakteren (*pl.*) wurden die Namen Elmar und Hannah gegeben.

___

___

___

148e **Schreiben Sie die Relativpronomen im Dativ in die Lücken.**

Die Familie, bei ____________ Janna-Berta gearbeitet hat, nahm sie nach der Arbeit im Auto mit.

Hier ist der Link zu der Webseite, auf ____________ du mehr Informationen zu den Grünen findest.

Janna-Berta und Lars waren gestern auf einem Protestmarsch (*m.*), bei ____________ gegen Atomenergie protestiert wurde.

Die Freund*innen, ____________ wir den Film „Die Wolke" geschenkt haben, fanden ihn super.

Politiker*innen, ____________ die Umwelt wichtig ist, sollten mehr gegen Klimawandel tun.

Kennst du die Person, mit ____________ sich Uli gerade unterhält?

149a **In MACHEN werden Sie sich den Trailer für den Film zum Buch „Die Wolke" anschauen. Sie sehen unten eine Reihe von Adjektiven, die bei der Aktivität in MACHEN hilfreich sind. Ordnen Sie den Adjektiven die richtige Definition zu. Wenn Sie Hilfe brauchen, können Sie ein Wörterbuch benutzen.**

a) fröhlich	___ keine Ordnung (Alle machen, was sie wollen.)
b) traurig	___ keine Hoffnung
c) dramatisch	___ frei von Spannung
d) angespannt	___ Liebesgefühle, emotional
e) chaotisch	___ viel Hoffnung (Die Zukunft sieht gut aus.)
f) düster	_a_ viel Freude, gute Stimmung, keine Sorgen
g) hoffnungslos	___ das Gegenteil von glücklich
h) romantisch	___ viel Spannung, eine kritische Situation
i) entspannt	___ eine drastische Situation
j) hoffnungsvoll	___ ziemlich dunkel

150a The Genitive Case for Proper Names

The genitive case is used to indicate possession or another relationship between two nouns or a proper name and a noun: one noun is part of, connected to, belongs to, or depends on the other noun. Here are some examples:

Gullivers Reisen, Der Besuch der alten Dame, Die Geschichte meines Lebens, Sofies Welt, Nachmittag eines Fauns, Die Rückkehr der Jedi-Ritter, Das Tagebuch der Anne Frank

Genitive of proper names:

Like in English, the main noun like ***der Bericht*** takes the second position, while the preceding "modifying attribute" *Annas* is marked by a simple *-s*. Unlike in English, no apostrophe is used in German (unless the name ends in **-s**, **-ss**, **-ß**, **-x**, or **-z**).

Proper Name (Nominative)	**Proper Name (Genitive)**	
Anna	Annas Bericht	*Anna's report*
Europa	Europas Grenzen	*Europe's borders*
Professor Pill	Professor Pills Fahrrad	*Professor Pill's bicycle*
Frau Mörike	Frau Mörikes Meinung	*Ms. Mörike's opinion*
Hans[1]	Hans' Position Hans**en**s[1] Position	*Hans's position*

[1] The older form of a genitive marker for names ending in **-s**, **-ss**, **-ß**, **-x**, or **-z** is the addition of **-ens** to the name. We don't ask you to produce this form, but you might see it when reading older texts.

150b Kombinieren Sie die beiden Elemente zu einem Genitivattribut, das Sinn ergibt.

Hut + Opa: *Opas Hut (Huts Opa ergibt keinen Sinn.)*

Uschi + Buch: ______________________

Film + Frau Walter: ______________________

Jens + Jacke: ______________________

Dr. Yıldırım + Seminar: ______________________

Blumen + Mutter: ______________________

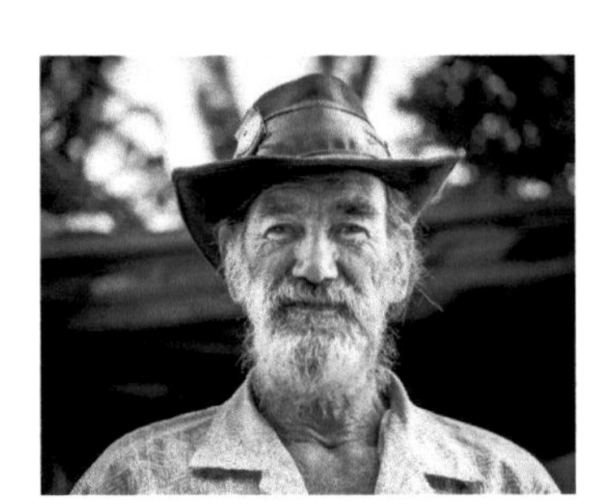

150c The Genitive Case

As mentioned before, in order to express possession or another modifying relationship between two nouns or between a proper name and a noun, we use the genitive case. In German genitive constructions, the **main noun** (which can be in the nominative, accusative, or dative form) comes first. The noun that possesses or modifies the main noun follows in the genitive case (unless it is a proper name, as presented in 150a).

Here is an overview of definite and indefinite articles in the genitive case:

DEFINITE ARTICLES	Nominative	Accusative	Dative	Genitive
masculine	**der** Abfall	**den** Abfall	**dem** Abfall	des Abfalls
neuter	**das** Klima	**das** Klima	**dem** Klima	des Klimas
feminine	**die** Industrie	**die** Industrie	**der** Industrie	der Industrie
plural	**die** Vorschläge	**die** Vorschläge	**den** Vorschläge**n**	der Vorschläge

The noun itself only displays genitive markers with masculine and neuter nouns. The genitive markers for masculine and neuter nouns are *-s* or *-es* (except for in the **n-declension**):

1. When the noun is short (monosyllabic) you can add *-es* or just *-s*: der Sturm → **die Stärke** des Sturm(e)s
2. When the noun consists of two or more syllables, just an *-s* is added: das Gewitter → **die Folgen** des Gewitters
   However, when the noun ends in an *-s*, *-ss*, *-ß*, *x*, or *-z*, you add an *-es*: der Ausstoß → **die Folgen** des Ausstoßes
3. Masculine nouns that belong to the n-declension group do not mark the genitive with an *-es* or *-s*, but with an ***-en*** or ***-n*** instead: der Planet → **die Probleme** des Planet**en**

DEFINITE ARTICLES	Nominative	Accusative	Dative	Genitive
masculine	**der** Planet	**den** Planet**en**	**dem** Planet**en**	des Planet**en**

150d Die Bürger*inneninitiative „Besser leben in Neudorf" hat ein Umwelt-Poster geschrieben. Welcher Artikel im Genitiv ist richtig: „des" oder „der"?

Wir alle müssen beim Schutz ____________ Umwelt (*f.*) helfen!

Das bedeutet die Reduzierung ____________ Erdölverbrauchs (*m.*), denn die Ölindustrie verschmutzt die Umwelt.

Wir brauchen Alternativen für die Nutzung ____________ Energiequellen (*pl.*), die wir sauber gewinnen können.

Egal, was wir wählen: Wir verbessern die Qualität ____________ Lebens (*n.*) nur mit sauberer Energie.

Deshalb wollen wir die Reduzierung ____________ Kernenergie (*f.*) in unserer Region.

Wir unterstützen die Gruppe ____________ Atomkraftgegner*innen (*pl.*) in Wyhl!

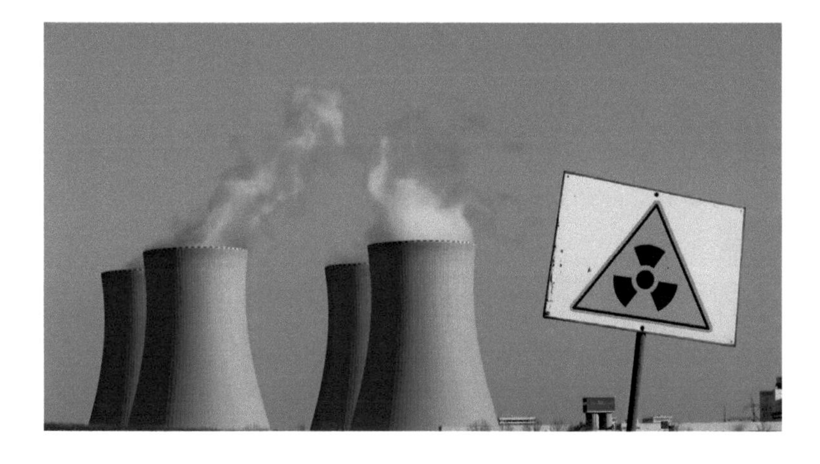

150e **Schulwahlen: Wienke, Carsten und Kathrin diskutieren über ein Wahlplakat in ihrer Schule. Setzen Sie die passenden bestimmten Artikel (des, der), Demonstrativartikel (dieses, dieser) oder unbestimmten Artikel (eines, einer) im Genitiv ein.**

Kathrin: Habt ihr das Wahlplakat __________ Anti-Atomkraft-Partei gesehen?

Carsten: Ist das eine neue Partei in unserer Schule?

Wienke: Ja. Die AAP versteht sich als Partei __________ Sonnenenergie. Hier ist das Motto __________ vier AAP-Politiker*innen: Für die Bewegung __________ Sonne.

Kathrin: Das klingt absurd. Die Sonne bewegt sich ja schon. Aber diese neue Partei braucht die Unterstützung __________ Schulbevölkerung. Sollen wir der AAP helfen?

Carsten: Ja! Ihr Ziel ist super, nur die Sprache ist nicht effektiv. Wir helfen ihr bei der Realisierung __________ Zieles. Welches Motto klingt besser? Lasst uns einen stärkeren Spruch finden.

K&W: Hmmmm ...

151a **Schreiben Sie vier Sätze – Hauptsatz plus Relativsatz – und sagen Sie, was Sie auf dem Bild sehen. Beginnen Sie die Sätze mit „Im Vordergrund gibt es ...", „Im Hintergrund gibt es ..." oder „Daneben/Dahinter/Davor gibt es ...".**

Im Vordergrund gibt es ein Pärchen, das sich küsst.

____

____

____

____

151b **Was ist das? In MACHEN Aktivität 151 werden Sie mit den anderen Kursteilnehmer*innen über Plakate sprechen, in denen die folgenden Begriffe vorkommen. Üben Sie die Begriffe hier, indem Sie den Wörtern die korrekten Definitionen zuordnen. Schreiben Sie für „Bevölkerung" und „Demonstration" selbst eine kurze Definition.**

Die Bedeutung des Wortes „Atomkraft" ist: __

Die Bedeutung des Wortes „Bewegung" ist: __

Die Bedeutung des Wortes „Kernkraftwerk" ist: __

Die Bedeutung des Wortes „Umwelt" ist: __

a) ein Gebäude, in dem Energie aus Atomkraft gewonnen wird

b) die Natur um uns herum

c) die Energie, die beim Spalten eines Atoms freigesetzt wird

d) eine Gruppe von Menschen, die gemeinsam ein Ziel verfolgen

Die Bedeutung des Wortes „Bevölkerung" ist:

____

Die Bedeutung des Wortes „Demonstration" ist:

____

46: Deutschland, grünes Vorbild°

153a **Deutschland und Umweltschutz: Assoziationen. Woran denken Sie spontan, wenn Sie „Deutschland und Umweltschutz" hören? Machen Sie eine Liste.**

____

____

____

____

153b **Deutschland als grünes Vorbild: Ein Diktat. Sie hören nun einen langsam gesprochenen Text zum Thema „Umweltschutz in Deutschland". Schreiben Sie mit. Hören Sie den Text mindestens zweimal.**

____

____

____

____

____

____

____

____

154a **Textvorbereitung: Lesen Sie in MACHEN Aktivität 154 die 15 Bausteine für die „Stadt der Zukunft" vom Umweltbundesamt (UBA) in Deutschland. Schlagen Sie unbekannte Wörter im Wörterbuch nach, sodass Sie am Ende alle 15 Bausteine verstehen. Welchen der Bausteine finden Sie am wichtigsten/interessantesten? Warum?**

____

____

____

47: Deutschland, grünes Vorbild?

156a Genitive Form Versus *von* + Dative

Like in English, there are two ways to express a possessive or otherwise modifying relationship between nouns:

a genitive construction (see 150c)	der Protest des Mitglieds das Fällen der Bäume Bärbels Kind	*the member's protest* *"the trees' felling"* *Bärbel's child*
a prepositional construction with ***von*** followed by articles and nouns in the dative case	der Protest **von dem** Mitglied das Fällen **von** (**den**) Bäum**en** das Kind **von** Bärbel	*the protest **of** the member* *the felling **of** (the) trees* *the child **of** Bärbel*

In both languages, there are certain criteria in texts, contexts, and style that decide which form is more suitable, so in many cases, the alternative forms are not interchangeable (Anna's love ≠ the love of Anna).

1. In spoken German, there is a tendency to use the prepositional construction ***von*** **+ dative** more often.
2. The genitive form with -s is, however, very suitable in written German, especially in scientific texts that strive to be as concise as possible.
3. A combination of both forms is indicated when you come across a series of nouns in specific relationships:

   Die Relevanz **von** Dr. Spocks Forschung — *The relevance **of** Dr. Spock's research*

156b Zuordnung: Was ist eine Genitivkonstruktion und was eine Präpositionalkonstruktion und welche zwei gehören zusammen?

Genitivkonstruktion		Präpositionalkonstruktion
a	=	d
	=	
	=	
	=	
	=	

a) die Veränderung des Klimas
b) das Klima der Welt
c) das Klima von der Welt
d) die Veränderung von dem Klima
e) die Produktion von dem Plastikmüll
f) der Schutz der Natur
g) die Webseiten von den Supermarktketten
h) der Schutz von der Natur
i) die Produktion des Plastikmülls
j) die Webseiten der Supermarktketten

156c Wie heißen die Filmtitel wirklich? Ändern Sie die Präpositionalkonstruktion in eine Genitivkonstruktion und umgekehrt.

Die Ökonomie von Glück (*n.*) Die Ökonomie des Glücks

Der Alptraum von Darwin ____________________

Uranium – is it a country? Eine Spurensuche nach der Herkunft des Atomstroms ____________________

____

Cowspiracy – Das Geheimnis von Nachhaltigkeit ____________________

Das geheime Leben von Bäumen ____________________

Der Kleiderhaken – Die Schattenseiten von Freihandel (*m.*) in der globalen Bekleidungsindustrie ____________________

____

156d Relative Clauses and Pronouns in the Genitive

In this chapter, we already covered relative clauses that start with relative pronouns in the nominative, accusative, and the dative case. Since you have now been introduced to the *Genitiv*, too, we can now look at relative sentences that start with genitive pronouns. These sentences will be used when the matching element in the second sentence is either in the genitive case (like *Leo**s** Wörterbuch*, *das Wörterbuch mein**es** Freund**es** Leo*) or when there is a matching possessive article (***sein** Wörterbuch*).

Ken trainiert jeden Tag im Fitnessstudio. Seine Boxhandschuhe liegen hier.	*Ken works out at the gym daily.* *His boxing gloves are here.*
Kim geht lieber zum Yoga. Ihre Interessen liegen woanders.	*Kim prefers to go to yoga.* *Her interests are elsewhere.*
Ken trainiert in einem Fitnessstudio. Die Öffnungszeiten des Fitnessstudios sind günstig.	*Ken works out at a gym.* *The opening hours of the gym are convenient.*
Ken findet seine Trainer*innen sehr kompetent. Ihre Methoden sind unterschiedlich.	*Ken finds his trainers very competent.* *Their methods are different.*

In contrast to the other relative pronouns, the relative pronouns in the genitive case don't look like their article counterparts but have their own forms instead: *dessen* (for masculine and neuter) and *deren* (for feminine and plural). In English, they translate to "whose," and their use is very similar to English.

DEFINITE ARTICLES	**Nominative**	**Accusative**	**Dative**	**Genitive**
masculine	**der** Abfall	**den** Abfall	**dem** Abfall	des Abfalls
neuter	**das** Klima	**das** Klima	**dem** Klima	des Klimas
feminine	**die** Industrie	**die** Industrie	**der** Industrie	der Industrie
plural	**die** Vorschläge	**die** Vorschläge	**den** Vorschläge**n**	der Vorschläge

RELATIVE PRONOUNS	**Nominative**	**Accusative**	**Dative**	**Genitive**
masculine	Abfall, **der**	Abfall, **den**	Abfall, **dem**	Abfall, dessen
neuter	Klima, **das**	Klima, **das**	Klima, **dem**	Klima, dessen
feminine	Industrie, **die**	Industrie, **die**	Industrie, **der**	Industrie, deren
plural	Vorschläge, **die**	Vorschläge, **die**	Vorschläge, **denen**	Vorschläge, deren

We can insert the additional information from the second sentences into the main sentences (first sentence) by changing them into relative clauses. The relative pronouns in the genitive case (*dessen* or *deren*) plus their nouns (*Boxhandschuhe*/*Interessen*) will start the relative clauses. As usual for relative clauses, the verb (***liegen***) will be at the end.

Ken [ ] trainiert jeden Tag im Fitnessstudio. dessen ~~Seine~~ Boxhandschuhe liegen hier **liegen**.	*Ken works out at the gym daily.* *whose ~~His~~ boxing gloves are here.*
Kim [ ] geht lieber zum Yoga. deren ~~Ihre~~ Interessen liegen woanders **liegen**.	*Kim prefers to go to yoga.* *whose ~~Her~~ interests are elsewhere.*

Now, let's insert the relative clauses into the spaces we marked, right after the nouns they specify.

Ken, dessen Boxhandschuhe hier **liegen**, trainiert jeden Tag im Fitnessstudio.	*Ken, whose boxing gloves are here,* *works out at the gym daily.*
Kim, deren Interessen woanders **liegen**, geht lieber zum Yoga.	*Kim, whose interests are elsewhere,* *prefers to go to yoga.*

Before moving to the next activity, you can do the same with the other sets of sentences from the examples above.

156e **Benutzen Sie Relativsätze, um alle Zusatzinformationen in den Hauptsatz zu integrieren.**

Hauptsatz: Claudia geht mit ihrem Freund Ben vor Gericht.

Zusatzinformationen: Claudias (*f.*) Debatte war spektakulär.
Bens (*m.*) Stiftung senkt den Verbrauch von CO_2.
Der Saal des Gerichts (*n.*) ist riesig.

____

____

____

Hauptsatz: Das Wahlplakat unterstützt die Atomkraftgegner*innen bei der bundesweiten Bewegung.

Zusatzinformationen: Die Farbe des Wahlplakats (*f.*) ist lila.
Die Botschaft der Atomkraftgegner*innen (*pl.*) ist klar.
Die Unterstützer*innen der Bewegung (*f.*) sind nicht gewaltsam.

____

____

____

156f **Eine Reflexion über die deutsche Anti-Atomkraft-Bewegung. Welches Relativpronomen passt zu den kursiv geschriebenen Nomen: „dessen“ oder „deren“?**

Seit Mitte der 1960er Jahre gab es *Kernkraftwerke*, deren Energie die Befürworter*innen (*proponents*) sicher und wirtschaftlich fanden.
Die Ölkrise im Jahr 1973 verursachte einen *Energieschock*, __________ Lösung in mehr alternativer Energie lag.
Ein neues Kernkraftwerk sollte 1975 in der *Stadt* Wyhl entstehen, __________ Einwohner*innen aber dagegen kämpften.
Die Wyhler*innen versuchten zuerst juristische *Prozesse*, __________ Effektivität sich als nicht stark genug erwies.
Dann besetzten sie den *Bauplatz* des Kernkraftwerkes, __________ brutale Räumung durch die Polizei die deutsche Anti-Atomkraft-Bewegung startete.

156g **Grüne Parteien in der Welt: Global Greens (GG). Ergänzen Sie die Sätze mit den Bezugswörtern aus dem Kasten.**

Die Global Greens sind eine Organisation, **deren** Föderation vier globale Regionen hat: Asien, Afrika, Amerika und Europa.
Viele __________________, **deren** Bürger*innen Interesse an effektiver Umweltpolitik zeigen, haben Grüne Parteien.
Die erste __________________, **deren** Ziele auf ökologischer Nachhaltigkeit lag, fand 1972 in Australien statt.
Danach folgten die ersten __________________, **deren** bekannteste Politikerin die deutsche Ökofeministin Petra Kelly war.
Die Global Greens sind 84 Grüne Parteien in Europa. Ihr __________________, **dessen** erstes planetarisches Treffen 1992 in Rio de Janeiro war, kommt einmal im Jahr zusammen.
Die __________________, **deren** Ziele partizipatorische Demokratie, soziale Gerechtigkeit, Nachhaltigkeit und mehr sind, gibt es seit dem Jahr 2001.

Charter der GG | ~~Organisation~~ | Kongress | Grünen Parteien in Europa | Parteitagung | Länder

157a Summary: Articles and Relative Pronouns

We have now learned and practiced all four grammatical cases. Here is a summary of all definite articles and relative pronouns. As you can see, the relative pronouns are mostly the same as the definite articles, except in the genitive case, and for dative plural:

DEFINITE ARTICLES	Nominative	Accusative	Dative	Genitive
masculine	**der** Baum	**den** Baum	**dem** Baum	**des** Baum**es**
neuter	**das** Gesetz	**das** Gesetz	**dem** Gesetz	**des** Gesetz**es**
feminine	**die** Erde	**die** Erde	**der** Erde	**der** Erde
plural	**die** Kinder	**die** Kinder	**den** Kinder**n**	**der** Kinder

RELATIVE PRONOUNS	Nominative	Accusative	Dative	Genitive
masculine	Baum, **der**	Baum, **den**	Baum, **dem**	Baum, **dessen**
neuter	Gesetz, **das**	Gesetz, **das**	Gesetz, **dem**	Gesetz, **dessen**
feminine	Erde, **die**	Erde, **die**	Erde, **der**	Erde, **deren**
plural	Kinder, **die**	Kinder, **die**	Kinder, **denen**	Kinder, **deren**

48: KOMMUNIKATION

159a Jeden Tag kommunizieren wir miteinander. Sie kennen bestimmt Situationen, in denen Sie etwas sagen und die andere Person etwas ganz anderes versteht, aber nicht das, was Sie sagen wollten. Lesen Sie die Sätze unten und spekulieren Sie, was die sprechende Person sagen möchte und was die andere Person, also der*die Empfänger*in, wahrscheinlich versteht.

Szenario 1: Maria zu Peter: „Der Mülleimer ist schon wieder ziemlich voll!"

Maria möchte kommunizieren: *Der Mülleimer ist voll. Das ist ein Fakt.*

Peter versteht: *Sie möchte, dass ich den Mülleimer leere.*

Szenario 2: Beim Abendessen sagt der Mann zu seiner Frau: „Ist das ein neues Rezept?"

Der Mann möchte kommunizieren: ______________________

Die Frau versteht: ______________________

Szenario 3: Eine Mutter sagt im Schuhladen zu ihrem Sohn: „Max, diese Schuhe kosten 300 Euro."

Die Mutter möchte kommunizieren: ______________________

Max versteht: ______________________

Szenario 4: Eine Schwester sagt zu ihrem Bruder: „Hast du schon wieder mein iPad aus meinem Zimmer geholt?!"

Die Schwester möchte kommunizieren: ______________________

Der Bruder versteht: ______________________

159b **War es in Aktivität 159a immer klar, was die Botschaft der sprechenden Person ist? Bei welchem Beispiel gibt es Ihrer Meinung nach am meisten Potential für ein Missverständnis? Warum? Schreiben Sie 2–3 Sätze.**

____

____

____

159c **Sie haben schon gemerkt, dass Kommunikation nicht immer eindeutig ist. Der deutsche Kommunikationswissenschaftler Friedemann Schulz von Thun entwickelte ein Modell, das dieses Phänomen erklärt. In diesem Text lernen Sie das Modell kennen. Lesen Sie den Text und ordnen Sie unten die Satzanfänge den Satzenden zu.**

Der Kommunikationswissenschaftler Friedemann Schulz von Thun hat ein Modell entwickelt, mit dem sich Kommunikation beschreiben lässt. Auch hilft dieses Modell, Probleme zu verstehen, die Menschen beim Kommunizieren haben.

Das Modell besagt, dass jede Aussage vier Botschaften enthält. Das bedeutet, wenn eine Person etwas zu einer anderen Person sagt, dann wird diese Nachricht auf unterschiedlichen Ebenen kommuniziert. Jede Ebene zeigt eine andere Perspektive auf die Aussage und wie man die Aussage unterschiedlich verstehen kann.

Der **Sachinhalt** beschreibt die Situation auf einer sachlichen, also objektiven Ebene. Das bedeutet, dass jede Aussage einen Fakt kommuniziert. Der Sachinhalt der Aussage „Das Wasser in der Badewanne ist kalt" ist einfach, dass das Wasser kalt ist, ein Fakt.

Der **Appell** beschreibt eine Aufforderung des*der Sprecher*in an den*die Empfänger*in. In unserem Wasserbeispiel könnte der Appell so aussehen: „Mach bitte das Wasser wärmer."

Mit der **Selbstaussage** gibt der*die Sprecher*in eine Information über sich selbst. In unserem Wasserbeispiel könnte er*sie als Selbstaussage das meinen: „Ich mag kaltes Wasser nicht."

Hier ist noch ein Beispiel. Pia benutzt die Toilette und sieht, dass das Toilettenpapier alle ist. Sie ruft laut, damit ihr Mitbewohner Ole sie hören kann: „Das Toilettenpapier ist alle!" Der Sachinhalt ist klar: „Es gibt kein Toilettenpapier mehr im Badezimmer." Der Appell ist: „Hol mir neues Toilettenpapier!" Pias Selbstaussage lautet: „Ich brauche Hilfe."

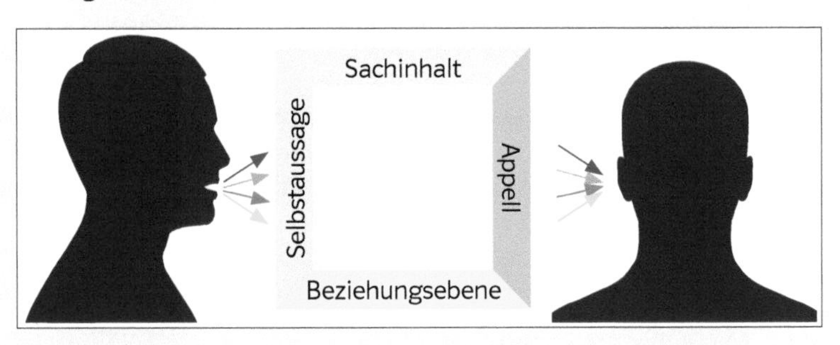

Die **Beziehungsebene** macht eine implizite Aussage über die Beziehung zwischen Sender*in und Empfänger*in. Vor allem bei dieser letzten Ebene kann es schnell zu Konflikten kommen, wenn der*die Empfänger*in eine Nachricht anders interpretiert, als sie gemeint war. Im Wasserbeispiel ist auch die Beziehungsebene am kompliziertesten. Die Beziehungsebene könnte hier sein: „Ich habe dir doch schon oft gesagt, dass ich kaltes Wasser nicht mag. Ich erwarte, dass du das weißt."

Bei der Beziehungsebene wird es nun interessant. Vielleicht ist das leere Toilettenpapier für Pia ja gar kein großes Problem und sie will nur signalisieren, dass sie Hilfe braucht. Trotzdem könnte Ole die Nachricht „Das Toilettenpapier ist alle!" als Kritik interpretieren. Und wenn Ole tatsächlich oft vergisst, neues Toilettenpapier ins Bad zu legen, dann wird der Unterton in Pias Nachricht, also die Beziehungsebene, bestimmt dieser sein: „Nie füllst du das Toilettenpapier auf!" Für die Beziehungsebene ist es also sehr wichtig, <u>wie</u> etwas gesagt wird und <u>wie</u> es verstanden wird.

a) Das Vier-Seiten-Modell zeigt …	____ gibt es die meisten Verständigungsprobleme.
b) Der Sachinhalt …	_a_ , dass mit jeder Nachricht mehr als eine Botschaft gesendet wird.
c) Der Appell beschreibt …	____ liefert Fakten.
d) Mit der Selbstaussage …	____ , wie die sprechende zur empfangenden Person steht.
e) Die Beziehungsebene zeigt …	____ , was der*die Empfänger*in tun soll.
f) Auf der Beziehungsebene …	____ sagt der*die Sprecher*in etwas über sich selbst.

159d **Sie haben in Aktivität 159c das Vier-Seiten-Modell kennengelernt. Um sich die vier Ebenen besser zu merken, können Sie für jede Ebene zwei Fragen formulieren, eine aus der Perspektive der sprechenden Person und eine aus der Perspektive der zuhörenden Person. Schreiben Sie die Fragen aus der Liste an die richtige Stelle in der Tabelle.**

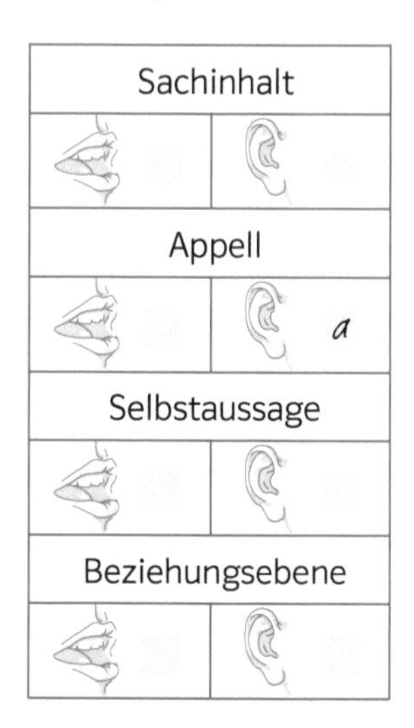

Fragen:
a) Was soll ich machen?
b) Was will ich über unsere Beziehung sagen?
c) Was will ich über mich selbst sagen?
d) Welche Fakten soll ich verstehen?
e) Welche Aktion erwarte ich von der anderen Person?
f) Was sagt die Person über sich selbst?
g) Welche Fakten möchte ich kommunizieren?
h) Was bedeutet das für unsere Beziehung?

159e **Jetzt üben Sie die Theorie etwas praktischer. Tom und Andres sitzen beim Abendessen. Tom sagt: „Warum ist das Essen so scharf?" Wählen Sie in der Tabelle, was Tom auf jeder Ebene wahrscheinlich kommunizieren möchte (Mund) und was Andres versteht (Ohr).**

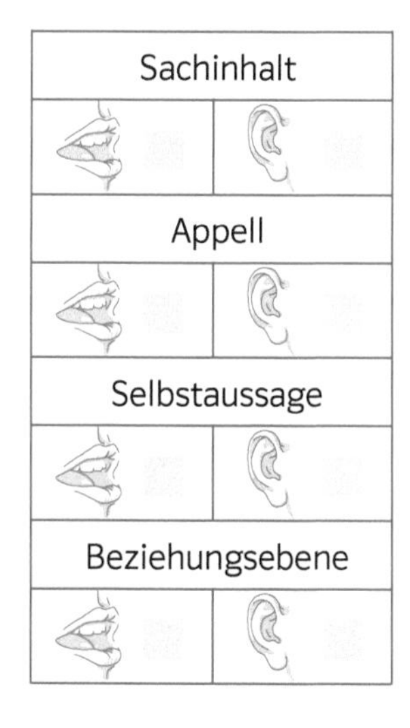

Was wird kommuniziert?
Was wird verstanden?
a) Das Essen ist scharf.
b) Sag mir, warum es so scharf ist.
c) Du weißt, warum es so scharf ist.
d) Ich bin ein schlechter Koch.
e) Ich esse (nicht) gern scharfes Essen.
f) Das Essen ist scharf.
g) Koch weniger scharfes Essen.
h) Er mag (nicht) gern scharfes Essen.

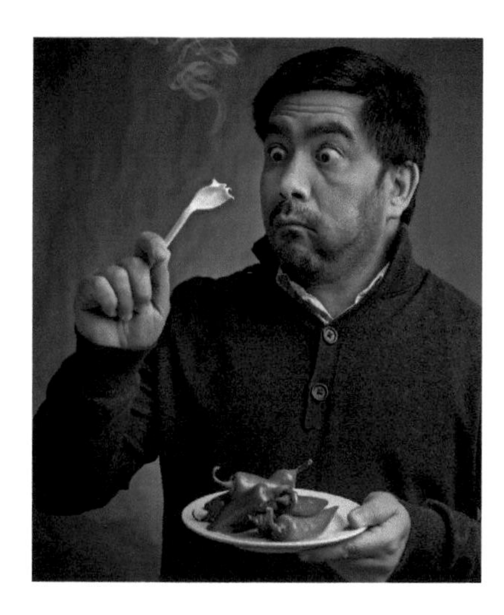

159f **Auch wenn eine Person nicht weiß, wie die andere Person eine Nachricht meint, muss sie trotzdem reagieren. Tom und Andres sitzen jetzt im Auto. Andres fährt 60 km/h und Tom sagt: „Du darfst hier 70 km/h fahren." Wählen Sie jetzt aus, wie Andres die Nachricht verstehen kann (Ohr) und wie er darauf basierend reagieren würde (Mund).**

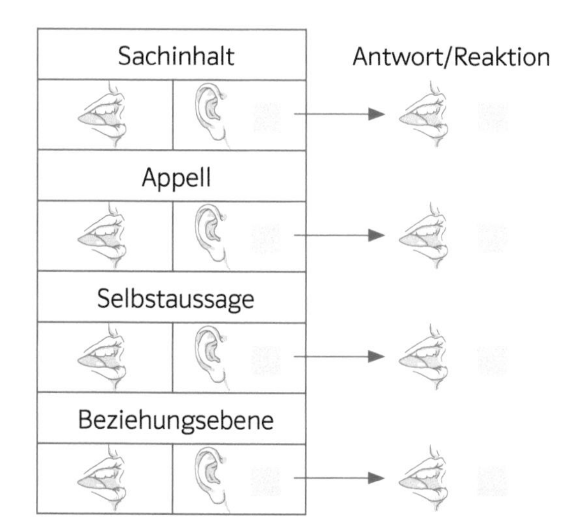

Was versteht Andres?
a) Ich bin ein schlechter Autofahrer.
b) Tom ist gestresst und möchte schnell nach Hause.
c) Auf dieser Straße kann 70 km/h gefahren werden.
d) Ich soll schneller fahren.

Wie antwortet/reagiert Andres?
e) Lass uns nächstes Mal eher los, dann hast du weniger Stress.
f) Oh danke, das wusste ich nicht.
g) Fahr selber, wenn du es besser kannst.
h) Ok, ich fahre schneller.

Aussprache: Das R

162a **Hören und Sprechen: Hören Sie die Wörter mit den verschiedenen R-Lauten und sprechen Sie dann nach.**

[r] = das konsonantische „r“	**[ɐ] = das vokalische „r“**
braun	der Bär

162b **Hören: Hören Sie die Sätze und lesen Sie mit. Achten Sie auf die R-Laute.**

Ich bin der berühmte Bär von Bern. Viele Touristen reisen nach Bern. Und auch viele Besucher aus der Region. Und alle kommen zu mir – dem braunen Bären von Bern. Denn ich bin interessant, ich bin eine Attraktion! Alle sind fröhlich und machen immer Fotos von mir. Ein Maler malt ein abstraktes Bild von mir und verkauft den Besuchern das Original gleich hier. Der Park von uns Bären ist wirklich das Zentrum von Bern!

162c **Hören Sie einzelne Wörter noch einmal und achten Sie auf die R-Laute. Wann sprechen wir das „r“ konsonantisch [r], wann vokalisch [ɐ]? Kreuzen Sie an.**

Wo ist das R?	**Beispiele**	**[r]**	**[ɐ]**
am Anfang von einem Wort oder einer Silbe	Region, Touristen		
nach kurzen Vokalen	Bern, Park		
nach langen Vokalen am Ende von einer Silbe	Bär, mir		
nach Konsonanten	braun, Attraktion		
in den unbetonten Vorsilben er-, ver-, zer-	verkaufen		
bei -er am Wortende (auch: -ert, -erst, -ern, -ernd)	Besucher, Besuchern		

162d **Hören Sie die Wörter noch einmal. Was fällt auf? Kreuzen Sie an.**

Das konsonantische „r“ hört man	deutlich.	undeutlich, klingt fast wie ein „a“.
Das vokalische „r“ hört man	deutlich.	undeutlich, klingt fast wie ein „a“.

162e **Hören und Sprechen: Hören Sie das Wortpaar. Was fällt auf? Kreuzen Sie an.**

„Bär“ — konsonantisches „r“, vokalisches „r“, denn nach langem Vokal am Ende einer Silbe.

„Bären“ — konsonantisches „r“, vokalisches „r“, denn am Anfang einer Silbe.

162f **Sprechen Sie die Beispielwörter in Aktivität 162c und dann den Text in Aktivität 162b.**

49: Was bewegt zu nachhaltigem Handeln?

163a **Nachhaltigkeit in meinem Alltag. In den vorherigen Einheiten haben Sie schon viel zum Thema „Nachhaltigkeit" gelernt und auch darüber mit anderen Kursteilnehmer*innen diskutiert. Beantworten Sie die Fragen.**

Wie definieren Sie „Nachhaltigkeit"? Sehen Sie sich zur Hilfe noch einmal die vorherigen Einheiten an, benutzen Sie aber Ihre eigenen Worte für die Definition.

____

____

Wo und wie handeln Sie in Ihrem Alltag nachhaltig?

Ich ______________________________

Ich ______________________________

Ich ______________________________

Ich ______________________________

164a Prepositions Followed by Genitive

Prepositions are powerful little words: they impose a case change on the following noun (and its article) and on pronouns.

der Planet → für den Planeten, auf dem Planeten

So far we have seen prepositions that require the accusative and/or the dative. Today, we will look at the last group of prepositions. They require the genitive case for the following (pro)noun (and its article). The most important and frequent ones are:

wegen (because of), ***während*** (during), ***statt*** (instead of), ***trotz*** (in spite of).

der Regen	**Wegen** des Regens fuhr Helga gestern nicht mit dem Fahrrad.	*Because of the rain, Helga didn't ride her bike yesterday.*
das Gewitter	**Während** des Gewitters saß sie am Busbahnhof.	*During the thunderstorm, she sat at the bus station.*
das Fahrrad	**Statt** des Fahrrads nimmt sie auch manchmal den Bus.	*Instead of the bike, she sometimes takes the bus.*
das Wetter	**Trotz** des guten Wetters hat sie ihr Fahrrad heute zu Hause gelassen.	*In spite of the good weather, she left her bike at home today.*

In spoken or colloquial dialogue, Germans often use the dative instead of the genitive after these prepositions, so be prepared to encounter both versions.

Ich gehe **wegen** des Regens nicht zum Training. (grammatically correct)	*Because of the rain, I am not going to the training.*
Ich gehe **wegen** dem Regen nicht zum Training. (grammatically incorrect, but often used colloquially)	*Because of the rain, I am not going to the training.*

164b **Ein Notfall im Atomkraftwerk! Lesen Sie den Text und kreisen Sie die passenden Präpositionen ein.**

Meine Freund*innen und ich wohnten 1979 in Neustadt, aber während | trotz des Sommers fuhren wir oft mit dem Fahrrad nach Altstadt zum Schwimmen am Altstädter See. Statt | Trotz seiner romantischen Lage hatte die Altstadt ein Geheimnis (*secret*): Es gab ein Atomkraftwerk hinter dem Altstädter Forst! An einem warmen Sommertag bekamen wir wegen | während dieses Atomkraftwerks einen Riesenschock. Wegen | Statt der Vögel und des Wassers hörten wir am See einen sehr lauten Alarm! Karen sagte sofort: „Das ist ein ABC-Alarm!" Und wir liefen trotz | wegen ihrer Warnung schnell zu unseren Fahrrädern. Am Ende war es nur ein Probealarm, aber während | statt der ganzen Radfahrt nach Hause hatten wir große Angst …

164c **Welche Fragen und Antworten bilden ein logisches Paar?**

Warum gibt es immer mehr Tiere im Klimastress?

Wegen des Klimawandels hat sich ihr Habitat verändert.

Aus welchem Grund ist Nachhaltigkeit so wichtig?

____

Wieso gibt es immer mehr Waldbrände in Deutschland?

____

Weshalb begann die Anti-Atomkraft-Bewegung in Deutschland?

____

Warum gibt es Subventionen für E-Bikes in manchen deutschen Städten und Bundesländern?

____

Wieso sind viele Deutsche mit dem Umweltschutz in ihrem Land nicht zufrieden?

____

Wegen des extremen Wetters werden die Wälder trockener.
Wegen der Umweltfreundlichkeit dieses Transportmittels.
Wegen der Angst um die Gesundheit und Sicherheit der Menschen.
Wegen der Umweltpolitik, die ihrer Meinung nach schlecht war.
Wegen der Perspektive auf die Zukunft unseres Planeten.
~~Wegen des Klimawandels hat sich ihr Habitat verändert.~~

164d **Umweltbewusstsein und globale Vernetzung. Ergänzen Sie die korrekten Artikel im Genitiv.**

Trotz *des* Klimawandels fördern viele Länder lieber das Wachstum. Wegen ________ globalen Vernetzung sollten Kund*innen sich während ________ Einkaufs über die Herkunft der Produkte informieren. Und das sollten sie nicht nur wegen ________ Transportwege, sondern auch wegen ________ Einsatzes von Dünger und Pestiziden tun. Kund*innen sollten also trotz ________ höheren Preises lieber Bio-Obst wegen ________ niedrigeren CO_2-Ausstoßes kaufen. Aber wegen ________ Aussehens kaufen viele Menschen importiertes Obst statt ________ Produkte vom Öko-Bauernhof nebenan.

Wegen ________ globalen Erwärmung sind viele Leute wieder für Atomkraft trotz ________ Katastrophen wie in Tschernobyl. Wegen ________ sauren Regens haben auch manche schon in den siebziger Jahren trotz ________ Risiken die Atomkraft befürwortet. Heute wird oft darüber diskutiert, ob es Sinn macht, die Atomkraft trotz ________ höheren Kosten zu fördern, vor allem wegen ________ Wetters, das Wind- und Solarenergie stark beeinflusst.

165a Fixed Prepositions and Prepositions in Relative Clauses

Here is a chart of the most frequent prepositions sorted by their required case:

Accusative	Accusative (for destinations) or Dative (for locations)	Dative	Genitive
bis	an	aus	statt
durch	auf	außer	trotz
für	hinter	bei	während
gegen	in	mit	wegen
ohne	neben	nach	
um	über	seit	
	unter	von	
	vor	zu	
	zwischen		

Prepositions stand directly before nouns or pronouns and determine their cases. This is also true for relative sentences. Since prepositions are always attached to a noun or pronoun, they precede a relative pronoun. As prepositions require specific cases, the relative pronouns follow the same rules: e.g. dative relative pronoun after *mit* or genitive relative pronoun after *wegen*.

Linda hat einen Hund [ ] und eine Katze.
Sie trainiert **mit** ihrem Hund jeden Tag.

Linda has a dog and a cat.
She works out ***with*** *her dog daily.*

Linda hat einen Hund, **mit** dem sie jeden Tag trainiert, und eine Katze.

Linda has a dog, ***with*** *whom she works out daily, and a cat.*

165b Greenpeace. Integrieren Sie die Informationen zu einem Hauptsatz mit Relativsatz, wie im Beispiel.

Greenpeace ist eine transnationale Non-Profit-Organisation. **Bei** der Organisation geht es um Umweltschutz.

____

____

Die Aktivist*innen arbeiten oft mit Aktionen. **Für** die Aktionen stellen sie Regierungen und Konzerne an den öffentlichen Pranger (*to pillory*).

____

____

Wichtig für den Erfolg ist eine Lobby- und Pressearbeit. **Ohne** die Lobby- und Pressearbeit können die Aktionen nicht medial wirksam werden.

____

____

Gegen gefährliche Textilchemikalien engagiert sich Greenpeace mit der Kampagne Detox. **Wegen** der Kampagne Detox wollen viele Unternehmen die gefährlichsten Stoffe nicht mehr einsetzen.

____

____

166a Suchen Sie eine Werbeanzeige für ein Produkt oder eine Dienstleistung, bei dem/der Nachhaltigkeit im Fokus steht. (Die Werbeanzeige kann auch auf Englisch sein.)

Name des Produkts / der Dienstleistung: ______________________________

Wie kann das Produkt / die Dienstleistung zu einer höheren Nachhaltigkeit führen?

____

Bringen Sie Ihre Werbeanzeige mit in den Kurs.

50: Nachhaltigkeit im Uni-Alltag°

167a **Meine Ressourcen: Nachhaltigkeit ist ein Thema, das nicht nur unsere Umwelt oder unser Verhalten als Konsument*innen betrifft. Im Alltag kann nachhaltiges Handeln zu innerer Balance, höherer Zufriedenheit und auch mehr Erfolg im Berufs- oder Student*innenleben führen. Die Ressourcen, die in diesem Kontext die wichtigste Rolle spielen, sind Zeit, Geld und Gesundheit. Was glauben Sie: Wie gut managen Sie diese Ressourcen? Füllen Sie den folgenden Fragebogen aus, indem Sie die passende Zahl auf der Skala von 1–5 ankreuzen.**

Wie gestresst fühlen Sie sich am Ende der Woche?	Wie oft machen Sie nach Mitternacht Hausaufgaben?
komplett gestresst ① ② ③ ④ ⑤ extrem entspannt	jede Nacht ① ② ③ ④ ⑤ nie

Wie oft arbeiten Sie mit To-do-Listen?	Wie viel Bewegung bekommen Sie jeden Tag?
nie ① ② ③ ④ ⑤ jeden Tag	Ich laufe vom Auto zum Kursraum. ① ② ③ ④ ⑤ Ich mache jeden Tag Sport.

Wie oft essen Sie frisches Gemüse?	Wie oft fühlen Sie sich überwältigt (*overwhelmed*)?
vielleicht einmal pro Woche ① ② ③ ④ ⑤ fünf Portionen pro Tag	jeden Tag ① ② ③ ④ ⑤ selten

Wie viel Geld haben Sie am Ende des Monats übrig?	Wie oft kaufen Sie etwas, das Sie nicht brauchen?
Ich bin pleite. ① ② ③ ④ ⑤ genug, um etwas zu sparen	mindestens einmal pro Woche ① ② ③ ④ ⑤ selten

168a **Was ist was? Ordnen Sie die folgenden deutschen Wörter und Redemittel der richtigen englischen Übersetzung zu.**

das Ziel d
das Praktikum ___
einen guten Eindruck hinterlassen ___
entspannt ___
etwas ausnutzen ___
tagsüber ___
Zeit verbringen ___
dieselben ___

a) *to spend time*
b) *relaxed*
c) *to make use of, take advantage of*
d) *goal*
e) *during the day*
f) *internship*
g) *the same*
h) *to make a good impression*

169a **Was sind typische Probleme, mit denen Sie als Student*in zu tun haben? Was tun Sie? Versuchen Sie, das Problem alleine zu lösen? Suchen Sie sich Hilfe? Schreiben Sie vier Probleme auf und wie Sie damit umgehen.**

Problem: Ich vergesse wichtige Deadlines.
Was ich tue: Ich speichere alle Deadlines in meinem Handy.
Problem: ___
Was ich tue: ___
Problem: ___
Was ich tue: ___
Problem: ___
Was ich tue: ___
Problem: ___
Was ich tue: ___

Wer sind wir?
Deutsch im Plural

52: PROMINENTE

der*die Prominente, -n (ein*e Prominente*r)	celebrity (*gender-neutral*)
die Persönlichkeit, -en	personality; celebrity
erklären, erklärte, hat ... erklärt	to explain
so ... wie	as ... as
so schnell wie	as fast as
so viel wie	as much as
repräsentativ	representative
vielfältig	diverse

Weitere Wörter: der Lyriker, - (poet (*male*)); **die Lyrikerin, -nen** (poet (*female*)); **der*die Dichtende, -n** (poet (*gender-neutral alternative*)); **das Privatleben, -** (personal life)

53: WOHER KOMMEN WIR?

der Migrationshintergrund, ¨-e	migration background
der Ausländer, -	foreigner (*male*)
die Ausländerin, -nen	foreigner (*female*)
die ausländische Person, die ausländischen Menschen	foreigner (*gender-neutral alternative*)
die Erfahrung, -en	experience
die Staatsangehörigkeit, -en	citizenship, nationality
der Migrant, -en	migrant (*male*)
die Migrantin, -nen	migrant (*female*)
die Person, -en mit Migrationshintergrund	migrant (*gender-neutral alternative*)
bald	soon
rassistisch	racist
diskriminieren, diskriminierte, hat ... diskriminiert	to discriminate
zurück·kehren, kehrte ... zurück, ist ... zurückgekehrt	to return, come back
weiterhin	furthermore; still
hoffen (auf + *akk.*), hoffte, hat ... gehofft	to hope (for)
dadurch	therefore
stehen (für + *akk.*), stand, hat ... gestanden	to stand (for)
die Diversität	diversity
der Einwanderer, -	immigrant (*male*)
die Einwanderin, -nen	immigrant (*female*)
die Einwandernden/ Eingewanderten (*pl.*)	immigrants (*gender-neutral alternative*)
die Herkunft, ¨-e	origin, descent

Weitere Wörter: der Vorfahr[e], -n (ancestor (*male*)); **die Vorfahrin, -nen** (ancestor (*female*)); **die Verwandten der Vergangenheit (*pl.*)** (ancestor (*gender-neutral alternative*)); **ein·wandern, wanderte ... ein, ist ... eingewandert** (to immigrate); **abwertend** (derogatory); **die Besatzungsmacht, ¨-e** (occupation force); **die Hautfarbe, -n** (skin color); **das Besatzungskind, -er** (child with a foreign military parent); **sich (*akk.*) identifizieren (mit + *dat.*), identifizierte, hat ... identifiziert** (to identify (with)); **die Ethnie, -n** (ethnicity); **homogen** (homogeneous); **die Homogenität, -en** (homogeneity); **das Einwanderungsland, ¨-er** (country of immigration); **heterogen** (heterogeneous); **die Heterogenität** (heterogeneity)

54: DIASPORA

das Heimatland, ¨-er	home country
innerhalb	within
gemeinsam	common; together
jüdisch	Jewish
der Jude, -n	Jew (*male*)
die Jüdin, -nen	Jew (*female*)
die jüdische Person, die jüdischen Menschen	Jew (*gender-neutral alternative*)
der Kurde, -n	Kurd (*male*)
die Kurdin, -nen	Kurd (*female*)
die kurdische Person, die kurdischen Menschen	Kurd (*gender-neutral alternative*)
der Abschnitt, -e	paragraph; section
überleben, überlebte, hat ... überlebt	to survive
der Transport, -e	transport
streng religiös	devout

Weitere Wörter: zusammen·gehören, gehörte ... zusammen, hat ... zusammengehört (to belong together); **grenzenlos** (limitless); **die Nationalität, -en** (nationality); **der Kommunismus** (communism); **(das) Hebräisch(e)** (Hebrew); **der Kumpel, -** (buddy (*male*)); **der Glaube** (faith; belief); **die Umgangssprache, -n** (colloquial/informal language)

56: EIN KRIEG GEGEN HETEROGENITÄT UND SEINE FOLGEN

die Folge, -n	consequence; episode (*TV show*)
mindestens	at least
das Gebiet, -e	area; territory
multikulturell	multicultural
bekämpfen, bekämpfte, hat ... bekämpft	to combat, fight (against)
verfolgen, verfolgte, hat ... verfolgt	to persecute
entsprechen (+ *dat.*) (entspricht), entsprach, hat ... entsprochen	to conform (to/with)
vertreiben, vertrieb, hat ... vertrieben	to expel, displace
der*die Vertriebene, -n (ein*e Vertriebene*r)	displaced person (*gender-neutral*)
heutzutage	nowadays
zu·nehmen (nimmt ... zu), nahm ... zu, hat ... zugenommen	to increase; to gain (weight)

Weitere Wörter: fremdsprachig (foreign-language); **die Volkszählung, -en** (population census); **die Muttersprache, -n** (native language); **inhaftieren, inhaftierte, hat ... inhaftiert** (to imprison); **ermorden, ermordete, hat ... ermordet** (to murder, assassinate); **das Konzentrationslager, -** (concentration camp); **die Besatzungszone, -n** (occupation zone); **der Zeitzeuge, -n** (witness of a (time) period (*male*)); **die Zeitzeugin, -nen** (witness of a (time) period (*female*)); **der*die Bezeugende, -n der Zeit** (witness of a (time) period (*gender-neutral alternative*))

57: MadGermanes

der See, -n	lake
der Berg, -e	mountain
an·kommen, kam ... an, ist ... angekommen	to arrive
anschließend	afterwards, subsequent
die Erholung	rest, recovery
fremd	foreign, different (*unfamiliar*)
zurück	back
vermissen, vermisste, hat ... vermisst	to miss
vertraut	familiar; intimate
die Rückkehr	return
ein·schätzen, schätzte ... ein, hat ... eingeschätzt	to evaluate, assess
prägen, prägte, hat ... geprägt	to shape, influence
die Lage, -n	location, position
fordern, forderte, hat ... gefordert	to demand
schwanger	pregnant
das Gehalt, ¨-er	salary, wage
nie	never
regelmäßig	regular(ly)
nachträglich	subsequent(ly), retrospectively

Weitere Wörter: die Korruption, -en (corruption); **der Bürgerkrieg, -e** (civil war); **das Kurvendiagramm, -e** (curve chart); **offen für (+ *akk.*)** (receptive to; open for); **die Unabhängigkeit, -en** (independence)

59: Flucht, Ankunft, Kunst

die Ankunft, ¨-e	arrival
der Flüchtling, -e	refugee (*legal*)
der*die Geflüchtete, -n (ein*e Geflüchtete*r)	refugee (*also serves as gender-neutral alternative*)
damals	back then, in those days
die Flüchtlingskrise, -n	refugee crisis
die Solidarität, -en	solidarity
sich (*akk.*) streiten (über + *akk.*), stritt, hat ... gestritten	to argue (about)
die Welle, -n	wave
die Schönheit	beauty
das Theaterstück, -e	play

Weitere Wörter: die Lawine, -n (avalanche); **überrollen, überrollte, hat ... überrollt** (to roll over); **schüren, schürte, hat ... geschürt** (to stir up, fuel (*e.g. conflict or fear*))

60: „Tatort DaF" (Teil 1)

der*die Schuldige, -n (ein*e Schuldige*r)	culprit (*gender-neutral*)
die Verhaftung, -en	detention, arrest
ermitteln, ermittelte, hat ... ermittelt	to investigate
überraschend	surprising
unschuldig	innocent
der*die Hauptverdächtige, -n (ein*e Hauptverdächtige*r)	main suspect (*gender-neutral*)
die falsche Fährte, -n	red herring
der Krimi, -s	crime story
einen Fall lösen, löste, hat ... gelöst	to solve a case

Weitere Wörter: rätselhaft (mysterious, puzzling); **der Detektiv, -e** (detective (*male*)); **die Detektivin, -nen** (detective (*female*)); **die ermittelnde Person, die Ermittelnden** (detective (*gender-neutral workaround*)); **die Wiederherstellung, -en** (restoration; recovery); **der Alptraum, ¨-e** (nightmare); **die Besichtigung, -en** (tour, sightseeing)

61: Was sprechen wir?

(das) Plattdeutsch(e)	Low German
(das) Jiddisch(e)	Yiddish
Sprichst du Jiddisch?	Do you speak Yiddish?
raten (rät), riet, hat ... geraten	to guess
kurz	short; brief(ly)
die Schreibweise, -n	spelling
anders	different
Pech haben (hat), hatte, hat ... gehabt	to be unlucky
sich (*akk.*) dumm an·stellen, stellte ... an, hat ... angestellt	to act stupid (*on purpose*)
umgangssprachlich	colloquial
die Einführung, -en	introduction
die Varietät, -en	variety
verschieden	different
der Ausdruck, ¨-e	expression
aus·drücken, drückte ... aus, hat ... ausgedrückt	to express
das Phänomen, -e	phenomenon

Weitere Wörter: der Buchstabe, -n (letter); **der Vokal, -e** (vowel); **der Konsonant, -en** (consonant); **verwandt** (related); **die Bereicherung, -en** (enrichment)

63: Heimat in der Musik

ausländerfeindlich	xenophobic
die Ausgrenzung, -en	exclusion, marginalization
die Abstammung, -en	descent
die Wurzel, -n	root
der Steckbrief, -e	profile
das Geräusch, -e	noise, sound
die Ähnlichkeit, -en	similarity
definieren, definierte, hat ... definiert	to define
auf·klären, klärte ... auf, hat ... aufgeklärt	to clarify, resolve
die Stille	silence

Weitere Wörter: schwer beladen (heavily laden); **aus·grenzen, grenzte ... aus, hat ... ausgegrenzt** (to exclude, marginalize); **provokant** (provocative(ly)); **die Äußerung, -en** (statement); **unterdrückt** (suppressed)

53: WOHER KOMMEN WIR?

173a Review: Nominative, Accusative, and Dative

The nominative case is for the **subject** of the sentence. In the active voice, the subject tells you who or what performs the action of the verb. It can be a person or a thing.

The government implemented the policy. The journalist wrote a story about the policy.

The accusative case is the **direct object** of the verb. It receives the action of the verb. It can be a person or a thing.

The government implemented the policy. The journalist wrote a story about the policy. He criticized the chancellor sharply.

The primary function of the dative case is to indicate the **indirect object** of the verb. The indirect object benefits from the action performed in the sentence. The indirect object is in most cases a person and usually translates as "to whom" in English.

The chancellor sent the document to the president for her signature.

In German, there are also specific dative verbs that require the dative case. In English, these verbs are usually translated with a direct object.

Der Abgeordnete half der Kanzlerin.	*The representative helped the chancellor.*
Die Kanzlerin dankte dem Abgeordneten.	*The chancellor thanked the representative.*

Lastly, remember that some prepositions require the accusative and dative cases as prepositional objects. (These are not direct or indirect objects of which you can only have one per sentence.)

always accusative:	bis, durch, für, gegen, ohne, um
accusative for destinations:	an, auf, hinter, in, neben, über, unter, vor, zwischen
dative for locations:	an, auf, hinter, in, neben, über, unter, vor, zwischen
always dative:	aus, außer, bei, mit, nach, seit, von, zu

	Nominative	Accusative	Dative
masculine	der Vertrag	den Vertrag	dem Vertrag
	ein Vertrag	einen Vertrag	einem Vertrag
	kein Vertrag	keinen Vertrag	keinem Vertrag
	mein Vertrag	meinen Vertrag	meinem Vertrag
neuter	das Dokument	das Dokument	dem Dokument
	ein Dokument	ein Dokument	einem Dokument
	kein Dokument	kein Dokument	keinem Dokument
	mein Dokument	mein Dokument	meinem Dokument
feminine	die Regierung	die Regierung	der Regierung
	eine Regierung	eine Regierung	einer Regierung
	keine Regierung	keine Regierung	keiner Regierung
	meine Regierung	meine Regierung	meiner Regierung
plural	die Verträge	die Verträge	den Verträgen
	---- Verträge	---- Verträge	---- Verträgen
	keine Verträge	keine Verträge	keinen Verträgen
	meine Verträge	meine Verträge	meinen Verträgen

173b **Durch Europa als Tourist*in: das Privileg der Reisefreiheit. Lesen Sie die Sätze und geben Sie für die unterstrichenen Satzelemente an: Akkusativ oder Dativ?**

Letzten Sommer sind wir mit unserem Wohnmobil durch den Süden Europas gereist. (Akk | Dat) Zuerst sind wir über die Autobahn nach Bayern gefahren. (Akk | Dat) Wir sind fünf Tage in Bayern am Königssee geblieben und haben dort lange Wanderungen gemacht. (Akk | Dat) Danach stand Italien auf unserer Liste. (Akk | Dat) Zuerst aber haben wir uns in der Schweiz so viel guten Käse gekauft, wie in unser Wohnmobil passte. (Akk | Dat) In Italien haben wir viele Restaurants besucht, weil wir die italienische Küche lieben. (Akk | Dat) Nach zwei Wochen Italien ging es weiter nach Frankreich. (Akk | Dat) Einer Tour durch die französischen Alpen folgten ein paar schöne Tage in Paris. (Akk | Dat) Eigentlich wollten wir dann in England ein paar Freund*innen besuchen, aber unser Wohnmobil hatte ein technisches Problem. (Akk | Dat) In der Werkstatt konnte der Mechaniker unserem Wohnmobil nicht helfen, deshalb mussten wir wieder nach Deutschland zurückfahren. (Akk | Dat)

173c **Susanne, Maryam und Thorsten machen gemeinsam Guacamole. Das ist auch bei Deutschen ein sehr beliebter Dip. Identifizieren Sie in den Sätzen das Akkusativ- und das Dativobjekt.**

Susanne bringt ihrem Bruder eine Avocado für die Guacamole.

Was ist das Akkusativobjekt? ____________________

Was ist das Dativobjekt? ____________________

Ihrem Freund Thorsten schneidet Maryam die Zwiebeln für die Guacamole.

Was ist das Akkusativobjekt? ____________________

Was ist das Dativobjekt? ____________________

Thorsten bringt seinen Mitbewohnerinnen fertige Guacamole.

Was ist das Akkusativobjekt? ____________________

Was ist das Dativobjekt? ____________________

173d **Tom und Layla planen eine Winterparty für internationale Studierende in ihrer WG. Vervollständigen Sie die Sätze, indem Sie die korrekten Artikelendungen einsetzen.**

Tom: Wir sollten heute zuerst zum_ Supermarkt gehen. Dort gibt es doch heute ein___ Sonderaktion für Bioprodukte.

Layla: Ja, ich will etwas von d____ Biogemüse kaufen, für d____ Buffet (*n.*) morgen Abend. Biogemüse kann ich mir sonst nicht leisten.

Tom: Brauchen wir ein____ oder zwei Tische fürs Buffet? Was meinst du?

Layla: Zwei wären gut. Ich frage gleich unser____ Nachbarin, Frau Lindner, ob wir wieder ihren Klapptisch haben können.

Tom: Oh ja, gute Idee. Ich muss nachher mein____ Bruder bei ein____ Computerproblem helfen, aber wenn ich zurück bin, können wir d____ Tisch zusammen heruntertragen.

Layla: Haben wir genug Getränke?

Tom: Wasser und Bier haben wir genug. Aber könntest du noch ein____ Kasten (*m.*) Cola besorgen?

Layla: Klar! Okay, letzter Punkt auf d____ Liste: Wollen wir jede____ Person ein____ Namensschild (*name tag*) geben?

Tom: Warum nicht? Dann lernen wir alle unser____ Namen schneller.

Layla: Super, danke. Ich freue mich schon richtig auf d____ Party!

173e Review: Pronouns

Pronouns literally stand in "for nouns," which means that they replace nouns or proper names. They can refer to people (I, you, he/it/she, we, you, they), but they can also refer to a previously mentioned noun. In contrast to English where we replace nouns with "it," the German pronouns correspond to the grammatical gender of the word, which means that *der* becomes *er*, *die* becomes *sie*, and *das* becomes *es*. Pronouns exist in all cases.

Nominative	Accusative	Dative
ich	mich	mir
du	dich	dir
er	ihn	ihm
es	es	ihm
sie	sie	ihr
wir	uns	uns
ihr	euch	euch
sie	sie	ihnen
Sie	Sie	Ihnen

Examples for replacing nouns:

Das Thema ist kontrovers. **Es** ist kontrovers.	*The topic is controversial.* *It is controversial.*
Minh bekam **einen Arbeitsplatz** in der DDR. Minh bekam **ihn**.	*Minh got a job in the GDR.* *Minh got it [him].*
Ich habe nur einen Teil **von der Geschichte** gelesen. Ich habe nicht viel **von ihr** verstanden.	*I have only read part of the story.* *I didn't understand much of it [her].*

173f Review: Gender-Neutral Pronouns

There are several gender-neutral pronouns in German. Throughout the book, several activities include people who prefer gender-neutral pronouns, but we purposefully did not include gender-neutral pronouns in our grammar tables (except for the one on the right-hand side). Because there are many competing gender-neutral pronouns currently being used by different communities in Germany, we do not want to present one of them as the "correct" one. That being said, the most widely used one is *xier* (see right), though *nin* is also very common.

If you prefer that others refer to you with gender-neutral pronouns or want to learn more about them, you can ask your instructor for more resources. We also encourage you to explore different options online, including their individual pros and cons, and decide on the ones you feel most comfortable with.

Nominative	Accusative	Dative
ich	mich	mir
du	dich	dir
er	ihn	ihm
es	es	ihm
sie	sie	ihr
xier	xien	xiem
wir	uns	uns
ihr	euch	euch
sie	sie	ihnen
Sie	Sie	Ihnen

173g Welche Personalpronomen im Nominativ und Akkusativ brauchen wir hier? Ergänzen Sie.

Eine Kölner Firma stellte 1955 mehr als 2.000 Gastarbeiter*innen ein. _Sie_ kamen aus Italien und Griechenland.

Auch Tímon war ein Gastarbeiter. Seine Frau blieb in Griechenland und vermisste _____ sehr.

Minh war eine Vertragsarbeiterin in der DDR. Helmuth lernte _______ 1976 in Halle kennen.

Minh und Helmuth hatten einen Sohn, Peter. _______ lebt heute in Wernigerode.

Drei Geflüchtete aus Syrien gehen auf meine Schule. Ich sehe _______ jeden Tag in der Klasse.

Mein Freund heißt Enis. _______ kommt auch aus Syrien.

173h **Andreas erzählt von seiner Tante Irma. Welche Personalpronomen im Dativ brauchen wir hier? Ergänzen Sie.**

Gudrun: Andreas, wusstest du das? Im Jahr 1979 gab es in der DDR rund 191.000 Ausländer*innen. Die DDR hatte ihnen Arbeit oder eine Ausbildung angeboten.

Andreas: Ja, 16.000 von ihnen kamen aus Mosambik. Das liegt in Ostafrika. Einer von ihnen war Filipe. Meine Tante Irma hat ___________ damals geholfen, ein Fahrrad zu kaufen.

Gudrun: Das war nett von ___________. Was ist dann passiert?

Andreas: Tante Irma erzählte oft von Filipe. Sie erzählte ___________ und meiner Familie , wie oft sie mit ___________ Fahrradtouren gemacht hat. Filipe mochte diese Touren sehr. Tante Irma hat ___________ viele neue deutsche Wörter beigebracht (*taught*).

Gudrun: Und als es zur Wiedervereinigung kam?

Andreas: Leider musste Filipe zurück nach Mosambik. Er und meine Tante tranken ein letztes Mal zusammen Kaffee. Dann schenkte er ___________ ein Souvenir aus seiner Heimatstadt Quelimane: eine kleine Makonde-Maske.

Makonde-Maske

Gudrun: Warte mal! Ist das die Maske in deinem Zimmer?

Andreas: Genau! Ich habe sie ___________ schon das letzte Mal gezeigt, nicht wahr? Tante Irma hat sie ___________ gegeben, weil ich sie so schön finde.

173i **Deutschland war schon immer ein Einwanderungsland. Die folgenden Punkte sind nur ein paar Beispiele dafür. Lesen Sie sich alle Beispiele durch. Suchen Sie sich dann einen Punkt aus, finden Sie dazu mehr Informationen und schreiben Sie 3–4 Sätze darüber.**

Recherche

- Vom 4. bis zum 6. Jahrhundert gab es die sogenannte **Völkerwanderung**, das heißt, die Migration vor allem **germanischer Gruppen** in Mittel- und Südeuropa.
- Im 17. und 18. Jahrhundert fanden **Hugenotten** (Protestant*innen aus Frankreich) Asyl in **Preußen**.
- Um 1890 erlebte das **Ruhrgebiet** (im heutigen Nordrhein-Westfalen) einen Industrieboom. Viele **Pol*innen** zogen in dieser Zeit dorthin, um Arbeit zu finden.
- In den 1960ern wurden **Gastarbeiter*innen** aus dem europäischen Ausland für die **Bundesrepublik Deutschland** sowie **Vertragsarbeiter*innen** aus sozialistischen Ländern für die **DDR** angeworben, um beim wirtschaftlichen Aufbau zu helfen.
- In den 1990er Jahren kamen hunderttausende **Kriegsflüchtlinge** nach Deutschland, z. B. aus Jugoslawien und Rumänien, aber auch aus verschiedenen afrikanischen Ländern, wie z. B. Nigeria und Zaire.
- 2004 und 2007 gab es die sogenannte **Osterweiterung**, d. h. die Aufnahme neuer Staaten aus Mittel- und Osteuropa in die EU. Als Folge immigrierten (und immigrieren) viele Menschen nach Deutschland. Sie hoffen, dort bessere Arbeitskonditionen zu finden.
- Seit **2015** suchen erneut viele Menschen, vor allem Menschen, die vor **Kriegen und Krisen** flüchten, temporären Schutz oder ein neues Leben in Deutschland. 2015 waren es mehr als 1 Million. Die meisten von ihnen kommen aus Syrien, Afghanistan und dem Irak.

____

____

____

____

____

____

173j **Flüchtlinge oder Geflüchtete? Lesen Sie den Text und kreuzen Sie an, was korrekt ist.**

The traditional translation for the word "refugee" in German—*der Flüchtling*—has been criticized for several reasons. It is rather static, for instance, and solely defines the person in terms of their displacement. The term, however, also defines a legal status, and it is still commonly used in everyday language. In this book, you will see the term *der*die Geflüchtete* ("person who fled") more often. It is more dynamic and still acknowledges the experience of fleeing while indicating that this flight is in the past. In contrast to <u>der</u> *Flüchtling*, it's also gender-neutral.

We use the word *Flüchtling* as a legal category because …
- the status grants certain rights to a person.
- it isn't otherwise used.

We prefer the word *Geflüchtete* because …
- it sounds better.
- it is more dynamic.

173k **Schreiben Sie 3–4 Sätze zu Migration in Ihrem Land. Folgen Sie dem Beispiel von Aktivität 173i.**

____

____

____

174a **Sehen Sie sich die Afrikakarte in MACHEN an und identifizieren Sie die Länder. Tipp: Schreiben Sie die Ländernamen auf die Karte in MACHEN, wenn Sie die Länder nicht gut kennen. Sie brauchen sie im Kurs.**

Algerien | Angola | Äthiopien | Burundi | Eritrea | Ghana | Kamerun | Marokko | Mosambik | Namibia | Nigeria | Ruanda | Senegal | Somalia | Sudan | Südsudan | Tansania | Togo | Tunesien

Länder in Rot: ________ ________ ________

Länder in Hellblau: ________ ________

Länder in Gelb: ________ ________ ________
________ ________ ________

Länder in Grün: ________ ________ ________
________ ________ ________
________ ________

Länder in Dunkelblau: ________ ________

175a **Blickpunkt: Rafik Schami. Lesen Sie den Text und markieren Sie auf der nächsten Seite, ob die Aussagen richtig oder falsch sind.**

Der syrisch-deutsche Schriftsteller Rafik Schami (in der genormten Transliteration der arabischen in die lateinische Schrift: Rafīq Šāmī) wurde 1946 als Suheil Fāḍel geboren. Er studierte Chemie, Physik und Mathe in Damaskus, beschäftigte sich aber auch schon früh mit Literatur. 1971 wanderte er nach Deutschland aus, wo er in Chemie promovierte. Gleichzeitig arbeitete er als Hilfsarbeiter in Fabriken, Restaurants und auf Baustellen. Dort lernte er einige Gastarbeiter*innen kennen.

Bald fing er an zu schreiben, erst auf Arabisch, später auch auf Deutsch. Sein erstes Buch in deutscher Sprache erschien 1978. Zusammen mit Franco Biondi, der aus Italien kam und in Deutschland arbeitete, gründete er eine Literatur-Reihe für Migrant*innen. Darin berichteten Migrant*innen über ihr Leben in Deutschland. Diese Literatur wurde anfangs auch „Gastarbeiterliteratur" genannt.

Schamis eigene Literatur handelt vor allem von dem Thema „Migration", aber er schrieb auch einige Märchen. Viele seiner Bücher spielen in Damaskus. Er schreibt Bücher für Erwachsene und Kinder, ist einer der erfolgreichsten deutschsprachigen Autor*innen und hat viele Preise gewonnen. Sein Pseudonym bedeutet: Freund aus Damaskus.

richtig falsch

- Rafik Schami ist in Deutschland geboren.
- Sein richtiger Name ist Suheil Fāḍel.
- Er studierte Chemie.
- Schami war Gastarbeiter.
- Er schrieb Bücher nur auf Arabisch.
- Seine Literatur handelt von Migration.

54: DIASPORA

178a **Lesen Sie den Text in Aktivität 178 in MACHEN und schlagen Sie unbekannte Wörter nach, um den Text global zu verstehen (es geht hier nicht um Details). Erstellen Sie eine Liste der Wörter und bringen Sie diese mit in den Kurs. Sie brauchen dafür nicht alle Linien unten zu benutzen.**

178b **Suchen Sie die folgenden Informationen im Text in Aktivität 178 in MACHEN.**

Name: ______

Alter: ______

Wohnort: ______

Glaube: ______

178c **Bar/Bat Mitzvah. Wissen Sie, was die Bar und Bat Mitzvah sind? Beschreiben Sie sie in 2–3 Sätzen. Wenn Sie es nicht wissen, recherchieren Sie.**

Recherche

178d **Blickpunkt: Olga Grjasnowa. Lesen Sie den Text und füllen Sie den Steckbrief aus.**

Olga Grjasnowa wurde 1984 geboren. 1996 zog sie mit ihrer Familie von Aserbaidschan nach Deutschland. Sie lebt heute in Berlin. Nach ihrer Ankunft in Deutschland lernte Grjasnowa Deutsch und besuchte eine deutsche Schule. Nach der Schule studierte sie zuerst Kunstgeschichte und Slawistik, dann wechselte sie an das Deutsche Literaturinstitut Leipzig und wurde Schriftstellerin. Ihr erster Roman kam 2012 heraus. Er hieß „Der Russe ist einer, der Birken liebt" und gewann mehrere Literaturpreise. In dem Roman schreibt sie auch über autobiografische Themen: deutsche und jüdische Identität und Migration aus Aserbaidschan, in der ehemaligen Sowjetunion.

Name: ____________________ Studium: ____________________

Geburtsjahr: ____________________ Beruf: ____________________

In Deutschland seit: ____________________ Erster Roman: ____________________

Aktueller Wohnort: ____________________

55: WAS ERZÄHLT UNSERE DNA?°

182a **Blickpunkt: Patrick Owomoyela. Lesen Sie die Biografie und beantworten Sie unten die Fragen.**

Patrick Owomoyela wurde am 05.11.1979 geboren und fühlt sich vor allem in Norddeutschland zu Hause. Er ist ein ehemaliger deutscher Fußballspieler. Seine größten Erfolge feierte er mit dem Bundesligaverein BVB Dortmund, der 2011 und 2012 zweimal Deutscher Meister wurde. Heute arbeitet er als Kommentator im Radio und Fernsehen. Er ist auch aktiv gegen Rassismus und hat 2006 den Udo-Lindenberg-Preis für sein Engagement bekommen. Mit einigen seiner BVB-Kollegen machte Owomoyela DNA-Tests. Vorher sagte er, dass er sich nicht wundern würde, wenn er 50 % deutsch und 50 % nigerianisch wäre. Tatsächlich kam bei dem Test heraus, dass ungefähr 50 % seiner DNA mit der häufig in Nigeria vorkommenden DNA übereinstimmt. Das überraschte ihn nicht, weil sein Vater aus einer Gegend kam, in der es kaum Migration oder Tourismus gab. Die andere Hälfte war sowohl norddeutsch als auch skandinavisch. Von der skandinavischen Seite seiner Familie wusste er vorher nichts, vor allem der kleine finnische Anteil überraschte ihn. Viel überraschender war der DNA-Test aber für einen anderen seiner Kollegen, zu dem wir in ZEIGEN etwas lesen werden.

Welchen Sport hat Owomoyela professionell gemacht?

- Handball
- Basketball
- Fußball

Bei welchem Verein hat Owomoyela gespielt?

- BVB Dortmund
- Schalke 04
- Hertha BSC Berlin

Was kam bei seinem DNA-Test heraus?

- 50 % nigerianisch, 50 % nordwesteuropäisch
- 50 % nigerianisch, 20 % englisch, 30 % nordwesteuropäisch
- 50 % nigerianisch, 40 % nordwesteuropäisch, 10 % skandinavisch

Was hat ihn beim DNA-Test überrascht? Warum?

- Dass er nordwesteuropäisch ist, weil er aus dem Süden Deutschlands kommt.
- Dass er finnische Wurzeln hat, weil er davon nichts wusste.
- Dass er nigerianische Wurzeln hat, weil sein Vater aus einer Region mit viel Handel und Austausch kam.

56: Ein Krieg gegen Heterogenität und seine Folgen

184a The Definition of the Middle Field

The middle field is the space in the sentence between the conjugated verb in the second position and the second (part of the) verb (for instance, a prefix of a separable verb, an infinitive, or a past participle) at the end of the sentence.

I	II	III				L
Subject	Verb	Subject	Time	Manner (how?)	Place	2nd Verb (part)
Susanne	kommt		heute	zufrieden	aus Paris	zurück.
Sie	will		im Juli	mit dem Rad	in die Schweiz	fahren.

We have already learned that the subject is either in first position, like in the examples above, or directly after the verb in the middle field if the first position is occupied by another element. You can move any of the elements (time, manner, or place) to the first position in order to stress it. The subject then moves right after the verb, and the rest of the order stays the same.

I	II	III				L
	Verb	Subject	Time	Manner (how?)	Place	2nd Verb (part)
Petra	ist		im Mai	mit ihrer Familie	in Italien	gewesen.
Im Mai	ist	Petra		mit ihrer Familie	in Italien	gewesen.
In Italien	ist	Petra	im Mai	mit ihrer Familie		gewesen.

The elements in the middle field have certain preferences when it comes to positions. **Time-manner-place** is a good compass, as long as the context does not imply a different order.

Accusative and dative objects find their respective places according to an intricate set of rules that we will introduce in this chapter.

184b Die dänische Sprache in Norddeutschland. Setzen Sie die markierte Zeitangabe an den Satzbeginn.

Das alte dänische Territorium Schleswig-Holstein ist **seit dem 14. August 1855** eine deutschsprachige Region.

Seit dem 14. August 1855 ist das alte dänische Territorium Schleswig-Holstein eine deutschsprachige Region.

Die Bewohner*innen durften die dänische Sprache in Schleswig-Holstein **ab 1842** nicht mehr sprechen.

____

Österreich und Preußen begannen **im Jahr 1854** einen Krieg mit Dänemark.

____

Es gibt **bis heute** eine dänische Minderheit mit dänischen Schulen in Schleswig-Holstein.

____

Es gab **zwischen 1933 und 1945** nur ungefähr 750 Schüler*innen an neun dänischen Schulen.

____

Circa 7.500 junge Leute lernen **heutzutage** an dänischen Schulen und Kindergärten.

____

184c **Die Sorb*innen in Deutschland. Sortieren Sie die Elemente im Mittelfeld.**

als feudale Vasall*innen / vor 1.400 Jahren / in die Lausitzer Region

Die slawischen Sorb*innen kamen vor 1.400 Jahren als feudale Vasall*innen in die Lausitzer Region.

auf der Straße / nicht mehr oft

Die sorbische Sprache wird ________________ gesprochen.

in Sachsen und Brandenburg / heutzutage noch bei Festen

Traditionelle sorbische Kleidung wird ________________ getragen.

ab 1815 / in Leipzig

Mit Handrij Zejler begann ________________ eine sorbische Nationalliteratur.

schon seit 2011 / auf Facebook

Eine sorbische Fan-Seite für das Rapper-Duo Serbska GmbH gibt es ________________.

Sorbisch / auf Konzerten / bis heute

Das Duo singt ________________.

184d **Schwarze Deutsche: Ihre Geschichte(n) zwischen den Weltkriegen. Der folgende Text beschreibt die Vorgeschichte von Schwarzen Deutschen im Dritten Reich. Lesen Sie den Text und kreuzen Sie unten die richtigen Antworten an.**

Der erste Weltkrieg endete am 11. November 1918. Am 28. Juni 1919 wurde der Friedensvertrag von Versailles unterzeichnet. In diesem Vertrag wurde entschieden, wie Deutschland für seine Verbrechen[1] während des Krieges bestraft[2] werden sollte. Unter anderem wurde beschlossen, dass Frankreich das Rheinland besetzen[3] sollte. Frankreich stationierte dort afrikanische Truppen aus den französischen Kolonien. Diese Truppen kamen aus Ländern wie Madagaskar, Mosambik und Algerien. Viele Deutsche waren schockiert, dass Schwarze Truppen über die weiße, deutsche Bevölkerung wachen[4] sollten. Die konservative Presse startete eine Propaganda-Kampagne mit dem Namen „Die Schwarze Schmach"[5]. Sie warnte vor den afrikanischen Truppen, weil sie angeblich eine Bedrohung für die Frauen im besetzten Gebiet waren.

[1] das Verbrechen – *crime* [2] bestrafen – *to punish* [3] besetzen – *to occupy* [4] wachen – *to keep watch* [5] die Schmach – *disgrace*

Der Friedensvertrag von Versailles hatte für Deutschland ____ Konsequenzen.

- ☐ positive ☐ negative ☐ keine

Truppen aus ____ wurden im Rheinland stationiert.

- ☐ Frankreich ☐ Frankreichs Kolonien ☐ Deutschland

Ein großer Teil der Menschen im Rheinland hatte ____ damit, dass Schwarze Menschen ihre Region besetzten.

- ☐ ein Problem ☐ kein Problem

Die Kampagne „Die Schwarze Schmach" verbreitete rassistische Stereotype über ____.

- ☐ Schwarze Frauen ☐ weiße Frauen ☐ Schwarze Männer

184e **Blickpunkt: Anne Frank. Eine der bekanntesten Zeitzeug*innen des Holocaust ist Anne Frank. Schreiben Sie ein paar Sätze: Was wissen Sie über Anne Frank und ihre Geschichte?**

____

____

____

____

____

184f **Blickpunkt: Leo Clasen. Lesen Sie den Text zu Leo Clasen, einem weiteren Zeitzeugen, der seine persönlichen Erfahrungen aufgeschrieben hat.**

Einer der wichtigsten Berichte für und über die homosexuellen Opfer der Nationalsozialist*innen wurde von Leo Clasen verfasst. Er lebte von 1896 bis 1972. Er war Arzt. Während des Dritten Reichs wurde er im Konzentrationslager Sachsenhausen bei Berlin gefangen gehalten (*held captive*). In den 1950er Jahren schrieb er über seine Erfahrungen und veröffentlichte (*published*) sie unter einem Pseudonym.

Reflektieren Sie nun auf Deutsch, Englisch oder in beiden Sprachen: Why are diaries and reports such significant documents when it comes to our knowledge about the Holocaust and its victims? Some diaries are written for publication to be read by others; other diaries are initially only written to be re-read by the writer and are later published. How do you think the type of diary affects what is written and how they are written? Which purposes do these different types of diaries fulfill?

185a Dative and Accusative Word Order: Two Nouns

Many verbs like *geben*, *schenken*, *zeigen*, *erklären*, *leihen*, *empfehlen*, *anbieten*, etc., require a direct and an indirect object. Very often both objects will be in the middle field, and there are some rules that govern the order in which you place them.

When both objects (the accusative object and the dative object) are nouns, most often the dative object (which is most likely a person) will be first, and the accusative object will follow (unless you purposefully move the dative object after the accusative in order to stress it, which is a rare occurrence).

I	II	III		L
Subject	**Verb**	**Dative Object**	**Accusative Object**	**2nd Verb (part)**
Susanne	bietet	ihrer Kollegin	einen Keks	an.
Toni	gibt	dem Hund	einen Knochen.	
Esme	schenkt	Marie	das Buch.	

185b **Das Leben im besetzten Deutschland. In welcher Reihenfolge erscheinen diese Satzelemente?**

Viele Menschen verkauften	2	ihre Wertsachen (z. B. Silber)	1	Tauschhändler*innen	.
Die Alliierten verboten		den Deutschen		den illegalen Handel	.
Die Bevölkerung bot		Kaffee und Zigaretten		den Tauschhändler*innen	.
Manche G.I.s schenkten		Schokolade oder Obst		kleinen Kindern	.
Deutschamerikaner*innen schickten		Care Packages		ihren deutschen Verwandten	.
Polizisten erteilten		Schieber*innen (*dealers*)		harte Strafen	.

57: Madgermanes

186a **Länderprofil Mosambik. Was wissen Sie über Mosambik?**

Recherche

____

____

____

____

____

____

____

Recherchieren Sie Informationen über Mosambik und bringen Sie Ihre Notizen mit in den Kurs. Sie werden Ihre Rechercheergebnisse präsentieren. Ihr Nachname bestimmt das Thema für Ihre Recherche.

Mit welchem Buchstaben beginnt Ihr Nachname? ________ (Der Nachname Smith beginnt z. B. mit einem S.)

Ihr Nachname beginnt mit A–E:	Demografie (Volksgruppen, Sprachen, Religion, soziale Lage etc.)
Ihr Nachname beginnt mit F–K:	Geografie (Lage, Klima, Flora und Fauna, größere Städte etc.)
Ihr Nachname beginnt mit L–R:	Politik/Geschichte (Unabhängigkeit, Kolonialismus, Bürger*innenkrieg, politisches System etc.)
Ihr Nachname beginnt mit S–Z:	Kulturelles (Sehenswürdigkeiten, Musik, Medien, Literatur, Essen etc.)

187a **Kulturschock: Wie nennt man das?**

Die geografische Region, wo mein Zuhause ist, nenne ich meine …

Heimat   Haus   Heimweh

Wenn ich ins Ausland reise, erlebe ich eine …

Interkultur   Fremdkultur   Eigenkultur

Wenn ich im Ausland meine Kultur und Familie vermisse, habe ich …

Euphorie   Heimweh   Erholung

Wenn ich mich kulturell nicht mehr orientieren kann, habe ich einen …

Heimschock   Fremdschock   Kulturschock

Ich verstehe die neue Kultur und navigiere in ihr. Das ist …

Harmonie   Akkulturation   Disintegration

Die Kultur aus meiner eigenen Heimat ist meine …

Fremdkultur   Außenkultur   Eigenkultur

188a Sie lernen jetzt etwas über die Madgermanes, eine Gruppe von Vertragsarbeiter*innen aus der DDR, die heute wieder in Mosambik leben. Es gibt sowohl historische Fakten als auch Informationen über die Madgermanes heute. Hören Sie gut zu und beantworten Sie die Fragen in Stichworten.

Woher kamen die Madgermanes?

____

Warum kamen diese Personen in die DDR?

____

Wie war das Leben der Madgermanes in der DDR? Nennen Sie positive und negative Elemente.

____

____

Welchen Skandal gab es mit der Bezahlung der Madgermanes?

____

____

Was fordern (*demand*) die Madgermanes von der Bundesrepublik Deutschland?

____

____

188b **Blickpunkt: Birgit Weyhe. Lesen Sie den Text.**

Birgit Weyhe wurde 1969 geboren. Sie ist Illustratorin und Autorin von Graphic Novels.

Ihre Kindheit und Jugend verbrachte Weyhe in Ostafrika, in den Ländern Uganda und Kenia. Als sie 19 Jahre alt war, kehrte sie nach Deutschland zurück und studierte Germanistik und Geschichte. Nach ihrem Diplom in Illustration begann sie, Comics und Graphic Novels zu schreiben und zu zeichnen. Ihr Stil wird von der europäischen Comic-Avantgarde und afrikanischen Zeichnungen beeinflusst.

2016 kam ihre Graphic Novel „Madgermanes" heraus, die von mosambikanischen Vertragsarbeiter*innen in der DDR handelt. Sie erhielt zwei Preise für das Buch, darunter den Max-und-Moritz-Preis für den besten deutschsprachigen Comic.

Schreiben Sie einen biografischen Steckbrief für Birgit Weyhe. Identifizieren Sie dabei die wichtigsten Lebensdaten und Informationen.

______________: ______________________________

______________: ______________________________

______________: ______________________________

______________: ______________________________

______________: ______________________________

______________: ______________________________

______________: ______________________________

188c Dative and Accusative Word Order: One Noun and One Personal Pronoun

We can replace nouns with personal pronouns, which changes the word order. Remember that for two nouns, dative comes before accusative. But personal pronouns have a tendency to be as close as possible to the left side of the middle field, preferably directly after the verb. Thus, a personal pronoun will always precede the noun, regardless of the object's case.

I	II	III		L	
Subject	**Verb**	**Dative Object (Noun)**	**Accusative Object (Noun)**		Observation: two nouns Rule: **dative before accusative**
Susanne	erklärt	ihrer Kollegin	den Plan.		
		Dative Object (Personal Pronoun)	**Accusative Object (Noun)**		Observation: noun + personal pronoun Rule: **personal pronoun goes first**
Susanne	erklärt	ihr	den Plan.		
		Accusative Object (Personal Pronoun)	**Dative Object (Noun)**		Observation: noun + personal pronoun Rule: **personal pronoun goes first**
Susanne	erklärt	ihn	ihrer Kollegin.		

188d Schreiben Sie diese Sätze um: Benutzen Sie Personalpronomen für die Objekte.

	mit Personalpronomen im Akkusativ:	Personalpronomen im Dativ:
Dana kauft ihrer Oma einen Pullover.	*Dana kauft ihn ihrer Oma.*	______
Chris leiht seinem Mann das Buch.	______	______
Ben leiht seinem Bruder die Hose.	______	______

188e Grammatik entdecken: Sie kennen nun schon die Wortstellung von Akkusativ- und Dativobjekten, wenn man entweder zwei Personalpronomen oder ein Personalpronomen und ein Nomen hat. Aber was passiert, wenn beide Objekte ein Personalpronomen sind? Lesen Sie die Sätze unten und beantworten Sie die Frage.

Ich erkläre meiner Freundin den Plan. → Ich erkläre ihn ihr.

Ich schenke meinem Vater das Buch. → Ich schenke es ihm.

Ich empfehle meinen Freund*innen eine neue Band. → Ich empfehle sie ihnen.

Welches Objekt steht in einem Satz zuerst, wenn beide Objekte ein Personalpronomen sind?

☐ das Akkusativobjekt ☐ das Dativobjekt

188f Dative and Accusative Word Order: Two Personal Pronouns

As a last possibility, we could encounter two personal pronouns in the middle field. If that happens, the cases actually switch positions and the accusative pronoun will precede the dative pronoun.

I	II	III		L	
Subject	**Verb**	**Dative Object (Noun)**	**Accusative Object (Noun)**		Observation: two nouns Rule: **dative before accusative**
Susanne	erklärt	ihrer Kollegin	den Plan.		
		Accusative Object (Personal Pronoun)	**Dative Object (Personal Pronoun)**		Observation: two personal pronouns Rule: **accusative before dative**
Susanne	erklärt	ihn	ihr.		

188g Eine Reise nach Namibia. Wo stehen die Personalpronomen?

Letztes Jahr zeigte meine Freundin Tsakana meiner Familie das Land Namibia.

Ja, wirklich! Letztes Jahr zeigte Tsakana _es ihr_ ________ (ihr / es).

Wir brachten unseren Gastgeber*innen in Windhoek signierte Fußbälle mit.

Was? Ja, wir brachten ________________ (ihnen / sie) mit.

Tsakana erklärte meinem Vater das ostafrikanische Bao-Spiel. Stimmt das?

Ja, Tsakana erklärte ________________ (ihm / es).

Tskanas Bruder gab meinen Schwestern eine Tour im Etosha-National-Park.

Ist das wahr? Tsakanas Bruder gab ________________ (ihnen / sie).

Tsakanas Familie schenkte dem Namibia-Haus in unserer Stadt einen traditionellen Schafwollteppich (*sheep wool carpet*).

Ist das so? Tsakanas Familie schenkte ________________ (ihm / ihn).

188h Ergänzen Sie jeweils das Personalpronomen für die Akkusativobjekte (unterstrichen) oder Dativobjekte (fett).

Die Eltern gaben **ihrem Sohn** den Namen Ernesto.

Die Eltern gaben ihn _ihm_ ____________.

Der Großvater José vererbte (*bequeathed*) **Ernestos Vater Luís** eine Uhr.

Der Großvater José vererbte ______________ **ihm.**

Ernesto brachte **seiner Familie** große Anerkennung[1].

Ernesto brachte sie ______________.

Er wurde Lehrer und brachte **vielen Kindern** die Geschichte seines Landes näher.

Er wurde Lehrer und brachte ______________ **ihnen** näher.

In einem Buch erzählte er **den Leser*innen** Anekdoten aus seinem Land.

In seinem Buch erzählte er sie ______________.

[1] die Anerkennung – *recognition*

58: Grenz-Identitäten°

190a **Die deutschsprachigen Länder in Europa. Markieren Sie die Grenzen mit farbigen Linien und die Dreiländerecke mit farbigen Kreuzen oder Kreisen dort, wo drei Länder zusammenkommen.**

deutsche Grenze mit ...
Dänemark: rot
Luxemburg: grün
Schweiz: blau
Polen: pink

österreichische Grenze mit ...
der Schweiz: gelb
der Slowakei: lila

Schweizer Grenze mit ...
Italien: orange

Dreiländereck ...
Deutschland-Belgien-Niederlande: rot
Schweiz-Österreich-Italien: blau
Deutschland-Tschechien-Polen: grün

3. Luxemburg
4. Liechtenstein

191a **Görlitz in der Mitte Europas. Sortieren Sie die Informationen zu den Überschriften.**

Lage/Geografie	Interessantes	Wissenschaften
Nummer ______	Nummer ______	Nummer ______
Nummer ______	Nummer ______	Nummer ______
Nummer ______	Nummer ______	Nummer ______

1) 2019 wurde hier CASUS (*Center for Advanced Systems Understanding*) gegründet.

2) am Fluss Neiße, in der Region Lausitz in Sachsen

3) Lernlabor Cybersicherheit des Fraunhofer Instituts

4) Geplant ist ein Kompetenzzentrum für Hydrotechnologie.

5) Die Görlitzer Altstadt wurde im Krieg nicht zerstört und ist gut erhalten.

6) In der Stadt wurden viele Filme gedreht, z. B. „M", „Der Vorleser" und „Inglourious Basterds".

7) Internationaler Brückepreis für Menschen, die sich für Völkerverständigung engagieren

8) auf dem 15° Meridian, genau in der Mitte Europas

9) östlichste Stadt Deutschlands

191b **Blickpunkt: Margarete Stokowski. Lesen Sie den Text und beantworten Sie die R/F-Fragen.**

Margarete Stokowski wurde am 14. April 1986 geboren. Seit sie zwei Jahre alt ist, ist sie in Berlin zu Hause. Sie studierte Philosophie und Sozialwissenschaften an der Humboldt-Universität in Berlin. Ihre Abschlussarbeit war über Simone de Beauvoir. Stokowski schreibt feministische und politisch-progressive Kolumnen für Zeitungen und Zeitschriften und publiziert auch Bücher. Ihr Buch „Untenrum frei" von 2016, eine Art feministische Autobiografie, war ein großer Erfolg.

In einer Kolumne im Spiegel schrieb sie über eine Kuriosität zur Frage ihres Geburtsortes: Obwohl die Stadt Zabrze heißt und in Polen liegt, steht in ihrem deutschen Pass „Hindenburg". So hieß die Stadt, als sie vor 1945 zu Schlesien gehörte, aber 1986 schon lange nicht mehr. Ihrer Recherche zufolge ist dies auch bei anderen Pol*innen der Fall, fast so als wäre Schlesien immer noch eine deutsche Region.

richtig	falsch	
		Stokowski ist in Polen zu Hause.
		Sie ist Feministin.
		In ihrem deutschen Pass steht der korrekte Geburtsort.

59: Flucht, Ankunft, Kunst

192a **Flucht nach Deutschland. Im Jahr 2015 kamen so viele Geflüchtete wie noch nie nach Europa. Der folgende Text und die Grafiken geben Ihnen ein Bild darüber, woher die geflüchteten Menschen kamen und welche Rolle Deutschland dabei spielte. Lesen Sie den Text und beantworten Sie die R/F-Fragen auf der nächsten Seite.**

Berichte der Vereinten Nationen (UN) zeigen, dass 2015 mehr als 240 Millionen Menschen auf der Flucht waren. Die Gründe: Krieg, Armut, Verfolgung (*persecution*). Mehrere Krisenregionen befinden sich in der Nähe Europas. Deswegen entschieden sich viele Menschen, Schutz in europäischen Ländern zu suchen. 2015 kamen mehr als eine Million Flüchtlinge nach Deutschland, die meisten davon flohen vor dem Bürger*innenkrieg in Syrien.

Es gab viele Deutsche, die den Geflüchteten halfen: Sie spendeten Geld, vergaben an Bahnhöfen Hilfspakete oder unterstützten Geflüchtete im Alltag, z. B. beim Besuch von Behörden. Doch es gab auch viele Menschen, die negativ reagierten und wollten, dass Deutschland keine weiteren Geflüchteten aufnimmt. Bundeskanzlerin Angela Merkel zeigte sich aber optimistisch und sagte in einem berühmten Interview: „Wir schaffen das."

Es stimmt, dass Deutschland in keinem Jahr so viele Geflüchtete aufgenommen hat wie 2015. Die meisten Geflüchteten leben aber außerhalb von Europa, z. B. in der Türkei, in Pakistan und Uganda, und der Libanon ist das Land, das prozentual die meisten Geflüchteten aufgenommen hat: Etwa jede*r sechste Einwohner*in im Libanon gehört zur Gruppe der Geflüchteten.

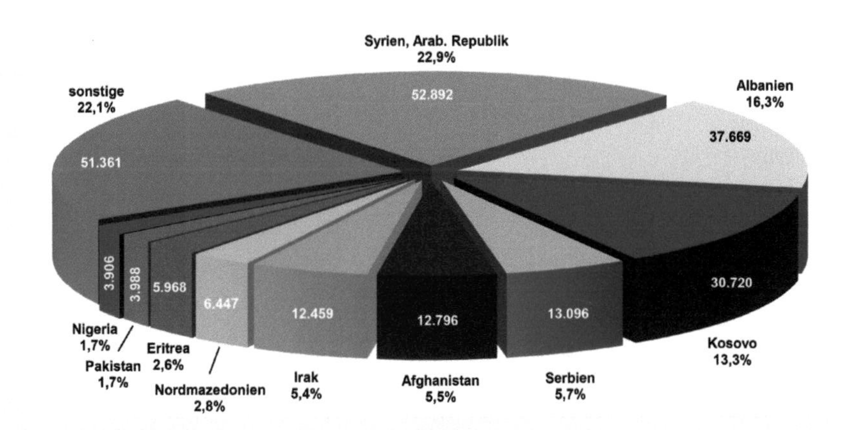

richtig	falsch	
		Viele Geflüchtete kamen nach Europa, weil das der Nachbarkontinent war.
		Die meisten Geflüchteten, die 2015 nach Deutschland flohen, kamen aus Afrika.
		Nicht alle Deutschen fanden es gut, dass so viele Geflüchtete nach Deutschland kamen.
		Die meisten Geflüchteten kommen nach Europa.

192b **Schauen Sie sich diese Statistik an. In welchen vier Ländern Europas wohnten 2018 die meisten Geflüchteten?**

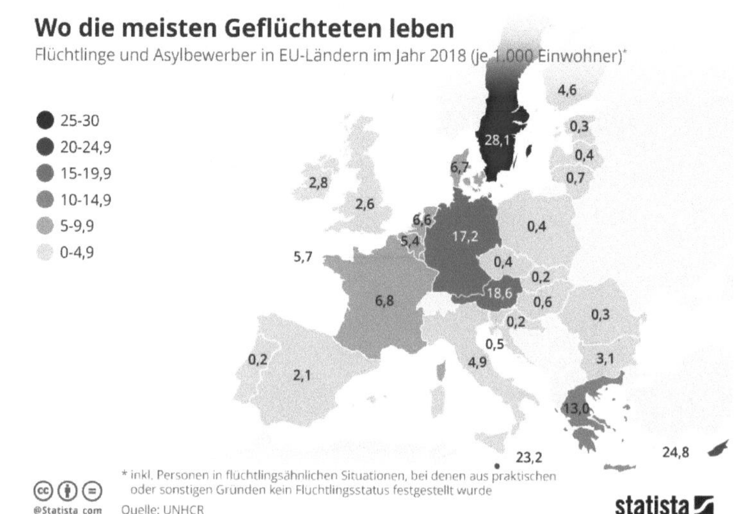

193a Review: Relative Pronouns

Relative pronouns mostly look like articles. When you write a relative clause that describes a noun, you will need to determine the grammatical gender, number, and case of the relative pronoun. You can easily see **grammatical gender** and **number** by looking at the main clause and the noun you are describing:

Der Mann, **den** Ai Weiwei trifft … — *The man whom Ai Weiwei meets …*
[masc., sg.]

To determine the **case**, you have to think about the function that the relative pronoun serves in the relative clause.

Der Mann ist nett. Ai Weiwei trifft **den** Mann. — *The man is nice. Ai Weiwei meets the man.*
Der Mann, **den** Aiwei trifft, ist nett. — *The man, whom Ai Weiwei meets, is nice.*

Der Mann ist nett. Ai Weiwei zeigt **dem** Mann das Projekt. — *The man is nice. Ai Weiwei shows the project to the man.*
Der Mann, **dem** Ai Weiwei das Projekt zeigt, ist nett. — *The man, to whom Ai Weiwei shows the project, is nice.*

Der Mann ist nett. Ai Weiwei kennt die Frau **des** Mannes. — *The man is nice. Ai Weiwei knows the man's wife.*
Der Mann, **dessen** Frau Ai Weiwei kennt, ist nett. — *The man, whose wife Ai Weiwei knows, is nice.*

Remember that when there is a preposition, it comes directly before the relative pronoun:

Der Mann, **mit dem** Ai Weiwei das Projekt bespricht, … — *The man, with whom Ai Weiwei discusses the project, …*

	Nominative	Accusative	Dative	Genitive
masculine	Tag, **der**	Tag, **den**	Tag, von **dem**	Tag, **dessen**
neuter	Boot, **das**	Boot, **das**	Boot, in **dem**	Boot, **dessen**
feminine	Insel, **die**	Insel, **die**	Insel, auf **der**	Insel, **deren**
plural	Geflüchtete, **die**	Geflüchtete, **die**	Geflüchtete, **denen**	Geflüchtete, **deren**

193b **Blickpunkt: Ai Weiwei. Welche Relativpronomen stimmen hier?**

Ai Qing ist ein Aktivist und Künstler, (der | den | dem) man unter dem Künstlernamen Ai Weiwei kennt.

Ai Weiweis Vater war der Dichter Ai Qing, (die | der | den) als „Kapitalist" in ein Arbeitslager (*labor camp*) musste, als sein Sohn ein Jahr alt war.

Nach zwei Jahren Arbeitslager schickte man die Familie in die Stadt Shihezi, in (der | die | dem) es Bauernhöfe im militärischen Stil gab, wo die Familie sechzehn Jahre lang arbeitete.

Ai Weiwei, (der | den | dem) Film-Animateur werden wollte, besuchte zuerst die Filmakademie in Beijing.

Jetzt arbeitet Ai Weiwei in Berlin, aber die deutsche Kultur, (das | die | den) er nicht toleranter als die chinesische findet, mag er nicht sehr.

Ai Weiwei und seine Frau Lu Qing ziehen bald nach Cambridge. Das ist eine Stadt, (der | die | das) sie aber auch nicht so tolerant finden.

60: „TATORT DAF" (TEIL I)

195a **Ordnen Sie die folgenden Städte oder Orte auf der Karte zu: Berlin, Chiemsee, Leipzig, Heidelberg, Hamburg, Essen. Wenn Sie nicht weiter wissen, dürfen Sie auch die Karte in Ihrem Kursbuch zur Hilfe nehmen.**

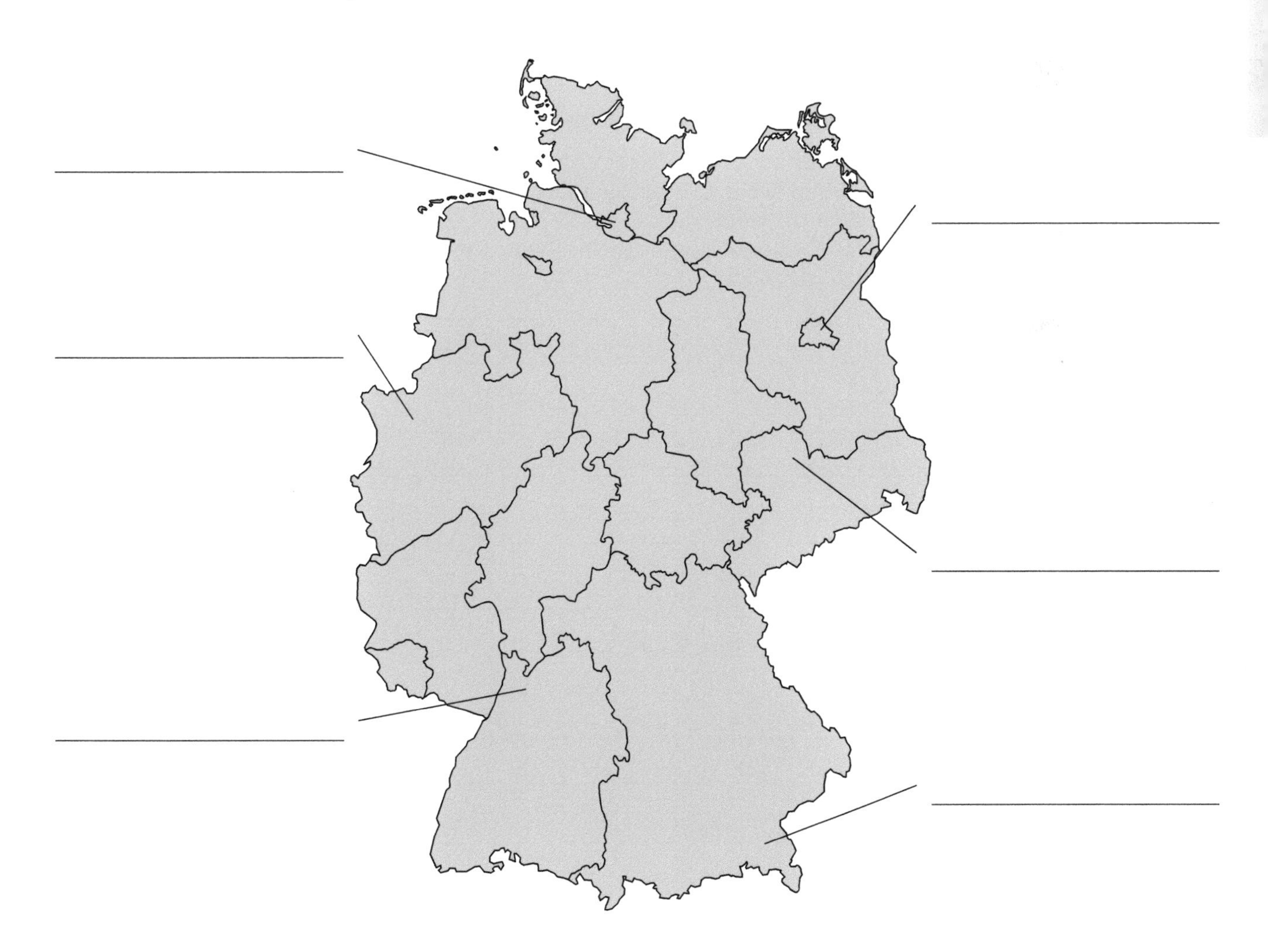

196a **Blickpunkt: Deutsche Krimis I – Christine Urspruch. Lesen Sie den Text und schreiben Sie einen Steckbrief mit allen wichtigen Informationen über Christine Urspruch.**

Krimis sind in Deutschland sehr beliebt. Über die Jahre gehen nicht mehr nur ältere weiße Männer auf Verbrecher*innenjagd (*„hunt for criminals“*), sondern die deutsche Krimilandschaft ist vielfältiger geworden. Die Pluralität bezieht sich sowohl auf die ethnische Herkunft der Teams als auch auf andere Aspekte. Wir stellen Ihnen hier eine Schauspielerin vor, die in der beliebten TV-Krimireihe „Tatort“ mitspielt und darin zur Vielfalt beiträgt.

Christine Urspruch wurde am 16. September 1970 geboren. Sie spielt im Theater und auch im Fernsehen. Sie war schon an Theatern in Bonn, Berlin, München, Wiesbaden, Basel, Bregenz und Wien zu sehen.

Seit 2002 spielt sie im „Tatort“ aus Münster neben Axel Prahl und Jan-Josef Liefers, dem beliebtesten „Tatort“-Team, eine Gerichtsmedizinerin (*coroner*). Sie hat außerdem von 2014 bis 2019 in einer Fernsehserie eine Ärztin gespielt.

Urspruch schreibt ihren eigenen Vornamen ChrisTine und sagt, dass sie damit Größe zeigen möchte. Urspruch ist 1,32 m groß und meint, dass ihre Kleinwüchsigkeit im Alltag keine Rolle spielt.

______________: ______________________________

______________: ______________________________

______________: ______________________________

______________: ______________________________

______________: ______________________________

______________: ______________________________

197a **In MACHEN lernen Sie sechs Krimis kennen. Gehen Sie zu Aktivität 197 in MACHEN. Dort sehen Sie die Cover der sechs Bücher mit dem jeweiligen Klappentext. Schauen Sie sich die Cover an und lesen Sie die Klappentexte. Formulieren Sie dann für jedes Buch eine Frage oder eine Beobachtung: Was wollen Sie wissen? Was wird in der Geschichte Ihrer Meinung nach passieren?**

Buch 1: ______________________________

Buch 2: ______________________________

Buch 3: ______________________________

Buch 4: ______________________________

Buch 5: ______________________________

Buch 6: ______________________________

61: WAS SPRECHEN WIR?

198a Review: W Questions and Yes/No Questions

Let's have a look at two types of questions: W questions and yes/no questions.

W questions begin with a question word, followed by the **conjugated verb**, then the subject (if there is one), and the rest of the question, ending with the second part of the verb (if there is one):

Wer **hat** das Video gemacht?	*Who made the video?*
Wen **zeigt** das Video?	*Whom does the video show?*

The most important questions words to remember are:

Wer/Was?	*who or what*	(asks for the subject of the sentence, person/thing)
Wen/Was?	*who(m) or what*	(asks for the accusative of the sentence, person/thing)
Wem?	*(to) whom*	(asks for the dative of the sentence, usually a person)
Wie?	*how*	
Warum?	*why*	
Wo?	*where*	
Woher?	*where from*	
Wohin?	*where to*	
Wann?	*when*	

Yes/No questions begin with the **conjugated verb**, then the subject, then the rest of the question, ending with the second part of the verb (if there is one):

Hat sie das Video gemacht?	*Did she make the video?*
Zeigt das Video Yared?	*Does the video show Yared?*

198b Blickpunkt: Biografie von Yared Dibaba. Lesen Sie die Biografie und formulieren Sie Fragen und Antworten auf der nächsten Seite.

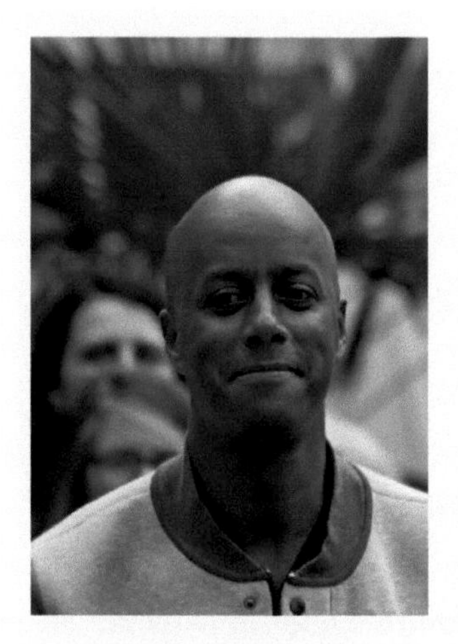

Yared Dibaba kam das erste Mal 1973 nach Deutschland, weil sein Vater an der Uni in Osnabrück studieren wollte. 1976 ist seine Familie noch einmal in sein Geburtsland Äthiopien gegangen, aber dann mussten sie wieder vor dem Bürger*innenkrieg dort fliehen. Dibaba ging in Delmenhorst in Norddeutschland auf die Schule, deshalb kann er auch Plattdeutsch (= Niederdeutsch). Er hat eine Ausbildung zum Kaufmann gemacht und Schauspiel und Musik studiert. Heute wohnt er in Hamburg-Altona.

Er spielte einige Rollen im Ohnsorg-Theater, das Stücke auf Plattdeutsch inszeniert. Abgesehen davon arbeitete er für mehrere Fernsehsender als Moderator. In den letzten Jahren hat er einige Bücher auf Plattdeutsch geschrieben, z. B. „Mien Welt blifft Platt" (2011). Er hat auch einige CDs aufgenommen, darunter „Dat groote plattdüütsche Bibel-Hörbook. For lüttje un groote Kinder", ein Hörbuch über Plattdeutsch in der Kirche.

Sein Lebensmotto ist: „Alles, was ich kann, habe ich auch gelernt", und damit meint er nicht nur Schauspiel, Schreiben und Musik, sondern auch Fechten, Ballett und Hip-Hop (z. B. in dem Lied „De Fofftig Penns" von De Biet).

Warum (nach Deutschland gehen / Bürge*innenkrieg)

Frage: *Warum ist die Familie Dibaba nach Deutschland gegangen?*

Antwort: *Wegen des Bürger*innenkriegs in Äthiopien. / Weil es in Äthiopien einen Bürger*innenkrieg gab.*

Was (lernen / Ausbildung zum Kaufmann machen, Schauspiel und Musik studieren)

Frage: ______

Antwort: ______

Wo (eine Rolle spielen / Ohnsorg-Theater)

Frage: ______

Antwort: ______

Wie (Titel eines Buchs von Dibaba lauten / „Mien Welt blifft Platt")

Frage: ______

Antwort: ______

Worüber (CD aufnehmen / Platt in der Kirche)

Frage: ______

Antwort: ______

Mit wem (ein Hip-Hop-Lied aufnehmen / De Biet)

Frage: ______

Antwort: ______

AUSSPRACHE: W ODER F

200a **Hören und Sprechen: Hören Sie die Namen und sprechen Sie nach.**

a	b	a	b
☐ Wahrenberg	☐ Fahrenberg	☐ Wichte	☐ Fichte
☐ Wehler	☐ Fehler	☐ Wiemer	☐ Fiemer
☐ Wetter	☐ Vetter	☐ Wollmer	☐ Vollmer
☐ Sommerwein	☐ Sommerfein	☐ Wuhlert	☐ Fuhlert

200b **Hören: Sie hören jetzt immer nur einen Namen. Was hören Sie: a oder b? Kreuzen Sie oben in Aktivität 200a an.**

200c **Hören: Was hören Sie: einen„F"-Laut oder einen „W"-Laut? Kreuzen Sie an.**

1. vier: ☐ f ☐ w	4. Krawatte: ☐ f ☐ w	7. Wäsche: ☐ f ☐ w
2. Verb: ☐ f ☐ w	5. Phonetik: ☐ f ☐ w	8. Pullover: ☐ f ☐ w
3. Farbe: ☐ f ☐ w	6. vorsichtig: ☐ f ☐ w	9. intensiv: ☐ f ☐ w

200d **Ordnen Sie die Wörter von Aktivität 200c richtig zu.**

Hier sprechen wir „f“:

f: füllen, höflich

v: der Vorschlag, versuchen, viel

ph: das Alphabet, die Atmosphäre

Hier sprechen wir „w“:

w: das Wetter, weiß

v[1]: das Klavier, privat

[1] Bei Fremdwörtern spricht man „v“ wie „w“. Auch am Wortende + Endung wird „v“ wie „w“ gesprochen (z. B. eine intensive Farbe).

200e **Hören und Sprechen: Hören Sie den Satz. Sprechen Sie ihn dann nach: erst langsam, dann so schnell wie möglich.**

Wir Wiener Waschweiber wollen weiße Wäsche waschen, weiße Wäsche wollen wir Wiener Waschweiber waschen.

62: KULINARISCHE EINFLÜSSE°

201a **Lebensmittel. Sortieren Sie die Wörter aus dem Kasten nach den vorgegebenen Kategorien.**

das Brot | die Currywurst | die Möhre | die Zwiebel | der Knoblauch | der Kuchen | der Supermarkt | die Gurke | der Brokkoli | der Imbisswagen | das Fast-Food-Restaurant | der Sauerbraten | das Schnitzel | das Vollkornbrot | die Banane | die Ananas | die Metzgerei | der Kartoffelsalat | das Brötchen | der Wochenmarkt | die Bratkartoffeln | die Bäckerei | der Rotkohl | der Apfel | die Königsberger Klopse | die Rostbratwurst | das Toastbrot | der Mais | die Spaghetti Bolognese | der Döner | das Gulasch | der Bagel | die Orange

Gemüse

______

______

______

Gerichte

______

______

______

Obst

______

______

______

Orte

______

______

______

Backwaren

____

____

____

201b **Brainstorming: Welche Gerichte sind ursprünglich typisch für Österreich, die Schweiz oder Deutschland? Recherchieren Sie.**

Recherche

Nürnberger Bratwürstchen	Österreich	die Schweiz	Deutschland
Faschierte Laibchen	Österreich	die Schweiz	Deutschland
Rösti	Österreich	die Schweiz	Deutschland
Sauerbraten	Österreich	die Schweiz	Deutschland
Sauerkraut	Österreich	die Schweiz	Deutschland
Kaiserschmarrn	Österreich	die Schweiz	Deutschland
Müsli	Österreich	die Schweiz	Deutschland
Tafelspitz	Österreich	die Schweiz	Deutschland
Kohlroulade	Österreich	die Schweiz	Deutschland
Steirisches Wurzelfleisch	Österreich	die Schweiz	Deutschland
Zürcher Geschnetzeltes	Österreich	die Schweiz	Deutschland
Bündner Nusstorte	Österreich	die Schweiz	Deutschland

201c **Blickpunkt: Sarah Henke ist eine Sterneköchin. Sie leitet das Restaurant YOSO in Andernach. Außerdem ist sie Jurorin bei der Fernsehshow „Die Küchenschlacht". Suchen Sie online Informationen zu Sarah Henke und ihrem Kochstil (z. B. auf den Webseiten von ihrem Restaurant, der Fernsehshow oder auf Wikipedia). Notieren Sie sich die Informationen und schreiben Sie dann einen kurzen Text (mindestens drei Sätze) über die Sterneköchin.**

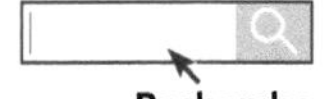

Recherche

Name: ______________________________

Geburtsdatum: ______________________________

Ausbildung: ______________________________

Arbeit: ______________________________

Restaurant (Name): ______________________________

Restaurant (Gründung): ______________________________

Restaurant (Ort): ______________________________

Kochstil/Küche: ______________________________

Text über Sarah Henke:

____

____

____

____

____

KULTURPUNKT: HEIMAT

"Hold on a second: …

what do the Germans mean when they talk about *Heimat*?" The German word *Heimat* is one of these untranslatable words (like *Fernweh* and *Schadenfreude*) because it carries much more meaning than can be expressed in a single word. *Heimat* means an emotionally charged space that applies to a place (usually) of origin. We often see it translated as "home" or "homeland," but the emotional bond to the place through family, ancestors, memories, traditions, languages, etc., are not included in these English words.

The word has had a difficult history throughout which it has served to differentiate between those who "belong" to a place and those who don't. Originally, it was a legal term: *Heimatrecht* meant that anyone who was born in a specific place would receive food and shelter from their community if they were unable to provide for themselves. This charge fell to the nation state after the German Empire was founded in 1871. But Germans didn't feel a strong sense of belonging to that large state. Therefore, *Heimat* art, literature, and music tried to create this sense of belonging and to forge a bond among local, regional, and national entities.

During the Third Reich, however, *Heimat* became a ethnonationalist concept that was used to include some and exclude others. It served both expansionism and discrimination. On the one hand, *Heimat* meant the German mainland to which ethnic Germans in other countries, for instance the Sudeten Germans in Czechoslovakia, supposedly felt allegiance. Nazi occupation, then, served to bring those Germans who lived far away from their *Heimat* "home." At the same time, the German *Heimat* was an excluding concept that built on the idea of an ethnically homogeneous nation state. It was used to rob unwanted minorities—Jews, Sinti and Romanies, people of color as well as people with disabilities and homosexuals—of their home/*Heimat* but also of their civil and ultimately human rights. After the war, German territories East of the river Oder, which was determined as the Eastern border of the new Germany, fell to the Soviet Union, Poland, and other countries. These countries expelled those who they perceived as German. These expellees longed to go back to their *Heimat*, which also included a political charge of making these territories "German" again. They celebrated their traditions in so-called *Heimatvereinen*, in which they remembered the old homes as "German," although they had been quite multicultural.

Heimat carries with it nostalgia for an idyllic landscape and a simple (and better) past. These sentiments were expressed, for example, in the *Heimatfilme* after the Second World War. These traditional *Heimat* films were set in rural areas and villages and dealt with friendship, love, and family. They avoided politics while also perpetuating an image of an ideal world that was rural and homogeneous. Today, the far-right uses this (for them) idyllic, nostalgic image of homogeneity to create a narrative of fear that "their" *Heimat* is being taken away by migrants. *Heimat* today is, thus, a term that is experienced as exclusionary for people of color and (post-)migrants. Some authors have written about their experiences with the concept of *Heimat* in a 2019 book called *Eure Heimat ist unser Alptraum (Your Heimat is Our Nightmare)*. The authors make clear that *Heimat* can describe a deep sense of belonging, but not everyone is allowed to belong to this "German" *Heimat*. Today, then, we find tensions between the far-right party AfD that terms itself *Heimatpartei* and aims to recreate a homogeneous *Heimat* (that never really existed) and people like *Heimat* ambassador Lamya Kaddor from North Rhine-Westphalia who wants to redefine *Heimat* as (plural) *Heimaten* in which many people can find their homes and which reflect diversity.

204a Reflektieren: Kennen Sie noch andere Wörter, die nicht übersetzbar sind? Was bedeuten sie ungefähr? Was bedeutet *home* für Sie? Wo ist *home*, wer gehört dazu und was empfinden Sie, wenn Sie daran denken? Haben Sie Angst, dass Sie ihr *home* verlieren könnten? Warum (nicht)? Was bedeutet es für Menschen, ihr *home* zu verlieren?

204b **Die Heimat in uns. Identifizieren Sie zuerst Kasus und Genus der kursiv markierten Pronomen. Entscheiden Sie dann: Welches Relativpronomen passt hier?**

Für Erwin ist Heimat eine Mischung von Gefühlen und dem Parfum seiner Oma. Er vermisst *sie* manchmal.

Für Erwin ist Heimat eine Mischung von Gefühlen und dem Parfum seiner Oma, die ________ er manchmal vermisst.

Für Mia ist Heimat ein Geräusch von Stimmen und Musik. Sie hörte *es*, als sie mit sechs Jahren im Bett lag.

Für Mia ist Heimat ein Geräusch von Stimmen und Musik, ________ sie hörte, als sie mit sechs Jahren im Bett lag.

Zoe denkt bei „Heimat" an den Geschmack von Saras Tomatensuppe. Sie fand *ihn* einmalig.

Zoe denkt bei „Heimat" an den Geschmack von Saras Tomatensuppe, ________ sie einmalig fand.

Jörg und Uwe finden Heimatgefühle in Rosen. *Sie* standen bei ihrem Lieblingsonkel vor dem Haus.

Jörg und Uwe finden Heimatgefühle in Rosen, ________ bei ihrem Lieblingsonkel vor dem Haus standen.

205a **Politik. Finden Sie die passenden Begriffe für die folgenden Definitionen.**

konzentriert sich auf Probleme zwischen Gruppen von Menschen:	sozialistisch | sozialkritisch
eine Reaktion zeigen:	reagieren | realisieren
negativer Aspekt, der die ganze Gesellschaft betrifft:	systematisches Problem | semantisches Problem
etwas mit Worten beschreiben:	erklären | aufklären
zwei oder mehr Dinge in einen Kontext bringen:	in Verbindung bringen | in Rage bringen
der zentrale Punkt ist:	es geht um | es geht nicht
die Atmosphäre, das Gefühl:	die Stille | die Stimmung
etwas indirekt sagen:	implizieren | implodieren

205b **Welche der Formulierungen und Wörter, die Sie in Aktivität 205a markiert haben passen in die Lücken?**

Es geht meistens um Politik, wenn ich mit meinen Freund*innen diskutiere. Wir denken alle sehr sozialkritisch ________, weil wir Politikwissenschaft, Soziologie oder Geschichte studieren. Es ist sehr interessant, wenn Bernd (Soziologie) und Yvette (Geschichte) ihre akademischen Disziplinen miteinander ________________, weil man dann viele Dinge besser verstehen kann. Ich lerne an der Uni, wie die Politik ein ________________ wie Rassismus verstärken oder verbessern kann. Bernd arbeitet als Sozialarbeiter und kann uns ________________, welche konkreten rassistischen Probleme er sieht.

205c **Blickpunkt: Namika. Ergänzen Sie den Text mit den Informationen aus dem Steckbrief.**

Bürgerlicher Name:	Hanan Hamdi
Geburtstag:	23.08.1991
Zuhause:	Frankfurt am Main
Beruf:	Sängerin und Rapperin
Größter Erfolg:	Lied „Lieblingsmensch"

Die ________________ Namika heißt eigentlich ________________.
Sie wurde am ________________ geboren und ist in ________________ zu Hause. Die Eltern ihrer Mutter kamen in den 1970er Jahren aus Marokko nach Deutschland. Ihre Musikrichtung ist Hip-Hop. Im Jahr 2015 hatte sie viel Erfolg mit dem Lied ________________, das ein Nummer 1-Hit wurde.

Wie unterhalten wir uns?

Alte und neue Medien

Wortschatz

65: Heute im Radioprogramm

die Medien (*pl.*)	media
das Medium, Medien	medium
die Wahrheit, -en	truth
die Sendung, -en	program, broadcast; shipment
mündlich	oral(ly), verbal(ly)
lügen, log, hat ... gelogen	to lie, tell a lie
die Lüge, -n	lie
ehrlich	honest(ly)
der Zuhörer, -	listener (*male*)
die Zuhörerin, -nen	listener (*female*)
die zuhörende Person, die Zuhörerschaft	listener (*gender-neutral alternative*)
die Show, -s	show
im Schnitt	on average
verraten (verrät), verriet, hat ... verraten	to reveal, disclose; betray
betonen, betonte, hat ... betont	to stress, emphasize
auffällig	conspicuous(ly), striking(ly)
starren, starrte, hat ... gestarrt	to stare
spontan	spontaneous(ly)
ab·lenken, lenkte ... ab, hat ... abgelenkt	to distract, divert
die Not, ¨e	emergency; distress; hardship
aus Versehen	by accident
stimmen, stimmte, hat ... gestimmt	to be true/right
außergewöhnlich	extraordinary(ly)

Weitere Wörter: auf der Spur sein (ist), war, ist ... gewesen (to be on the scent); **los·gehen, ging ... los, ist ... losgegangen** (to start, begin); **verpassen, verpasste, hat ... verpasst** (to miss); **glauben, glaubte, hat ... geglaubt** (to believe); **nun** (now); **überhaupt** (anyway); **erfahren (erfährt), erfuhr, hat ... erfahren** (to find out); **ertappen (bei + *dat.*), ertappte, hat ... ertappt** (to catch (at)); **der Lügner, -** (liar (*male*)); **die Lügnerin, -nen** (liar (*female*)); **die lügende Person, die Lügenden** (liar (*gender-neutral alternative*)); **ungelogen** (truly, honestly); **kreativ** (creative); **wahr** (true); **als Wahrheit gelten (gilt), galt, hat ... gegolten** (to count as truth)

67: „Tatort DaF" (Teil 2)

die Handlung, -en	plot; action
die Aktion, -en	action
gemeint sein (ist), war, ist ... gewesen	to be meant
bisher	until now, so far
neugierig	curious
interessiert	interested
langweilig	boring
ernst	serious(ly)
sympathisch	likeable
intelligent	intelligent
sich (*akk.*) erholen, erholte, hat ... erholt	to relax; get better (*health*)

Weitere Wörter: die Figur, -en (character; figure); **die Nacherzählung, -en** (reproduction, re-telling); **der Einleitungssatz, ¨e** (introductory phrase, topic sentence); **der Hauptteil, -e** (main part, body); **nervös** (nervous(ly))

68: Nachrichtenmedien

die Nachrichten (*pl.*)	news, newscast
schauen, schaute, hat ... geschaut	to watch
die Quelle, -n	source
komplex	complex
intellektuell	intellectual(ly)
die Grippe, -n	flu
aus·brechen (bricht ... aus), brach ... aus, ist ... ausgebrochen	to break out
berichten, berichtete, hat ... berichtet	to report
ernst nehmen (nimmt), nahm, hat ... genommen	to take seriously
der Beitrag, ¨e	article (*news*); contribution
die Infektion, -en	infection
der Fall, ¨e	case
die Wahl, -en	election; choice
die Verspätung, -en	delay
der Sturm, ¨e	storm
inzwischen	in the meantime, by now

Weitere Wörter: analytisch (analytical); **der Nachrichtenbericht, -e** (news report); **der Zeitungsartikel, -** (newspaper article); **die sozialen Medien (*pl.*)** (social media); **seriös** (reputable, reliable); **die Nachrichtenquelle, -n** (source of information); **sensationalistisch** (sensationalist); **simplifizierend** (simplifying)

69: Serienmarathon

das Fernsehen	television, TV
an·sehen (sieht ... an), sah ... an, hat ... angesehen	to watch; look at
streamen, streamte, hat ... gestreamt	to stream
die Serie, -n	series (TV)
die Auswahl, -en	choice; selection
jemals	ever
die Folge, -n	episode; consequence
der Charakter, -e	character
je ... desto ...	the ... the ... (*e.g. the sooner the better*)
das Drehbuch, ¨er	script
die Darstellerin, -nen	actress, performer (*female*)
der Darsteller, -	actor, performer (*male*)
die darstellende Person, die Darstellenden	actor/actress, performer (*gender-neutral workaround*)
nebenbei	on the side, besides
der Schluss, ¨e	ending
enttäuschen, enttäuschte, hat ... enttäuscht	to disappoint
unheimlich	uncanny, eerie, scary
die Werbung, -en	commercials, advertisement

die Reklame, -n	advertisement

Weitere Wörter: das Kabelfernsehen (cable TV); **die Werbepause, -n** (commercial break); **aus·strahlen, strahlte … aus, hat … ausgestrahlt** (to broadcast)

71: Inklusives Fernsehen transnational

das Format, -e	format
die Vermutung, -en	assumption, guess
die Staffel, -n	season (*TV, radio*)
gestalten, gestaltete, hat … gestaltet	to design, shape
der Kandidat, -en	candidate (*male*)
die Kandidatin, -nen	candidate (*female*)
die antretende Person, die Antretenden	competing person (*gender-neutral workaround for candidate*)
loben, lobte, hat … gelobt	to praise
aufmerksam	attentive
der Kommentar, -e	comment
schwach	weak
die Kritik, -en	critique
die Haltung, -en	attitude; posture
zukünftig	prospective, future
der Produzent, -en	producer (*male*)
die Produzentin, -nen	producer (*female*)
die Produktionsleitung, die Produzierenden	producer (*gender-neutral alternative*)
die Verbesserung, -en	improvement
die Unterhaltung, -en	entertainment; conversation
übertragen (überträgt), übertrug, hat … übertragen	to broadcast; transmit
jdm. (*dat.*) etw. vor·werfen (wirft … vor), warf … vor, hat … vorgeworfen	to accuse so. of sth.

Weitere Wörter: der Rundfunk (broadcast, radio); **sehenswert** (worth seeing); **die Sichtbarkeit** (visibility)

72: „Tatort DaF" (Teil 3)

ab·holen, holte … ab, hat … abgeholt	to pick up
der Moment, -e	moment
der Blickkontakt, -e	eye-contact
die Notiz, -en	note
das Paket, -e	package
mit·teilen, teilte … mit, hat … mitgeteilt	to inform, communicate
plausibel	plausible, feasible
das Szenario, Szenarien	scenario
die Hauptperson, -en	main person
die Entführung, -en	abduction
das Geheimnis, -se	secret
die Spekulation, -en	speculation
wieder·geben (gibt … wieder), gab … wieder, hat … wiedergegeben	to describe, reproduce
spekulieren, spekulierte, hat … spekuliert	to speculate
strukturieren, strukturierte, hat … strukturiert	to structure

Weitere Wörter: spekulativ (speculative); **chronologisch** (chronological(ly))

73: Im Kino

das Kino, -s	cinema
bestehend	existing
das Jubiläum, Jubiläen	anniversary, jubilee
entlassen (entlässt), entließ, hat … entlassen	to dismiss
die Herrschaft, -en	rule, reign
produzieren, produzierte, hat … produziert	to produce
der Besuch, -e	visit
der Untertitel, -	subtitle
synchronisieren, synchronisierte, hat … synchronisiert	to synchronize, dub
die Stimme, -n	voice
die Synchronisation, -en	synchronization, dubbing
unbedingt	absolute(ly), desperately
gespannt sein (ist), war, ist … gewesen	to be curious

Weitere Wörter: die Filmgeschichte (film history); **der Stummfilm, -e** (silent film); **der Synchronsprecher, -** (dubbing artist, voice-over artist (*male*)); **die Synchronsprecherin, -nen** (dubbing artist, voice-over artist (*female*)); **die synchronsprechende Person, die Synchronsprechenden** (dubbing artist, voice-over artist (*gender-neutral alternative*))

75: Postmigrantisches Theater

der Gegenstand, ⸚e	item, object
das Gerät, -e	device, appliance
der Zweck, -e	purpose, objective
die Verwendung, -en	usage
das Archiv, -e	archive
die Art und Weise	kind, manner
sich (*akk.*) auseinander·setzen (mit + *dat.*), setzte … auseinander, hat … auseinandergesetzt	to discuss, deal with (*subject, theme, problem*)
demnächst	soon, in the near future
auf·führen, führte … auf, hat … aufgeführt	to perform
künstlerisch	artistic(ally)
berühren, berührte, hat … berührt	to touch
sogar	even
schrecklich	dreadful
freiwillig	voluntary/voluntarily
der Witz, -e	joke
das Gift, -e	poison
die Karriere, -n	career
die Bühne, -n	stage
unerwartet	unexpected(ly)
das Verhältnis, -se	relationship

Weitere Wörter: die Motivation, -en (motivation); **improvisieren, improvisierte, hat … improvisiert** (to improvise); **das Bühnenbild, -er** (stage set); **das Programm, -e** (program, schedule); **die Regieanweisung, -en** (stage direction); **ambitioniert** (ambitious(ly)); **die Effizienz, -en** (efficiency); **die Uraufführung, -en** (premiere (*of a play, movie, etc.*))

76: Virtuelle Realitäten

virtuell	virtual
die Realität, -en	reality
das Videospiel, -e	video game
die Konsole, -n	console
mehrmals	repeatedly, multiple times
die Luft, ¨-e	air
der Teilnehmer, -	participant (*male*)
die Teilnehmerin, -nen	participant (*female*)
die teilnehmende Person, die Teilnehmenden	participant (*gender-neutral alternative*)
erweitern, erweiterte, hat ... erweitert	to expand
sich (*akk.*) befinden, befand, hat ... befunden	to be located
der Wissenschaftler, -	scientist (*male*)
die Wissenschaftlerin, -nen	scientist (*female*)
die forschende Person, die Forschenden	scientist (*gender-neutral alternative*)
besprechen (bespricht), besprach, hat ... besprochen	to discuss

Weitere Wörter: gesundheitlich (healthwise); **digital** (digital(ly)); **vorteilhaft** (advantageous)

77: „Tatort DaF" (Teil 4)

fallen (fällt), fiel, ist ... gefallen	to fall
aus·füllen, füllte ... aus, hat ... ausgefüllt	to fill out/in, complete
flüstern, flüsterte, hat ... geflüstert	to whisper
der Schreibstil, -e	writing style
die Buchempfehlung, -en	book recommendation
basierend (auf + *dat.*)	based (on)

65: Heute im Radioprogramm

209a Overview: Tenses in German

When we imagine time as a concept, we usually think in terms of the **past** (*die Vergangenheit*), the **present** (*die Gegenwart*), and the **future** (*die Zukunft*). The German language has six grammatical tenses to express these concepts of time: the *Präsens*, the *Perfekt*, the *Präteritum*, the *Plusquamperfekt*, the *Futur I*, and the *Futur II*.

Vergangenheit		Gegenwart	Zukunft	
Plusquamperfekt	Perfekt	Präsens	Futur II	Futur I
	Präteritum			Präsens

While the distribution of these grammatical tenses mostly follows logic and intuition (like "the present time is expressed by the *Präsens*, DUH!"), you might come across some overlaps, inconsistencies with English, and stylistic variations.

Here are some example sentences for each tense.

Times	Grammatical tense to express times		
die Vergangenheit	Plusquamperfekt	Kim hatte den Text gelesen.	*Kim had read the text.*
	Perfekt	Kim hat den Text gelesen.	*Kim read the text.* *Kim has read the text.*
	Präteritum	Kim las den Text.	*Kim read the text.*
die Gegenwart	Präsens	Kim liest den Text.	*Kim is reading the text.* *Kim (usually) reads the text.* *Kim does read the text.* *Kim has been reading the text.*
die Zukunft	Futur II	Kim wird (bis Mittag) den Text gelesen haben.	*Kim will have read the text (by noon).*
	Futur I	Kim wird den Text lesen.	*Kim is going to read the text.*
	Präsens	Kim liest den Text (morgen).	*Kim will read the text (tomorrow).*

In this chapter, we will look into these tenses and talk about the situations and contexts in which specific grammatical tenses are used.

209b Review: Past Tenses

When we speak of the "past tense," we are referring to events or actions that took place before the present time. In German, there are two main tenses that express the past: the ***Perfekt***, which is the conversational past, and the ***Präteritum***, which is mainly used in writing.

Vergangenheit		Gegenwart	Zukunft	
Plusquamperfekt	**Perfekt**	Präsens	Futur II	Futur I
	Präteritum			Präsens

The *Perfekt* looks similar to the English present perfect tense, but both the *Perfekt* and the *Präteritum* correspond to the simple past, the present perfect, and the past progressive. *Perfekt* and *Präteritum* are interchangeable in terms of function (= both refer to past events), but the context matters: Germans generally use the *Perfekt* when speaking, but they prefer the *Präteritum* for auxiliary verbs and modal verbs.

Perfekt — Anton **hat** ein Radio **gekauft.** — *Anton has bought a radio.* *Anton bought a radio.*

Präteritum — Anton **kaufte** ein Radio. — *Anton bought a radio.*

In addition, there is a third tense to express the past: the *Plusquamperfekt* is sometimes inserted in texts that are otherwise spoken or written in the *Perfekt* or the *Präteritum*. This form expresses an action that has happened before the other actions in the text.

Plusquamperfekt — Er **hatte** das Radio eine Woche vorher in einem Schaufenster **gesehen**. — *He **had seen** the radio in a shopping window a week before.*

Here is an overview of the situation from the example sentences put into the chart from above to help you better visualize the different time frames. Read the sentences from right to left to go from the action in the present (Anton is gifting the radio to his sister) to the past (He bought the radio) to the action before that past action (He had seen the radio in the shopping window a week before).

Vergangenheit		Gegenwart
Er hatte das Radio eine Woche vorher in einem Schaufenster gesehen.	Anton hat das Radio gekauft.	Anton schenkt seiner Schwester das Radio.
	Anton kaufte das Radio.	

In the following units, we will mainly focus on the *Perfekt* and the *Präteritum*, and we will review how to form and use these two tenses. If you would like to review the *Plusquamperfekt*, have a look at activity 30b in Chapter 1.

209c **Uschi berichtet von einem spannenden Krimi-Podcast. Lesen Sie, worum es im Podcast ging, und entscheiden Sie, in welchem Tempus die Sätze sind: Perfekt (PE), Präteritum (PR) oder Plusquamperfekt (PL)?**

Letzte Woche hörte ich im Auto den Podcast „Wahre Lügen" mit meinem Freund Ekon und seiner Schwester Carla (PE | PR | PL), als wir in die Stadt fuhren (PE | PR | PL). Dieser Podcast war interessant (PE | PR | PL): Eine anonyme Person hatte einem Museum ein Picasso-Gemälde geschenkt (PE | PR | PL). Die Museumsdirektorin hat zuerst nicht geglaubt (PE | PR | PL), dass das Gemälde echt war (PE | PR | PL). Immer wieder ging sie zu dem Bild (PE | PR | PL), denn sie wollte die Reaktion der Museumsbesucher*innen sehen (PE | PR | PL). Anfangs waren wir frustriert (PE | PR | PL): Warum hatte die Direktorin das Gemälde nicht geprüft (PE | PR | PL)? Warum wusste sie nicht (PE | PR | PL), dass es keine unregistrierten Picasso-Bilder gibt? Sie hat doch gewusst (PE | PR | PL), dass Picasso alle Kunstwerke signiert hatte (PE | PR | PL)! Am Ende haben Ekon, Carla und ich klar erkannt (PE | PR | PL), wer die wirkliche Malerin des neuen Picasso-Gemäldes war (PE | PR | PL): die Museumsdirektorin!

209d Review: *Perfekt*

Today, we are reviewing how to talk about an event in the past using the *Perfekt*, the conversational past.

Vergangenheit		**Gegenwart**	**Zukunft**	
Plusquamperfekt	**Perfekt** / Präteritum	Präsens	Futur II	Futur I / Präsens

The *Perfekt* is a compound tense, meaning that it is made up of two elements, a **helping/auxiliary verb** (*Hilfsverb*), which is always a form of ***haben*** or ***sein*** (more details on when to use which one will follow), and a **past participle** (*Partizip Perfekt*).

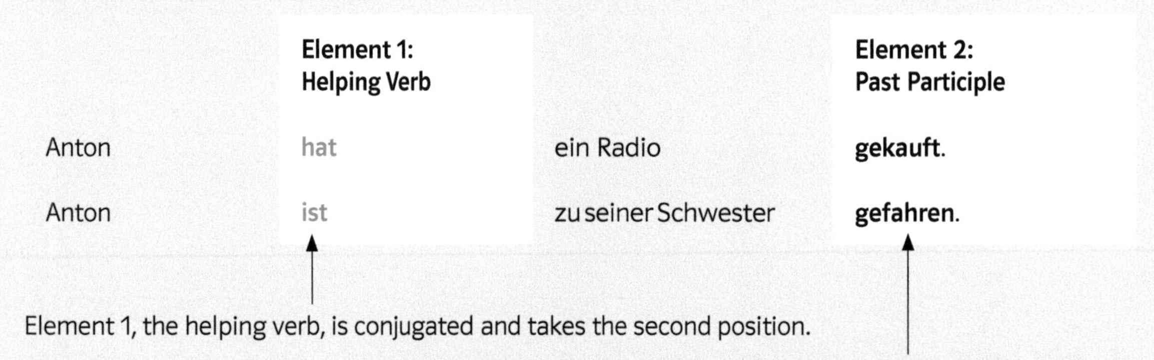

	Element 1: Helping Verb		**Element 2: Past Participle**
Anton	hat	ein Radio	**gekauft**.
Anton	ist	zu seiner Schwester	**gefahren**.

Element 1, the helping verb, is conjugated and takes the second position.

Element 2, the past participle takes the last position in the main clause.

The past participle forms differ for **weak verbs**, **strong verbs**, and **mixed verbs**.

	Infinitive	Past Participle
Weak verbs usually form the past participle with the prefix ***ge-*** and the suffix ***-t***.	kaufen hören schenken	**ge**kauf**t** **ge**hör**t** **ge**schenk**t**
Strong verbs usually form the past participle with the prefix ***ge-*** and the suffix ***-en***. Like in English, they often have a vowel change.	gehen lesen sprechen	**ge**gang**en** **ge**les**en** **ge**sproch**en**
Mixed verbs often have a vowel change like strong verbs but the ***-t*** suffix of weak verbs.	denken wissen bringen	**ge**dach**t** **ge**wuss**t** **ge**brach**t**
Separable-prefix verbs can be weak or strong verbs. Thus the ending of their past participle can result in a ***-t*** or an ***-en***. The ***ge-*** is now a "circumfix" and is inserted between the prefix and the verb.	aufwachen aussehen nachdenken	auf**ge**wach**t** aus**ge**seh**en** nach**ge**dach**t**

There are some exceptions when it comes to **weak verbs** that you need to keep in mind:

- Verbs with their stem ending in ***-d*** or ***-t*** add an ***e***.
- Verbs with inseparable prefixes like ***be-***, ***er-***, ***ver-***, ***ent-*** don't add the prefix ***ge-***.
- International verbs that end in ***-ieren*** don't add the prefix ***ge-*** either.

Infinitiv	**Partizip**	
duschen	**ge**dusch**t**	
arbeiten	**ge**arbeit**et**	(As in the present tense, verb stems ending in ***-d*** or ***-t*** add an ***e***.)
bestellen	bestell**t**	(Verbs with inseparable prefixes like ***be-***, ***er-***, ***ver-***, ***ent-*** don't add the prefix ***ge-***.)
studieren	__studier**t**	(International verbs that end in ***-ieren*** don't add the prefix ***ge-*** either.)

209e **Xenia erzählt eine komische Geschichte von ihrer Freundin Aisha. Lesen Sie ihre Erzählung und entscheiden Sie, welche Form das unterstrichene Partizip hat: schwach, gemischt oder stark?**

Heute hat meine Schwester Aisha mir eine komische Geschichte erzählt. (schwach | gemischt | stark)

Sie ist gestern zur Uni gefahren. (schwach | gemischt | stark)

Da hat sie ihren Wagen auf den Parkplatz vor ein Café gestellt. (schwach | gemischt | stark)

Aber als sie am Nachmittag zurückgekommen ist, war das Auto nicht mehr da! (schwach | gemischt | stark)

Aisha hat die Polizei angerufen. (schwach | gemischt | stark)

Mit der Polizei hat sie die ganze Straße abgesucht. (schwach | gemischt | stark)

Doch der Wagen war weg.

Erst nach einer Stunde ist Aisha wieder zu dem Café gegangen. (schwach | gemischt | stark)

Und da stand der Wagen wieder da!

Warum? Ihr Freund Ottmar hatte das Auto da gefunden. (schwach | gemischt | stark)

Er war schnell damit nach Hause gefahren. (schwach | gemischt | stark)

Ottmar hat gedacht, dass Aisha das Auto nicht brauchte. (schwach | gemischt | stark)

Er hat ihr zum Geburtstag eine neue Autostereoanlage installiert. (schwach | gemischt | stark)

Eine Stunde später hat er das Auto mit dem neuen Radio zurückgebracht. (schwach | gemischt | stark)

Ich habe zuerst nicht gewusst, ob ich ihr glauben sollte. (schwach | gemischt | stark)

Dann ist mir eingefallen: Es ist ja der erste April! (schwach | gemischt | stark)

209f Review: *Perfekt* – Helping Verb *haben* or *sein*

As mentioned before, the *Perfekt* is formed with two verbs: an auxiliary verb *haben* or *sein* in the second position and another verb in the past participle form in the last position. The question now is how to decide which auxiliary verb to choose.

The norm: ***haben***
Most verbs use the auxiliary *haben* to form the *Perfekt*.

Anton hat ein Radio im Schaufenster **gesehen**.	*Anton saw a radio in the store window.*
Anton hat das Radio gekauft.	*Anton bought the radio.*
Anton hat sich über das Radio **gefreut**.	*Anton was happy about the radio.*

The exception: ***sein***
Sein is only used as an auxiliary for the *Perfekt* tense when two conditions are met (one from each box).

Condition 1	Verb does not take direct object.

+

Condition 2 (one of these four)		
	1) Change of condition	Er **ist aufgewacht**. (*He woke up.*) → going from being asleep to being awake
	2) Verb indicates motion or movement from one place to another (e.g. *fliegen* = to fly).	Er **ist** nach Italien **geflogen**. (*He flew to Italy.*) → He was not in Italy. Now he is.
	3) Verb indicates an event, achievement.	Was **ist** heute **passiert**? (*What happened today?*) Der Test **ist gelungen**. (*The test was successful.*)
	4) *sein*, *bleiben* and *werden*	Petra **ist** in Paris **gewesen**. (*Petra was in Paris.*) Sie **ist** 5 Tage **geblieben**. (*She stayed for 5 days.*) Petra **ist** Mutter **geworden**. (*Petra became a mother.*)

209g Was ist passiert? Welches Hilfsverb brauchen wir hier: „haben" oder „sein"? Ergänzen Sie den Text mit den konjugierten Verbformen.

Gestern __________ Ulla und Madeleine sehr spät aufgewacht. In der Nacht zuvor __________ sie sehr lange wach geblieben: bis zwei Uhr morgens! Warum? Madeleine __________ lange mit ihrem Freund Oscar aus Peru über eine Radiosendung diskutiert. Oscar __________ vor fünf Jahren aus Peru nach Bremen gezogen. Drei Jahre lang __________ er jetzt schon an der Uni in Bremen Kulturwissenschaften studiert. Dort __________ er auch Ulla und Madeleine kennengelernt. Ulla, Madeleine und Oscar __________ zusammen eine Radioreportage über Peru gehört. Der Radiobericht __________ über Kriminalität in Peru informiert, aber nicht alles __________ korrekt gewesen. Deshalb __________ Ulla viele Fragen an Oscar gehabt. Madeleine __________ dann irgendwann eingeschlafen.

211a **Fragen, Fragen, Fragen. In MACHEN sollen Sie durch Fragen herausfinden, ob eine Person lügt oder nicht. Üben Sie hier, indem Sie zu einer der beiden Aussagen vier Fragen schreiben. Schreiben Sie mindestens zwei Fragen im Perfekt.**

Beispiel: Wo hast du das gemacht? Hast du Fotos gemacht? Wie alt warst du? Wer hat dich gesehen?

Aussage 1: Ich habe als Kind einen Wurm gegessen.
Aussage 2: Ich habe vor einem großen Publikum gesungen.

Frage 1: ______________________________

____

Frage 2: ______________________________

____

Frage 3: ______________________________

____

Frage 4: ______________________________

____

211b **Lügen. Kinder sollen nicht lügen und im Deutschen gibt es das Sprichwort „Lügen haben kurze Beine" – das bedeutet, dass Lügen schnell/immer ans Licht kommen. Wie denken Sie über Lügen? Ergänzen Sie den folgenden Fragebogen in Stichworten.**

Was denken Sie, wie oft lügt ein Mensch jeden Tag? Mit „Lügen" sind hier auch Übertreibungen (*exaggerations*) oder das Auslassen (*omission*) von relevanten Informationen gemeint.[1]

- 3-mal pro Tag
- 25-mal pro Tag
- 200-mal pro Tag

Ist es okay zu lügen? Wählen Sie die Antworten, mit denen Sie sich am meisten identifizieren.

- Zu lügen ist immer falsch.
- Ich fühle mich schlecht, wenn ich lüge, auch wenn es nur eine Notlüge ist.
- Notlügen sind manchmal okay.
- Ohne Lügen könnte menschliche Kommunikation nicht funktionieren.
- Ich habe kein Problem damit zu lügen, auch wenn es sich um eine schwerwiegende (*serious*) Lüge handelt.

In welchen Situationen könnte es besser sein zu lügen? Nennen Sie zwei oder drei Beispiele.

____

____

____

____

____

Ideen: Warum lügen Menschen?

aus Angst
aus Unsicherheit
aus Höflichkeit (*out of courtesy*)
aus Not
aus Scham (*out of shame*)
aus Verlegenheit (*out of embarrassment*)
um Gefühle nicht zu verletzen
um Kritik zu vermeiden
um einer Strafe zu entgehen
um Zeit zu sparen

Welche Sprichwörter zum Thema „Lügen" gibt es in Ihrer Sprache?

____

____

[1] Übrigens: Unter Wissenschaftler*innen gibt es keinen Konsens darüber, wie oft wir am Tag lügen. Manche behaupten, dass es ungefähr 25 Lügen pro Tag sind. Benutzt man aber eine breitere Definition von Lüge, dann könnte es bis zu 200-mal pro Tag passieren, dass wir die Unwahrheit sagen.

211c **Zwei Wahrheiten und eine Lüge. In MACHEN werden Sie einer anderen Person im Kurs zwei Wahrheiten und eine Lüge erzählen. Die andere Person soll dann durch Fragen herausfinden, was wahr und was gelogen ist. Schreiben Sie hier Ihre drei Sätze im Perfekt auf.**

Beispiel: Ich habe ein Start-up-Unternehmen gegründet. Ich habe noch nie einen Zoo besucht. Ich bin schon durch 15 verschiedene Länder gereist.

Wahrheit: ______________________________

Wahrheit: ______________________________

Lüge: ______________________________

66: PODCASTS°

212a **Podcasts. Nehmen Sie eine Audiodatei auf und beantworten Sie die folgenden Fragen. Sprechen Sie dabei frei, ohne zu lesen. Schicken Sie die Aufnahme an Ihre*n Professor*in.**

Was ist ein Podcast? Definieren Sie.

Welche Podcasts kennen Sie? Nennen Sie zwei oder drei Beispiele.

Hören Sie Podcasts? Wenn ja, welche?

Warum hören Sie diese Podcasts?

Hören Sie Podcasts in mehr als einer Sprache?

Wenn Sie keine Podcasts hören: Warum nicht?

213a **Tontechniker*innen bei der Arbeit. Welches Wort passt hier am besten?**

Aufnahme | aufnehmen | aufgenommen | Ausstattung | ausstatten | ausgestattet | Schnittprogramm | schneiden | geschnitten

Madjid hat ein Interview mit seiner Schwester ____________, um ihr Schulleben zu dokumentieren. Dann hat er die ____________ nach Belgien geemailt, wo ihre Freundin Godelieve wohnt. Godelieve will auch Szenen von ihrer Schule in Tienen ____________ und beide Schuldokumentationen in ihrem Podcast über internationale Freundschaften senden.

Nicole hat ihren Podcast über ihr Leben mit Downsyndrom mit einer coolen Melodie ____________. Sie hat einen Elektro-Beat gewählt und will auch ihren Hintergrund komplett mit Elektro-Beat ____________. Diese musikalische ____________ ist ihr wichtig, weil sie dadurch junge Leute erreichen möchte.

Claas und Jasper haben ein ____________ gekauft, um bessere Podcasts zu machen. Ihre alte Software hat es nicht mehr geschafft, die Interviewszenen scharf zu ____________. In den letzten Monaten hatten sie immer wieder das Problem, dass die alte Software nicht so gut ____________ hat.

213b Review: *um ... zu*

In German, ***um ... zu*** is used to express an intention, a goal, or the purpose of an action. This construction can usually be translated by "in order to:"

Anna kauft einen Minivan,
um ihr Werkzeug **zu** transportieren.

Anna is buying a minivan
***in order to** transport her tools.*

The ***um ... zu*** sentence is an infinitive sentence, which is a special type of a subordinate clause. The verb in these sentences is placed at the end of the clause, and it is in the infinitive form preceded by ***zu***. If the verb is separable, the ***zu*** will be placed between the prefix and the verb.

Heute benutzt Anna ihren Minivan,
um Baumaterial ab**zu**holen.

Today Anna uses her minivan
***in order to** pick up building material.*

213c **Martin und Gesine arbeiten für den Tourismusverband der Stadt Fürth in Bayern. Sie sollen durch eine Podcast-Serie mehr Tourist*innen nach Fürth bringen. Bevor sie an den Strategien für dieses Jahr arbeiten, werden noch einmal ihre Strategien vom letzten Jahr zusammengefasst. Was haben sie im letzten Jahr gemacht?**

Sie sind ins Fürther Rundfunkmuseum gegangen,
um die Podcasts interessanter zu machen. .

Dann haben sie das Jüdische Museum Franken besucht,
____.

Martin hat im Januar ein neues Schnittprogramm gefunden,
____.

Im Juli ist Gesine im Fürther Stadtpark gewesen,
____.

Sie haben ein neues Mikrofon gekauft,
____.

Im Herbst haben sie mit einer Online-Lotterie begonnen,
____.

Informationen über die jüdische Geschichte für die Fürther Webseite sammeln
einen Podcast über die alten Grundig-Radios aufnehmen
~~die Podcasts interessanter machen~~
einen Restaurantbesuch in Fürth an Hotelgäst*innen verlosen.
das Vogelzwitschern (*birds' twittering*) mit dem Audiorecorder auffangen
die Stimmen von Fürther Bürger*innen in den Interviews besser hören

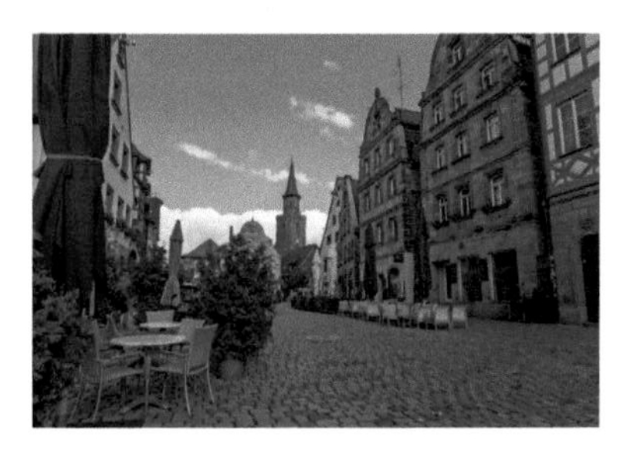

214a **Stellen Sie sich vor, Sie machen einen Podcast über ein Thema, das in der Vergangenheit liegt. Was interessiert Sie? Welches Thema würden Sie wählen? Schreiben Sie erst ein paar Ideen auf.**

____

____

Entscheiden Sie sich jetzt für ein bestimmtes Thema und schlagen Sie zehn Vokabeln nach, die mit dem Thema zu tun haben und die Sie für einen Beitrag benutzen würden.

____

____

____

67: „Tatort DaF" (Teil 2)

Bitte machen Sie die Aktivitäten, die zu dem Buch gehören, das Sie lesen.

„Böses Erwachen in Heidelberg"

215a **Wie finden Sie Emma und Professor Vogt? Schreiben Sie ein E für Emma oder ein P für Professor Vogt in die Kästchen. Es ist auch okay, ein Attribut für beide zu wählen. (Kapitel 1)**

nervös	interessiert	langweilig	sympathisch	neugierig
fröhlich	dumm	offen	intelligent	ernst

216a **Was ist richtig? Kreuzen Sie an. (Kapitel 1)**

Wohin möchte Emma Mörk in Urlaub fahren?

- nach Norwegen
- nach Stuttgart zu ihrer Cousine
- nach Heidelberg zu ihrer Au-pair-Familie

Wie fühlt sie sich?

- Sie ist müde, weil sie so viel gearbeitet hat.
- Sie hat viel Energie, weil sie jetzt in den Urlaub fährt.
- Sie ist traurig, weil in Deutschland so viel Schnee liegt.

Warum fahren die Züge nicht weiter?

- Emma hat den falschen Zug genommen.
- Es steigen zu viele Menschen in Heidelberg aus.
- Es gibt zu viel Schnee.

Für Professor Vogt war seine Zeit in Heidelberg so spannend, weil

- er gerne an der Universität Heidelberg gearbeitet hat.
- er so viel Bahn fahren konnte.
- er mit dem Knochen des „Heidelbergmenschen" forschen konnte.

Emma fühlt sich unwohl, weil

- der Zug nicht weiter fährt.
- ein Mann mit schwarzen Haaren sie und Professor Vogt beobachtet.
- Professor Vogt so viel redet.

Warum bleibt Emma in Heidelberg?

- Weil sie die Universität in Heidelberg besuchen möchte.
- Weil sie heute nicht mehr zu Beate fahren kann.
- Weil sie ihre Au-pair-Familie besuchen möchte.

216b **Was passiert? Bringen Sie die Sätze in die richtige Reihenfolge. (Kapitel 2)**

Sie beschließt für eine Nacht im Hotel Ritter zu bleiben, aber vor dem Hotel sieht sie den Mann mit den dunklen Haaren aus dem Zug. Emma bekommt Angst.

Als sie die Heidelberger Schlosskugeln im Schaufenster des Cafés Gundel sieht, bekommt sie Hunger.

Im Café ist es sehr voll. Emma muss sehr laut sprechen, damit die Verkäuferin sie versteht. Ihre Handtasche stellt sie auf den Boden.

Schnell versucht sie, die anderen Leute wegzuschieben und hinterher zu laufen. Ein Mann hilft ihr und findet die Handtasche draußen vor der Tür des Cafés.

1 Emma geht zu Fuß in das Zentrum von Heidelberg. Heute fahren keine Züge mehr und sie möchte einen Tag hier bleiben.

Da merkt Emma, dass jemand ihre Handtasche wegnimmt.

Am Nachmittag geht Emma zum Marktplatz in Heidelberg, zur Heiliggeistkirche, aber es ist sehr kalt und ungemütlich dort. Emma beschließt, zum Heidelberger Schloss zu fahren.

Nach einem kurzen Moment geht Emma trotzdem weiter. Sie will nicht ängstlich sein und nimmt im Hotel ein Zimmer für eine Nacht.

Jetzt hat sie aber keinen Hunger mehr. Sie möchte nur noch schnell zum Schloss.

Emma kontrolliert die Handtasche: Handy, Portemonnaie, Taschentücher ... alles ist noch drin.

216c **Emma ist in Heidelberg unterwegs. Was ist richtig oder falsch? Kreuzen Sie an. (Kapitel 2)**

richtig	falsch	
		Das Hotel Ritter ist ein sehr altes Gebäude in Heidelberg.
		Es ist auch das Rathaus der Stadt.
		In der Kirche kann man Brot und Blumen kaufen.
		In der Mauer der Heiliggeistkirche gibt es Ladenanbauten, wo Tourist*innen Souvenirs und Bücher kaufen können.
		Heidelberger Schlosskugeln ist der Name einer Spezialität aus Heidelberg.
		Zum Schloss fährt Emma vom Karlsplatz aus mit dem Bus.

„Die Lerche aus Leipzig"

215a **Was ist richtig? Kreuzen Sie an. (Kapitel 1)**

Warum ist Dagmar Geißler wütend?

- Udo Geißler heiratet und er hat seine Schwester nicht eingeladen.
- Udo Geißler hat nicht auf die Einladung zu Dagmars Hochzeit geantwortet.
- Udo Geißler kommt nicht zu Dagmars Hochzeit.

Was gibt es für ein Problem mit der Post?

- Udo hat keine Post bekommen.
- Udo hat keinen Briefkasten.
- Udo lügt. Er hat die Post bekommen.

Was denkt Udo Geißler über die Hochzeit?

- Er freut sich auf die Hochzeit.
- Er weiß noch nicht, ob er zur Hochzeit kommt.
- Er freut sich nicht auf die Hochzeit.

216a **Welche Wörter passen nicht zum Thema „Hochzeit"? Streichen Sie diese durch. (Kapitel 1)**

Trauung | Briefkasten | Herzlichen Glückwunsch! | Feier | ~~lügen~~ | Kirche | Familie | hassen | heiraten | Einladung | wütend

216b **Was macht Udo Geißler? Wie ist die richtige Reihenfolge? (Kapitel 2)**

- Er kauft sich in der Mädler-Passage zwei Leipziger Lerchen.
- 1 Er geht von zu Hause in die Innenstadt. Er kommt an der Nikolaikirche vorbei.
- Er kauft sich eine Leipziger Lerche.
- Er kauft eine Vase aus Meißner Porzellan.
- Am Telefon hört er, dass seine Karten gesperrt sind.
- Ein Mann rempelt ihn von hinten an. Die Vase geht kaputt.
- Er will das Geschenk noch einmal kaufen, aber seine Karten funktionieren nicht.

„Gefährliches Spiel in Essen"

215a **Was passt zusammen? Kombinieren Sie. (Kapitel 1)**

Als was arbeiten die Männer?

a)	Friso Breugel	Referent
b)	Hartwig Köhler	Journalist
c)	Martin Faber	Bauunternehmer

Wie sind die drei Männer?

a)	Friso Breugel	mürrisch und unruhig
b)	Hartwig Köhler	freundlich und aufgeschlossen
c)	Martin Faber	jung und dynamisch

216a **Richtig oder falsch? Kreuzen Sie an. (Kapitel 1)**

richtig	falsch	
		Friso Breugel will einen Artikel über Industriedenkmäler schreiben.
		Köhler will mit Breugel über die Finanzen seiner Wohnanlage sprechen.
		Faber will Breugel Sehenswürdigkeiten in Essen zeigen.
		Hartwig Köhler ist bei der Führung durch die Zeche Zollverein dabei.
		Friso Breugel weiß noch nichts über die Zeche Zollverein.

216b **Ergänzen Sie die Lücken mit den passenden Wörtern. (Kapitel 2)**

Rundblick | Rundgang | Ausgang | Maschinen | Höhepunkt

Martin Faber und Friso Breugel machen zusammen mit Horst Briske einen ______________________ durch die Zeche Zollverein. Briske zeigt und erklärt den beiden auch verschiedene Werkzeuge und ______________________. Kurz vor dem ______________________ verletzt sich Breugel an der Hand. Das ist sehr schade. Faber und Breugel verpassen den ______________________ der Führung. Sie können nicht den ______________________ über das Ruhrgebiet von dem Aussichtsturm der Kokerei sehen.

„Kalt erwischt in Hamburg"

215a **Was ist richtig? Kreuzen Sie an. (Kapitel 1)**

Wo arbeitet Klaas Hansen?
- im Hamburger Hafen
- auf dem Michel
- auf einem Schiff

Wie ist das Wetter in Hamburg?
- Es regnet.
- Die Sonne scheint.
- Es ist bewölkt.

Wann spielt Klaas Hansen immer auf dem Michelturm auf seiner Trompete?
- fast jeden Tag um 10 Uhr
- fast jeden Tag um 10 Uhr und um 21 Uhr
- nur jeden Sonntag um 21 Uhr

215b **Was macht Klaas Hansen? Was ist die richtige Reihenfolge? (Kapitel 1)**

- die Trompete auspacken
- die Fenster schließen
- 1 die Stufen nach oben gehen
- Wasser, Schiffe und viele Leute sehen
- die Fenster öffnen
- auf dem Turm ankommen
- Lieder spielen
- die Treppe hinuntergehen

216a **Was passt? Kreuzen Sie an. (Kapitel 2)**

Was ist das Thema von Kapitel 2?
- Klaas Hansen ist verschwunden.
- Klaas Hansen und Nele Lühders hatten Streit.
- Pastor Dirkheide und Nele Lühders verstehen sich nicht.

Welche zwei Personen handeln in Kapitel 2?
- der Turmbläser Klaas Hansen
- Pastor Dirkheide
- Nele Lühders, die Freundin von Klaas Hansen

An welchem Ort spielt Kapitel 2?
- bei Pastor Dirkheide zu Hause
- im Büro von Pastor Dirkheide
- im Büro von Nele Lühders

216b **Richtig oder falsch? Kreuzen Sie an. (Kapitel 2)**

richtig	falsch	
		Pastor Dirkheide muss noch seine Predigt schreiben.
		Pastor Dirkheide weiß, wo Klaas ist.
		Pastor Dirkheide mag Nele nicht.
		Nele und der Pastor machen sich Sorgen um Klaas.
		Klaas isst normalerweise zu Mittag bei Nele im Goldenen Anker.
		Das Lieblingsgericht von Klaas ist Aalsuppe.
		Nele und Klaas hatten Streit. Klaas hat den Pastor angerufen.

216c **Ergänzen Sie den Text. (Kapitel 3)**

verschwunden | suchen | Birgit Brandt | Mann | umbringt | Alarm | Reportage | komisch | Exfreund | klingelt | los

Im dritten Kapitel kommt ______________________ zum Büro des Pastors. Sie ist Journalistin und macht eine ______________________ über den Michel. Sie sieht die besorgten Gesichter von Pastor Dirkheide und von Nele Lühders und fragt die beiden: „Was ist denn ______________________?" Nele und der Pastor sagen ihr, dass Klaas ______________________ ist. Birgit findet es ______________________, weil sie Klaas kurz vorher gesehen hat. Sie erzählt, dass ein ______________________ bei ihm war, ein Typ ganz in Schwarz. Da weiß Nele, dass es ihr ______________________ Ole Wilken ist. Nele hat Angst, dass Ole Klaas ______________________. Nele, der Pastor und Birgit Brandt wollen Klaas ______________________. Plötzlich ______________________ das Handy von Birgit Brandt. Sie muss zum Container-Terminal Altenwerder. Dort hat es ______________________ gegeben. Nele ist sehr aufgeregt.

„Verschollen in Berlin"

215a **Was ist richtig? Kreuzen Sie an. (Kapitel 1)**

Jan arbeitet als
- Reiseführer und Kellner.
- Student und Kellner.
- Student und Reiseführer.

Wo ist Jan mit Maja verabredet?
- an der Glaskuppel
- am Dachgartenrestaurant
- am Aufzug

Die ältere Dame hat eine Bitte an Jan. Er soll ihr
- den Stadtplan von Berlin erklären.
- den Reichstag und die Glaskuppel zeigen.
- die Sehenswürdigkeiten Berlins von oben zeigen.

215b **Wo liegt das? Ordnen Sie zu. (Kapitel 1)**

	Norden	Süden	Osten	Westen
Charité				
Siegessäule				
Filmmuseum				
Unter den Linden				
Potsdamer Platz				

216a **Was stimmt? Kreuzen Sie an. (Kapitel 2)**

„Schon halb zwei vorbei und Maja ist immer noch nicht da!"

Wie lange wartet Jan schon?
- etwa 45 Minuten
- mehr als eine Stunde
- etwa eine Viertelstunde

Maja kommt nicht. Jan denkt:
- „Sie muss heute aber lange arbeiten!"
- „Dieser Privatdetektiv hat sie in seiner Gewalt!"
- „Sie hat die Verabredung vergessen!"

216b **Wie geht es Jan, als Maja nicht kommt. Welche Adjektive passen? (Kapitel 2)**

- glücklich
- froh
- neugierig
- böse
- nervös
- kompliziert
- unruhig

216c **Richtig oder falsch? Kreuzen Sie an. (Kapitel 3)**

richtig	falsch	
		Jan möchte mit Herrn Dr. Welsch sprechen.
		Jan will wissen, wann Dr. Welsch ins Wochenende fährt.
		Frau Martini sagt Jan, wann Maja gegangen ist.
		Frau Martini sagt Jan, wie Maja die Kanzlei verlassen hat.
		Frau Martini weiß nichts von einem braunen Umschlag.

„Der Schützenkönig vom Chiemsee"

215a **Was ist richtig? Kreuzen Sie an. (Kapitel 1)**

Mathias hört einen Schuss. Was ist da los?

- Sein Vater sieht ein Video vom letzten Schützenfest.
- Sein Vater übt schon das Schießen.
- Sein Vater testet seine Waffe und macht einen Fehler.

Was denkt Ludwig über das Schießen im Verein? Finden Sie zwei richtige Antworten.

- Das macht mehr Spaß als Fußball.
- Das ist Sport.
- Das ist eine alte Tradition.

Wer fährt zum Schützenfest? Kreuzen Sie an.

- Ludwig S.
- Rosi
- Edelgard S.
- Mario, der Freund von Rosi
- Mathias

215b **Die Kameraden vom Schützenverein begrüßen Ludwig und Mathias. Wer sagt was? (Ludwig = L, Mathias = M, die Kameraden = K, Xaver = X) (Kapitel 2)**

- „Ich bin noch nicht euer Schützenkönig!"
- „Wo sind denn Edelgard und Rosi?"
- „Die machen was anderes."
- „Klar, die Rosi und der Mario …"
- „Das geht dich nix an."

216a **Was kommt zuerst, was kommt später? Nummerieren Sie. (Kapitel 2)**

- Ludwig gewinnt und ist Schützenkönig.
- Das Schießen beginnt.
- *1* Das Fest beginnt.
- Alle trinken auf Ludwig und Mathias.

68: NACHRICHTENMEDIEN

218a **Mein Medienkonsum. Notieren Sie alle Nachrichtenquellen, die Sie nutzen: Fernsehsender, spezifische soziale Medien, (Online-)Zeitungen etc. Schreiben Sie auch dazu, welche Quellen Sie am häufigsten/wenigsten benutzen.**

Beispiel: Spiegel Online (3-4 mal pro Woche), Tagesschau (täglich), Reddit (täglich)

____

____

____

____

218b **Mein Medienkonsum: Fortsetzung. Sind die Nachrichtenquellen, die Sie benutzen, eher alt, neu, links, neutral oder rechts? Liefern diese Quellen kurze Inhalte, die nur die wichtigsten Fakten beschreiben, oder lange Beiträge, die ins Detail gehen? Ordnen Sie den Quellen in Aktivität 218a die Kategorien unten zu. Jede Quelle kann in mehr als eine Kategorie fallen.**

- links
- neutral
- rechts
- alt
- neu

- intellektuell
- analytisch
- hoher Standard
- Basisinformationen
- sensationalistisch
- simplifizierend
- Clickbait

220a Review: *Präteritum*

Now, let's review the other option to talk about an event in the past: the *Präteritum*.

Vergangenheit		Gegenwart	Zukunft	
Plusquamperfekt	Perfekt **Präteritum**	Präsens	Futur II	Futur I Präsens

While the *Perfekt* tense is used in oral communication and "conversational" writing (emails, text messages, etc.), the second past tense, the *Präteritum*, is the primary past tense used in print/writing (newspapers, books, fairy tales, narratives, etc.) and is thus considered the more "formal" of the past tenses in German.

Like we he have seen with past participles in the last chapters, the *Präteritum* also has three conjugations for **weak**, **strong**, and **mixed** verbs.

weak verbs:
The *Präteritum* marker for weak verbs is a ***t*** after the stem (***et*** after a stem ending in *-t* or *-d*), followed by specific endings. (The he/it/she-form does not end in *-t*.)

ich	machte	arbeitete
du	machtest	arbeitetest
er/es/sie	machte	arbeitete
wir	machten	arbeiteten
ihr	machtet	arbeitetet
sie/Sie	machten	arbeiteten

strong verbs:
The marker for the strong verbs is the vowel change, personal endings are very reduced: *ich* and *er/es/sie* don't have endings at all.

ich	ging_	fuhr_
du	gingst	fuhrst
er/es/sie	ging_	fuhr_
wir	gingen	fuhren
ihr	gingt	fuhrt
sie/Sie	gingen	fuhren

mixed verbs:
Mixed verbs display a double set of markers: the ***t*** marker with the respective endings like the weak verbs plus a vowel change.

ich	kannte	dachte
du	kanntest	dachtest
er/es/sie	kannte	dachte
wir	kannten	dachten
ihr	kanntet	dachtet
sie/Sie	kannten	dachten

Modal verbs in the *Präteritum* behave like mixed verbs: they all have a ***t*** marker, and they have a vowel change (except *wollen* and *sollen*).

	müssen	**können**	**dürfen**	**sollen**	**wollen**	**mögen**
ich	musste	konnte	durfte	sollte	wollte	mochte
du	musstest	konntest	durftest	solltest	wolltest	mochtest
er/es/sie	musste	konnte	durfte	sollte	wollte	mochte
wir	mussten	konnten	durften	sollten	wollten	mochten
ihr	musstet	konntet	durftet	solltet	wolltet	mochtet
sie/Sie	mussten	konnten	durften	sollten	wollten	mochten

220b Lesen Sie den Artikel von Ende Februar 2020 zum Coronavirus und unterstreichen Sie alle Verben im Präteritum.

Coronavirus – Die aktuelle Situation

In Echtzeit zeigt die Realtime-Karte der Johns Hopkins University, wie viele Menschen sich weltweit bisher mit dem neuen Virus ansteckten und daran starben. Danach gibt es bis heute 75.191 bestätigte Infektionen und 2.014 Todesfälle. 15.084 Menschen erholten sich bereits vollständig wieder von der Krankheit.

Die meisten Todesopfer forderte das Virus bisher in China. Dort stieg die Zahl im Vergleich zum Vortag um 136 auf nun mehr als 2.000 Tote, wie die Gesundheitskommission in Peking mitteilte. Chinesische Staatsmedien berichteten, dass auch die Zahl des infizierten medizinischen Personals weiter angestiegen ist. Demnach infizierten sich bisher über 3.000 Ärzt*innen und Krankenhausmitarbeiter*innen. Besonders ernst ist die Lage in der Provinz Hubei, in deren Hauptstadt Wuhan das Virus Ende Dezember ausbrach.

Mittlerweile wurden in ca. 30 Ländern Infektionsfälle bestätigt. Auch in Deutschland ist das Virus angekommen. 16 Deutsche bekamen die Krankheit bislang, davon 14 in Bayern. Beim Automobilzulieferer Webasto in Stockdorf bei München waren die ersten Fälle bekannt geworden. Ärzt*innen isolierten Patient*innen in Krankenhäusern und testeten alle Personen, die Kontakt zu ihnen hatten. Webasto schloss für zwei Wochen komplett und die Mitarbeiter*innen mussten von zu Hause arbeiten.

Die Weltgesundheitsorganisation WHO erklärte wegen der Epidemie den internationalen Gesundheitsnotstand. So soll sichergestellt werden, dass der Umgang mit der Krankheit international koordiniert wird.

220c **Sind die Verben, die Sie im Text von Aktivität 220b unterstrichen haben, starke, schwache oder gemischte Verben? Ordnen Sie zu.**

Starke Verben: ______________________________

____

Schwache Verben: ______________________________

____

Gemischte Verben: ______________________________

____

220d **Dumme Clickbait-Geschichten! Welche Verben brauchen diese Clickbait-Nachrichten? Wählen Sie das beste Verb für jede Situation und setzen Sie es im Präteritum ein.**

kommen | gehen | fahren | schlafen | springen | schreiben | trinken | fliegen | stehen | sitzen | verlieren | liegen

Medien-Influencerin ____________ ihren Ferrari ins Casino, um Federboa zu holen!

Kleiner Pudel ____________ in heißes Bad, um seinen Besitzer vor dem Ertrinken zu retten!

Britische Kinder ____________ Briefe an die Königin, um Brexit zu stoppen!

Helikopter ____________ auf das Dach von unserem Kindergarten!

Auf der Foto-Safari ____________ drei Giraffen vor unserem Jeep!

Ohne Geld ____________ drei Studentinnen aus Berlin im Zug nach Rom!

220e **Wer wird neue*r CDU-Vorsitzende*r? Lesen Sie den Ausschnitt aus einem Zeitungsartikel vom Februar 2020 und setzen Sie die Verben im Präteritum ein.**

Es ____________ (beginnen) mit den Ereignissen in Thüringen: Eine Woche nach der skandalösen Wahl von Thomas Kemmerich zum Ministerpräsidenten und seinem Rücktritt ____________ (ziehen) Annegret Kramp-Karrenbauer Konsequenzen. Sie ____________ (geben) bekannt, dass sie den Parteivorsitz abgeben möchte. In den Medien ____________ (sprechen) man daraufhin über drei mögliche Kandidaten für ihre Nachfolge: Jens Spahn, Friedrich Merz und Armin Laschet. Heute ____________ überraschend ein vierter Kandidat – Umweltminister Norbert Röttgen – seine Kandidatur ____________ (ankündigen). In einer Pressekonferenz ____________ (sagen) Röttgen, dass es in der Diskussion bisher nur um das Personal und nicht um eine Zukunftsidee für die Partei und für Deutschland ____________ (gehen). Außerdem ____________ (fordern) er eine Entscheidung über den Parteivorsitz noch vor der Sommerpause.

221a **Campusnachrichten. In MACHEN werden Sie einen Text im Präteritum über die wichtigsten Ereignisse auf Ihrem Campus schreiben. Worüber möchten Sie berichten? Schreiben Sie unten zwei Campusereignisse auf, die im letzten Monat passiert sind. Finden Sie dann für jedes Ereignis fünf Wörter (jeweils mindestens zwei Verben), die Sie brauchen, um das Ereignis zu beschreiben. Listen Sie für alle Verben den Infinitiv und die Präteritumform für die 3. Person Singular (er/es/sie) auf.**

Recherche

Ereignis 1: ____________________

____

Wörter: ____________________

____

____

____

Ereignis 2: ____________________

____

____

____

Wörter: ____________________

____

____

69: Serienmarathon

222a Overview: The Present Tense

After talking about past events in the last few units, let's review how to talk about an event in the present, using the *Präsens*.

Vergangenheit		Gegenwart	Zukunft	
Plusquamperfekt	Perfekt	**Präsens**	Futur II	Futur I
	Präteritum			Präsens

The *Präsens* is used to describe what is happening currently or in the present time, what is happening regularly, and what has been ongoing up to now. (Pay close attention to the difference in the English translations.)

Anton **hört** gerade Radio. — *Anton is listening to the radio.*
Anton **hört** abends Radio. — *Anton (usually) listens to the radio in the evening.*
Anton **hört** zwar Radio, aber er passt nicht auf. — *Anton does listen to the radio, but he is not paying attention.*
Anton **hört** schon seit zwei Stunden Radio. — *Anton has been listening to the radio for two hours.*

222b Review: *Präsens*

In this unit, you will get a review of the *Präsens* which comes in different forms: weak/regular verbs, strong verbs, modal verbs, and irregular verbs.

The *Präsens* of weak verbs is formed in the following manner: verb stem + **personal endings**:

ich	lern**e**	schau**e**	rechn**e**	hör**e**	reis**e**
du	lern**st**	schau**st**	rechn**est**	hör**st**	reis_**t**
er/es/sie	lern**t**	schau**t**	rechn**et**	hör**t**	reis**t**
wir	lern**en**	schau**en**	rechn**en**	hör**en**	reis**en**
ihr	lern**t**	schau**t**	rechn**et**	hör**t**	reis**t**
sie/Sie	lern**en**	schau**en**	rechn**en**	hör**en**	reis**en**

When the verb stem ends in a *-t*, *-d*, and consonant clusters like *-ffn* or *-chn*, an additional e is inserted before the personal endings ***-st*** and ***-t***.

When the stem ends in an *-s*, *-ss*, *-ß*, *-x*, and *-z*, the *du*-form ending will change from an ***-st*** to a simple ***-t***.

To form the *Präsens* of strong verbs, you add the same personal endings to the verb stem like you do with the weak verbs. The difference is that strong verbs change their vowels in the *du*-form and in the *er/es/sie*-form.

	e → i	**e → ie**	**a → ä**
ich	geb**e**	seh**e**	trag**e**
du	gib**st**	sieh**st**	träg**st**
er/es/sie	gib**t**	sieh**t**	träg**t**
wir	geb**en**	seh**en**	trag**en**
ihr	geb**t**	seh**t**	trag**t**
sie/Sie	geb**en**	seh**en**	trag**en**

222c Ein Gespräch in der Mensa. Ergänzen Sie die Lücken mit den Präsensformen.

Ahmad: Tina, welches Buch ______________ du da? (lesen)

Tina: Ich ______________ Nietzsche. ______________ du „Jenseits von Gut und Böse"? (lesen; kennen)

Ahmad: Ja, aber ich ______________ ihn schlecht. ______________ du auch Quizsendungen? (verstehen; sehen)

Tina: Haha, weil Nietzsches Texte wie eine Quizsendung ____________? Das ____________ ich gut! (sein; finden)

Ahmad: ______________ du übrigens auch die neue Serie mit Franziska Weisz? (sehen)

Tina: Nein, wir __________________ keine Satellitensendungen mehr. (empfangen)

Ahmad: Warum? ______________ ihr pleite? (*broke*)? (sein)

Tina: Ja, genau.

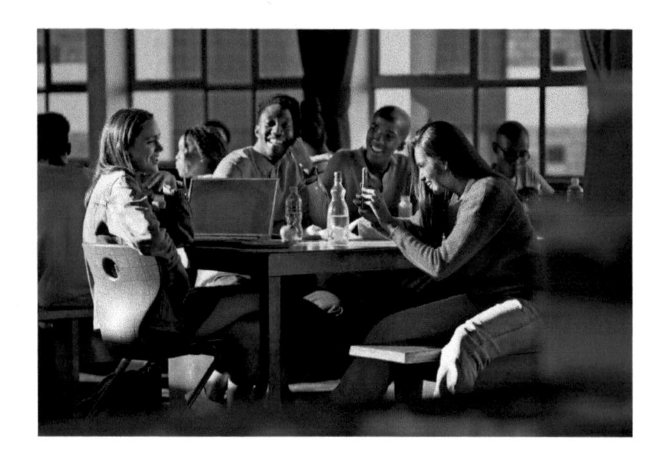

222d Was kommt heute im Fernsehen? Beschreiben Sie Ihrer Urgroßmutter, die nicht mehr so gut sieht, das Fernsehprogramm für heute Abend im Ersten. Lesen Sie zuerst die nützlichen Wörter rechts im Kasten.

Beispiel: Um 20:15 Uhr kommt im ARD die Quizsendung „Ich weiß alles!" mit Jörg Pilawa und Günther Jauch. Die Sendung ist für die ganze Familie und wird in Österreich, Deutschland und in der Schweiz ausgestrahlt.

Das Abendprogramm im Ersten (ARD)

20:15 „Ich weiß alles!" – Mit Jörg Pilawa und Günther Jauch
Quizsendung für die ganze Familie – A/D/CH

21:45 Tagesthemen – Nachrichten
Moderator: Ingo Zamperoni
Wetter und Hintergrundberichte – D

22:00 Tatort – „Franziska" – Krimi
Ort dieser Folge: Köln
Regie: Dror Zahavi | Darsteller*innen: Tessa Mittelstaedt u.v.a.
FSK 12 – D

23:30 „Die Kinder machen Druck!"
Dokumentation – D 2020
Drehbuch: Laura Borchardt und Lucas Stratmann
für die ganze Familie

> ausstrahlen; zeigen
>
> der Bericht
>
> Regie führen (*to direct*)
>
> Darsteller*innen, Schauspieler*innen
>
> das Drehbuch

____
____
____
____
____
____

222e Review: Modal Verbs and *wissen* in the *Präsens*

Modal verbs and the verb *wissen* follow a different pattern. With most of them (except *sollen*), the vowel in the singular forms differs from the infinitive and the plural forms. The endings look like the past tense endings of strong verbs): **--**, **-st**, **--**, **-en**, **-t**, **-en**. Note that the *ich*-form and the *er/es/sie*-form don't have personal endings. This pattern also applies to the verb *wissen*.

	dürfen *to be allowed to*	**können** *to be able to*	**wollen** *to want*	**müssen** *to have to*	**sollen** *to be supposed to*	**wissen** *to know*
ich	darf	kann	will	muss	soll	weiß
du	darf**st**	kann**st**	will**st**	muss**t**[1]	soll**st**	weiß**t**[1]
er/es/sie	darf	kann	will	muss	soll	weiß
wir	dürf**en**	könn**en**	woll**en**	müss**en**	soll**en**	wiss**en**
ihr	dürf**t**	könn**t**	woll**t**	müss**t**	soll**t**	wiss**t**
sie/Sie	dürf**en**	könn**en**	woll**en**	müss**en**	soll**en**	wiss**en**

[1] The stem forms *muss-* and *weiß-* end in an *-ss* and *-ß*, which will reduce the ending for the *du*-form to a ***-t***.

222f **Was, wann und warum (nicht)? Diese sechs Personen wissen, was sie gerne sehen. Ordnen Sie die passenden Informationen aus der Tabelle zu und schreiben Sie einen Text über drei Personen: Was sehen sie gern? Warum? Welches Problem gibt es? Was ist die Lösung?**

Name + Was sieht die Person gern?	Warum?	Problem	Lösung
~~Alyssa: Horror~~	mache ich selbst	zu spät	DVR
Ahmet: Sport	entspannend	langweilig	nebenbei telefonieren
Bernd: Quizsendungen	~~spannend~~	zu früh	mit anderen anschauen
Britta: Familiensendungen	Nervenkitzel	zu alt	~~bei Freund*innen anschauen~~
Chloe: SciFi	interessant	~~zu jung~~	heimlich anschauen
Christian: Doku-Dramas	man lernt was	zu lang	aufnehmen

*Alyssa sieht gern Horrorfilme, weil sie spannend sind. Sie darf sie aber nicht sehen, weil ihre Eltern sagen, dass sie zu jung ist. Alyssa kann Horrorfilme bei Freund*innen anschauen.*

____

____

____

____

____

____

70: „TATORT" – EINE LEIDENSCHAFT°

224a **Fernsehen. Finden Sie die englische Bedeutung der Wörter im Kasten und setzen Sie sie dann in die Lücken ein.**

Spielfilm | Einschaltquote | Marktanteil | Folge | Sendung | Beteiligung

Durch die Fusionierung konnte der Medienkonzern seinen ____________ um zehn Prozent vergrößern.

Die ____________ an der Demonstration gegen Rechtsradikale war sehr hoch.

Die Regisseurin hat für ihren letzten ____________ viele Preise bekommen.

Die erste ____________ der zweiten Staffel (*season*) habe ich mindestens zehnmal gesehen – so gut war sie!

Wie findest du diese neue ____________ über die Goldenen Zwanziger?

Die ____________ für „Tatort" ist immer noch sehr hoch, obwohl es die Serie schon so lange gibt.

226a **Krimi. In Einheit 68 sind Ihnen schon viele Vokabeln zum Thema „Krimi" begegnet. Welche Wörter kennen Sie schon? Übersetzen Sie. Schauen Sie dann in einem Wörterbuch nach, ob Sie alles richtig haben, und ergänzen Sie, wenn nötig. Vervollständigen Sie anschließend die drei Sätze.**

der*die Täter*in	______________	der Tatort	______________
ermitteln	______________	der*die Verdächtige	______________
der*die Kommissar*in	______________	verhaften	______________
der*die Gerichtsmediziner*in	______________	untersuchen	______________

Ein*e Kommissar*in ist eine Person, die ______________________________.

Ein*e Täter*in ist eine Person, die ______________________________.

Ein*e Gerichtsmediziner*in ist eine Person, die ______________________________.

AUSSPRACHE: DAS H

226b **Hören: Hören Sie die Wortpaare.**

hin – in   halt – alt   Hände – Ende   hoffen – offen   heiß – Eis

226c **Sprechen: Nehmen Sie ein Blatt Papier und halten Sie es vor Ihren Mund. Sprechen Sie dann die Wortpaare nach. Sprechen Sie so:**

Wörter oder Silben mit „h" am Anfang = gehauchter Vokaleinsatz (das Papier bewegt sich)

Wörter oder Silben mit einem Vokal am Anfang = fester Vokaleinsatz (das Papier bewegt sich nicht)
Es klingt hart und knackt leise, deshalb heißt das auch „Knacklaut".

226d **Hören und Sprechen: Hören Sie die Namen und sprechen Sie sie nach.**

Hast	Ast	Haubert	Aubert
Herzfeld	Erzfeld	Hopper	Opper
Heisler	Eisler	Humann	Uhmann

226e **Sie hören jetzt immer nur einen Namen. Welchen? Kreuzen Sie oben an.**

226f **Hören Sie die Sätze und ergänzen Sie die Namen.**

1) Herr ______________ ist Hausmeister.
2) Frau ______________ lebt in Hagen.
3) Herr ______________ liebt die Alpen.
4) Frau ______________ arbeitet an der Uni.
5) Herr ______________ hat Hunde.
6) Frau ______________ mag Hörbücher.

226g **Hören und Sprechen: Hören Sie, was Tante Hertha hat und was sie gern hätte. Sprechen Sie nach. Achten Sie auf das [h].**

Tante Hertha hat
- braune Haare.
- einen kleinen Hund.
- ein hässliches Haus.
- heute viel zu tun.

Tante Herta hätte gern
- schwarze Haare.
- einen großen Hund.
- ein hübsches Haus.
- Hilfe im Haushalt.

71: Inklusives Fernsehen transnational

227a Overview: Talking About the Future

After talking about present events in the last few units, let's review how to talk about an event in the future, using the *Präsens*, the *Futur I*, or the *Futur II*.

<table>
<tr><th colspan="2">Vergangenheit</th><th>Gegenwart</th><th colspan="2">Zukunft</th></tr>
<tr><td rowspan="2">Plusquamperfekt</td><td>Perfekt</td><td rowspan="2">Präsens</td><td rowspan="2">Futur II</td><td>Futur I</td></tr>
<tr><td>Präteritum</td><td>Präsens</td></tr>
</table>

When Germans talk about things which will happen in the future, **they mostly use the *Präsens* in everyday conversations.** More formally used and also important to know is a form that is specifically used to express the future: the *Futur I*.

Futur I	Anton **wird** seiner Schwester nächsten Monat ein Radio zum Geburtstag **schenken**.	*Next month, Anton will give his sister a radio for her birthday.*
Präsens	Anton **schenkt** seiner Schwester nächsten Monat ein Radio zum Geburtstag.	*Next month, Anton will give his sister a radio for her birthday.*

In addition, there is a third tense to express the future: the *Futur II*. This form expresses an action that has happened before the other actions in the future.

Futur II	Anton **wird** hoffentlich eine Woche vor dem Geburtstag seiner Schwester ein Radio **gekauft haben**.	*Anton will hopefully have bought a radio a week before his sister's birthday.*

Here is an overview of the situation from the example sentences put into the chart from above to help you better visualize the different time frames. Read the sentences from left to right to go from the action in the present (Anton's sister would like a radio for her upcoming birthday) to the action that happens right before the other event in the future (Anton will hopefully have found a radio by then) to the action in the future (Anton will buy a new radio for his sister next month).

<table>
<tr><th>Gegenwart</th><th colspan="2">Zukunft</th></tr>
<tr><td rowspan="2">Antons Schwester möchte ein Radio zum Geburtstag.</td><td rowspan="2">Hoffentlich wird Anton bis dann ein Radio gekauft haben.</td><td>Anton wird seiner Schwester nächsten Monat ein Radio schenken.</td></tr>
<tr><td>Anton schenkt seiner Schwester nächsten Monat ein Radio.</td></tr>
</table>

In the following units, we will focus on the *Präsens* and the *Futur I*, and will review how to form and use these two tenses.

227b Review: *Präsens* for Future Events

In daily conversation, Germans tend to use the ***Präsens*** to express future events, especially when the context gives a clear indication that we are talking about future times. Most of the time, an adverb, another time expression, or the context will indicate that a future time is being expressed (like *bald, gleich, in fünf Minuten, heute Abend, morgen, nächste Woche, am Samstag, nächstes Jahr, in der Zukunft*).

Morgen **kauft** Anton ein Radio.	*Anton is going to buy a radio tomorrow.*

227c Jetzt oder bald? Zwei Freundinnen sprechen über Situationen – in der Gegenwart oder Zukunft?

Adya:	Kommst du morgen zu Franks Geburtstagsparty?	Gegenwart	(Zukunft)
Marlene:	Nee, ich arbeite morgen den ganzen Tag.	Gegenwart	Zukunft
	Ich bringe ihm aber nächste Woche ein Geschenk.	Gegenwart	Zukunft
Adya:	Hast du schon eins?	Gegenwart	Zukunft
Marlene:	Ja. Kennst du Anne Will, die Fernsehjournalistin?	Gegenwart	Zukunft
Adya:	Klar. Ich sehe „Anne Will", immer wenn ich im Fitnessstudio bin.	Gegenwart	Zukunft
Marlene:	Ich schenke Frank ein Ticket zu ihrer Sendung im Juni.	Gegenwart	Zukunft
Adya:	Tolle Idee!	Gegenwart	Zukunft

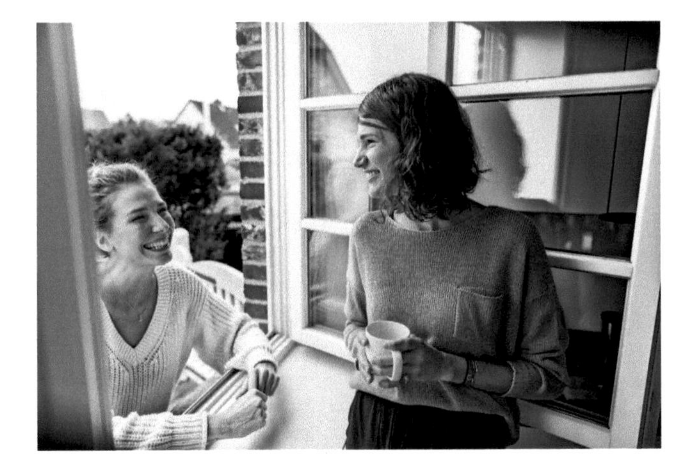

227d Review: *Futur I* for Future Events

Less frequent but also important to know is a form specifically used to express that the described action will only happen in future times. This form is called *Futur I* and it is constructed with the forms of the auxiliary verb ***werden*** in the second position of the sentence and an infinitive form of the main verb in the end of the sentence. Obviously, all you need to know is the conjugation of the verb ***werden***:

Ich	**werde**	in Wien	studieren.	*I will study in Vienna.*
Du	**wirst**	viel Erfolg	haben.	*You will have lots of success.*
Er*Sie	**wird**	als Pilot*in	arbeiten.	*S/he will work as a pilot.*
Wir	**werden**	Deutsch	sprechen.	*We will speak German.*
Ihr	**werdet**	nach Berlin	fahren.	*You will go to Berlin.*
Sie	**werden**	mich bald	besuchen.	*They will visit me soon.*
Sie	**werden**	die Situation	verstehen.	*You will understand the situation.*

227e **Dirk ist ein Fußballfan. Er ist fünf Jahre alt und erzählt seiner Schwester, wie er sich sein Leben in 30 Jahren vorstellt. Helfen Sie ihm dabei, indem Sie die korrekte Form von „werden" einsetzen.**

Wie __________ mein Leben in 30 Jahren aussehen? Also, erstens __________ ich 35 Jahre alt sein. Meine Schwestern __________ nicht mehr zu Hause leben. Meine Mutter __________ nicht mehr arbeiten. Aber mein Vater arbeitet gerne, er __________ noch jeden Tag ins Büro fahren, wie immer. Er __________ mich fragen: „Dirk, wann __________ du dein Zimmer aufräumen?" Weil ich dann groß bin, __________ ich antworten: „Nie, Papa!"

Zweitens __________ sich mein Leben rund um den Fußball drehen. Meine Freund*innen und ich __________ natürlich für den besten Fußballclub spielen. Wir __________ alle als Stürmer*innen spielen, außer Marcel, er __________ ein Torwart sein.

Drittens __________ ich in meinen Fernseher einsteigen können, wie in ein Auto. Wenn ich ein Fußballspiel sehen möchte, __________ ich einfach auf einen Knopf drücken und – schwupps! – bin ich mitten im Stadion. So einfach __________ das sein!

227f **TV in 100 Jahren – Wie wird es sich verändern? Diskussion im Fernsehen: Die TV-Moderatorin Gina Paschalle diskutiert mit ihren Gäst*innen darüber, wie die Fernsehkultur sich entwickeln wird. Schreiben Sie die Sätze im Futur.**

Liebe Zuschauer*innen, heute schreiben wir das Jahr 2020 und wir wollen unsere Fernsehkultur unter die Lupe nehmen (*take a close look at*). Was wird es Neues in den nächsten 100 Jahren geben?

2051: Das Jahr der TV-Revolution! Wir **beginnen**, unsere Fernsehsendungen persönlich zu entwerfen. Wer einen achtzigjährigen Afro-Deutschen als „Tatort"-Kommissar sehen will, **programmiert** das problemlos **ein**.

____

____

____

2073: Wir **können** jetzt riechen, was im Fernsehen **passiert**. Eine Kochshow mit einem leckeren Kuchen **wird** noch besser, wenn das köstliche Aroma in unsere Nasen **fliegt**.

____

____

____

2099: Das Jahrhundert **endet** mit einem TV-Spektakel. nX59 **ist** der erste Fernseher, der mit uns **spricht**. Alle **kaufen** einen nX59 und **starten** ihre TV-Freundschaften mit ihrem persönlichen Modell.

____

____

____

2105: Ab diesem Jahr **gibt** es keine Horrosendungen mehr ohne simultane Psychotherapie.

Es wird keine Horrorsendungen mehr ohne simultane Psychotherapie geben.

230a **Diskussion im Produzent*innen-Team einer Kabelfernsehsendung. Schreiben Sie den Dialog neu und zwar im Futur.**

Alan: Wir <u>verlieren</u> Zuschauer*innen, wenn wir unser Format nicht progressiver gestalten.

Gisi: Aber was <u>sagen</u> unsere Sponsor*innen, wenn wir unsere Themen nicht mehr so traditionell präsentieren?

Luigi: In den kommenden Jahren <u>ist</u> es klüger, dass wir keine geschlossenen Positionen beziehen, sondern offen diskutieren.

Alan: Diversity und Toleranz <u>werden</u> immer wichtiger, weil alle unsere Zuschauer*innen sich repräsentiert sehen wollen.

Gisi: Gut, aber unsere Sponsor*innen <u>verstehen</u> vielleicht nicht, warum wir unsere traditionelle Grundhaltung verändern.

Hannes: Wenn sie sehen, dass sich Diversity gut verkauft, <u>sind</u> sie bestimmt überzeugt.

Alan: *Wir werden Zuschauer*innen verlieren* ,
wenn wir unser Format nicht progressiver gestalten.

Gisi: ______________________________ ,
wenn wir unsere Themen nicht mehr traditionell präsentieren?

Luigi: ______________________________ ,
dass wir keine geschlossenen Positionen beziehen, sondern offen diskutieren.

Alan: ______________________________ ,
weil alle unsere Zuschauer*innen sich repräsentiert sehen wollen.

Gisi: ______________________________ ,
warum wir unsere traditionelle Grundhaltung verändern.

Hannes: Wenn sie sehen, dass sich Diversity gut verkauft,
______________________________ .

72: „Tatort DaF" (Teil 3)

Bitte machen Sie die Aktivitäten, die zu dem Buch gehören, das Sie lesen.

„Böses Erwachen in Heidelberg"

231a Ergänzen Sie den Text mit den folgenden zwölf Wörtern. (Kapitel 4)

Angst | Handtasche | allein | überfallen | Papiertaschentüchern | unterwegs | machen | Wetters | Akku | Raum | Tür | rennt

Im vierten Kapitel besucht Emma das Deutsche Apothekenmuseum im Schloss von Heidelberg. Wegen des schlechten ________________ sind nur wenig Leute ________________. Im Museum ist sie ganz ________________. Nur die Aufsichtsperson am Informationsstand ist da. Aber sie telefoniert und sieht Emma nicht. Sie geht langsam durch das Museum. Aber im ________________ mit den medizinischen Geräten wird ihr plötzlich kalt. Die Fenster sind nicht richtig zu. Emma sucht in ihrer Tasche nach ________________ – und findet den Unterkiefer des „Homo heidelbergensis". Sie kann es nicht glauben: Warum ist er in ihrer ________________? Was soll sie jetzt ________________? Emma beschließt, die Aufsicht um Hilfe zu bitten. Aber als sie aus dem Raum kommt, wird sie ________________. Ein Mann versucht, ihre Tasche zu klauen. Emma schafft es, sich zu befreien. Sie ________________ in einen neuen Raum und drückt die ________________ hinter sich zu. Der Mann folgt ihr und zieht an der Tür. Emma hat ________________. Sie holt ihr Handy aus der Tasche, aber der ________________ ist leer ...

231b Was macht Emma? Wie ist die richtige Reihenfolge? (Kapitel 5)

- ☐ sich im Raum umschauen
- ☐ die Chilischoten mit dem Schlüssel zerdrücken
- ☐ eine Lösung suchen
- 1 einen Stuhl unter die Türklinke schieben
- ☐ eine Idee bekommen
- ☐ hinter der Tür warten

232a Was ist richtig oder falsch? Kreuzen Sie an. (Kapitel 6)

richtig	falsch	
☐	☐	Plötzlich kommt Inge Schmidt, die Frau von der Information.
☐	☐	Frau Schmidt ist wütend und schreit den Mann an, er soll von der Tür weggehen.
☐	☐	Der Mann hat Angst vor Inge Schmidt und versucht wegzulaufen.
☐	☐	Er erzählt ihr, dass Emma seine Frau ist und sich selbst in dem Zimmer eingeschlossen hat.
☐	☐	Durch die Tür warnt Emma Frau Schmidt und erklärt ihr, dass der Mann gefährlich ist.
☐	☐	Frau Schmidt glaubt Emma und ruft die Polizei.
☐	☐	Der Mann schlägt Frau Schmidt zu Boden.
☐	☐	Emma wirft dem Mann das Chilipulver ins Gesicht und läuft an ihm vorbei aus dem Raum.

„Die Lerche aus Leipzig"

231a **Was passt? Kreuzen Sie an. (Kapitel 4)**

Was ist das Thema des Kapitels?

- Udo Geißler bekommt Angst.
- Udo Geißlers Liebe zu Miriam Becker
- die Hochzeitsfeier

An welchen Orten spielt das Kapitel?

- im Büro von Udo Geißler
- in der Innenstadt von Leipzig
- bei Udo Geißler zu Hause

Welche Personen kommen in dem Kapitel vor?

- Udo Geißler
- Dagmar Geißler/Fischer
- René Hartmann

231b **Erklären Sie die Wörter mit einem Satz. (Kapitel 4)**

das Senior*innenheim

____

das Handy

____

die Lampe

____

teuer

____

die Wanze

____

232a **Zwei Ereignisse sind falsch. Schreiben Sie die falschen Ereignisse auf. (Kapitel 5)**

Udo Geißler träumt. | Das Telefon von Udo klingelt. | Udo spricht mit Miriam. | Udo wäscht sein Hemd. | Udo fährt mit dem Auto zum Dittrichring. | Udo parkt sein Auto. | Udo ruft die Polizei an. | Udo geht zu Miriam und umarmt sie. | Um Udo herum wird alles dunkel.

Falsches Ereignis 1:

____

Falsches Ereignis 2:

____

232b **Ergänzen Sie den Text mit den Wörtern aus dem Kasten. (Kapitel 6)**

gefesselt | Museum | Stasi | Zelle | Raum | erinnert | Bett | Miriam | Lerche

Udo Geißler wacht in einer _______________ auf. Er liegt auf einem _______________ und seine Hände sind _______________. Udo Geißler hat von _______________ einen Stromstoß bekommen. Er denkt an sein früheres Leben. Er hat für die _______________ gearbeitet. Sein Deckname war _______________ und er hat vielen Leuten Probleme gemacht. Dann steht er vom Bett auf und geht durch den _______________. Dieser _______________ Udo Geißler an früher. Er weiß, er ist im _______________ in der Runden Ecke.

232c **Richtig oder falsch? Kreuzen Sie an. (Kapitel 7)**

richtig	falsch	
		Udo Geißler sieht, wer in die Zelle kommt.
		Udo Geißler bekommt Wasser und Brot mit Schimmel.
		Geißler hat großen Hunger, deshalb isst er das Brot.
		Er liegt auf dem Bett und kann nicht schlafen.
		Die Tür öffnet sich wieder und Geißler hält die Tür fest.
		Dann ist die Tür ganz offen. Geißler sieht den Mann.
		Udo Geißler hört die Stimme von dem Mann und weiß, wer er ist.

„Gefährliches Spiel in Essen"

231a **Faber und Breugel fahren durch Essen. Wie ist die richtige Reihenfolge? (Kapitel 4)**

Colosseum   Villa Hügel   *1* Baldeneysee   Margarethenhöhe   Grugapark

231b **Was ist richtig? Kreuzen Sie an. (Kapitel 5)**

Warum spielen sie „Glück Auf" im Stadion?

- Die Fans sollen grölen und in Stimmung kommen.
- Das motiviert die Spieler zum Gewinnen.
- Im Ruhrgebiet wird dieses Lied immer und überall gespielt.

Wie geht das Fußballspiel aus?

- 3:1 für Essen
- 2:1 für Essen
- 3:1 für Dresden

232a **Was passiert Friso Breugel? Kreuzen Sie an. (Kapitel 6)**

- Ein schwarzer BMW kommt ihm entgegen und er fährt in den Graben.
- Ein großer BMW lässt ihn nicht vorbei und er hat fast einen schlimmen Unfall.
- Ein BMW blendet ihn mit seinen Scheinwerfern und er bremst neben der Straße.

232b **Finden Sie die richtige Antwort. (Kapitel 7)**

Wann treffen sich Friso Breugel und Martin Faber in Stoppenberg?

____

Was wollen Faber und Breugel hier machen?

____

Wer hat die Anlage geplant?

____

Wer hat die Anlage gebaut?

____

Welches Problem hat Familie Galanis?

____

Wie reagieren Faber und Breugel?

____

„Kalt erwischt in Hamburg"

231a **Was passt? Kreuzen Sie an. (Kapitel 4)**

Was ist das Thema des Kapitels?

- Ole Wilken will Klaas Hansen umbringen.
- Nele Lühders und Pastor Dirkheide suchen Klaas.
- eine schöne Fahrt durch Hamburg

Welche zwei Personen handeln in diesem Kapitel?

- der Turmbläser Klaas Hansen
- Nele Lühders, die Freundin von Klaas Hansen
- Ole Wilke, der Exfreund von Nele Lühders

An welchem Ort spielt das Kapitel nicht?

- auf einer Brücke
- in der Kneipe Goldener Anker
- im Container-Terminal Altenwerder

231b **Wie ist die richtige Reihenfolge? (Kapitel 5)**

- Nele und Ole streiten sich.
- Birgit geht auf das Gelände.
- Nele und der Pastor fesseln Ole und tragen ihn zum Eingang.
- Nele und der Pastor treffen Ole draußen vor dem Terminal.
- Nele und der Pastor kommen auf das Terminalgelände.
- *1* Birgit, Nele und der Pastor kommen am Container-Terminal Alterwerder an.
- Nele und der Pastor dürfen nicht auf das Gelände und machen einen Spaziergang.
- Nele und der Pastor treffen Birgit und sie suchen zusammen am Wasser nach Klaas.

232a **Richtig oder falsch? Kreuzen Sie an. (Kapitel 6)**

richtig	falsch	
		Klaas wacht auf und alles ist dunkel.
		Es geht Klaas gut.
		Klaas erinnert sich langsam, was passiert ist.
		Er ist in der Kiste gefangen.
		Es riecht gut dort.
		Klaas hat leider seine dicke Jacke nicht angezogen.

232b **Was passt zusammen? (Kapitel 6)**

1) die Augen	4) gegen die Wand	riechen	haben
2) nach links	5) an die weite Welt	denken	*1* aufmachen
3) nach Fisch	6) Streit	gehen	klopfen

232c **Wer sagt was? Nele (N) oder der Pastor (P)? Kreuzen Sie an. (Kapitel 7)**

N	P	
		„Sagen Sie, was hat Ole denn genau gesagt?"
		„Hm … Klaas ist bei den Fischen."
		„Sie meinen, er ist nicht im Wasser? Und er lebt vielleicht noch?"
		„Ganz klar. Er ist in einem Container. In einem Container mit Fischen."
		„Mist! Warum gibt es eigentlich diese Handys. Sie sind immer leer oder niemand geht ran."
		„Schnell … Ich weiß, wie wir Klaas finden können."
		„Ist das vielleicht Chinesisch?"
		„Nein, … aber hier ist ein Symbol für einen Kühlschrank und das ist international."

„Verschollen in Berlin"

231a **Welchen Weg geht Jan? Was sieht er? Finden Sie die richtige Reihenfolge. (Kapitel 4)**

Schlossbrücke	Berliner Dom	Jannowitzbrücke
Monbijoubrücke	1 Museumsinsel	Kupfergraben

231b **Antworten Sie. (Kapitel 4)**

Jans Handy klingelt. Wer ist dran? ____________________

Wie heißt der Steward? ____________________

231c **Ergänzen Sie die Steckbriefe von Maja und Kokoschka. (Kapitel 5)**

Steckbrief Maja

Haare: *lang …*

Alter: ____________________

Figur: ____________________

Kleidung: *Jeans …*

Steckbrief Kokoschka

Haare: ____________________

Alter: ____________________

Figur: ____________________

Kleidung: ____________________

232a **Finden Sie die richtige Antwort. (Kapitel 6)**

Woran erinnert sich Jan?

____

Wie kommt er zur Kanzlei von Dr. Welsch?

____

Wer öffnet ihm die Tür?

____

Aus welchem Material ist der Schreibtisch von Dr. Welsch?

____

Was war in dem braunen Umschlag?

____

Wohin sollte Maja den Umschlag bringen?

____

231a **Was passt? Kreuzen Sie an. (Kapitel 4)**

Was ist das Thema des Kapitels?

- Kommissar Weigl hat weitere Fragen für die Familie.
- Mathias ruft Kommissar Weigl an.
- Die Mutter möchte mit dem Kommissar sprechen.

Welche Personen handeln in diesem Kapitel?

- die Mutter und Mathias
- Mathias und Kommissar Weigl
- Kommissar Weigl, Mathias und Mario

An welchem Ort spielt das Kapitel nicht?

- im Haus der Familie Sonnleitner
- in den Bergen
- auf dem Schützenfest

231b **Was ist richtig? Kreuzen Sie an. (Kapitel 4)**

Warum mag Mathias nicht, dass Kommissar Weigl zu ihnen ins Haus kommt? Was ist der wichtigste Grund?

- Der Mutter geht es nicht gut und sie will nicht über Ludwig sprechen.
- Mathias hat ein Geheimnis und Weigl darf nichts merken.
- Rosi hat sich über Weigl geärgert und will ihn nicht sehen.

Der Kommissar denkt, es war vielleicht Selbstmord. Warum?

- Er findet keine*n Täter*in.
- Es gibt kein Motiv für einen Mord.
- An Ludwigs Hand sind Schmauchspuren.

Warum schickt Mathias den Kommissar unfreundlich weg? Es gibt mehrere Gründe. Kreuzen Sie alle an.

- Weigl stellt unangenehme und gefährliche Fragen.
- Es ist schon spät und Weigl ist schon zu lange da.
- Weigl soll nicht die Wahrheit finden.
- Weigl ist zu Mathias und seiner Familie unfreundlich.
- Weigl hat Ideen, die den guten Namen der Familie verletzen.
- Die Nachbar*innen sollen nichts merken.

231c **Warum ist die Familie so aufgeregt? Kreuzen Sie alle Möglichkeiten an. (Kapitel 5)**

- Sie haben nichts von der Krankheit gemerkt.
- Ludwig sagte nicht, dass er todkrank war.
- Der Arzt hat der Familie nichts gesagt.
- Wie konnte Ludwig so ein schreckliches Geheimnis haben?
- Warum wollte Ludwig nicht, dass die Familie das weiß?

232a Richtig oder falsch? Kreuzen Sie an. (Kapitel 6)

richtig	falsch	
		Mathias geht zu Fuß auf die Kampenwand.
		Es sind viele Leute auf dem Berg.
		Zuerst frühstückt Mathias mit seiner Mutter.
		Die Bergbahn fährt bis zum Gipfelkreuz.
		Von der Station aus geht Mathias zu Fuß auf den Gipfel.

233a Temporal Adverbs

Especially in written discourse, but also when speaking, it is important to link sentences to one another rather than just creating a succession of isolated sentences. One way of connecting sentences logically and in sequence is by using temporal adverbs. These adverbs often take the first position in the sentence and are followed by the verb, but they can also be placed in middle field.

Here are some of these useful words to learn:

zuerst	*first*	**Zuerst** ging sie zur Arbeit.	*First, she went to work.*
dann	*then*	**Dann** arbeitete sie eine Weile.	*Then, she worked for a while.*
danach	*afterwards*	**Danach** aß sie zu Mittag.	*Afterwards, she ate her lunch.*
anschließend	*after that*	**Anschließend** schrieb sie E-Mails.	*After that, she wrote emails.*
schließlich	*finally*	**Schließlich** ging sie nach Hause.	*Finally, she went home.*

233b Sortieren und erzählen: Ordnen Sie die Sätze und schreiben Sie sie mit temporalen Adverbien neu. Achtung: Die Sätze sind noch nicht in der richtigen Reihenfolge.

Der Kommissar besucht die Familie. / Er spricht mit Mathias. / Der Kommissar ruft Mathias an.

Zuerst ruft der Kommissar Mathias an, dann besucht er die Familie. Anschließend spricht er mit Mathias.

Die Polizei startet eine Suchaktion. / Ludwig ist verschwunden. / Ludwigs Leiche wird gefunden.

___

___

Der Pastor und Nele machen sich Sorgen. / Klaas kommt nicht nach Hause. / Die Polizei löst den Fall.

___

___

Er macht den Computer an und öffnet sein E-Mail-Postfach. / Udo Geisler kommt im Büro an. / Er ruft seine Schwester an und erzählt ihr von der E-Mail. / Er sieht eine unerwartete E-Mail und bekommt einen großen Schrecken.

___

___

___

73: Im Kino

234a **Die DEFA. In den folgenden Sätzen lernen Sie, was die DEFA war. Schreiben Sie hinter jeden Satz, ob es sich um eine Aussage in der Vergangenheit (V), Gegenwart (G) oder Zukunft (Z) handelt.**

DEFA steht für „Deutsche Film AG". ___

Sie ist die einzige Organisation für Filmproduktion in der DDR gewesen. ___

Zwischen 1946 und 1990 hat sie über 1.300 Filme und mehr als 2.250 Dokumentar- und Kurzfilme produziert. ___

Mehr als 2.000 Menschen haben für die DEFA gearbeitet. ___

Einige dieser Filme haben heute Kultstatus, wie zum Beispiel der Märchenfilm „Drei Haselnüsse für Aschenbrödel". ___

Auch in vielen Jahren wird es noch möglich sein, im deutschen Fernsehen Filme der DEFA zu sehen. ___

234b **Grit plant ihren Kinobesuch mit ihrer Freundin Suri. Am Telefon erzählt sie ihrem Freund Alex davon. Hören Sie, was Grit sagt, und lesen Sie dabei das Transkript.**

Transkript:
Ach ja, Alex, das wollte ich dir noch erzählen, Suri und ich gehen nächsten Samstag ins Kino, und zwar werden wir in den UFA-Palast gehen. Sie bringen am Wochenende zwei neue Filme, einen mit Untertiteln, den anderen ohne. Keine Frage, Suri wird den Film ohne Untertitel auswählen, sie wird sagen: „Das ist authentischer!" Ich werde sie zum Film einladen, weil sie ja, wie immer, für uns Getränke und die Snacks kaufen wird. Was wir danach machen, wissen wir noch nicht, aber vielleicht werden wir noch in eine Bar gehen. Nun erzähl, wie wirst du denn dein Wochenende verbringen? Triffst du dich mit …

Grit erzählt am Sonntag danach, wie es war:

Suri und ich sind gestern ins Kino gegangen, und zwar sind wir mit dem Taxi zum UFA-Palast gefahren.

Dieses Wochenende haben sie …

____

____

____

237a **Info: Stimmen beschreiben**

Eine der wichtigsten Komponenten im Film (und natürlich auch im Fernsehen oder auf der Bühne) ist die Stimme. Jede Stimme hat ihren eigenen Charakter, ihr individuelles Timbre. Schauspieler*innen trainieren darüber hinaus, wie sie mit ihrer Stimme unterschiedliche Emotionen ausdrücken können. Hier sehen Sie zwei Listen mit Wörtern, um die Stimmen von Schauspieler*innen zu beschreiben. Schauen Sie die Bedeutung der Wörter nach, die Sie nicht kennen.

Stimmcharakter		**Emotion**	
warm	markant	fröhlich	traurig
hell	kräftig	wütend	verzweifelt
mittel	rauchig	verbittert	selbstbewusst
jung	weich	skeptisch	wahnsinnig
alt	hoch	sarkastisch	geistesabwesend
tief	kratzig	albern	ängstlich
voll	fein	nervös	mitfühlend
klar	sinnlich	unsicher	überschwänglich
angenehm	unangenehm	optimistisch	aggressiv

237b **Stimmen und Emotionen. Sie hören vier Aufnahmen, die aus einem Film sein könnten. Beschreiben Sie den Stimmcharakter und die Emotion(en) mit Wörtern aus dem Info-Kasten in 237a.**

	Aufnahme 1	Aufnahme 2	Aufnahme 3	Aufnahme 4
Stimmcharakter				
Emotion(en)				

237c **Mit welchen Worten würden Sie den Charakter Ihrer Stimme beschreiben?**

____

____

74: Tanz und Performance°

238a **Morgenroutine als Performance. Ordnen Sie die Vokabeln zur Morgenroutine den passenden Bildern zu.**

sich kämmen	aufwachen	sich strecken	sich duschen
sich eincremen	sich die Zähne putzen	sich abtrocknen	sich anziehen

1 

2 

3 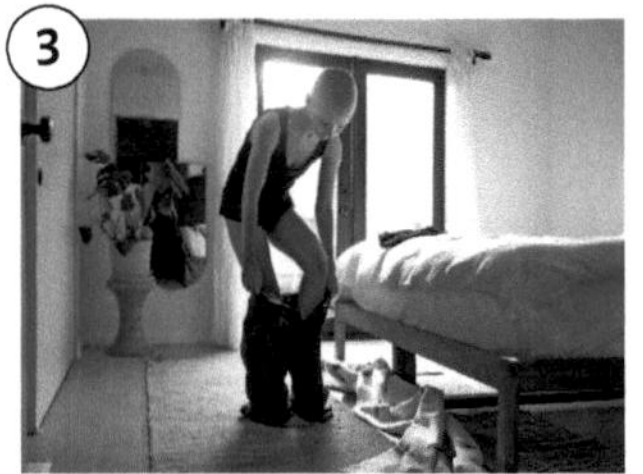

4 

5 

6 

7 

8 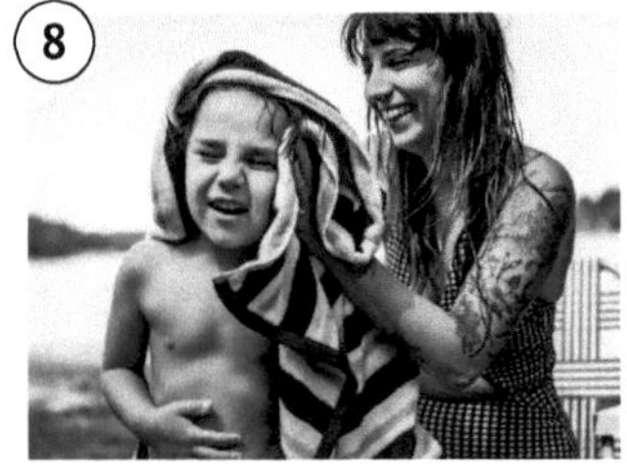

238b **Beschreiben Sie jetzt Ihre Morgenroutine in vier Sätzen: Was machen Sie zuerst, was danach und was am Ende?**

Beispiel: Zuerst strecke ich mich.

____

____

____

____

239a **Was ist ein Medium? Hier sehen Sie eine Variante des klassischen Sender-Empfänger-Modells, wie man es in den Kommunikations- und Medienwissenschaften benutzt. Lesen Sie die Definitionen und ergänzen Sie die folgenden Wörter: Empfänger*innen, Kanal/Kanäle, Botschaft, Signal und Störung (*interference*). Für jede Definition wird nur eines dieser Wörter benutzt.**

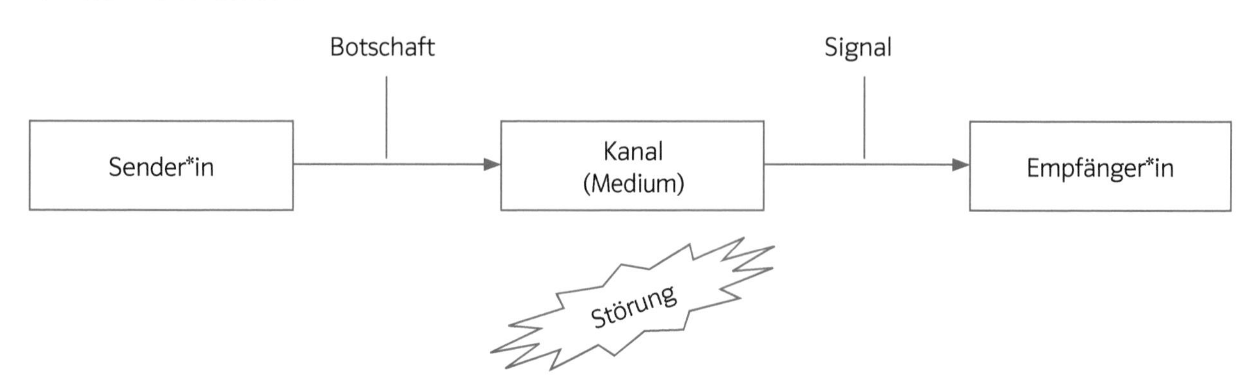

Die ________________________ ist die Nachricht, die die Sender*innen mit Hilfe eines Kanals verschicken. Oft sind es rein informative Nachrichten, z. B.: „Wir haben morgen um drei ein Meeting." Künstler*innen aber versuchen eine ________________________ zu transportieren, die etwas Wichtiges über unsere Gesellschaft sagt. Zur ________________________ gehören verbale und nonverbale Informationen.

Eine ________________________ verursacht Probleme im Kommunikationsprozess. Das können technische Probleme sein, wie z. B. schlechter Internetempfang, aber auch physischer Zugang (*access*) zum Kanal.

Der ________________________ ist das Vehikel, mit dem die Botschaften der Sender*innen transportiert werden. Ein ________________________ kann ein Fernsehsender oder ein Telefonkabel sein. Aber auch ein Buch oder ein Kunstwerk sind ________________________. Deshalb ist der ________________________ auch ein Medium.

Die ________________________ erhalten die Nachricht der Sender*innen. Ob sie die Nachricht so verstehen, wie die Sender*innen sie gemeint haben, hängt von vielen Faktoren ab: Sprache, Kultur, Emotionen etc.

Das ________________________ ist die kodierte Botschaft der Sender*innen, nachdem sie durch den Kanal (oder das Medium) transportiert wurde. Gab es Störungen im Kommunikationsprozess, kann das ________________________ verfälscht bei den Empfänger*innen ankommen.

239b **Was ist ein Medium? – Teil 2. Hier sehen Sie noch einmal die Definitionen für eine Botschaft und ein Medium (einen Kanal) in leicht variierter Form. Lesen Sie die Definitionen. Überlegen Sie dann, welche Dinge aus dem weißen Kasten die Rolle eines Mediums übernehmen können. Kopieren Sie sie in den grauen Kasten.**

Eine **Botschaft** ist die Nachricht, die der*die Sender*in mit Hilfe eines Mediums (Kanals) verschickt. Oft ist es eine rein informative Nachricht, z. B.: „Wir haben morgen um drei ein Meeting." Künstler*innen aber versuchen oft eine Botschaft zu transportieren, die etwas Wichtiges über unsere Gesellschaft aussagt. Zur Botschaft gehören verbale und nonverbale Informationen.

Das **Medium** (der Kanal) ist das Vehikel, mit dem die Botschaft der Sender*innen transportiert wird. Ein Medium kann ein Fernsehsender oder ein Telefonkabel sein. Aber auch ein Buch oder ein Kunstwerk sind ein Medium.

Das ist ein Medium

ein Lied

Kleidung
eine Katze
ein Lied
Tanz
ein Werbeplakat
ein Radiosender

239c **Schreiben Sie zum Schluss jeweils zwei Begründungen für die Objekte aus dem Kasten in Aktivität 239b. Folgen Sie dem Beispiel.**

*Ein Lied ist ein Medium, weil Künstler*innen eine direkte Botschaft an ihre Zuhörer*innen schicken. Die Botschaft kann informativ sein („Ich habe Liebeskummer"), aber es kann auch ein Appell sein („Sei mutiger!").*

240a **Lesen Sie die Beschreibungen. Beschreiben Sie sich selbst und dann eine wichtige Person in Ihrem Leben.**

Jeanne ist sehr fleißig. Sie arbeitet viel. Sie macht alle Hausarbeiten und hilft anderen Leuten bei ihren Problemen. Sie schreibt ihre Aufsätze pünktlich und hat genug Zeit für ihre Oma, ihre Katze und ihren Job.

Martin ist sehr interessant. Er hat exotische Hobbys und reist viel. Er hat schon Dinge gemacht, die andere Leute schockierend oder Angst erregend (*terrifying*) finden. Martin spricht nicht gerne mit anderen Menschen.

Susanne ist sehr korrekt und hat viel Humor. Sie kann gut Geschichten erzählen, aber sie mag keine pikanten Witze. Susanne ist immer höflich, auch wenn sie manchmal starke Schmerzen hat, weil sie chronische Migränen hat. Nett ist Susanne immer.

Ich:

Eine wichtige Person in meinem Leben:

75: POSTMIGRANTISCHES THEATER

242a **Impro-Theater: In MACHEN werden Sie einen kurzen Monolog improvisieren. Wählen Sie für den Monolog einen Gegenstand aus (z. B. ein Lebensmittel, Kleidungsstück oder Gerät). Stellen Sie sich vor, Sie sind dieser Gegenstand. Was für Merkmale (*characteristics*), Gefühle, Aufgaben/Zwecke (*purposes*) und Motivationen haben Sie? Notieren Sie sich unten für jede Kategorie ein paar Wörter oder kurze Sätze. Hier sehen Sie ein Beispiel für „Banane".**

Gegenstand	Merkmale	Gefühle	Aufgaben/Zwecke	Motivationen
Banane	*gelb, süß, krumm*	*Ich schäme mich, wenn die Leute mich ausziehen.*	*wachsen, warten, gegessen werden*	*Ich will den Leuten schmecken.*

Im Kurs werden Sie diese Wörter und Sätze benutzen, um Ihren Monolog zu improvisieren. Sie dürfen nicht sagen, was Sie sind – die anderen Kursteilnehmer*innen müssen raten! Hier ist ein Beispiel für den Monolog einer Banane, damit Sie eine Vorstellung davon haben, wie ein Monolog aussehen könnte:

„Ich bin gelb, süß und ein bisschen krumm. Ich schäme mich (I am embarrassed), wenn ich von Leuten oder von Tieren ausgezogen werde. Meine Aufgaben? Ich muss nur wachsen. Dann warte ich, bis ich gegessen werde. Manchmal werde ich gekocht, bis ich noch süßer werde, oder die Leute backen mich in einem Kuchen. Ich will den Leuten schmecken – und das auf der ganzen Welt! Was bin ich?"

242b **Was bin ich? Lesen Sie und tragen Sie den Gegenstand ein, der hier beschrieben wird.**

„Fast alle brauchen mich. Ganz viele haben mich. Ich habe meistens ein Kabel. Viele verbringen viel Zeit mit mir. Ich zeige der Welt viele Bilder und bringe das ganze Universum ins Haus. Aber wenn du mit mir sprichst, reagiere ich nicht darauf, außer wenn du Sprachassistenten (Google Assistant, Alexa, Siri …) hast, die mit mir kommunizieren können.

Ich bin ______________________________"

„Fast alle brauchen mich. Ganz viele haben mehr als eins von mir. Die meisten Menschen in deutschsprachigen Ländern (und auch in den USA) brauchen mich mehrmals am Tag. Aus Plastik komme ich oft in den Müll statt ins Recycling. Es gibt mich aus Holz, Edelstahl, Plastik, aber auch Silber und manchmal Gold. Suppe kann und will ich mit niemandem essen.

Ich bin ______________________________"

„Nicht alle brauchen mich. Ich stehe oft im Weg und brauche viel Platz. Man kann mich verbessern und reparieren. Fast alle sehen mich öfter am Tag, auch wenn sie mich nicht brauchen. Ich habe viele Farben und kann ganz teuer oder billig sein. Morgens und abends stehe ich oft in langen Staus auf der Straße und produziere CO_2.

Ich bin ______________________________"

„Fast alle brauchen mich. Ganz viele haben mich. Ich habe meistens ein Kabel. Viele verbringen viel Zeit mit mir. Ich zeige der Welt viele Bilder und bringe das ganze Universum ins Haus. Wenn du mir widersprechen willst, kannst du mir das durch Tippen sagen.

Ich bin ______________________________"

„Fast alle brauchen mich. Ganz viele haben mehr als eins von mir. Die meisten Menschen brauchen mich mehr als einmal am Tag. Aus Plastik komme ich oft in den Müll statt ins Recycling. Es gibt mich aus Holz, Edelstahl, Plastik, aber auch Silber und manchmal Gold. Suppe ist meine Spezialität."

Ich bin ______________________________"

„Nicht alle brauchen mich. Ich stehe oft im Weg und brauche viel Platz. Man kann mich verbessern und reparieren. Fast alle sehen mich öfters am Tag, auch wenn sie mich nicht brauchen. Ich habe viele Farben und kann ganz teuer oder billig sein. Morgens und abends fahre ich oft an langen Staus auf der Straße vorbei, die CO_2 produzieren.

Ich bin ______________________________"

242c **Hören Sie zu. Welche Gegenstände werden beschrieben?**

a) ______________ b) ______________ c) ______________

d) ______________ e) ______________ f) ______________

242d **Geht es bitte auch noch etwas komplizierter? Machen Sie acht Audioaufnahmen und beschreiben Sie diese vier Wörter, ohne sie zu nennen und ohne zu pausieren. Schreiben Sie kein Skript! Improvisieren Sie. Schicken Sie Ihre Aufnahmen an Ihre*n Professor*in.**

das Hemd	in 10 Sekunden	das Brot	in 30 Sekunden
das Hemd	in 20 Sekunden	das Brot	in 60 Sekunden
der Bleistift	in 20 Sekunden	das Handy	in 60 Sekunden
der Bleistift	in 40 Sekunden	das Handy	in 120 Sekunden

Tipps:
Sie starten mit dem größten gemeinsamen Nenner: Zu welcher Kategorie gehört es?
Wie viele Menschen haben es?
Haben Menschen mehr als eins davon?
Braucht man es einmal, zweimal ... am Tag?
Wozu braucht man es?
Ist es billig, teuer oder mal so, mal so?
Was unterscheidet den Gegenstand von anderen, ähnlichen Gegenständen?
...

243a **Postmigrantisches Theater. Dieser Text handelt von der Entstehung des postmigrantischen Theaters in Deutschland. Schlagen Sie zuerst alle fettgedruckten Wörter nach. Lesen Sie dann den Text und ordnen Sie unten die englischen Aussagen den drei Textabschnitten zu. Schreiben Sie dafür 1, 2 oder 3 hinter jeden Satz.**

Der Kanon des deutschsprachigen **Schauspiels** ist immer noch limitiert, antiquiert und eurozentrisch. Als Shermin Langhoff, eine der **Begründer*innen** des postmigrantischen Theaters, 2008 das Ballhaus neu aufmachte, war die Idee des postmigrantischen Theaters deshalb ein inspirierendes und **bemächtigendes** Konzept. Am Ballhaus Theater in Berlin hat sich ein Netzwerk aus Künstler*innen, Aktivist*innen und Wissenschaftler*innen gebildet. Ihre Ideen haben diese Personen dann zu anderen Bühnen gebracht, z. B. zum Gorki Theater, und **weiterentwickelt**.

Als sich in Berlin-Kreuzberg diese **Bewegung** formiert hat, wollte postmigrantisches Theater folgende Situation darstellen: In Deutschland gibt es eine Generation mit Migrations**erfahrung**, People of Color und Menschen mit nicht-deutsch klingenden Namen. Diese Menschen sehen sich als **Teil** der deutschen Gesellschaft und sie sind es auch. Aber die weiße Mehrheitsgesellschaft signalisiert diesen Menschen immer wieder, dass sie sie nicht als **zugehörig** versteht. (Strukturelle) Diskriminierung findet im Alltag statt, aber auch in allen Bereichen der Kunst, wo die postmigrantische Generation immer noch unterrepräsentiert ist.

Aus der Arbeit des postmigrantischen Theaters sind verschiedene neue Praktiken **entstanden**. Es gibt auch jetzt mehr **Unterstützung** für Autor*innen, um zu einer Diversifizierung des Kanons des deutschen Theater beizutragen.

From the concept of the postmigrant theater, new theatrical practices were developed. ___

The Ballhaus Theater was the place where artists, activists, and scientists alike came together to give rise to the concept of the postmigrant theater. ___

Postmigrant theater highlights the situation of individuals who are part of the German society but are constantly reminded that they don't belong. ___

Shermin Langhoff was one of the founders of the postmigrant theater movement in Germany. ___

There are now more means of support for writers to create a new theatrical canon. ___

244a **„Bitte hinterlassen Sie eine Nachricht, ich rufe bald zurück!" Improvisieren muss man nicht nur im Theater. Lesen Sie die Situation und hinterlassen Sie dazu auf der Mailbox jeweils eine Nachricht. (Mindestens 90 Sekunden pro Situation – improvisieren, nicht lesen.) Schicken Sie Ihre Mailbox-Nachrichten Ihrem*Ihrer Professor*in.**

Sie werden viel zu spät zu einer Party kommen, weil Sie die Snacks vergessen haben, die Sie mitbringen sollten. Sie hinterlassen dem Gastgeber eine Nachricht. Was ist passiert? Warum? Was müssen Sie jetzt machen? Wie lange dauert das? (Beschreiben Sie Ihren Weg.) Wann kommen Sie an? Was sollen die anderen jetzt so lange machen?

Sie haben einen Unfall mit dem Wagen Ihrer Eltern verursacht. Sie sind nicht verletzt, aber das Auto hat einen Totalschaden (*total loss*). Wie erklären Sie Ihren Eltern, was passiert ist? Sagen Sie ihnen direkt alles? Lassen Sie einige Details aus? Wie beruhigen Sie Ihre Eltern, damit sie sich nicht zu viele Sorgen machen?

Sie können nicht zu einem Kurs kommen. Sie erklären Ihrem*Ihrer Freund*in warum, was er*sie für Sie tun soll (z. B. Notizen machen) und wann Sie wieder kommen können.

76: VIRTUELLE REALITÄTEN

246a **Bestimmt kennen Sie den Begriff „Augmented Reality". Aber was ist das genau? Lesen Sie den Text und ergänzen Sie die fehlenden Verbformen.**

Augmented Reality, also erweiterte Realität, ist ein Konzept, das virtuelle und reale Welten ________________ (verbinden; Präsens). AR ________________ (erweitern; Präsens) die echte Realität mit zusätzlichen künstlichen Elementen. In Computerspielen bringt AR Spielwelten, Charaktere und Gebäude in unsere reale Welt. „Pokémon Go" ist ein sehr bekanntes AR-Spiel. Vor „Pokémon Go" ________________ es schon das Spiel „Ingress" ________________ (geben; Perfekt), das aber nur Kenner*innen ________________ ________________ (spielen; Perfekt). Und die Pokémon-Firma hat inzwischen noch ein neues Spiel kreiert: „Wizards Unite", bei dem die Spieler*innen mit Harry Potter, Ron und Hermine schwarze Magier*innen fangen können. Dabei ________________ (sehen; Präsens) sie auf der Karte im Smartphone Hexenhäuser und magische Gegenstände. AR wird auch in Schulbüchern benutzt. Zum Beispiel können Hologramme in einem Architektur-Buch Gebäude realistisch in 3D darstellen. Aber wie funktioniert das alles technisch? Es ist nicht einfach, virtuelle Objekte in die Realität einzubauen. Zuerst ________________ eine Person das reale Bild ________________ (aufzeichnen; Präsens). Dann ________________ (interpretieren; Präsens) ein Computer dieses Bild und ________________ es für die virtuellen Objekte ________________ (vorbereiten; Präsens). Dann fügen die Grafiker*innen die nicht-reellen Elemente ein. Was ________________ die Zukunft für AR ________________ (bringen; Futur)? Vielleicht ________________ wir es bald ________________ (benutzen; Futur), um uns bei virtuellen Meetings zu sehen. Oder vielleicht ________________ Museumsdesigner*innen virtuelle Ausstellungen mit AR ________________ (bauen; Futur). Es gibt grenzenlose (*endless*) Möglichkeiten, um AR zu benutzen.

246b **Lesen Sie den Text in Aktivität 246a noch einmal. Entscheiden Sie dann, ob die Aussagen richtig oder falsch sind.**

richtig	falsch	
		AR wird nur für Computerspiele benutzt.
		„Pokémon Go" war das erste Computerspiel, das AR benutzte.
		Auch Schulbücher können AR benutzen, um Dinge realistischer zu illustrieren.
		Das Kreieren von AR-Elementen ist ein relativ einfacher technologischer Prozess.
		In der Zukunft wird es noch viele neue Möglichkeiten für die Benutzung von AR geben.

246c **Das will ich spielen! Füllen Sie den folgenden Fragebogen aus, um ein Spiel zu kreieren, das Sie gerne spielen würden. Schreiben Sie unten zwei weitere Fragen und Antworten zu Ihrem Spiel, z.B. Plattform, Alter, Titel.**

Für wie viele Spieler*innen ist das Spiel?

- 1
- 2–5
- mehr als 5

Was für ein Spiel ist es?

- Puzzle
- Simulation
- Rollenspiel
- Click-and-point
- Strategie
- ______________

Welches Genre bzw. Thema hat das Spiel?

- Science Fiction
- Fantasy
- Horror
- Geschichte
- Krimi
- ______________

Was ist das Ziel des Spiels?

- so viele Punkte wie möglich sammeln
- eine*n Gegner*in (*opponent*) besiegen
- eine Handlung durch Entscheidungen steuern
- alle Rätsel lösen
- kooperativ eine Geschichte schreiben
- ______________________________

____?

____.

____?

____.

246d **Das will ich spielen! Teil 2. Zeichnen Sie hier ein Logo für Ihr Spiel aus Aktivität 246c, die Hauptfigur(en) oder andere Elemente.**

77: „Tatort DaF" (Teil 4)

Bitte machen Sie die Aktivitäten, die zu dem Buch gehören, das Sie lesen.

„Böses Erwachen in Heidelberg"

249a **Welche Erklärung passt. Verbinden Sie. (Kapitel 7)**

ist es manchmal im Winter, da kann man leicht hinfallen	stolpern
beim Gehen gegen etwas treten und dabei fast hinfallen	glatt
ist es, wenn es geregnet hat	der Tunnel
ein Weg durch einen Berg	nass

249b **Was denken Sie? Beantworten Sie die Fragen. (Kapitel 7)**

Warum will der Mann Emmas Handtasche haben?

____

____

Warum läuft sie zu Fuß durch den Tunnel?

____

____

Warum bewegt sich auf einmal alles?

____

____

250a **Wie ist die richtige Reihenfolge? (Kapitel 8)**

- ☐ Der Schaffner kontrolliert Emmas Fahrkarte.
- ☐ Ihre Cousine Beate fragt, wo sie ist. Sie wartet schon seit einer halben Stunde in Stuttgart auf den Zug.
- ☐ Emma bekommt einen großen Schreck.
- ☐ Professor Vogt erinnert sich an Rudolf Kuhn und ist begeistert: Die beiden fangen an zu diskutieren.
- ☐ Der Mann hinter ihnen steht auf und kommt zu Emma und Professor Vogt.
- ☐ Emma erzählt Beate von der Verspätung in Heidelberg.
- ☐ Beate schlägt vor, einen Ausflug nach Heidelberg zu machen. Aber Emma möchte erst einmal in Stuttgart ankommen.
- *1* Emma wacht auf: Ihr Tag in Heidelberg war nur ein Traum.
- ☐ Er erzählt, dass er Rudolf Kuhn heißt und ein alter Student von Professor Vogt ist. Die Paläontologie ist immer noch sein großes Hobby.
- ☐ Als Emma die Fahrkarte zurücksteckt, sieht sie den Mann mit den schwarzen Haaren: Er sitzt hinter ihr und schaut sie an.
- ☐ Emmas Handy klingelt.

„Die Lerche aus Leipzig"

249a **Was ist richtig? Kreuzen Sie an. (Kapitel 8)**

Was ist das Thema des Kapitels?

- ☐ Udo Geißler hört René Hartmann ab.
- ☐ das frühere Leben von René Hartmann
- ☐ die Familie von Udo Geißler

Welche Personen kommen in dem Kapitel vor?

- ☐ Udo Geißler
- ☐ René Hartmann
- ☐ Miriam Becker

Wie geht es Udo Geißler?

- ☐ Er freut sich auf René Hartmann.
- ☐ Er ist müde und hat Hunger, aber es geht Geißler gut.
- ☐ Er hat Angst. Er weiß nicht, was René Hartmann mit ihm macht.

249b **Wie ist die richtige Reihenfolge? (Kapitel 9)**

- Geißler schläft ein.
- 1 Jemand trägt Udo Geißler aus der Zelle.
- Geißler möchte mit Hartmann sprechen.
- Jemand fesselt Geißler an einen Stuhl.
- Geißler muss etwas trinken.
- Udo Geißler wacht auf. Er fühlt Spinnen an seinen Beinen.
- Udo Geißler sieht nichts. Eine Lampe zeigt genau in sein Gesicht.
- Udo Geißler hört einen Schuss.
- Miriam Becker kommt in das Büro.
- Udo Geißler entschuldigt sich.

250a **Was denken Sie? Beantworten Sie die Fragen. (Kapitel 10)**

Warum will Geißler die Spinne nicht zertreten?

___

Hat sich das Leben von Udo Geißler für immer verändert?

___

Udo Geißler geht aus dem Museum. Ist er traurig oder fröhlich?

___

Wollte René Hartmann Udo Geißler töten?

___

„Gefährliches Spiel in Essen"

249a **Wer sagt das? Faber (F) oder Breugel (B)? (Kapitel 8)**

F	B	
		„Nun schauen Sie sich das mal an … !"
		„Überall schiefe Gardinen an den Fenstern … !"
		„Ja, … stimmt! Und wie kommt das an?"
		„Denken Sie dasselbe wie ich?"
		„Sie meinen, genau das passiert auch da … in Stoppenberg?"
		„Kennen Sie den?"
		„Was … was soll das denn?"
		„Ja, ich glaube schon."

249b **Richtig oder falsch? Kreuzen Sie an. (Kapitel 9)**

richtig	falsch	
		Nur Faber und Koslowski fahren zum Haus von Hartwig Köhler.
		Köhler wohnt in einer Villa im Norden von Essen.
		Eine junge Frau öffnet die Haustür.
		Köhler will mit seinem BMW flüchten.
		Koslowski hat die Polizei informiert.

250a **Welche Schlagzeile passt am besten zu dem Artikel in der Zeitung? Was denken Sie? (Kapitel 10)**

- Bauunternehmer drohen mehrere Jahre Haft
- Bauunternehmen baut nie wieder
- Auf Zechengelände ohne Genehmigung gebaut

„Kalt erwischt in Hamburg"

249a **Was macht Klaas Hansen? Wie ist die richtige Reihenfolge? (Kapitel 8)**

aufstehen wollen	zurückfallen	1 frieren	nicht schaffen
müde sein	wach bleiben	nicht schlafen	liegen bleiben

249b **Antworten Sie. (Kapitel 9)**

Welche Personen kommen in diesem Kapitel vor?

____

Mit wem kommt Birgit zu Nele und dem Pastor?

____

Warum geht es um Leben und Tod?

____

Was hat der Polizist bei sich?

____

Woran sieht Nele, in welchem Container Klaas ist?

____

250a **Was ist richtig? Kreuzen Sie an. (Kapitel 10)**

Klaas bekommt
- seine Trompete.
- seine Tabletten.

Die Trompete ist
- wie neu.
- ein bisschen kaputt.

Klaas ist
- im Krankenhaus.
- zu Hause.

Klaas
- hat Schmerzen.
- geht es sehr gut.

Ole ist
- auch im Krankenhaus.
- im Gefängnis.

Nele und der Pastor
- sind Freund*innen geworden.
- mögen sich nicht.

Plötzlich will Klaas
- etwas essen.
- zum Michel.

Am Sonntag muss Klaas
- Trompete spielen.
- nicht Trompete spielen.

„Verschollen in Berlin"

249a **Richtig oder falsch? Kreuzen Sie an. (Kapitel 7)**

richtig	falsch	
		Jan glaubt, Maja ist im Filmmuseum.
		Das Filmmuseum ist ab 18 Uhr geschlossen.
		Die Dame an der Kasse geht abends durch das Museum.
		Sie erinnert sich nicht an Maja.
		Im Museum waren an diesem Tag nur wenige Leute.

249b **Warum verliert Jan die Geduld? (Kapitel 7)**

- Frau Rogalla will Jan nicht helfen.
- Frau Rogalla verbietet Jan, Maja zu suchen.
- Frau Rogalla erzählt zu viel über das Museum.

250a **Richtig oder falsch? Kreuzen Sie an. (Kapitel 9)**

richtig	falsch	
		Graf von Sawitzky ist der Großonkel von Maja.
		Herr Kokoschka findet noch andere Verwandte.
		Der Graf hat keinen Kontakt zu seinen Kindern.
		Maja hat eine Villa in Grunewald.
		Sie hat Herrn Kokoschka getroffen.
		Maja hat ihren Großonkel noch nie gesehen.

„Der Schützenkönig vom Chiemsee"

249a **Beantworten Sie die Fragen. (Kapitel 7)**

Content Warning
Chapter 7: Death by suicide.

Wer kümmert sich um das Begräbnis von Ludwig?

___

Was findet Edelgard plötzlich?

___

Warum ist für Edelgard und Rosi jetzt alles klar?

___

249b **Warum wollte Ludwig gerade jetzt sterben? Was steht in seinem Brief? Kreuzen Sie an. (Kapitel 7)**

- Er wollte kein Ende mit Schmerzen.
- Er wollte nicht, dass die Familie Probleme hat.
- Er hatte Angst vor einem Tod mit Schmerzen.
- Er wollte in einem Moment sterben, wo er glücklich war.
- Er wollte möglichst schnell Familie und Freund*innen verlassen.
- Er wollte etwas Gutes tun.

78: „Yolocaust"°

251a **Unten sehen Sie vier Bilder vom Denkmal für die ermordeten Juden Europas in Berlin. Ordnen Sie die Bilder einem der vier kurzen Texte zu.**

Text: ____________________

Text: ____________________

Text: ____________________

Text: ____________________

Text 1: Unter dem Denkmal gibt es ein Dokumentationszentrum, in dem die Besucher*innen Informationen über die Opfer des Holocaust erhalten. Die Besucher*innen können zum Beispiel auf dem Boden eines Raumes Teile von Briefen lesen, die Menschen aus Konzentrationslagern an ihre Familie geschickt haben. Sie lernen so mehr über die Geschichte und das Leid der Naziopfer. Die Positionierung der Briefe im Boden schafft eine besonders emotionale Stimmung.

Text 2: Wenn Besucher*innen zwischen den einzelnen Blöcken des Denkmals gehen, fühlen sie sich teilweise wie in einem Labyrinth. Viele Besucher*innen haben diese Erfahrung als desorientierend beschrieben.

Text 3: Das Denkmal für die ermordeten Juden Europas besteht aus 2.711 quaderförmigen Blöcken. Die Blöcke sind unterschiedlich groß. Wegen der unterschiedlichen Größe der Blöcke sieht das Denkmal von oben wellenförmig (*wavy*) aus.

Text 4: Im Dokumentationszentrum gibt es auch einen dunklen Raum, den sogenannten „Raum der Namen", in dem die Namen aller Opfer des Holocaust vorgelesen werden. In diesem Raum gibt es keine Bilder. Mit einem Beamer (*projector*) werden die Namen an die Wand projiziert. Die Biografien werden laut vorgelesen.

251b **Recherchieren Sie: Wo befindet sich in Berlin das Denkmal für die ermordeten Juden Europas? Ist es in der Stadtmitte oder außerhalb?**

Recherche

Ort des Denkmals: ____

WOFÜR/WOGEGEN SIND WIR?

PROTEST, WIDERSTAND, MITBESTIMMUNG

Wortschatz

80: Unsere Stimmen auf dem Campus

der Protest, -e	protest
der Widerstand, ¨-e	resistance; opposition
wofür	for what
wogegen	against what
protestieren, protestierte, hat ... protestiert	to protest
demonstrieren, demonstrierte, hat ... demonstriert	to demonstrate, rally
sich (*akk.*) engagieren (für + *akk.*), engagierte, hat ... engagiert	to commit oneself (to), become involved (in)
die Demonstration, -en	demonstration
gegen (+ *akk.*)	against
für (+ *akk.*)	for
kontrovers	controversial, contentious
das Kreuz, -e	cross
die Skala, Skalen	scale
dafür	for it, for that
dagegen	against it, against that
gültig	valid
die Studiengebühren (*pl.*)	tuition

Weitere Wörter: die Mitbestimmung, -en (participation, co-determination); **kund·geben (gibt ... kund), gab ... kund, hat ... kundgegeben** (to announce, make sth. known); **verantwortungsvoll** (responsible)

81: Karneval kontrovers

der Karneval, -s	Carnival, Mardi Gras
die Politik	politics
das Mittel, -	means (*pl.*)
ab·schneiden, schnitt ... ab, hat ... abgeschnitten	to cut off
das Rathaus, ¨-er	townhall, city hall
ab·nehmen (nimmt ... ab), nahm ... ab, hat ... abgenommen	to take off; lose weight; decrease
der Schlüssel, -	key
das Mittelalter	Middle Ages
kirchlich	clerical, church-related
der Papst, ¨-e	pope (*male*)
die Päpstin, -nen	pope (*female*)
das Oberhaupt der römisch-katholischen Kirche	head of the Roman-Catholic Church (*gender-neutral workaround for pope*)
der Teufel, -	devil
enden, endete, hat ... geendet	to end
die Uniform, -en	uniform
die Opposition, -en	opposition
die Figur, -en	figure
werfen (wirft), warf, hat ... geworfen	to throw
kritisch	critical(ly)
denken (an + *akk.*), dachte, hat ... gedacht	to think (about/of)
informieren (über + *akk.*), informierte, hat ... informiert	to inform (about)
zeichnen, zeichnete, hat ... gezeichnet	to draw
die Band, -s	band
glauben (an + *akk.*), glaubte, hat ... geglaubt	to believe (in)
nach·denken (über + *akk.*), dachte ... nach, hat ... nachgedacht	to think (about), reflect (on)

Weitere Wörter: Preußen (Prussia); **die Krawatte, -n** (tie); **parodieren, parodierte, hat ... parodiert** (to parody, satirize); **der Narr, -en** (fool, jester (*male*)); **die Närrin, -nen** (fool, jester (*female*)); **die närrische Person, die närrischen Personen** (fool, jester (*gender-neutral alternative*)); **das Militär, -s** (military); **die Parodie, -n** (parody); **preußisch** (Prussian); **sich (*akk.*) einigen (auf + *akk.*), einigte, hat ... geeinigt** (to agree (on)); **sich (*akk.*) ärgern (über + *akk.*), ärgerte, hat ... geärgert** (to be/get annoyed (at)); **sich (*akk.*) freuen (auf + *akk.*), freute, hat ... gefreut** (to look forward (to)); **sich (*akk.*) freuen (über + *akk.*), freute, hat ... gefreut** (to be happy (about)); **warten (auf + *akk.*), wartete, hat ... gewartet** (to wait (for))

82: Widerstand im Dritten Reich

das Dritte Reich	Third Reich
dennoch	nevertheless, still
sammeln, sammelte, hat ... gesammelt	to collect
sondern	but rather
aber	but
da	since, as
an·fangen (mit + *dat.*) (fängt ... an), fing ... an, hat ... angefangen	to start (with)
beginnen (mit + *dat.*), begann, hat ... begonnen	to begin (with)
streiten (mit + *dat.*), stritt, hat ... gestritten	to argue (with)
sich (*akk.*) beschweren (über + *akk.*), beschwerte, hat ... beschwert	to complain (about)
jdm. (*dat.*) helfen (bei + *dat.*) (hilft), half, hat ... geholfen	to help (with)
etw. (*akk.*) verlangen (von + *dat.*), verlangte, hat ... verlangt	to demand sth. (from)
erwischen, erwischte, hat ... erwischt	to catch, arrest
die Front, -en	foresite, front
furchtbar	terrible

Weitere Wörter: Widerstand leisten, leistete, hat ... geleistet (to resist, make a stand, offer resistance); **der Widerständler, -** (insurgent, resister (*male*)); **die Widerständlerin, -nen** (insurgent, resister (*female*)); **der*die Widerständige, -n** (insurgent, resister (*gender-neutral alternative*)); **jdn. (*akk.*) überreden (zu + *dat.*), überredete, hat ... überredet** (to persuade sb. (to)); **das Flugblatt, ¨-er** (flyer, leaflet); **einer Meinung sein (mit + *dat.*) (ist), war, ist ... gewesen** (to agree (with), share an opinion (with))

84: Automatisierung – Protestieren oder mitbestimmen?

die Automatisierung, -en	automatization, automation
mechanisch	mechanical(ly)
das Element, -e	element
die künstliche Intelligenz	artificial intelligence
der Greifer, -	gripper, claw
optisch	visual(ly), optical(ly)
der*die Beschäftigte, -n (ein*e Beschäftigte*r)	employee (*gender-neutral*)
die Branche, -n	sector, branch
der Einzelhandel	retail industry
sich (*akk.*) Sorgen machen (um + *akk.*), machte, hat ... gemacht	to worry (about)
Angst haben (vor + *dat.*) (hat), hatte, hat ... gehabt	to be afraid (of)
sich (*akk.*) verändern, veränderte, hat ... verändert	to change
übertreiben, übertrieb, hat ... übertrieben	to exaggerate, overstate
beschäftigen, beschäftigte, hat ... beschäftigt	to employ
entstehen, entstand, ist ... entstanden	to emerge, arise
deshalb	therefore
die Stelle, -n	position, job
die Strahlung, -en	radiation
künstlich	artificial(ly)
automatisch	automatic(ally)
bedrohlich	threatening
die Weiterbildung, -en	further education, further training

Weitere Wörter: die Fernsteuerung, -en (telecontrol, remote control); **die Fortbewegung, -en** (locomotion, movement); **optimistisch** (optimistic(ally)); **pessimistisch** (pessimistic(ally)); **die Überwachung, -en** (surveillance); **das Organ, -e** (organ); **der Organismus, Organismen** (organism)

85: Street Art

das Kriterium, Kriterien	criterion
auf·fallen (fällt ... auf), fiel ... auf, ist ... aufgefallen	to attract attention
der Künstler, -	artist (*male*)
die Künstlerin, -nen	artist (*female*)
die kunstschaffende Person, die Kunstschaffenden	artist (*gender-neutral alternative*)
meiner Meinung nach	in my opinion
bedenken, bedachte, hat ... bedacht	to consider
der Entwurf, ¨-e	draft
das Kunstwerk, -e	artwork
umstritten	controversial, disputed
Geld verdienen, verdiente, hat ... verdient	to earn money
akzeptieren, akzeptierte, hat ... akzeptiert	to accept
meinen, dass	to mean/guess that
sicher sein, dass	to be sure that
wissen, dass	to know (as a fact) that
finden, dass	to find that
denken, dass	to think that
glauben, dass	to believe that

Weitere Wörter: illegal (illegal(ly)); **legal** (legal(ly)); **das Graffiti, -s** (graffiti); **der Kritiker, -** (critic (*male*)); **die Kritikerin, -nen** (critic (*female*)); **die kritische Stimme, die kritischen Stimmen** (critic (*gender-neutral alternative*)); **an·kündigen, kündigte ... an, hat ... angekündigt** (to announce); **symbolisieren, symbolisierte, hat ... symbolisiert** (to symbolize)

86: Mit Möhren gegen koloniale Spuren

die Möhre, -n	carrot
die Spur, -en	track, trace
der Ort, -e	location, place
um·benennen, benannte ... um, hat ... umbenannt	to rename
bezeichnen, bezeichnete, hat ... bezeichnet	to denote, designate, label
sichtbar machen, machte, hat ... gemacht	to make visible
jeweils	respectively, in each case
einheimisch	local, native
die Bedeutung, -en	meaning
das Straßenschild, -er	road sign, street sign
ehemalig	former
die Aufarbeitung, -en	coming to terms with sth., processing, reappraisal
die Einstellung, -en	attitude
in Verbindung stehen (mit + *dat.*)	to be connected/ communicate (with)

Weitere Wörter: benennen, benannte, hat ... benannt (to name, designate, label)

88: Über Erinnerung stolpern

stolpern (über + *akk.*), stolperte, ist ... gestolpert	to stumble (over)
der Stolperstein, -e	stumbling stone/block
das Denkmal, ¨-er	monument, landmark, memorial
das Mahnmal, -e	memorial
der Boden, ¨-	ground, floor
unterbrechen (unterbricht), unterbrach, hat ... unterbrochen	to disrupt, interrupt
verlegen, verlegte, hat ... verlegt	to lay, install; transfer; postpone
treten (tritt), trat, ist ... getreten	to step; kick

sich (*akk.*) entscheiden (für + *akk.*), entschied, hat ... entschieden	to decide (in favor of); choose
das Grundstück, -e	property, premise
hingegen	in contrast, on the contrary
ab·lehnen, lehnte ... ab, hat ... abgelehnt	to refuse, reject
beschädigen, beschädigte, hat ... beschädigt	to damage
jds. (*gen.*) gedenken, gedachte, hat ... gedacht	to commemorate, remember sb.
Berlin gedenkt der Opfer mit einem Mahnmal.	Berlin commemorates the victims with a memorial.
das Bauwerk, -e	structure, building
zusammen·leben, lebte ... zusammen, hat ... zusammengelebt	to live together
obwohl	although, despite

Weitere Wörter: der Besitzer, - (owner (*male*)); **die Besitzerin, -nen** (owner (*female*)); **die besitzende Person, die Besitzenden** (owner (*gender-neutral alternative*)); **das Gedenken** (commemoration, remembrance); **der Gehweg, -e** (sidewalk)

89: #METWO

in Bezug auf (+ *akk.*)	in relation to
der Lohn, ⸚e	wage
die Steuer, -n	tax
fördern, förderte, hat ... gefördert	to promote, support
das Publikum	audience
der Benutzer, -	user (*male*)
die Benutzerin, -nen	user (*female*)
die [Service] benutzende Person, die [Service] Benutzenden	user of [service] (*gender-neutral workaround*)
gesellschaftlich	social(ly), societal(ly)
das Zeichen, -	character (*in a word*); sign
trotzdem	despite that, still, nevertheless

Weitere Wörter: der Aktivist, -en (activist (*male*)); **die Aktivistin, -nen** (activist (*female*)); **der politisch aktive Mensch, die politisch aktiven Menschen** (activist (*gender-neutral alternative*)); **die Empfehlung, -en** (recommendation); **erreichen, erreichte, hat ... erreicht** (to achieve); **bei·bringen, brachte ... bei, hat ... beigebracht** (to teach)

80: Unsere Stimmen auf dem Campus

255a Verbs With Prepositional Objects: *für, gegen*

In this chapter, we will not only focus on connecting sentences into paragraphs but also on adding information in such sentences to explain something in detail. One way to do this is by using prepositions.

We have already learned and reviewed the way that prepositions are always followed by an object in a specific case:

accusative:	bis, durch, für, gegen, ohne, um
dative:	ab, außer, bei, gegenüber, mit, nach, seit, von, zu
accusative or dative:	an, auf, hinter, in, neben, über, unter, vor, zwischen
genitive:	(an)statt, außerhalb, trotz, während, wegen

Some of these prepositions are used in combination with specific verbs. Unfortunately, not all of these verb-preposition combinations will correspond to English directly; therefore, we will introduce them as vocabulary and practice them in chunks.

We will start by looking at verbs that are often used in combination with the accusative prepositions ***für*** (for) and ***gegen*** (against). Using these two prepositions helps you, for example, to not only say that you are "protesting" but what you are "protesting against," or not only that you are "fighting" but what you are "fighting for."

Here are some useful ones:

etwas (*akk.*) brauchen	**für** + *akk.*	*to need something (sth.) for sth./someone (so.)*
demonstrieren	**für/gegen** + *akk.*	*to demonstrate for/against sth./so.*
sich engagieren	**für/gegen** + *akk.*	*to campaign for/against sth./so.*
sich entscheiden	**für/gegen** + *akk.*	*to decide in favor of/against sth./so.*
sich interessieren	**für** + *akk.*	*to be interested in sth./so.*
kämpfen	**für/gegen** + *akk.*	*to fight for/against sth./so.*
protestieren	**für/gegen** + *akk.*	*to protest for/against sth./so.*

Examples:

Viele Menschen demonstrieren **für** den Weltfrieden.	*Many people demonstrate for world peace.*
Viele Menschen protestieren **gegen** den Stellenabbau.	*Many people protest against job cuts.*
Wir brauchen neue Poster **für** die Demonstration.	*We need new posters for the demonstration.*
Die Studierenden interessieren sich auch **für** das Thema.	*The students are also interested in the issue.*
Viele entscheiden sich **für** gewaltlosen Widerstand.	*Many students opt for nonviolent resistance.*

255b Anke, Hasnaa, Ingo und Jenny unterhalten sich im Café Revoluzzer. Sie organisieren einen Protest, weil sie denken, dass Tiere in Freiheit (und nicht in Zoos) leben sollten. Welche Präpositionen passen?

Anke: Wir brauchen mehr Leute ____________ (für | gegen) die Protestaktion am Montag. Habt ihr eure Bekannten eingeladen?

Hasnaa: Ja, alle! Viele interessieren sich wirklich ____________ (für | gegen) unseren Protest, denn sie haben viele Fragen. Sie wollen wissen: Kämpfen wir ____________ (für | gegen) die Rechte der Zootiere oder protestieren wir ____________ (für | gegen) den Zoo?

Ingo: Also, ich demonstriere ____________ (für | gegen) die Freiheit der Tiere. Das heißt, ich engagiere mich ____________ (für | gegen) Institutionen, in denen Tiere eingesperrt sind, wie z. B. Zoos und Zirkusse.

Jenny: Ich finde, wir müssen uns jetzt klar für *eine* Perspektive entscheiden: entweder ____________ (für | gegen) die Freiheit der Tiere oder ____________ (für | gegen) die Institutionen. Dann verfolgen (*pursue*) wir ein klareres Ziel.

255c **Dafür oder dagegen? Lesen Sie die Aussagen und beschreiben Sie in jeweils einem Satz, wofür oder wogegen die Personen sind und warum.**

Jasper (xier, 22), Salzburg: „Es wird immer wieder über ein Tempolimit auf der Autobahn diskutiert. Ich finde das Quatsch. Jede Person sollte so schnell fahren dürfen, wie sie will."

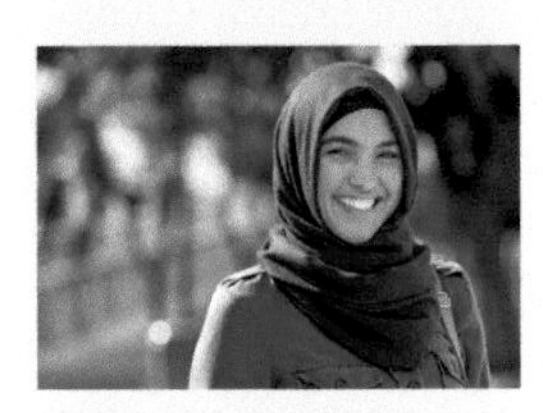

Lena (sie, 35), Münster: „Als für das Wintersemester 2006/2007 allgemeine Studiengebühren eingeführt wurden, haben meine Mitstudierenden und ich bei mehreren Protestaktionen mitgemacht. Jede Person sollte das Recht auf freie Bildung haben, auch an der Uni. Studiengebühren sorgen dafür, dass nur privilegierte Menschen sich ein Studium leisten können."

Noah (er, 51), Kiel: „Ich denke, dass Jugendliche schon mit 16 an der Bundestagswahl teilnehmen sollten. Viele glauben, dass Teenager in dem Alter nicht wirklich wissen, was sie wollen, aber das halte ich für Unsinn. Es geht ja um ihre Zukunft, und das nehmen sie ernst. Vor allem, wenn es zum Beispiel um Umweltschutz oder eine offenere Gesellschaft geht."

Neslihan (sie, 19), Dresden: „Ich verstehe nicht, warum es in Deutschland immer noch nicht erlaubt ist (bis auf ein paar Ausnahmen), dass Supermärkte und andere Geschäfte am Sonntag öffnen. Unterschiedliche Menschen haben unterschiedliche Lebensstile. Manche Personen würden gerne sonntags arbeiten und andere gerne sonntags einkaufen. Ich denke, wir brauchen neue Gesetze für die Ladenöffnungszeiten."

Jasper ist gegen ein generelles Tempolimit auf der Autobahn, weil für xien jede Person das Recht hat, so schnell zu fahren, wie sie will.

255d **Was denken Sie? Wählen Sie eines der vier Themen von Aktivität 255c. Sagen Sie in 2–3 Sätzen, ob Sie dafür oder dagegen sind und warum.**

256a Connecting Sentences: Overview

In this chapter, we will provide you with the tools to move from writing individual sentences to connected sentences and paragraphs. We will introduce connecting words that help us do so and think about them in terms of use. That means that we will talk about connecting words that express reasons or contrasts, for instance. At the same time, we will also discuss the different impact these connecting words have on the structure of the sentence. There are three main categories of connecting words in this regard. Let's consider these two sentences:

Die Arbeitskräfte fordern mehr Lohn. — *The workers demand higher wages.*
Die Arbeitskräfte streiken heute. — *The workers are on strike today.*

Coordinating conjunctions connect two main clauses and keep the word order intact (verb in second position). The coordinating conjunction counts as position zero when you determine the verb position.

Die Arbeitskräfte fordern mehr Lohn
und (sie) streiken heute.

The workers demand higher wages
and are on strike today.

Subordinating conjunctions connect a subordinate clause to a main clause and cause the verb of the subordinate clause to move to the end of that part of the sentence.

Die Arbeitskräfte streiken heute,
weil sie mehr Lohn fordern.

The workers are on strike today
because they demand higher wages.

Connecting adverbs connect two main clauses and count as a regular position within the sentence (verb remains in second position). That means they can take a position on either side of the verb (before or after).

Die Arbeitskräfte fordern mehr Lohn,
deshalb streiken **sie** heute.

The workers demand higher wages;
therefore, they are on strike today.

Die Arbeitskräfte fordern mehr Lohn,
sie streiken **deshalb** heute.

The workers demand higher wages;
therefore, they are on strike today.

256b Hauptsatz oder Nebensatz? Markieren Sie zuerst den Konnektor. Sagen Sie dann für Satz 1 und Satz 2, ob es sich um einen Hauptsatz oder einen Nebensatz handelt. Die Verbposition hilft Ihnen dabei.

Wir wollen morgen demonstrieren (und) übermorgen schreiben wir dann gemeinsam einen Protestbrief.

Satz 1 = ~~Nebensatz~~ | Hauptsatz   Satz 2 = ~~Nebensatz~~ | Hauptsatz

Weil wir keine Studiengebühren bezahlen möchten, protestieren wir.

Satz 1 = Nebensatz | Hauptsatz   Satz 2 = Nebensatz | Hauptsatz

Wir gehen morgen nicht in die Vorlesung, weil wir demonstrieren werden.

Satz 1 = Nebensatz | Hauptsatz   Satz 2 = Nebensatz | Hauptsatz

Die Unipräsidentin wird uns vielleicht nicht zuhören, aber wir werden weiter protestieren.

Satz 1 = Nebensatz | Hauptsatz   Satz 2 = Nebensatz | Hauptsatz

Dieses Thema ist uns wichtig, deshalb engagieren wir uns dafür.

Satz 1 = Nebensatz | Hauptsatz   Satz 2 = Nebensatz | Hauptsatz

256c Connecting Sentences: *weil*, *da*, and *denn*

The first connections we are going to look at are **causal** ones. With these connecting words, we can express the outcome of an action and also add more detail to a sentence. We use these connections in our spoken language all the time when we explain **the reason for doing something**.

Denn, *weil*, and *da* all mean "because," but they behave differently because of the type of connecting word they are.

As a coordinating conjunction, ***denn*** connects two main clauses and takes position zero while the rest of the word order is not impacted (verb in second position).

Die Arbeitskräfte streiken heute, **denn** sie fordern mehr Lohn.	*The workers are on strike today* *because they are demanding higher wages.*

As subordinating conjunctions, ***weil*** and ***da*** cause the verb of the subordinate clause to move to the end.

Die Arbeitskräfte streiken heute, **weil** sie mehr Lohn fordern.	*The workers are on strike today* *because they are demanding higher wages.*
Die Arbeitskräfte streiken heute, **da** sie mehr Lohn fordern.	*The workers are on strike today* *because they are demanding higher wages.*

In addition to the word order, there is another difference between *denn* on the one hand and *weil* and *da* on the other hand: while a *denn*-clause cannot stand first, it is possible to begin a sentence with a *weil*- or *da*-clause. If you do so, remember that the whole subordinate clause takes position one of the main clause, and the verb goes right after the comma.

Da die Arbeitskräfte mehr Lohn fordern, streiken sie heute.	*Because the workers are demanding higher wages,* *they are on strike today.*

When do you use what? The short answer is: it is up to you because they all mean the same thing. However, *denn* is more common in written than in spoken language, and when you start with the causal subordinate clause, it is more common to use *da* rather than *weil*. *Denn* and *da* also sound a bit more formal, and you could translate them as "since" or "as," whereas *weil* should always be translated as "because."

256d Schreiben Sie die Sätze um. Beginnen Sie mit dem jeweils angegebenen Konnektor. Achten Sie darauf, dass sich dabei die Verbposition verändert.

Die Campus-Zeitung schreibt heute über einen Studierendenprotest,
weil viele Studierende sich dafür interessieren.

…, denn *viele Studierende interessieren sich dafür.*

Die Studierenden protestieren gegen Studiengebühren,
denn sie glauben an das Recht auf Bildung.

…, da ______________________________.

Die Uni hatte Studiengebühren eingeführt,
denn sie wollte mehr Geld in die Lehre investieren.

…, weil ______________________________.

Die Studierenden meinen, dass Studiengebühren nicht sozial gerecht sind,
da Studierende mit weniger Geld benachteiligt werden.

…, denn ______________________________.

81: KARNEVAL KONTROVERS

258a Connecting Sentences With *und*

Und means "and." It is used, just like in English, for **lists of two or more elements**, bringing together elements that are equally valid at the same time:

Die Karnevalszüge in Köln, Düsseldorf **und** Mainz finden am Rosenmontag statt.	*The Karneval parades in Cologne, Dusseldorf, and Mainz take place on Carnival Monday.*

The last element in the list will either be separated by a comma or *und*, never both. As a coordinating conjunction, *und* can also **connect two main clauses when the two clauses are equally valid.**

Ali war unzufrieden mit der Entscheidung. Er hat einen Protest organisiert.	*Ali was unhappy with the decision.* *He organized a protest.*
Ali war unzufrieden mit der Entscheidung **und** (er) hat einen Protest organisiert.	*Ali was unhappy with the decision* *and (he) organized a protest.*

In this case, the person does both things. Because the subject is the same, it can be left out. If the verb is the same, you can omit it, too. These potential omissions mean that *und* also makes sentences flow better by connecting them.

258b Connecting Sentences With *oder*

Oder (or) also works like in English and connects several elements of which only one can apply, be valid, or happen at the same time. This is true for **lists**:

Am Rosenmontag fahre ich nach Köln **oder** Düsseldorf.	*On Carnival Monday, I will go to Cologne or Dusseldorf.*

and also when *oder* **connects two main clauses as a coordinating conjunction:**

Sie wollten demonstrieren. Sie wollten eine Petition schreiben.	*They wanted to stage a demonstration.* *They wanted to compose a petition.*
Sie wollten demonstrieren **oder** (sie wollten) eine Petition schreiben.	*They wanted to stage a demonstration,* *or they wanted to compose a petition.*

In German, there is usually no comma between two main clauses that are connected with *und* and *oder*.

258c Was passiert während der Basler Fasnacht? Setzen Sie die passenden Konnektoren in die Lücken: „und", „oder" oder „denn". Entscheiden Sie dabei, ob der Satz ein Komma braucht. Setzen Sie – wenn nötig – das Komma vor dem Konnektor ein.

Der Morgestraich ist der erste Tag der Basler Fasnacht ____________ beginnt um 4 Uhr morgens, wenn die Stadt die Straßenlaternen ausschaltet. Die Cliquen (*established Fasnacht groups*) laufen mit ihren berühmten Kopflaternen durch die dunklen Straßen. Zur gleichen Zeit öffnen viele Basler Restaurants ____________ sie bleiben den ganzen Tag offen. Gastronomiebetriebe (*restaurants and catering businesses*) freuen sich auf diesen Tag ____________ viele Cliquen beenden ihren Straßenlauf mit einer traditionellen Mehlsuppe und vielen Getränken. Die Basler Cliquen basteln ihre Kopflaternen schon Monate vorher ____________ kaufen Hüte, Make-up oder Perücken (*wigs*). Taxifahrer*innen arbeiten extralange Schichte ____________ es gibt viele beschwipste (*tipsy*) Fahrgäst*innen. Manche Familien bleiben in der Fasnachtszeit zu Hause ____________ sie fahren in den Urlaub. Die Basler Fasnacht ist ein großes Ereignis für die Region ____________ sie bringt viele Tourist*innen in die Stadt.

258d **Karneval. Unten sehen Sie eine Liste mit wichtigen Vokabeln zum deutschen Karneval. Finden Sie die richtige Definition. Versuchen Sie es zuerst selbst. Anschließend können Sie die Wörter nachschlagen, wenn Sie sich nicht sicher sind.**

die Weiberfastnacht (der Rathaussturm) ____

der Fasching / die Fastnacht ____

die Karnevalssitzung ____

die Büttenrede ____

jeck, der*die Jeck*in ____

der*die Närr*in ____

die Kamelle ____

das Kostüm ____

der (Um)Zug ____

die Garde ____

Helau!/Alaaf! ____

a) das ziehen Menschen an, um wie eine andere Person (oder ein Tier, ein Ding etc.) auszusehen
b) eine Parade von Karnevalswagen, auf denen Menschen feiern
c) regionale Synonyme für „Karneval"
d) ein Karnevalsevent, bei dem es ein Showprogramm auf einer Bühne mit Reden, Tanzeinlagen und Musik gibt
e) ein Karnevalsvortrag, der sich reimt und oft im regionalen Dialekt gehalten wird
f) Grüße, die beim Karneval gerufen werden
g) dieser Karnevalstag gehört den Frauen, die zum Beispiel Männern die Krawatten als Symbol von Macht abschneiden
h) das sind Süßigkeiten, die von den Karnevalswagen geworfen werden
i) im Mittelalter waren das Menschen im Kostüm, die König*innen kritisieren durften; heute ist es ein Wort für Menschen, die Karneval feiern
j) das Adjektiv bedeutet „verrückt" und das Nomen steht für „Menschen, die Karneval feiern"
k) beim Karneval ist das entweder eine Tanzgruppe oder eine Gruppe, die das Militär parodiert

259a **Kölsche Karnevalslieder. Sortieren Sie die Liedtitel und Bands „op Kölsch" zu den übersetzten Liedtiteln auf Hochdeutsch.**

Op Kölsch
Höhner: „Hey Kölle! Du bes e Jeföhl"
Brings: „Su lang mer noch am Lääve sin"
Paveier: „Leev Marie"
Colör: „Kölsche Mädcher sin jefährlich"
Höhner: „Mer stonn zo dir, FC Kölle"
Querbeat: „Stonn up un danz"
Bläck Fööss: „Dat Wasser vun Kölle"
Brings: „Superjeile Zick"
Paveier: „Mir sin Kölsche us Kölle am Rhing"
Micky Brühl Band: „Zo Fooss noh Kölle jonn"

Auf Hochdeutsch
„**Das** Wasser von Köln"
„Steh **auf** und tanz"
„Zu Fuß nach Köln **gehen**"
„**Liebe** Marie"
„Wir sind Kölner aus Köln am Rhein"
„So lange **wir** noch am Leben sind"
„Hey Köln! Du **bist** ein Gefühl"
„Wir **stehen** zu dir, FC Köln"
„Kölsche Mädchen sind **gefährlich**"
„Super**geile** Zeit"

Finden Sie die im hochdeutschen Titel markierten Wörter im kölschen Titel und kreisen Sie sie ein. Was wird aus diesen Buchstaben im Kölner Dialekt?

Aus „i" (z.B. bist, wir, liebe) wird ______ (z.B. ______________, ______________, ______________), aus „s" am Wortende (z.B. das) wird ______ (z.B. ______________), aus „g" (z.B. Gefühl, gefährlich, geil) wird ______ (z.B. ______________, ______________, ______________).

259b Kölsches Wörterbuch. Ergänzen Sie die Wörter auf Hochdeutsch oder Kölsch.

auf
das Herz
denn
der Zug
mein(e)

sin/ben/best
han
wat
~~kumme/kütt~~
jonn/jeit
lije/litt
luure
dat

Kölsch	Hochdeutsch
	das
	was
	sein/bin/bist
	haben
ming	
dann	
op	
kumme/kütt	kommen/kommt
	schauen
	liegen/liegt
	gehen/geht
Hätz	
Zoch	

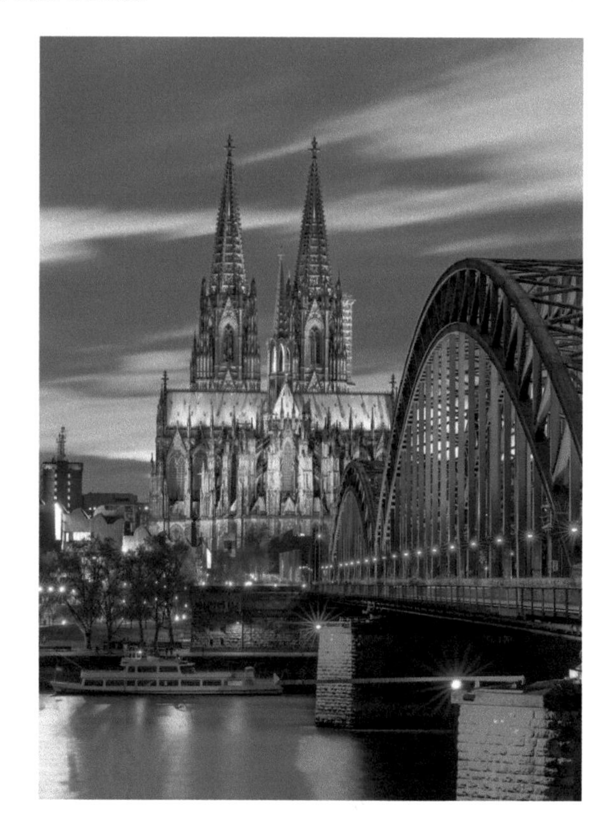

260a Idiomatic Use of the Prepositions: *an, auf, über*

You are familiar with the prepositions *an*, *auf*, and *über* in the context of two-way prepositions. They describe physical relationships between persons / things which will either take accusative (destination) or dative (location) forms (*Senta sitzt am Computer* but *Sally geht an den Computer*).

In addition to describing physical relationships (location / destination), ***an***, ***auf***, and ***über*** are also used in a more figurative sense when combined with certain verbs. Very often, a verbal translation to English is not possible.

Here are some high frequency verbs used with the prepositions ***an***, ***auf***, and ***über***. *Auf* and *über* always require the accusative case, while *an* can take either accusative or dative.

etwas (*akk.*) ändern	**an** + *dat.*	Ich ändere etwas **an** meiner Frisur.	*I am changing sth. about my hair.*
arbeiten	**an** + *dat.*	Wir arbeiten **an** der Kampagne.	*We are working on the campaign.*
sich ärgern	**über** + *akk.*	Er ärgert sich **über** die Politik.	*He is annoyed about politics.*
denken	**an** + *akk.*	Wir denken **an** die Tiere.	*We are thinking of the animals.*
(sich) erinnern	**an** + *akk.*	Ich erinnere mich **an** die Ferien.	*I am remembering the vacation.*
jdn. (*akk.*) erinnern	**an** + *akk.*	Ich erinnere Noah **an** die Aufgabe.	*I remind Noah about the assignment.*
sich freuen	**auf** + *akk.*	Wir freuen uns **auf** die Ferien.	*We are looking forward to the holidays.*
sich freuen	**über** + *akk.*	Sie freut sich **über** das Geschenk.	*She is happy about the gift.*
glauben	**an** + *akk.*	Sie glauben **an** den Fortschritt.	*They believe in progress.*
(sich) informieren	**über** + *akk.*	Er informiert **über** die Wahl.	*He informs (so.) about the elections.*
nachdenken	**über** + *akk.*	Denkt ihr **über** den Protest nach?	*Do you think about the protest?*
sprechen	**über** + *akk.*	Wir sprechen **über** die Demo.	*We are talking about the demonstration.*
schreiben	**über** + *akk.*	Ich schreibe **über** den Protest.	*I am writing about the protest.*
schreiben	**an** + *akk.*	Wir schreiben **an** die Zeitung.	*We are writing to the newspaper.*
warten	**auf** + *akk.*	Sie wartet **auf** eure Neuigkeiten.	*She is waiting for your news.*
zweifeln	**an** + *dat.*	Er zweifelt **an** seinen Worten.	*He is doubting his words.*

260b **Mottowagen: Ein wichtiger Teil des deutschen Karnevals sind die sogenannten „Mottowagen". Auf diesen Wagen sind keine feiernden Menschen. Stattdessen gibt es satirische bzw. kritische Figuren und Szenen aus Pappmaché, die aktuelle Ereignisse aus Politik und Gesellschaft kommentieren. Machen Sie eine Bildersuche online. Was sehen Sie? Beantworten Sie die Fragen.**

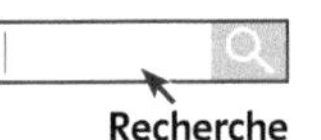
Recherche

Wagen 1 – Suchbegriffe: Rosenmontag, Mottowagen, Greta Thunberg, Fridays for Future

Welche Objekte, Wörter oder Sprüche sehen Sie?

___

Was ist die Botschaft dieses Mottowagens?

___

___

Wie effektiv finden Sie den Wagen?

___

___

Wagen 2 – Suchbegriffe: Rosenmontag, Mottowagen, Coronavirus

Welche Objekte, Wörter oder Sprüche sehen Sie?

___

Was ist die Botschaft dieses Mottowagens?

___

___

Wie effektiv finden Sie den Wagen?

___

___

Wagen 3 – Suchbegriffe: Rosenmontag, Mottowagen, Facebook, Hass

Welche Objekte, Wörter oder Sprüche sehen Sie?

___

Was ist die Botschaft dieses Mottowagens?

___

___

Wie effektiv finden Sie den Wagen?

___

___

Wagen 4 – Jedes Jahr gibt es viele Karnevalswagen, die Personen aus der nationalen und internationalen Politik scharf kritisieren. Finden Sie online ein Foto von einem solchen Wagen.

Welche Objekte, Wörter oder Sprüche sehen Sie?

___

Was ist die Botschaft dieses Mottowagens?

___

___

Wie effektiv finden Sie den Wagen?

___

___

82: Widerstand im Dritten Reich

261a Verbs With Prepositional Objects: *Dativ*

Thus far, you have encountered verbs that always take accusative prepositions, such as *für* and *gegen*, and verbs with the prepositions *an*, *auf*, and *über*. Out of the many dative prepositions you know, the following small selection also is commonly found in combination with selected verbs: ***bei***, ***mit***, ***von***, and ***zu***. Look at the following examples to see how these verb + **prepositions** + dative combinations are used.

anfangen	**mit** + *dat.*	Morgen fangen wir **mit** dem Streik an.	*Tomorrow, we will start the strike.*
beginnen	**mit** + *dat.*	Wir beginnen **mit** der Protestaktion.	*We are beginning with the protest.*
aufhören	**mit** + *dat.*	Er hört **mit** dem Protest nicht auf.	*He doesn't stop protesting.*
streiten	**mit** + *dat.*	Wir streiten **mit** dem Mann.	*We are arguing with the man.*
(sich) beschweren	**bei** + *dat.*	Sie beschwerte sich **bei** ihm.	*She complained to him.*
jdm. (*dat.*) helfen	**bei** + *dat.*	Er hilft ihm **bei** den Hausaufgaben.	*He helps him with the homework.*
etwas (*akk.*) verlangen	**von** + *dat.*	Wir verlangen **von** ihr ein Geschenk.	*We demand a present from her.*
jdn. (*akk.*) überreden	**zu** + *dat.*	Ich überrede meinen Freund **zu**m Lesen.	*I am persuading my friend to read.*

Many verbs can have two objects connected to them with the help of prepositions. Some of the ones above, for example, can also add ***über*** (about), saying what somebody is complaining or arguing about. Remember that *über* requires the accusative:

Sie beschwerte sich **bei** ihm über die vielen Hausaufgaben. — *She complained to him about all the homework.*
Wir streiten **mit** dem Mann über den Streik. — *We are arguing with the man about the strike.*

261b Eine Reportage über die Edelweißpiraten. Ergänzen Sie die Lücken mit den passenden Verben und Präpositionen.

Die Edelweißpiraten waren junge Leute im westlichen Deutschland. Circa 1938 __________________ sie ______ ihrem Protest gegen die Nazis. (überredeten zu | begannen mit)

Die nationalsozialistische Ideologie __________________ ______ Jugendlichen eine Trennung in Jungen und Mädchen, obwohl die Jugendbewegung seit 1896 für beide Gruppen offen gewesen war. (verlangte von | half bei)

Die Edelweißpiraten wollten so ein Leben aber nicht. Sie suchten Freiheit und Autonomie und deshalb ____________________ sie ______ den konservativen und nationalsozialistischen Jugendgruppen. (änderten an | stritten mit)

Zuerst ____________________ sich die lokalen Nazis nur ______ die Edelweißpiraten in ihren Städten, aber später verhafteten sie die jungen Rebell*innen. (beschwerten über | überredeten zu) Dreizehn von ihnen wurden exekutiert.

261c **Anne Frank. Lesen Sie die folgenden Sätze über Anne Frank und setzen Sie die passende Verbform ein.**

verlangen | sich beschweren | ändern | helfen | beginnen | sich streiten

Freund*innen und Bekannte der Familie Frank haben bei dem Plan ______________, Anne, ihre Eltern Edith und Otto und ihre Schwester Margot zu verstecken. Das haben sie freiwillig getan, ohne etwas von der Familie zu ______________. Während der Zeit im Versteck hat Anne mit dem Schreiben eines Tagebuchs ______________, das sie „Kitty" nannte. Dem Tagebuch hat Anne alles erzählt, z. B. dass sie ______________ oft mit ihrer Mutter und ihrer Schwester ______________. Aber Anne hat ______________ nicht nur bei Kitty über andere Menschen ______________, sondern sie hat auch viele schöne Momente aufgeschrieben. Anne war auch selbstkritisch. So hat sie Kitty erzählt, dass sie gerne etwas an sich ______________ möchte, um nicht immer so schnell wütend zu werden.

262a **Hören Sie den Text über die Weiße Rose und machen Sie sich Notizen zu den Fragen. Schreiben Sie Ihre Notizen zu den letzten beiden Fragen in die Tabelle in MACHEN Aktivität 262.**

Wer waren die Mitglieder der Weißen Rose?

____

Worauf reagierten sie mit ihrem Widerstand?

____

Für MACHEN: Was waren die Themen der Flugblätter? Was war besonders am 6. Flugblatt der Gruppe?

____

262b Connecting Sentences: *aber* and *sondern*

Aber and ***sondern*** express **contrasting information**. They both mean "but" in English, though a more accurate translation for *sondern* would be "but instead." While *aber* is used to express any kind of contrast between two statements, the meaning of *sondern* is to negate or correct a statement in the first main clause that usually contains a negation already.

They belong to the same group of coordinating subjunctions as *und* and *oder*. This means that they combine two main clauses without consequences for the word order.

Im Dritten Reich gab es auch Widerstand, **aber** die Widerständigen mussten sehr vorsichtig sein.	*There was also resistance in the Third Reich, but the resisters had to be very careful.*
Sophie und Hans Scholl waren keine Nazis, **sondern** (sie)[1] schrieben Flugblätter gegen das Regime.	*Sophie and Hans Scholl weren't Nazis, but instead they wrote leaflets against the regime.*

[1] In *sondern*-clauses: when the subject is the same for both main clauses, it is often left out.

262c **Die Geschwister Scholl. Welcher Konnektor fehlt: „sondern" oder „aber"?**

Hans und Sophie Scholl kamen nicht aus Berlin, ____________ aus der Stadt Forchtenberg in Baden-Württemberg.

Sophie Scholl war im Bund Deutscher Mädel, ____________ sie war keine Nazi-Sympathisantin.

Hans und Sophie Scholl studierten zur gleichen Zeit, ____________ Hans war drei Jahre älter als Sophie.

Sie studierten nicht in Stuttgart, ____________ in München.

Hans Scholl studierte nicht Philosophie und Biologie, wie seine Schwester, ____________ Medizin.

Die Studierenden in der Weißen Rose waren nicht nur moralisch engagiert, ____________ sie waren auch sehr mutig.

262d **Was stimmt hier nicht? Florian hat eine Biografie über Christoph Probst geschrieben, ein Mitglied der studentischen Widerstandsgruppe Weiße Rose. Leider hat er Fehler gemacht. Korrigieren Sie seinen Text. Welcher Konnektor fehlt: „sondern" oder „aber"?**

Florian: Christoph Probst wurde am 6. November 1920 geboren.

Korrektur: Probst wurde nicht 1920, ____________ 1919 geboren.

Florian: Probsts Vater war Griechischlehrer.

Korrektur: Nein, sein Vater unterrichtete kein Griechisch, ____________ Sanskrit.

Florian: Probst studierte Physik an der Universität in München.

Korrektur: Ja, er studierte in München, ____________ es war Medizin, nicht Physik.

Florian: Obwohl Probst noch jung war, hatte er schon zwei Kinder, als die Nazis ihn verhafteten.

Korrektur: Richtig, Probst war jung und hatte Kinder, ____________ es waren drei. Das Baby war erst einen Monat alt.

Florian: Probst wurde am 22. Februar 1942 exekutiert. Er war erst 23 Jahre alt.

Korrektur: Das Datum ist korrekt, ____________ er war noch keine 23.

83: Die 68er – Jugend protestiert°

266a **Der Name „68er-Bewegung" bezieht sich auf unterschiedliche soziale Bewegungen in den 1960er Jahren, die besonders im Jahr 1968 weltweit für Aufmerksamkeit sorgten. Es war eine transnationale Bewegung in vielen Ländern. Lesen Sie den folgenden Text und markieren Sie in jedem Absatz die wichtigsten Informationen. Sie müssen diese Informationen im Kurs anwenden können.**

Die Proteste in den USA begannen schon in den 1950er Jahren unter der Führung von Martin Luther King. So war zum Beispiel der Busboykott von Montgomery im Jahr 1955 ein wichtiger Moment in der amerikanischen Bewegung. In den 60er Jahren formte sich eine starke Oppositionsbewegung gegen den Vietnamkrieg. In Mexiko gab es Studierendenproteste gegen die Partei der Institutionalisierten Revolution. Die Studierenden protestierten hier vor allem gegen die große Ungleichheit im Land. Auch in Japan protestierten in den 60er Jahren viele Studierende gegen den Sicherheitsvertrag mit der US-Armee und im Jahr 1965 begannen japanische Gewerkschaften, gegen den Vietnamkrieg zu demonstrieren.

In Europa war die Bewegung schon sehr früh in Großbritannien aktiv. Dort gab es die Campaign for Nuclear Disarmament. Sie war eine außerparlamentarische Bewegung, die gegen die atomare Aufrüstung der NATO protestierte. In Frankreich hatten in den 1960er Jahren die Arbeiter*innen wegen der politischen Zentralisierung keine gute Repräsentation in den Firmen. Da es ab 1967 zu einer immer stärkeren Rezession kam, wurden die Arbeiter*innenproteste immer radikaler. Aber auch die Studierenden kämpften in Frankreich für mehr Rechte und Freiheiten. So kam es im Mai 1968 zu starken Protesten an der Université Paris Nanterre. In Italien war die Bewegung hauptsächlich eine Reaktion auf die wirtschaftliche Ungleichheit zwischen Nord- und Süditalien.

In Österreich drückte sich die Bewegung vor allem durch den Wiener Aktionismus aus und in der Schweiz kam es ebenso zu Kämpfen zwischen jugendlichen Demonstrierenden und der Polizei. In Deutschland kämpfte die 68er-Bewegung für Demokratisierung, antiautoritäre Erziehung oder die Entnazifizierung an Universitäten. Die Studierenden kämpften auch gegen das Meinungsmonopol des Axel-Springer-Verlags, denn sie waren der Meinung, dass der Verlag versuchte, die öffentliche Meinung zu manipulieren. Die Bewegung in Deutschland wurde radikaler, nachdem es am 11. April 1968 ein Attentat auf Rudi Dutschke, einen Anführer der Bewegung, gab.

266b **1950er bis 1960er: Proteste gegen die herrschenden Kräfte. Welcher Konnektor fehlt hier?**

1955 gab es den Busboykott in Montgomery ________________ (oder | , denn) Afroamerikaner*innen durften ihre Bussitze nicht frei wählen.

In Mexiko protestierten Studierende zuerst nur gegen die Partido Revolucionario Institucional (Partei der Institutionalisierten Revolution) ________________ (, aber | oder) später protestierten sie auch für die soziale Unterschicht im Land.

Junge Japaner*innen kämpften gegen die US-Soldat*innen in ihrem Land ________________ (oder | und) die Arbeiter*innengewerkschaft kämpfte gegen den Vietnamkrieg.

Viele Brit*innen wollten keine Atomwaffen ________________ (, aber | oder) die NATO wollte diese Waffen benutzen.

In Frankreich wollten Arbeiter*innen mehr Rechte am Arbeitsplatz ________________ (und | , aber) die Unternehmen erlaubten trotz dieser Proteste keine Repräsentation.

Politisch aktive Deutsche protestierten gegen Polizeigewalt ________________ (oder | , denn) sie wollten antiautoritäre Strukturen.

267a **Wer war Studierendenführer Rudi Dutschke? Verbinden Sie die Sätze und entscheiden Sie, welcher Konnektor passt: „denn" oder „weil". Die Verbposition hilft Ihnen.**

In der DDR geboren, floh Rudi Dutschke 1961 nach Westberlin, (denn | weil) ____________ ____

Er studierte Soziologie, Philosophie und Geschichte in Berlin, (denn | weil) ____________ ____

1965 wurde er Mitglied des Sozialistischen Deutschen Studentenbundes (SDS), (denn | weil) ____________ ____

Der Christ Dutschke wurde ein Sozialist, (denn | weil) ____________ ____

Dutschke wollte die Studierenden nicht radikalisieren, (denn | weil) ____________ ____

a) der SDS Demonstrationen gegen die Vietnamkrieg organisierte.
b) er hoffte, dass sie die Regierung in der Zukunft legal reformieren würden.
c) er wollte nicht ostdeutscher Soldat werden.
d) er sah Jesus als ersten sozialistischen Freiheitskämpfer.
e) er sich für soziale Gerechtigkeit interessierte.

84: Automatisierung – Protestieren oder mitbestimmen?

268a **Länder im Vergleich. Lesen Sie die Informationen über die verschiedenen Länder. Benutzen Sie den Komparativ und den Superlativ, um die Daten zu vergleichen.**

Einwohner*innen: Deutschland 83 Millionen – Japan 126,8 Millionen – Indien 1,36 Milliarden

*Japan hat mehr Einwohner*innen als Deutschland. (Es gibt mehr Einwohner*innen in Japan als in Deutschland.) Indien hat die meisten Einwohner*innen. (Die meisten Einwohner*innen gibt es in Indien.)*

Fläche in Quadratkilometern: Italien 301.338 – USA 9.826.675 – Russland 17.075.400

Bruttoinlandsprodukt (BIP) in US-Dollar (2018): China 13,36 Millionen – USA 20,58 Millionen – Brasilien 1,86 Millionen

Bevölkerungsdichte (Einwohner*innen pro Quadratkilometer): Schweiz 213 – Südkorea 513 – Frankreich 103

Arbeitslosenquote (2019): Spanien 14 % – UK 3,7 % – Österreich 4,5 %

269a **Textvorbereitung: Wichtige Wörter. Schlagen Sie die folgenden Wörter in einem Wörterbuch nach und schreiben Sie damit einen Satz, der Ihnen hilft, sie im Kontext zu lernen.**

die Gewerkschaft, -en — In Ihrer Sprache: ____________

Satz auf Deutsch: ____________

der Arbeitsplatz, ¨-e — In Ihrer Sprache: ____________

Satz auf Deutsch: ____________

der*die Arbeitnehmer*in, -*innen — In Ihrer Sprache: ____________

Satz auf Deutsch: ____________

das Unternehmen, - — In Ihrer Sprache: ____________

Satz auf Deutsch: ____________

die Weiterbildung, -en — In Ihrer Sprache: ____________

Satz auf Deutsch: ____________

die Versicherung, -en — In Ihrer Sprache: ____________

Satz auf Deutsch: ____________

270a **Unten sehen Sie eine Liste von modernen Herausforderungen, die einen großen Einfluss auf unser Leben haben (werden). Welche Thematik passt zu welchem Bild bzw. zu welchen Bildern?**

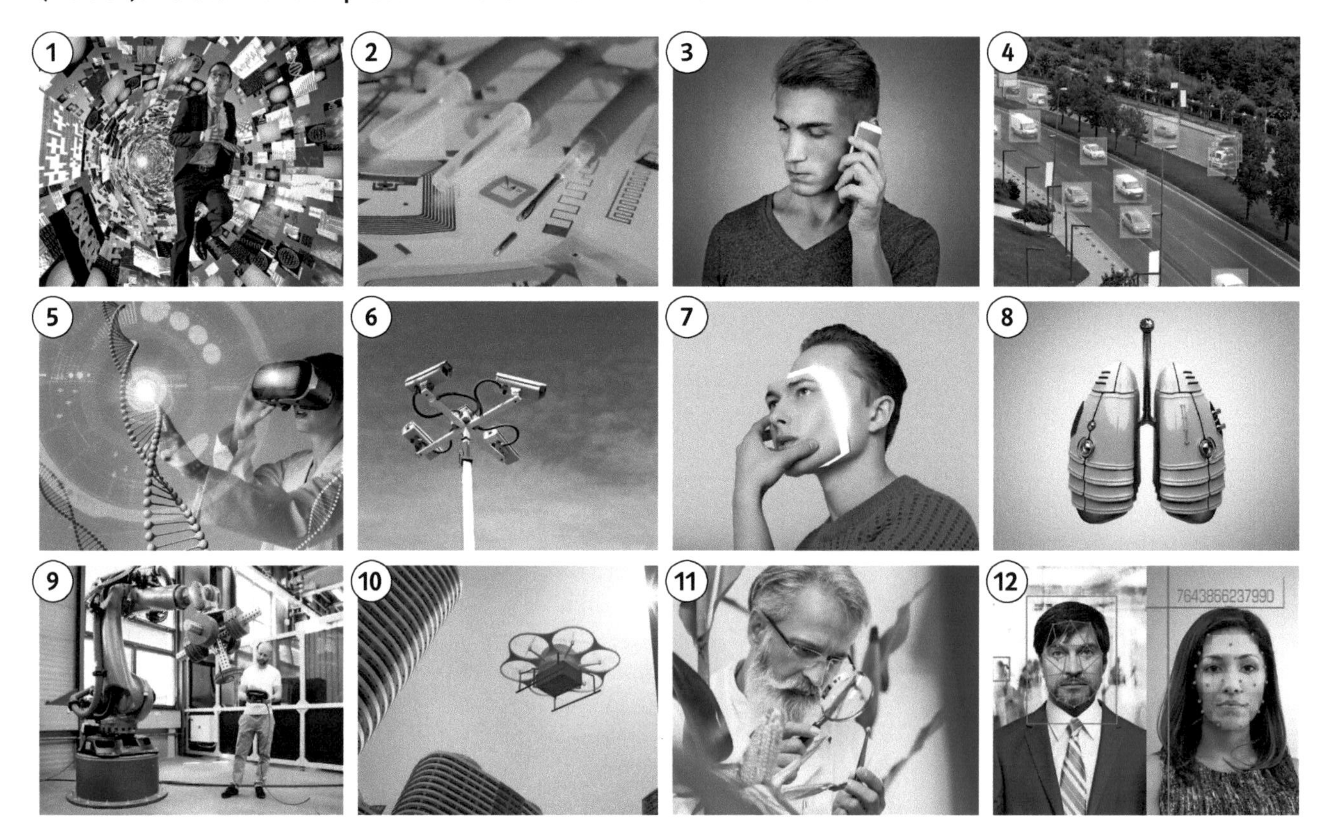

- Genmanipulation
- Massendaten
- Automatisierung
- Überwachung
- Strahlung
- künstliche Organe
- Mikrochipeinpflanzung
- Kfz-Kennzeichenerkennung
- selbstfliegende Drohnen bzw. Taxis
- automatische Gesichtserkennung
- gentechnisch veränderte Organismen
- menschliche Roboter

270b Review: *da-* and *wo-*Compounds

We have looked at a variety of prepositions and how they often pair with different verbs. In written texts and in daily communication, you often don't want to repeat a prepositional phrase (a noun or pronoun preceded by a preposition). But you can take a shortcut – at least for nouns that are not people or animals. Instead of repeating the noun with all its attributes and its preposition, you can refer to this previously mentioned information by attaching the prefix *da-* to the **preposition** → *da**mit***, *da**von***, *da**zu***. This comes in handy when using those verb + **preposition** + noun-phrases we have practiced before. Take a look at the following examples.

Interessierst du dich **für** die deutsche Kolonialgeschichte?	*Are you interested **in** German colonial history?*
Ja, ich interessiere mich **für** die deutsche Kolonialgeschichte.	*Yes, I am interested **in** German colonial history.*
Ja, ich interessiere mich da**für**.	*Yes, I am interested **in** it.*
Kümmerst du dich **um** die Verteilung der Flugblätter?	*Will you take care **of** the distribution of flyers?*
Ja, ich kümmere mich **um** die Verteilung der Flugblätter.	*Yes, I will take care **of** the distribution of flyers.*
Ja, ich kümmere mich dar**um**.	*Yes, I will take care **of** it.*

These very practical *da*-compounds can be built with most prepositions. If a preposition starts with a vowel, you have to insert the letter *-r-* between the *da-* and the **preposition**.

da**für**, da**gegen**, da**mit**, da**von**, da**vor**, da**zu**, dar**an**, dar**auf**, dar**aus**, dar**über**, dar**um**

The same principle applies when you need a question word that asks for an element with a **preposition**. For these, you will use the prefix <u>wo</u>-:

<u>Wo</u>r**auf** wartest du? Ich warte **auf** <u>einen Brief</u>.	*<u>What</u> are you waiting **for**?* *I am waiting **for** <u>a letter</u>.*
<u>Wo</u>r**über** habt ihr gesprochen? Wir haben **über** <u>die Demonstration gesprochen</u>.	*<u>What</u> did you talk **about**?* *We talked **about** <u>the demonstration</u>.*

You can attach the generic question particle <u>*wo*</u>- to the front of the **preposition** and create a whole list of new question words. Again, this question words are not applicable for people and animals. And don't forget to insert the -*r*- here, too, in front of the vowel.

<u>wo</u>**für**, <u>wo</u>**gegen**, <u>wo</u>**mit**, <u>wo</u>**von**, <u>wo</u>**vor**, <u>wo</u>**zu**, <u>wo</u>r**an**, <u>wo</u>r**auf**, <u>wo</u>r**aus**, <u>wo</u>r**über**, <u>wo</u>r**um**

270c **In Aktivität 270a haben Sie Zukunftstechnologien kennengelernt. Lesen Sie die kurzen Dialoge und setzen Sie die „wo"- und „da"-Komposita ein.**

Yael: Ich sorge mich **um** die Privatsphäre bei den neuen Technologien. Sorgst du dich auch ____________?

Philipp: Nein, ____________ sorge ich mich nicht.

Yael: ____________ sorgst du dich?

Philipp: Ich sorge mich um die Umwelt.

Yael: Ja, ____________ sorge ich mich auch.

Alina: Hast du Angst **vor** der Strahlung von Handys?

Sascha: Ja, ____________ habe ich schon ein bisschen Angst. Und ____________ hast du Angst?

Alina: Ich habe Angst vor der Genmanipulation. Damit kann so viel Negatives gemacht werden.

Sascha: Hm, ____________ habe ich eigentlich keine Angst.

270d **Und Sie? Welche Dinge aus Aktivität 270a finden Sie (nicht) bedrohlich? Welche Konsequenzen könnten sie haben?**

Was?	bedrohlich?	Konsequenz
Überwachung	*ja*	*Dadurch (= durch Überwachung) würde ich keine Privatsphäre mehr haben.*

270e **Roboter: Was passt zusammen? Ordnen Sie zu.**

Arten von Robotern

a) humanoide Roboter | b) autonome Transportroboter | c) Industrieroboter | d) Cobots | e) Roboter mit künstlicher Intelligenz

- Diese Roboter arbeiten schon sehr lange, vor allem im Autobau.
- Diese Fahrzeuge fahren ohne Fahrer*innen und transportieren Materialien, zum Beispiel in der Industrie.
- Diese Roboter sind recht neu. Sie arbeiten mit Menschen zusammen, das heißt, sie kooperieren.
- Diese Roboter sehen aus wie Menschen.
- Diese Roboter müssen nicht programmiert werden, sondern sie lernen selbst.

Steuerung

a) direkt (Fernsteuerung) | b) teilautonom | c) autonom

- Dieser Roboter erkennt seine Aufgaben und führt sie alleine aus.
- Dieser Roboter wird mit einem Gerät, zum Beispiel dem Handy, gesteuert.
- Hier definiert der Mensch eine Aufgabe, die der Roboter dann alleine ausführt.

Greifer

a) mechanisch | b) magnetisch | c) humanoide Hände

- Das sind Greifer aus der Industrie: pneumatisch für leichtes und hydraulisch für schweres Material.
- Sie können die gleichen Bewegungen wie menschliche Hände ausführen.
- Davon gibt es in zwei Varianten: permanent magnetisch oder elektromagnetisch.

Sensoren

a) Kraftsensoren | b) induktive Sensoren | c) kapazitive Sensoren | d) magnetische Sensoren | e) Tastsensoren | f) optische Sensoren

- Sie arbeiten mit einer Kamera und analysieren Bilder. Sie werden für die Navigation gebraucht.
- Sie erkennen Metallteile, ohne sie zu berühren, induktiv durch ein elektromagnetisches Feld.
- Diese Sensoren können die Position exakt erfassen (*determine*), durch GMR = Riesenmagnetowiderstand (*giant magnetoresistance*).
- Diese Sensoren sind im Greifer und erfassen Kräfte und Drehmomente (*torque*).
- Sie messen Distanz, z. B. zwischen Robotern und Menschen durch die Kapazität eines elektrischen Kondensators.
- Sie nehmen Objekte durch Berührung wahr und können den Griff anpassen.

270f **Gehen Sie auf die deutschsprachige Webseite der Münchner Firma Franka Emika, die Sie auf der Linkliste unter www.klett-usa.com/impuls2links finden. Schauen Sie sich den Franke Emika Roboterarm (auch „Panda" genannt) an. Beschreiben Sie ihn mit Informationen aus Aktivität 270e.**

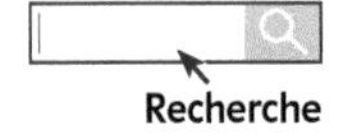
Recherche

___

___

85: Street Art

271a **Lesen Sie den Text und wählen Sie für jeden Abschnitt eine passende Überschrift aus dem Kasten (unten) aus.**

Street Art: Zwischen Kunst, Kommerz und Kriminalität

Überschrift für Absatz 1: ______________________________

Street Art ist eine künstlerische Ausdrucksform im öffentlichen Raum, die für alle zugänglich ist. Graffiti gilt oft auch als Street Art, obwohl es Unterschiede gibt. Während Street Art meist bildbasiert ist, ist Graffiti schriftbasiert und grundsätzlich illegal. Es entstand im urbanen Raum. Vor allem junge Menschen nutzen Graffiti. Die Sprayer*innen besprühen jede freie Fläche – ob Mülleimer, Hauswände oder Züge – mit ihren „Tags" und kommunizieren auf diese Weise untereinander. Viele Menschen denken, dass Graffitis die Städte verunstalten (*to disfigure*) und sie werden als Sachbeschädigung (*damage to property*) gesehen.

Überschrift für Absatz 2: ______________________________

Street Art zieht ihre Inspiration aus Graffiti, aber die Künstler*innen sind oft ausgebildet (*formally trained*). Deshalb sind ihre Kritik und Gestaltungsmöglichkeiten komplexer. Unter den Künstler*innen gibt es die Parole „Reclaim the Streets". Sie wollen die Straßen zurückerobern und kritisieren die flächendeckende (*extensive*) Werbung in den Städten und ein oft einheitliches, charakterloses Stadtbild. Mit ihren Bildern senden die Künstler*innen auch manchmal explizit gesellschaftskritische und politische Botschaften. Andere Werke sind dekorativ oder einfach witzig.

Überschrift für Absatz 3: ______________________________

Dabei kann auch Street Art illegal sein, wenn die Künstler*innen keine Genehmigung (*permission*) haben. Street Art ist aber viel akzeptierter als Graffiti. Oft werden Street Art-Künstler*innen sogar dafür engagiert und bezahlt, graue Flächen kunstvoll zu gestalten, um das Stadtbild damit zu verschönern. Street Art ist mittlerweile gesellschaftlich so etabliert, dass sie ihren Rebellionscharakter ein bisschen verloren hat. Weil viele Menschen Street Art cool und hip finden, gibt es zum Beispiel in vielen Städten Street Art-Touren oder Ausstellungen (*exhibitions*). Entgegen ihrer ursprünglichen Intention wird Street Art so teilweise kommerzialisiert.

- Wie sich der Charakter von Street Art verändert hat
- Unterschiede zwischen Street Art und Graffiti
- Strafen (*punishments*) fürs Graffitisprühen
- Wie man Street Art-Künstler*in wird
- Street Art-Künstler*innen und ihre Intention

271b **Entscheiden Sie (basierend auf dem Text in Aktivität 271a): Sind die Aussagen richtig oder falsch?**

richtig	falsch	
		Um Street Art zu sehen, müssen die Leute bezahlen.
		Viele Menschen finden Graffitis schön.
		Viele Street Art-Künstler*innen haben eine Agenda.
		Manche Street Art-Kunstwerke sollen einfach nur Spaß machen.
		Street Art ist umstrittener als Graffiti.
		Einige Street Art-Künstler*innen verdienen mit ihrer Kunst Geld.

271c **Vokabeln: Street Art. Welche Begriffe sind in diesem Kontext Gegenteile? Bilden Sie Paare.**

der Raum | hässlich | die Schrift | dekorativ | bunt | traditionell | verschönern | ~~illegal~~ | unzugänglich | umstritten

legal	*illegal*	schwarz-weiß	______	zugänglich	______
schön	______	innovativ	______	akzeptiert	______
politisch	______	verunstalten	______	die Fläche	______
das Bild	______				

271d Connecting Sentences: *dass*

Dass (that) is a subordinating conjunction frequently used with verbs that help you to express your opinions about something. We have learned these verbs that are complemented by a *dass*-clause before:

denken, dass	*to think that*	finden, dass	*to find that*
glauben, dass	*to believe that*	meinen, dass	*to mean/think/guess that*
sicher sein, dass	*to be sure that*	wissen, dass	*to know (as a fact) that*

Besides helping us to express our opinion, *dass* can also add more information to a sentence, much in the same way it would be used in English when you can add "that" to a verb:

Sie haben angekündigt, dass …	*They announced that …*
Wir wollen, dass …	*We want (that) …*
Er beschwert sich bei ihr, dass …	*He complains to her that …*

Dass connects a subordinate clause to a main clause. The two clauses are separated by a comma, and as a subordinating conjunction, *dass* causes the **conjugated verb** to move to the end of the clause.

Die Polizei **hat** gestern angekündigt,
dass für das Festival Graffiti erlaubt **ist**.

The police announced yesterday
that graffiti would be permitted for the festival.

The *dass*-clause can also come first and the main clause second (this doesn't work in English). If you create the sentence that way, your subordinate clause counts as position one, and the **conjugated verb** in the main clause will come right after the comma in the second position.

Dass Graffiti für das Festival erlaubt **ist**,
hat die Polizei gestern angekündigt.

(That graffiti would be permitted for the festival
the police announced yesterday.)

271e **Ist das Kunst? Hier sehen Sie, wie Kunstkritiker*innen ihre Meinung über verschiedene Künstler*innen und deren Werke ausdrücken können. Ergänzen Sie die „dass"-Sätze, wie im Beispiel.**

Ich bin sicher, dass *auch Monet dieses Werk lieben würde.*

Die Künstlerin hat angekündigt, dass ______.

Ich weiß, dass ______.

Ich finde, dass ______.

Haben Sie gehört, dass ______?

Ich glaube, dass ______.

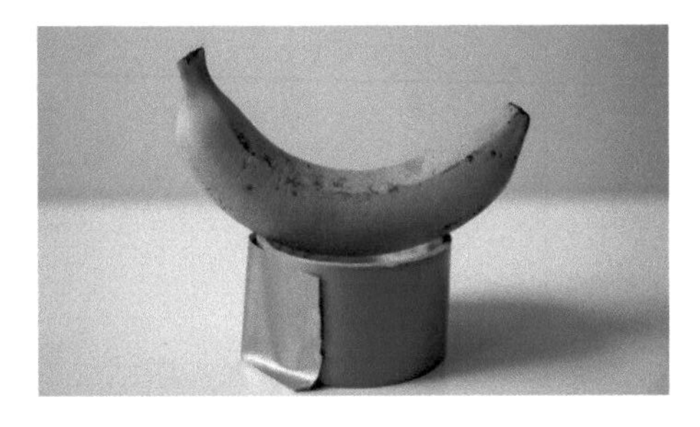

~~Auch Monet würde dieses Werk lieben.~~
Sie wird nächstes Jahr nach Shanghai ziehen.
Seine Ausstellung in Accra war umstritten.
Der Stil dieser Künstlerin ist traditionell und doch unzugänglich.
Die Stadt hat ihn für ein Wandgemälde (*mural*) am Bahnhof engagiert.
Seine Botschaft könnte politischer sein.

86: Mit Möhren gegen koloniale Spuren

274a **Namen des deutschen Kolonialismus. Sie lesen jetzt sechs Kurzbiografien von Deutschen, die in Verbindung mit dem Kolonialismus stehen. Entscheiden Sie nach dem Lesen: Sind die Aussagen unten richtig oder falsch?**

Hedwig Heyl: Sie kämpfte für Frauenrechte, aber Heyl war auch eine Begründerin (*founder*) des Frauenbundes im deutschen Kolonialverein. Ihre Denkweise war eindeutig rassistisch. Sie war verantwortlich für das Verschicken von sogenanntem „Mädchenmaterial". Das heißt, dass sie weiße, junge Frauen für die deutschen Kolonisten aussuchte. Heyl wollte nicht, dass die Kolonialherren sexuelle Kontakte zu den afrikanischen Frauen suchten.

Adolf Lüderitz: Der Bremer Kaufmann erwarb (*purchased*) im späten 19. Jahrhundert Land im heutigen Namibia. Durch einen Schwindel (*con*) erhielt er mehr Land als geplant. Lüderitz' Landerwerb und seine geschäftlichen Aktivitäten im heutigen Namibia legten den Grundstein für die spätere, gewalttätige Kolonialherrschaft in Deutsch-Südwestafrika.

Karl Peters (auch Carl Peters): Peters war Publizist und „Afrikaforscher" mit stark rassistischer Einstellung. Als Kolonialherr in Deutsch-Ostafrika war er für sein gewalttätiges Verhalten gegenüber der afrikanischen Bevölkerung bekannt – auch gegenüber Kindern.

Paul von Lettow-Vorbeck: Er war ein General der deutschen Kolonialkriege. Im heutigen Namibia beteiligte er sich am Genozid an den Herero. Im Ersten Weltkrieg führte er in Afrika eine skrupellose militärische Kampagne, bei der auch viele Zivilist*innen starben.

Adolph Woermann: Woermann war Kaufmann und Reeder (= Besitzer mehrerer Schiffe) und einer der Begründer der deutschen Kolonien in Afrika. Er profitierte vom Völkermord (= Genozid) an den Herero, weil er mit seinen Schiffen die deutschen Soldaten und Waffen transportierte, die im Kampf gegen die Herero benutzt wurden.

Lothar von Trotha: Von Trotha war ein General und der Vorgesetzte (*superior*) von Lettow-Vorbeck. Er gab den Befehl, auf alle Herero zu schießen, egal ob sie bewaffnet waren oder nicht, ob Mann, Frau oder Kind.

richtig	falsch	
☐	☐	Hedwig Heyl half, weiße Frauen in die Kolonien zu schicken, damit die Kolonisten keine Beziehungen mit einheimischen Frauen hatten.
☐	☐	Adolf Lüderitz kaufte sein gesamtes Land auf legalem Wege.
☐	☐	Karl Peters behandelte die afrikanische Bevölkerung mit Respekt.
☐	☐	Paul von Lettow-Vorbeck war mitverantwortlich für den Genozid im heutigen Namibia.
☐	☐	Durch seine Transportschiffe verdiente Adolph Woermann Geld mit dem Völkermord an den Herero.
☐	☐	Lothar von Trotha befahl, Frauen und Kinder der Herero nicht zu töten.

274b **Schreiben Sie zwei Fakten auf, die Sie beim Lesen der Biografien (Aktivität 274a) überrascht/schockiert haben oder die Sie besonders wichtig finden. Erklären Sie, warum Sie diese Fakten gewählt haben. Die Namen dieser Personen werden Sie in MACHEN wiedersehen.**

____

____

____

275a **Textvorbereitung: Straßen als Denkmäler. Lesen Sie die Textabschnitte und beantworten Sie die Fragen. Gehen Sie dabei Schritt für Schritt vor.**

Antizipieren. Überlegen Sie zuerst: Inwiefern können Straßen Denkmäler sein? Machen Sie sich auf der nächsten Seite Stichpunkte.

Lesen Sie den ersten Textabschnitt und beantworten Sie unten die Fragen: richtig oder falsch?

Straßennamen sind wie Denkmäler. Straßen können an bestimmte Menschen erinnern, die eine historische und/oder kulturelle Bedeutung haben. Diese Bedeutung kann sich natürlich ändern, weil sich die Werte (*values*) einer Gesellschaft auch ändern können.

richtig	falsch	
		Straßennamen erinnern an berühmte Personen.
		Die Bedeutung von Personen bleibt immer gleich.

Überlegen Sie: Straßennamen in den USA. An welche berühmten Personen wird auf vielen Straßenschildern in den USA erinnert? Können Sie sich vorstellen, nach welchen deutschen Personen vielleicht früher Straßen benannt waren, heute aber nicht mehr?

Lesen Sie den zweiten Textabschnitt. Sind die Aussagen richtig oder falsch?

Zur Zeit des Dritten Reichs gab es viele Straßen, die den Namen Hitler trugen. Diese Straßen wurden nach dem Zweiten Weltkrieg umbenannt. In der DDR gab es einige Straßen, die Stalin im Namen hatten, auch diese gibt es heute nicht mehr. Die Stalinallee in Berlin heißt heute zum Beispiel Karl-Marx-Allee. Heute gibt es in Deutschland keine Straßen mehr, die an Nationalsozialist*innen oder Diktatoren erinnern, aber es gibt einige Straßen und Plätze, die nach Menschen und Orten benannt sind, die mit dem Kolonialismus in Verbindung stehen.

richtig	falsch	
		Es gibt Straßen in Deutschland, die an Nationalsozialist*innen erinnern.
		Die Stalinallee in Berlin wurde umbenannt.

Überlegen Sie: Was könnte es für Gründe dafür geben, dass Straßen, die nach Kolonist*innen oder ehemaligen Kolonien benannt sind, weiter existieren?

Lesen Sie den dritten Textabschnitt. Sind die Aussagen richtig oder falsch?

Es gibt einige Organisationen, die sich dafür einsetzen, dass Straßennamen, die nach Menschen oder Orten des Kolonialismus benannt wurden, verändert werden. In einigen Fällen hatte das auch schon Erfolg: So heißt heute die ehemalige Von-Trotha-Straße in München Hererostraße und erinnert damit explizit an den Genozid statt an den Mann, der den Genozid befahl. In Berlin gibt es inzwischen ein May-Ayim-Ufer, das nun einer herausragenden Persönlichkeit der afrodeutschen Bewegung gewidmet (*dedicated*) ist. Und auch in Wien wurde der Dr.-Karl-Lueger-Ring neutral in Universitätsring umbenannt. Denn der Kommunalpolitiker Lueger (1844–1910) hat die Stadt nicht nur modernisiert, sondern war auch ein Populist und Antisemit.

richtig	falsch	
		Bisher wurden keine Straßen umbenannt.
		Die Hererostraße erinnert an den Genozid in Deutsch-Südwestafrika.

Überlegen Sie: Kennen Sie Straßen, die in Ihrer Stadt oder Ihrem Land umbenannt wurden? Welche?

Lesen Sie den vierten Textabschnitt.

Aber nicht immer haben die Bemühungen der Aktivist*innen Erfolg. Es gibt noch viele Straßen, die nach kolonialen Menschen und Orten benannt sind. Ein Argument, das oft gegen eine Umbenennung vorgebracht wird, ist, dass Deutsche sich auch an problematische Persönlichkeiten erinnern müssen, weil sie sonst ein Kapitel der deutschen Geschichte verschweigen (*conceal*) würden. Aber heißt das, dass wir Täter*innen (*perpetrators*) ehren sollten?

Überlegen Sie: Welches Argument gibt es gegen die Umbenennung von Straßen? Verstehen Sie dieses Argument? Welche Gegenargumente fallen Ihnen ein?

____

____

____

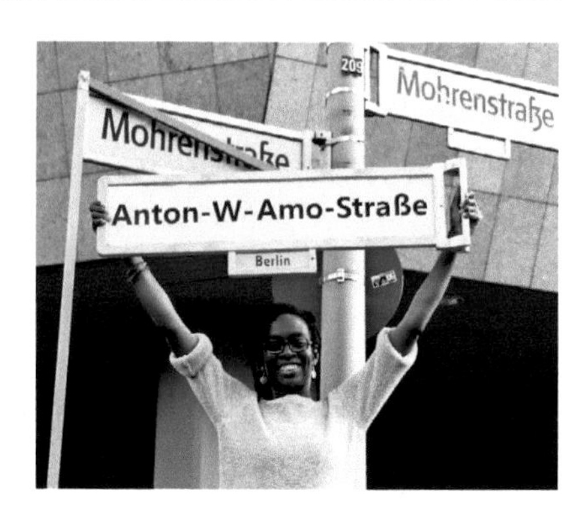

275b **M . . . : Lesen Sie die Informationen in der Kulturbox und beantworten Sie die Frage.**

INFO Terminologie: The German word *Mohr, Mohren* etymologically means Moors. It is originally a term for people from Morocco and particularly Muslim conquerors of Spain and Portugal but was also used for Black people in general. Today, it is perceived as archaic and offensive. But you can still find it in the names of chocolates, desserts, and streets. In *Impuls Deutsch*, we will not use the word and will mark it as M... when we point out colonial traces in Germany.

In „Impuls Deutsch" schreiben wir M . . . , weil ☐ das Wort alt ist. ☐ das Wort abfällig (*derogatory*) ist.

276a *Da*-Compound + *dass*-Clause

We are now bringing together the two topics of this chapter's grammar—prepositions and connecting sentences and thoughts—by looking at *da*-compounds with ***dass***-clauses. We need these constructions when we cannot express something with just one noun but want to express a more complex and longer thought.

As we have now seen, prepositions for certain verbs connect nouns to a verb:

Sie demonstrieren **gegen** Korruption.	*They demonstrate against corruption.*
Sie engagieren sich **für** die Umwelt.	*They are campaigning for the environment.*

If you want to add information that goes beyond a noun, you often need a full sentence. You connect that full sentence by using a *da*-compound that announces the bigger chunk of information to come, which is then expressed in a ***dass***-clause (verb at the end).

Sie **demonstrieren** da**gegen**, **dass** Politiker*innen Geld von Lobbyist*innen **nehmen**.	*They demonstrate against the fact* *that politicians take money from lobbyists.*
Sie **engagieren** sich da**für**, **dass** der Klimawandel ernst **genommen wird**.	*They are campaigning to ensure* *that climate change is taken seriously.*

As you can see, these constructions don't translate seamlessly into English. So, let's review the elements we need to construct such sentences: a verb that requires a specific preposition, da- plus that preposition followed by a comma, and a *dass*-clause after the comma. Let's look at a few more examples contrasting prepositions plus noun and prepositions plus subordinate clause with ***dass***:

Er ärgert sich **über** den Protest.	*He is annoyed by the protest.*
Er ärgert sich dar**über**, **dass** er wegen des Protests zu spät zur Arbeit kommt.	*He is annoyed about the fact* *that he will be late for work because of the protest.*
Sie schreibt einen Artikel **über** den Streik.	*She is writing an article about the strike.*
Sie schreibt einen Artikel dar**über**, **dass** die Menschen eine Lohnerhöhung fordern **und** deshalb streiken.	*She is writing an article about the fact* *that people are demanding higher wages* *and are therefore on strike.*
Wir haben **bei** dem Protest geholfen.	*We helped with the protest.*
Wir haben da**bei** geholfen, **dass** die Poster rechtzeitig fertig wurden.	*We helped* *so that the posters were finished on time.*
Ich warte **auf** meinen Freund.	*I am waiting for my friend.*
Ich warte dar**auf**, **dass** mein Freund die Poster bringt.	*I am waiting* *for my friend to bring the posters.*

276b Proteste gegen Kolonialismus und koloniale Spuren. Fügen Sie die korrekten „da"-Komposita ein.

Agneta: Die Gruppe IG-Metall-Jugend protestierte 1988 gegen den Bremer Elefanten, das war damals ein Kolonialdenkmal.

Christian: Wogegen protestierten sie denn?

Agneta: Die Gruppe protestierte dagegen, dass es ein Kolonialdenkmal in Bremen gab. Zwei Jahre später stimmten die Stadtpolitiker*innen für eine Veränderung des Denkmals.

Christian: Und wofür genau stimmten sie?

Agneta: Die Politiker*innen stimmten ____________, dass der Elefant ein Antikolonialdenkmal werden sollte. 2009 legten Bremer Politiker*innen etwas unter den Elefanten.

Christian: Ach ja?

Agenta: Ja, sie legten einen Brocken (*boulder*) vom Waterberg ____________, um an den Genozid zu erinnern.

Christian: Hm, verstehe, woran soll denn aber dieser Brocken ganz konkret erinnern?

Agneta: Der Waterberg-Brocken erinnert ____________, dass mehr als 50.000 Herero und Nama ermordet wurden. Es gab bundesweit auch andere Proteste. Der Verein AfrikaForum, zum Beispiel, demonstrierte 2014 in Berlin.

Christian: Wofür demonstrierte der Verein?

Agneta: Er demonstrierte ____________, dass Bremer*innen den Kolonialismus nicht vergessen und diesen aufarbeiten. Fünf Jahre später machten rund 8.000 Menschen bei der Ersten Antikolonialen Demonstration mit.

Christian: Ja, darüber habe ich etwas gelesen. Aber haben sie denn mit der Demo etwas erreicht?

Agneta: Ja, klar, durch die Demo konnten sie ____________ helfen, dass die Politiker*innen die antikolonialen Stimmen hörten.

277a **Lesen Sie den Text über die koloniale Geschichte in Hamburg und ergänzen Sie die Lücken. Was brauchen wir: „dass“ oder „da“-Komposita?**

Heute wissen nur wenige, ____________ der Hamburger Baakenhafen im Jahr 1904 durch die Verschiffung von Kolonialtruppen sehr wichtig wurde. (dass | darauf) Viele Hamburger Hafenarbeiter*innen halfen ____________, 14.000 Soldaten auf die Schiffe zu bringen. (dass | dabei) Diese Truppen und 12.000 Pferde reisten zur Kolonie Deutsch-Südwestafrika. Dort bekamen die Männer Waffen und kämpften ____________ gegen die Herero. (dass | damit) Aber zu wenige Hamburger Denkmäler erinnern an die Kolonialzeit von 1884 bis 1919 und ____________ (daran | damit), ____________ (dass | darin) die Deutschen in Afrika einen Völkermord verübt haben (*carried out*). Seit 1912 können Besucher*innen eine Gedenktafel mit den Namen von toten deutschen Afrika-Soldaten in der St. Michaelis-Kirche sehen, als Erinnerung an die Tatsache (*fact*), ____________ dieser Völkermord passiert ist. (dass | daran) Der Berliner Aktivist Israel Kaunatjike hat 2013 eine Protestaktion gegen das Denkmal in der Kirche gestartet: Er hat nämlich ein „Gegendenkmal“ für die toten Hereros ____________ gestellt. (dass | darunter)

87: Afrodeutscher Aktivismus°

278a **Uli und Nadia unterhalten sich darüber, was EOTO (Each One Teach One) macht. Lesen Sie das Gespräch und ersetzen Sie die unterstrichenen Informationen mit einem „da“-Kompositum.**

Uli: Was ist Each One Teach One (EOTO)?

Nadia: EOTO ist ein Empowerment-Projekt in Berlin. Es kämpft gegen Rassismus und Diskriminierung von Schwarzen Menschen.

Uli: Es kämpft gegen Rassismus und Diskriminierung?

Nadia: Ja, es kämpft *dagegen*. EOTO setzt sich aber besonders für das Empowerment von Schwarzen Menschen ein.

Uli: Wie setzt es sich ____________ ein?

Nadia: Es hat einen Film produziert, der über das Leben Schwarzer Menschen in Berlin-Wedding spricht.

Uli: Spricht der Film auch ____________, dass andere Minoritäten auch Probleme haben können?

Nadia: Natürlich! Aber der Film konzentriert sich auf afrodeutsche Themen.

Uli: Ich finde es gut, dass sich ein Film ____________ konzentriert.

Nadia: Eine Black Diaspora School und das Literaturfestival Afrolution gibt es auch in dem Haus von EOTO. Und Workshops. Durch diese Workshops lernen junge Schwarze etwas über die afrikanische Geschichte.

Uli. Wie bitte? Ich habe dich nicht verstanden. ____________ lernen sie etwas?

Nadia: Über die afrikanische Geschichte, aber auch über die afrodiasporische Geschichte.

279a **Ikonen der afrodeutschen (Frauen-)Bewegung. Recherchieren Sie online und finden Sie die folgenden Informationen über Audre Lorde, May Ayim und Ika Hügel-Marshall.**

Foto links: Gloria I. Joseph, Audre Lorde, Ika Hügel-Marshall, May Ayim

	Audre Lorde	May Ayim	Ika Hügel-Marshall
Geburtsdatum und Todestag			
Orte, an denen diese Frauen zu Hause waren			
Beruf(e)			
Welche Rolle spielt(e) diese Person innerhalb der afrodeutschen (Frauen-)Bewegung?			

88: Über Erinnerung stolpern

281a **Denkmal und Mahnmal. Der folgende Text erklärt den Unterschied zwischen Denkmälern und Mahnmalen. Lesen Sie zuerst den Text. Schauen Sie sich danach die Beispiele an und entscheiden Sie, ob es ein Denkmal (D) oder ein Mahnmal (M) ist.**

Ein Denkmal ist zum Beispiel eine Statue, die an eine berühmte Person aus der Wissenschaft, Politik oder Kultur erinnern soll. Denkmäler können aber auch Bauwerke sein, die ein Ereignis repräsentieren, mit dem eine Nation positive Gefühle assoziiert. Ein Mahnmal ist hingegen ein Bauwerk, das an ein negatives, traumatisches Ereignis erinnern soll. Das Verb „mahnen" bedeutet *to warn* oder *to admonish*. An einem Mahnmal gedenken Menschen zum Beispiel der Opfer eines Krieges oder Menschengruppen, die verfolgt bzw. ermordet wurden. Ein Mahnmal ist deshalb zugleich eine Warnung an die nachfolgenden Generationen.

Dieser Ort gedenkt der Opfer des Holocaust. ____

Diese Statuen gedenken der Schriftsteller Goethe und Schiller. ____

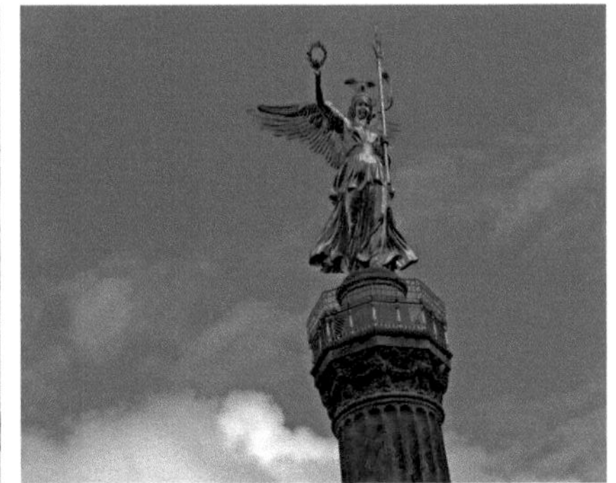

Die Siegessäule gedenkt der Einigungskriege des 19. Jahrhunderts. ____

281b Connecting Sentences: *obwohl*

To express contrast or a counter-argument, we can connect sentences with the subordinating conjunction **obwohl** (although). *Obwohl* behaves like the other subordinating conjunctions we have introduced in this chapter (*weil/da* to give reasons and *dass* to complement a sentence or express an opinion): the main clause and the subordinate clause with *obwohl* are separated by a comma, and *obwohl* causes the conjugated verb to move to the end of the subordinate clause. When the *obwohl*-clause comes first, the verb of the main clause will be directly after the comma.

Manche Menschen protestieren für Gerechtigkeit, **obwohl** sie Angst haben.	*Some people protest for justice although they are scared.*
Obwohl manche Menschen Angst haben, protestieren sie für Gerechtigkeit.	*Although some people are scared, they protest for justice.*

281c Verbinden Sie die Sätze mit „obwohl". Überlegen Sie zuerst: Welcher Satz (der erste oder der zweite) wird mit „obwohl" eingeführt?

Es gibt immer noch Denkmäler für Menschen, die früher Vorbilder waren. Sie sind es heute nicht mehr.

Es gibt immer noch Denkmäler für Menschen, die früher Vorbilder waren, obwohl sie es heute nicht mehr sind.

Denkmäler und Mahnmale erinnern beide an historische Ereignisse. Bei Denkmälern geht es um positive Erinnerungen und bei Mahnmalen um negative Ereignisse.

____

____

Es gibt auch in den USA Denkmäler und Mahnmale. Beide heißen auf Englisch *memorial*.

____

281d Welcher Konnektor passt in die Lücke: „obwohl" oder „aber"?

Ein Denkmal erinnert an positive Dinge und Personen, ____________ ein Mahnmal erinnert an negative Dinge.

____________ wir bei einem Denkmal vielleicht auch mal stehen bleiben und nachdenken, sollten wir das bei einem Mahnmal ganz bestimmt (*most definitely*) tun.

Manchmal interpretiert man ein altes Denkmal neu. ____________ die Menschen es früher positiv oder neutral gesehen haben, verstehen sie jetzt, dass hinter der erinnerten Figur negative Ereignisse stehen.

Denkmäler können Statuen, ____________ auch Bauwerke sein.

____________ die Begriffe „Denkmal" und „Mahnmal" beide auf -mal enden, haben sie verschiedene Pluralformen: „Denkmäler", aber „Mahnmale". („Denkmale" sagt man nur in sehr formellen Kontexten oder in poetischen Texten.)

282a Was sind Stolpersteine? Jana ist zum ersten Mal in Bamberg. Während sie mit ihrem besten Freund Carlos durch die Innenstadt von Bamberg läuft, sieht sie etwas, das sie vorher noch nie gesehen hat. Hören Sie das Gespräch. Sind die folgenden Aussagen richtig oder falsch?

richtig	falsch	
☐	☐	Der Stolperstein liegt am letzten Wohnort der Person.
☐	☐	Auf den Stolpersteinen stehen nur der Name und das Geburtsdatum der Person.
☐	☐	Stolpersteine gibt es nur in Bamberg.
☐	☐	Stolpersteine erinnern an die Menschen, die während der NS-Zeit verfolgt bzw. ermordet wurden.

283a **Textvorbereitung: Eine Kontroverse. In MACHEN lesen Sie einen Text darüber, dass Stolpersteine in einigen Städten sehr kontrovers sind. Schauen Sie sich hier zur Vorbereitung einige wichtige Vokabeln aus dem Text an. Schlagen Sie die Wörter aus dem Kasten nach, die Sie noch nicht kennen. Ergänzen Sie dann die folgenden Sätze.**

verlegen | Boden | treten | Tafel | Grundstück | ablehnen | Erinnerung | beschädigt

Wenn du Hinkelkästchen (*hopscotch*) spielst, darfst du nicht überall auf den Boden ____________________.

Früher gab es in allen Klassenzimmern eine traditionelle ____________________, auf der Lehrer*innen mit Kreide geschrieben haben.

Ich möchte gerne Teppichboden im Schlafzimmer ____________________, aber meine Freundin hätte lieber Laminat.

Letzte Nacht haben Unbekannte ein Mahnmal stark ____________________.

Der ____________________ in meiner Wohnung ist auch im Winter schön warm, weil es eine Heizung darunter gibt.

In meiner ____________________ sieht der Strand immer viel schöner aus, als er wirklich ist.

Auf dem ____________________ nebenan wird ein neues Haus gebaut.

Wir müssen das Projekt leider ____________________, weil die Stadt nicht genug Geld dafür hat.

283b **Lesen Sie die Sätze über die Stolpersteine und entscheiden Sie, welcher Konnektor passt: „obwohl" oder „weil".**

______________ es in vielen Orten Stolpersteine gibt, dürfen sie in manchen nur auf Privatgrundstücken verlegt werden. In vielen Städten gibt es sie nur auf privatem Boden, ______________ andere Städte Stolpersteine auf öffentlichem Boden erlauben.

______________ niemand auf die Opfer der Nazis „treten" soll, verbieten manche Städte Stolpersteine.

______________ Stolpersteine nicht viel kosten, sind sie trotzdem sehr effektiv, denn viele Menschen sehen sie.

______________ die Stolpersteine an Deportierte und Ermordete erinnern, hilft die Aktion dabei, dass diese Menschen nicht vergessen werden.

89: #METWO

284a **Soziale Medien. Füllen Sie die folgende Umfrage aus. Kreuzen Sie alles Zutreffende an oder ergänzen Sie.**

Welche sozialen Medien nutzen Sie?

- [ ] Facebook
- [ ] Tumblr
- [ ] TikTok
- [ ] Instagram
- [ ] Pinterest
- [ ] Discord
- [ ] Twitter
- [ ] YouTube
- [ ] WhatsApp
- [ ] Snapchat
- [ ] Reddit
- [ ] ______________

Mit wem kommunizieren Sie über soziale Medien?

- [ ] Freund*innen
- [ ] Familie
- [ ] Mitstudent*innen
- [ ] ____________________

Welche Themen besprechen Sie auf sozialen Medien am häufigsten?

- [ ] Privates
- [ ] Uni
- [ ] Hobbys
- [ ] aktuelle Ereignisse
- [ ] ______________

Haben soziale Medien einen direkten Einfluss auf Politik und Gesellschaft?

- [ ] ja
- [ ] nein
- [ ] Ich bin mir nicht sicher.

Begründen Sie Ihre Antwort auf die letzte Frage in 1–2 Sätzen.

____

____

285a Lesen Sie den Text zu #MeTwo. Sind die Aussagen unten richtig oder falsch?

#MeTwo ist ein Hashtag gegen die Diskriminierung von Menschen in deutschsprachigen Ländern, die sich mit mehr als einem Land oder einer Kultur verbunden fühlen. Der Aktivist Ali Can rief im Juli 2018 dazu auf, den Hashtag auf Facebook und Twitter zu benutzen und darunter über eigene Erfahrungen mit Diskriminierung zu erzählen. Grund für die Kampagne war eine Debatte um den Fußballspieler Mesut Özil.

Nachdem sich Özil mit dem türkischen Präsidenten Recep Tayyip Erdoğan getroffen hatte, wurde er stark kritisiert. Doch es blieb nicht bei politischer Kritik, sondern es ging um mehr. Özil erzählte von Rassismus, den er erlebt hatte. Er sagte: „Ich bin Deutscher, wenn wir gewinnen, aber ein Einwanderer, wenn wir verlieren."

Im neuen Hashtag steht, dass jeder Mensch mehr als eine Identität haben kann, damit sind vor allem zwei Heimaten gemeint. #MeTwo verbreitete sich wie ein Lauffeuer[1] und hat inzwischen viele tausend Tweets bekommen.

[1] sich verbreiten wie ein Lauffeuer – *to go viral*

richtig	falsch	
		Bei #MeTwo geht es um Rassismus und Diskriminierung.
		Der Hashtag wurde von Mesut Özil erfunden.
		Den Hashtag gibt es seit 2015.
		Özil hat Rassismus im Fußball erlebt.
		#MeTwo steht dafür, dass jeder Mensch nur ein Heimatland haben kann.

285b Recherchieren: Gehen Sie auf Twitter und benutzen Sie die Suchfunktion, um Tweets mit dem #MeTwo zu finden. Dafür sind die folgenden Schritte notwendig:

Recherche

- Klicken Sie auf „Erweiterte Suche".
- Schreiben Sie unter „Diese Hashtags": #MeTwo.
- Wählen Sie Deutsch als Sprache aus.
- Suchen Sie Tweets.

Machen Sie sich Notizen zu den folgenden Fragen:

Wie viele Tweets finden Sie? Wie populär sind diese Tweets?

___

___

#MeTwo

Welche anderen Hashtags sehen Sie in Verbindung mit #MeTwo? Schreiben Sie alle auf, die Sie finden.

___

___

___

Bringen Sie die fünf interessantesten Tweets mit in den Kurs.

287a Connecting Sentences: Adverbs

In this chapter, we have focused on connecting sentences based on the logic expressed by certain coordinating and subordinating conjunctions. Now we will introduce a third way of connecting sentences (adverbs) and give you three examples that each express a different connection: *deshalb* (therefore), *trotzdem* (despite that, still), and *also* (so, thus).

Adverbs often take the first position in the sentence. They count as a regular part of the sentence and are thus followed by the verb in the second position.

Deshalb (therefore) and ***also*** (so, thus) express a consequence:

Viele Menschen möchten mit ihren Freund*innen in Kontakt bleiben, **deshalb** sind sie in den sozialen Medien aktiv.	*Many people want to stay in touch with their friends; therefore, they are active on social media.*
Viele Menschen möchten mit ihren Freund*innen in Kontakt bleiben, **also** sind sie in den sozialen Medien aktiv.	*Many people want to stay in touch with their friends; so, they actively use social media.*

Although both *deshalb* and *also* indicate a cause-and-effect situation, and they can often be used interchangeably, *also* is more informal and you will hear it more often in spoken language.

Trotzdem (despite that, still) expresses something that could impede the action of the other clause but doesn't:

Viele Menschen sorgen sich um ihre Privatsphäre. **Trotzdem** sind sie in den sozialen Medien aktiv.	*Many people worry about privacy. Nevertheless, they are active on social media.*

287b Marieke Benja ärgert sich über Leute, die ihre Hunde zu wenig spazieren führen. Ergänzen Sie ihre Tweets. Welcher Konnektor passt am besten?

Manche Leute haben keine Zeit. ________________ kaufen sie einen Hund. #hundeliebe (trotzdem | also)

Ich sehe Hunde, die nur eine Stunde am Tag an die Luft kommen. ________________ protestiere ich hier. #hundeliebe (trotzdem | deshalb)

Manche Hunde sind den ganzen Tag allein zu Hause. ________________ werden sie neurotisch. #hundeliebe (deshalb | trotzdem)

Ich bin sauer auf Leute, die glauben, dass sie ihre Hunde lieben. ________________ sage ich ihnen meine Meinung. #hundeliebe (trotzdem | also)

Ich mag auch Hunde. ________________ kaufe ich keinen Hund, denn ich habe nicht genug Platz und Zeit. #hundeliebe (trotzdem | deshalb)

287c Twitter-Sprüche. Welche Tweets passen zusammen?

Ich vermisse meinen Opa; ____ Die Sonne tut Körper und Seele gut; ____ Ich liebe Bäume; ____

Wir brauchen mehr Bienen; ____ Morgen kommt ein besserer Tag; ____

a) deshalb stellt Blumen auf eure Balkons! #KeinHonigmehr
b) also videochatte ich mit ihm. #GemeinsamgegenCorona
c) also pflanze ich jedes Jahr einhundert neue. #Wald-im-Ort
d) trotzdem musst du heute genießen. #carpediem
e) trotzdem sind Sonnenschutzmittel wichtig. #Energietanken

AUSSPRACHE: DER NG/NK-LAUT

287d **Hören und Sprechen: Hören Sie die Laute und Wörter und sprechen Sie sie nach.**

[ŋ]	lang	singen	Junge	Engel
[ŋk]	Bank	sinken	danken	Enkel

Achtung: Sprechen Sie [ŋ] und [ŋk] nasal durch die Nase, wie wenn Sie Schnupfen haben.

287e **Hören und Sprechen: Hören Sie die Familiennamen und sprechen Sie nach.**

Tann	Tang	Tank
Renner	Renger	Renker
Sinnbach	Singbach	Sinkback
Bronn	Brong	Bronk

287f **Sie hören jetzt immer nur einen Namen. Was hören Sie? Kreuzen Sie oben an.**

287g **Hören Sie die Wörter und sprechen Sie sie nach. Achten Sie auf die Aussprache von „ng".**

die Buchhandlung – die Buchhandlungen
die Lesung – die Lesungen
die Wohnung – die Wohnungen
die Zeitung – die Zeitungen

287h **Hören und Markieren: Hören Sie die Sätze und markieren Sie „ng"- und „nk"-Verbindungen.**

1) Frank geht heute zur Bank. Er braucht eine Beratung und will Überweisungen machen.
2) Als er in der Bank ankommt, ist dort ein großes Gedränge. Viele Leute warten am Bankschalter.
3) Der Automat funktioniert heute nicht, denn man kann die PIN nicht eingeben.
4) Er fragt eine Angestellte: „Wie lange muss ich warten?" Sie antwortet: „Das ist unklar."
5) Er sagt: „Entschuldigung, ich komme morgen wieder."

In welchen Wörtern mit „ng"/„nk" hören Sie das „g" oder das „k" und in welchen nicht?

ng: ich höre [ŋ]: *Beratung,* ______ nk: ich höre [ŋk]: ______

ng: ich höre [ng]: *eingeben,* ______ nk: ich höre [nk]: ______

Was fällt Ihnen bei den Beispielen auf? Ergänzen Sie die Regeln.

Wenn eine Vorsilbe auf „-n" endet und ein „g" oder „k" folgt, z. B. „unklar", sprechen wir ______.

In den anderen Fällen (z. B. „Überweisungen", „Bank") sprechen wir ______.

90: WAS DARF COMEDY?°

288a **Was sind Ihre Lieblings-Comedyserien und -comedians? Erklären Sie, warum Sie diese Serien oder Comedians so gut finden. Achten Sie dabei auf die Verbstellung nach dem Konnektor.**

Meine absolute Lieblings-Comedyserie bzw. mein*e Lieblingscomedian ist: ______________________________,

weil ____.

Meine zweitliebste Comedyserie bzw. mein*e zweitliebste*r Comedian ist: ______________________________,

denn ____.

Schließlich ist meine dritte Wahl: ______________________________,

weil ____.

289a **Eine Rezension schreiben. Im letzten Kapitel haben Sie gelernt, wie Sie eine Rezension für eine Serie oder einen Film strukturieren. In diesem Kapitel werden Sie eine Rezension für einen Comedysketch schreiben. Lesen Sie unten noch einmal die Teile einer Kritik, hier an den neuen Kontext angepasst. Ordnen Sie den verschiedenen Elementen (links) die korrekte Definition (rechts) zu.**

die Überschrift ____

die Einleitung ____

die Handlung ____

die Bewertung ____

der Schluss _d_

a) Hier sagen die Kritiker*innen, ob ihnen das Programm oder ein spezifischer Sketch aus dem Programm gefallen hat und warum (nicht). Wichtige Punkte für die Kritik sind einerseits die Leistung der Comedians, andererseits oft die Reaktion des Publikums.

b) Sie ist in einer Rezension das erste Element, das die Leser*innen sehen, und sollte deshalb neugierig machen. Hier benutzen Kritiker*innen oft eine Frage oder provokante Adjektive, um einen Hinweis (*clue*) auf die Meinung der Kritik zu geben.

c) In den ersten Sätzen einer Rezension werden oft Zitate oder interessante Fakten über die Comedians und das aktuelle Programm (oder einen einzelnen Sketch) präsentiert.

d) Am Ende sagen die Kritiker*innen ganz kurz, ob sie das Programm (oder den Stil) der Comedians empfehlen würden.

e) In diesem Teil beschreiben die Kritiker*innen den Inhalt des Programms (oder eines einzelnen Sketches).

289b **Ist das nicht ironisch? Ordnen Sie die Adjektive zu.**

vulgär | gesellschaftskritisch | ironisch | bizarr | albern (*silly*) | absurd | klischeehaft | pointiert

Wenn zwei oder mehr Dinge nicht logisch zusammengehören (so wie „Bananen rauchen"), ist das ______________.

Wenn Humor mit Sexualität zu tun hat, ist er oft ______________.

Kinderwitze sind meistens ______________.

Witze über blonde Frauen, die nicht intelligent sind, oder über Männer und ihre Autos sind ______________.

Ein Witz, der soziale Probleme kritisiert, ist ______________.

Meine Freund*innen finden meinen Humor ______________, denn er ist zu privat und seltsam (*odd*).

Die Komikerin hat mit ihrem Witz zur LKW-Maut die Kritik auf den Punkt gebracht. Der Witz war ______________.

Wenn du schon zu spät bist, dein Fahrrad auch noch einen Platten hat und du kommentierst: „Heute ist mein Glückstag!", dann ist das ______________.

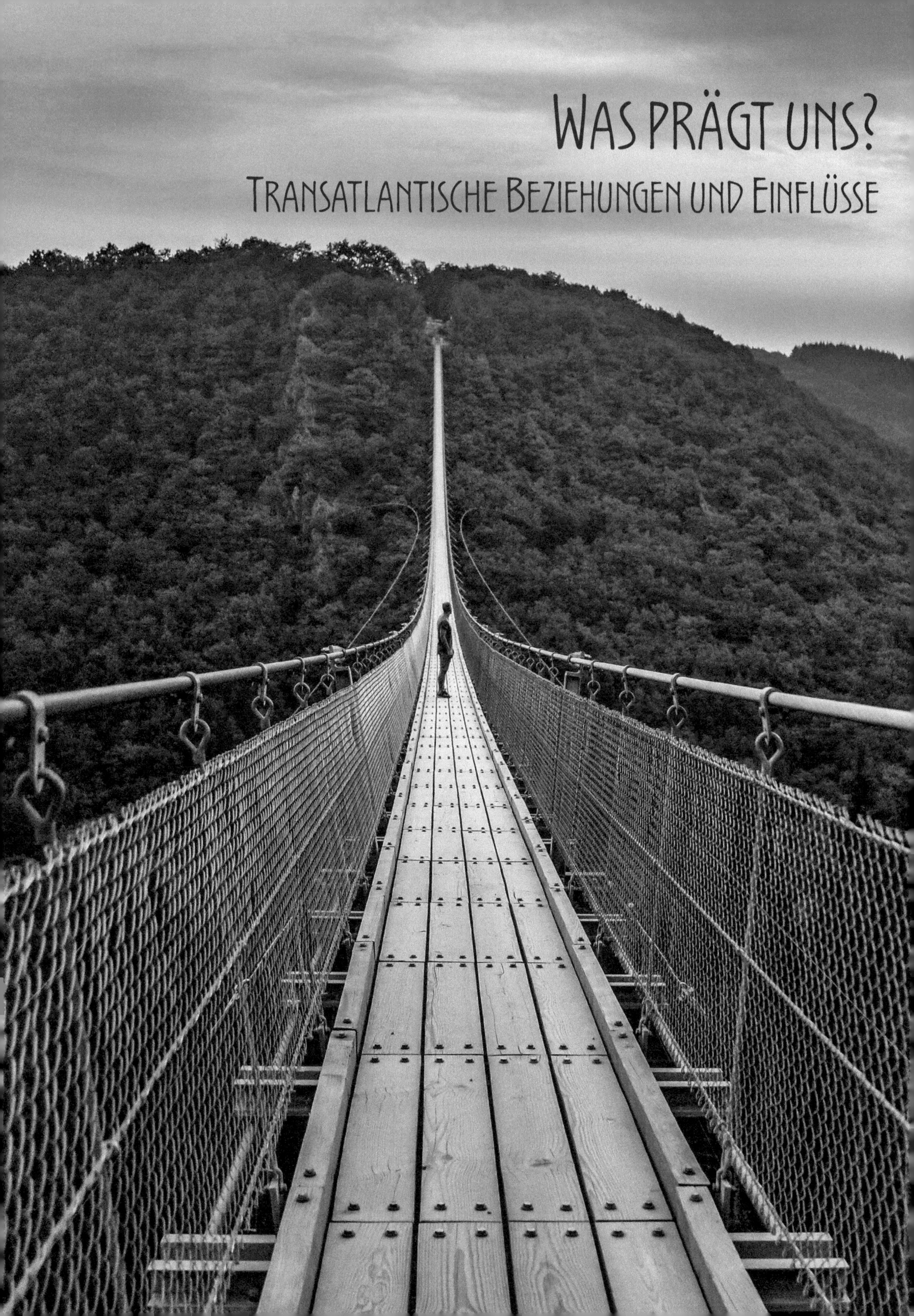
Was prägt uns?
Transatlantische Beziehungen und Einflüsse

WORTSCHATZ

92: KULTUR – WAS IST DAS EIGENTLICH?

die Praktik, -en	practice
das Ritual, -e	ritual
bilden, bildete, hat ... gebildet	to constitute, form
unsichtbar	invisible
behalten (behält), behielt, hat ... behalten	to keep; remember
um Hilfe bitten, bat, hat ... gebeten	to ask for help
vertreten (vertritt), vertrat, hat ... vertreten	to represent
der Verlag, -e	publisher
der Rahmen, -	frame
das Lob	praise
geheim	secret
jdm. (*dat.*) Recht geben (gibt), gab, hat ... gegeben	to prove sb. right
bestimmen, bestimmte, hat ... bestimmt	to determine
die Norm, -en	norm
das Stereotyp, -e	stereotype
das Vorurteil, -e	prejudice
der Kulturstandard, -s	cultural standard
die Verallgemeinerung, -en	generalization
alltäglich	everyday, common

Weitere Wörter: das Konzept, -e (concept); **die Studie, -n** (study); **der Außenstehende, -n** (outsider (*male*)); **die Außenstehende, -n** (outsider (*female*)), **die Umgangsform, -en** (way of behaving); **der*die Mitreisende, -n (ein*e Mitreisende*r)** (fellow traveler (*gender-neutral*)); **ironisch** (ironic)

93: AUF NACH NORDAMERIKA

die Auswanderung, -en	emigration
aus·wandern, wanderte ... aus, ist ... ausgewandert	to emigrate
stören, störte, hat ... gestört	to bother; disturb
sich (*akk.*) wohl·fühlen, fühlte ... wohl, hat ... wohlgefühlt	to feel comfortable
erkennen, erkannte, hat ... erkannt	to recognize
die Regierung, -en	government
bewusst	aware; conscious
die Germanistik	German studies
zurück·ziehen, zog ... zurück, ist ... zurückgezogen	to move back
die Einwanderung, -en	immigration
dauerhaft	permanent(ly)
der Schmelztiegel, -	melting pot
sich (*akk.*) assimilieren, assimilierte, hat ... assimiliert	to assimilate
ein·bringen, brachte ... ein, hat ... eingebracht	to contribute, bring in
die Bildung, -en	education; formation
erwähnen, erwähnte, hat ... erwähnt	to mention
das Zielland, ¨er	country of destination
die Sozialversicherung, -en	social security (*insurance*)
der Tellerwäscher, -	dishwasher (*male*)
die Tellerwäscherin, -nen	dishwasher (*female*)
die Spülhilfe, -n	dishwasher (*gender-neutral alternative*)
obdachlos	homeless; unsheltered
verklärt	glorified; idealized
die Kluft, ¨e	chasm

Weitere Wörter: die Überstunde, -n ((an hour of) overtime); **die Aufenthaltsgenehmigung, -en** (residence permit); **der Doktorand, -en** (Ph.D. student, doctoral candidate (*male*)); **die Doktorandin, -nen** (Ph.D. student, doctoral candidate (*female*)); **die promovierende Person, die Promovierenden** (Ph.D. student, doctoral candidate (*gender-neutral alternative*))

94: AUF NACH EUROPA

froh	happy
die Mannschaft, -en	team (*sports*)
erstellen, erstellte, hat ... erstellt	to create, compile, generate
das Stipendium, Stipendien	scholarship, grant
sich (*akk.*) verlieben (in + *akk.*), verliebte, hat ... verliebt	to fall in love (with)
selten	rare(ly)
zahlreich	numerous
die Tatsache, -n	fact, matter of fact
die Hochschule, -n	college, university
stolz (auf + *dat.*)	proud (of)
der Studiengang, ¨e	field of study, course of study
ausgerechnet	of all things
die Inszenierung, -en	production, staging
qualitativ	qualitative(ly)
die Bezahlung, -en	payment
die Studiengebühr, -en	tuition (*fees*)
sonst	else, otherwise

Weitere Wörter: die Liga, Ligen (league); **der Opernsänger, -** (opera singer (*male*)); **die Opernsängerin, -nen** (opera singer (*female*)); **die Opern singende Person, die Opern Singenden** (opera singer (*gender-neutral alternative*)); **staatlich gefördert** (state-sponsored); **die Arbeitsstelle, -n** (position, job); **das Wunder, -** (miracle); **finanziell** (financial(ly))

96: MUSIKALISCHE EINFLÜSSE AUS NORDAMERIKA

die Rezeption, -en	reception
zum Einsatz kommen, kam, ist ... gekommen	to be deployed, be used
aus·tauschen, tauschte ... aus, hat ... ausgetauscht	to exchange
wachsen (wächst), wuchs, ist ... gewachsen	to grow, increase
das Verständnis	understanding

gegenseitig	mutual(ly), reciprocal
der Ruf	reputation
die Presse	press
das Musical, -s	musical
die Platte, -n	record
keine Ahnung haben (hat), hatte, hat ... gehabt	to have no idea, have no clue
Lust haben (auf + *akk.*) (hat), hatte, hat ... gehabt	to be up/down for sth.

Weitere Wörter: die Musikrichtung, -en (music genre); **die Marschkapelle, -n** (marching band); **kraftvoll** (forceful, powerful)

97: Sprachliche Einflüsse aus D-A-CH-L

verschwinden, verschwand, ist ... verschwunden	to disappear
mittlerweile	(by) now, meanwhile
ein·treten (tritt ... ein), trat ... ein, ist ... eingetreten	to arise, occur
sprachlich	linguistic(ally)
publizieren, publizierte, hat ... publiziert	to publish
der Sprachgebrauch	use of language

99: Sport im Vergleich

draußen	outside
drinnen	inside
unabhängig	independent(ly)
aus·führen, führte ... aus, hat ... ausgeführt	to do, perform, carry out
gelegentlich	occasional(ly)
der Vorstand, ¨e	board, executive committee
der Widerspruch, ¨e	contradiction
der Sieger, -	winner (*male*)
die Siegerin, -nen	winner (*female*)
der*die Erstplatzierte, -n (ein*e Erstplatzierte*r)	winner (*gender-neutral alternative*)
der Radsport	cycling
Sport treiben, trieb, hat ... getrieben	to do sports, play sports
die Weltmeisterschaft, -en	world championship
der Bildhauer, -	sculptor (*male*)
die Bildhauerin, -nen	sculptor (*female*)
die bildhauende Person, die Bildhauenden	sculptor (*gender-neutral alternative*)
das Eislaufen	ice skating
die Medaille, -n	medal

Weitere Wörter: eis·laufen (läuft ... eis), lief ... eis, ist ... eisgelaufen (to ice-skate); **der Teamsport** (team sport); **der Einzelsport** (individual sport); **das Bergsteigen** (mountaineering, alpine climbing); **die Gymnastik, -en** (gymnastics); **der Fitnesssport** (fitness); **die Olympischen Spiele** (Olympic Games); **der Sportgeist** (sporting spirit)

100: Bildung im Vergleich

die Ausbildung, -en	apprenticeship, training, education (*for professions*)
das Abitur	secondary school diploma (*general qualification for university entrance*)
sich (*akk.*) bewerben (bewirbt), bewarb, hat ... beworben	to apply
die Note, -n	grade
Erfahrung sammeln, sammelte, hat ... gesammelt	to gain experience
die praktische Erfahrung, -	practical experience, hands-on experience
weiter·machen, machte ... weiter, hat ... weitergemacht	to continue
die Oberstufe, -n	final years in German secondary school (*equiv. junior and senior year in U.S. high school*)
der Betrieb, -e	business, enterprise
besuchen, besuchte, hat ... besucht	to attend (*a school*); visit
Ich habe die Geschwister-Scholl-Schule besucht.	I attended Geschwister-Scholl school.
eine Entscheidung treffen (trifft), traf, hat ... getroffen	to make a decision
sich (*akk.*) gewöhnen (an + *akk.*), gewöhnte, hat ... gewöhnt	to get used (to), get accustomed (to)
das Fachgebiet, -e	specialty, field of expertise
der Studienplatz, ¨e	place at college/university
das Hauptfach, ¨er	major
das Auslandssemester, -	semester abroad
benotet	graded
Kurse belegen, belegte, hat ... belegt	to take courses
das Nebenfach, ¨er	minor
das Vorlesungsverzeichnis, -se	course catalog

Weitere Wörter: das Bildungssystem, -e (education system); **die Eckdaten (*pl.*)** (key data, basic information); **der Bereich, -e** (sector); **die Schulform, -en** (type of school); **die Öffnungszeiten (*pl.*)** (business hours); **außerschulisch** (extracurricular); **die Zusage, -n** (acceptance (*of an invitation or appointment*)); **die Absage, -n** (rejection, refusal)

92: Kultur – Was ist das eigentlich?

292a **Was ist Kultur? Lesen Sie den Text und beantworten Sie die Fragen.**

Definition: Kultur ist nicht leicht zu definieren. Jede akademische Disziplin versteht unter Kultur etwas anderes. Für Kulturwissenschaftler*innen sind Kulturen Orientierungssysteme für Gruppen. Das heißt, eine Kultur definiert sich durch die Art und Weise, wie ihre Mitglieder sich verhalten und denken. So bestimmen Kulturen das gemeinsame Leben, also die Werte und Normen der Gruppe. Der Kulturwissenschaftler Geert Hofstede bezeichnet Kultur auch als eine Art von „mentaler Software", die jedem Menschen während seiner Sozialisation von Eltern, Schule und Gesellschaft einprogrammiert wird. Wir können also sagen, dass Kulturen ihre Mitglieder durch ein spezifisches System an Normen und Werten als Gruppe definieren. Alle Mitglieder lernen diese Normen und Werte während ihrer Sozialisation (sie kennen sie also, respektieren sie aber nicht unbedingt). Oft denken wir bei Kulturen vor allem an Nationalkulturen, zum Beispiel an die deutsche Kultur. Das kann dazu führen, dass wir Kulturen essentialisieren (wenn wir zum Beispiel sagen: Sie tut das, weil sie Deutsche ist). Das ist ein Problem, weil dabei die Heterogenität innerhalb eines Landes ignoriert wird. Deshalb ist es wichtig zu verstehen, dass Kulturen sowohl groß als auch klein sind. Sie sind auch nicht klar voneinander getrennt, sondern sie überlappen und verändern sich über die Zeit. Alle Menschen sind deshalb gleichzeitig Mitglieder vieler Kulturen.

richtig	falsch	
		Es gibt nur eine Kulturdefinition.
		Kulturen bestimmen, wie ihre Mitglieder sich fühlen, handeln und denken.
		Menschen lernen kulturelle Normen und Werte bereits, wenn sie aufwachsen.
		Kulturen sind immer Nationalkulturen.

292b **Sie haben jetzt eine Definition von Kultur gelesen, aber was heißt das konkret: Welche Elemente sind Teil einer Kultur? Machen Sie sich in der Tabelle Notizen: Schreiben Sie auf, welche Elemente Ihre eigene(n) Kultur(en) definieren und mit wem Sie diese Elemente teilen (z. B. Menschen in Ihrer Region, Menschen, die das gleiche Hobby haben etc.). Versuchen Sie, so viele Assoziationen wie möglich stichwortartig zu notieren.**

Kulturelle Elemente	Ich teile diese Elemente mit:
Uniregeln,	*anderen Studierenden*
Dialekt,	*Menschen in meiner Region*
	Menschen in meinem Land

292c **Eine Art, Kultur zu beschreiben, ist die Unterscheidung in „Produkte", „Praktiken" und „Perspektiven". Ordnen Sie die Definitionen den Begriffen zu.**

Produkte …	beschreiben Standpunkte und Positionen zu bestimmten Themen, also welche Werte und Meinungen in einem Kulturkreis wichtig sind.
Praktiken …	beschreiben Verhaltensweisen oder Rituale, die in einem Kulturkreis Standard sind. Ein Beispiel dafür wäre, dass man sich in Deutschland zur Begrüßung oft die Hand schüttelt.
Perspektiven …	beschreiben Dinge, die für einen bestimmten Kulturkreis wichtig sind. Ein Beispiel dafür wären die regionalen Varianten von Bratwurst in Deutschland (Thüringer, Nürnberger …).

292d **Reflektieren: Gehen Sie zurück zu Aktivität 292b und markieren Sie in der Tabelle, ob die Elemente, die Sie gesammelt haben, eher Produkte (Pro), Praktiken (Pra) oder Perspektiven (Per) sind. Schreiben Sie hier auf, aus welcher Kategorie Sie die meisten Elemente gewählt haben, und beantworten Sie dann die Reflexionsfragen.**

Die meisten Elemente in meiner Tabelle sind aus der Kategorie

Produkte
Praktiken
Perspektiven

Glauben Sie, dass „Meine Kultur" persönlich ist? Sind Ihre Elemente „typisch" für Ihr(e) Land/Region/Universität/Hobbys? Mit wie vielen Menschen teilen Sie wohl Elemente, die Sie hier aufgeschrieben haben? Wer hat vielleicht andere Elemente?

293a **Lesen Sie die Begriffsdefinitionen und die Beispiele von Kulturstandards, Stereotypen und Vorurteilen. Bestimmen Sie dann, welches Beispiel ein deutscher Kulturstandard, ein Stereotyp oder ein Vorurteil ist. Schreiben Sie anschließend – basierend auf der Definition und dem Beispiel – einen Kulturstandard aus einer Ihrer eigenen Kulturen auf. Sie können überlegen, wie dieser Kulturstandard ein Stereotyp produzieren könnte.**

Definitionen:
Kulturstandards sind Standards, die von den meisten Mitgliedern einer Kultur für das eigene Handeln und für die Interaktion mit den anderen Menschen akzeptiert werden. Es geht also um Praktiken, die aber meistens Perspektiven reflektieren. Diese Standards definieren, welche Verhaltensweisen kulturell als „Norm" angesehen werden. Kulturstandards sind also Orientierungspunkte, die Menschen dabei helfen, sich in einem Kulturkreis zu bewegen und zurechtzufinden. Weil Standards „nur" Orientierungspunkte sind, folgen nicht alle Menschen immer diesen Normen. Das ist ein wichtiger Unterschied zu Stereotypen. **Stereotype** generalisieren und simplifizieren das Verhalten einiger Menschen in einer Gruppe und vermitteln die Idee, dass sich alle Menschen dieser Gruppe immer so verhalten. Sie homogenisieren also große Gruppen und können deshalb nie wahr sein. Während Stereotype sowohl positiv als auch negativ sein können (z. B. eine Gruppe kann besonders gut/schlecht Auto fahren), sind **Vorurteile** immer negativ. Vorurteile entstehen nicht durch Beobachtung, sondern sind eine Vorab-Bewertung (*pre-judgment*), die wenig reflektiert wird.

Ein ______________________: Die Deutschen sind unhöflich und unfreundlich. Sie benutzen nie den Vornamen und wollen keine Freundschaften schließen.

Ein ______________________: In Deutschland wird kulturell erwartet, dass sich Personen mit dem förmlichen „Sie" ansprechen, wenn sie sich zum ersten Mal treffen und keine enge persönliche Beziehung zueinander haben (es gibt dabei für verschiedene Altersgruppen Unterschiede). Auch bei Menschen, die sich täglich sehen, ist das „Sie" nicht ungewöhnlich, vor allem in beruflichen Kontexten.

Ein ______________________: Deutsche sind distanziert und effizient. Sie schließen nicht so schnell Freundschaften und sprechen sich mit Nachnamen und „Sie" an, auch wenn sie miteinander arbeiten oder sich schon länger kennen.

Ein Kulturstandard in meiner Kultur:

____

____

____

____

294a Review: Predicate Adjectives and Adverbs in the Positive, Comparative, and Superlative

Adjectives not directly preceding a noun can function as adverbs or so-called "predicate adjectives" in English.

Adverbs describe the way an action is carried out. Unlike in English where the suffix -ly is added to an adjective, in German the adverb just consists of a "blank" adjective in this function.

Die Studentin spricht deutlich.	*The (female) student speaks clearly.*

Predicative adjectives describe the subject of a sentence. They accompany the verbs *sein*, *bleiben*, and *werden*, and they are positioned at the end of the sentence most of the time. They don't precede the noun and therefore don't receive adjective endings.

Die Professorin ist sehr pünktlich.	*The (female) professor is very punctual.*

Comparing the "quality" of these actions or subjects with others is done with the comparative and superlative forms, which are actually very similar to their English counterparts.

Comparative: Who/What is taller, heavier, smarter than others?
Who/What does something faster, smoother, more elegantly than others?

How?	Adjective + -er and the word ***als*** (*than*)	
Examples:	Prof. Schmidt ist pünktlicher **als** ich.	*Professor Schmidt is more punctual than me.*
	Die Studentin spricht deutlicher **als** mein Vater.	*The (female) student speaks more clearly than my father.*
Note:	*Mehr* (more) is not used for comparatives. If the items you are comparing are the same, use the word ***so***, an adjective, and the word ***wie***:	
	Die Studentin spricht **so** deutlich **wie** meine Mutter.	*The (female) student speaks as clearly as my mother.*

Superlative: Who/What is the tallest, heaviest, smartest?
Who/What does something in the fastest, nicest, smoothest, or most efficient way?

How?	The particle ***am*** and an adjective + -sten	
Examples:	Prof. Arnold ist **am** pünktlichsten.	*Professor Arnold is the most punctual.*
	Die Studentin spricht **am** deutlichsten.	*The (female) student speaks most clearly.*
Note:	Adjectives ending in a *-t* or *-s* sound or in a vowel form the superlative with an -e before -sten.	
	Die Aufgabe ist am leichtesten.	*This task is the easiest.*

294b An Overview of Common Adjectives and Their Comparative and Superlative Forms

Here are some samples of frequently used adjectives in their comparative and superlative forms. You will see that some of them show little deviation from the standard pattern, and the ones at the end of the list have to be memorized.

basic form **"positive" form A**	**comparison form** **A = B**	**comparative form** **A > B, A < B**	**superlative form** **A > B, C, D . . ., A < B, C, D . . .**	
standard comparative forms				
klein	**so** klein **wie**	kleiner **als**	**am** kleinsten	*small*
wenig	**so** wenig **wie**	weniger **als**	**am** wenigsten	*few, little*
additional *(e)* in the superlative form after ***-s, -ss, -ß, -x, -z,*** vowels				
interessant	**so** interessant **wie**	interessanter **als**	**am** interessantesten	*interesting*
nass	**so** nass **wie**	nasser **als**	**am** nassesten	*wet*
neu	**so** neu **wie**	neuer **als**	**am** neu(e)sten	*new*
most one-syllable adjectives containing the vowels ***a, o,*** or ***u*** add an *Umlaut* in the comparative and superlative forms:				
alt	**so** alt **wie**	älter **als**	**am** ältesten	*old*
warm	**so** warm **wie**	wärmer **als**	**am** wärmsten	*warm*
phonetic adjustments				
teuer	**so** teuer **wie**	teur_er **als**	**am** teuersten	*expensive*
dunkel	**so** dunkel **wie**	dunk_ler **als**	**am** dunkelsten	*dark*
hoch	**so** hoch **wie**	hö_her **als**	**am** höchsten	*high*
nah	**so** nah **wie**	näher **als**	**am** nächsten	*close*
lexic change / completely different forms				
gut	**so** gut **wie**	besser **als**	**am** besten	*good*
viel	**so** viel **wie**	mehr **als**	**am** meisten	*much*
gern	**so** gern **wie**	lieber **als**	**am** liebsten	*gladly*

294c Was passt hier: Positiv, Komparativ oder Superlativ? Ergänzen Sie die Lücken mit der richtigen Adjektivform.

Kulturen sind sehr ____________________ (komplex) aufgrund ihrer Heterogenität. Menschen versuchen häufig, Kulturen durch Abgrenzungen zu definieren. Zum Beispiel wird in Deutschland oft gesagt „Amerikaner*innen sind ____________________ (oberflächlich) als Deutsche". Diese Annahme ist aber ____________________ (problematisch), da sie auf einer Verallgemeinerung basiert, also einem Stereotyp. Man kann natürlich kulturelle Tendenzen beobachten. In manchen Kulturkreisen ist es beispielsweise wichtig, dass man immer ____________________ (pünktlich) ist. In anderen Kulturkreisen hingegen ist es viel ____________________ (wichtig), dass man sich Zeit nimmt, und es ist dabei egal, wer am ____________________ (pünktlich) ist. Am ____________________ (gut) ist es sowieso, wenn man die Heterogenität von Kulturen feiert, anstatt sie durch Stereotype zu beschreiben.

294d **Komparativ oder Superlativ: Was passt hier am besten? Ergänzen Sie die Sätze über kulturelle Dimensionen mit der richtigen Form. Die Grundform ist jeweils vorgegeben.**

Privatsphäre wird in jeder Kultur anders empfunden (*felt*). In der arabischen Welt oder in Lateinamerika gibt es ________________ (viel) Nähe und Körperkontakt zwischen den Menschen, während man zum Beispiel in nordeuropäischen Kulturen ________________ (gern) eine „Komfort-Distanz" zu anderen Menschen hat.
In einer durch Kollektivismus geprägten Kultur ist die Gruppe am ________________ (wichtig), während in den auf Individualismus ausgerichteten (*oriented*) Kulturen die Idee der Selbstverwirklichung (*self-realization*) viel ________________ (stark) definiert ist.
Beim Thema „Zeit" gibt es auch große Unterschiede. In Kulturen, die mit der sogenannten „Ereigniszeit" arbeiten, ist die Uhrzeit ____________________ (unwichtig) als in Kulturen, die ihre Pläne nach der Uhr ausrichten. In diesen Kulturen sind die am ____________________ (pünktlich), die zur entsprechenden (*appropriate*) Uhrzeit kommen.

93: Auf nach Nordamerika

295a **Das Schub- und Sog-Modell („Push-Pull"-Modell) ist eine Migrationstheorie von Everett Lee, die erklärt, warum Menschen auswandern. Schubfaktoren (*push factors*) sind negative Aspekte im eigenen Land und Gründe, warum Menschen flüchten oder sich dafür entscheiden, ihr Land zu verlassen. Sogfaktoren (*pull factors*) sind positive Aspekte in einem anderen Land, die Menschen dazu bewegen, dorthin zu gehen. Ordnen Sie die Faktoren aus dem Kasten den sechs Kategorien zu und sagen Sie, ob es sich jeweils um einen Schub- oder einen Sogfaktor handelt. Wenn nötig, schlagen Sie die Bedeutung der Wörter nach. Einige Faktoren passen in mehr als eine Kategorie.**

~~Arbeitslosigkeit~~ | ~~Religionsfreiheit~~ | Diktatur | Kriminalitätsrate | hohe Steuern | niedrige Steuern | Frieden | Folter | Wohnungsmangel | Armut | stabiles Bildungssystem | Bürger*innenkrieg | Hunger | Völkermord | Diskriminierung | Krieg | gute Sozialleistungen | Naturkatastrophen | Umweltverschmutzung | viele/wenige Jobangebote | Freundschaften über soziale Netzwerke | Meinungsfreiheit | freier Zugang zu Schulen und Universitäten | Toleranz | fehlende Naturressourcen | gutes öffentliches Gesundheitssystem | Verfolgung | günstige Einwanderungsgesetze | Rechtssicherheit | persönliche Freiheiten | kulturelle Vielfalt | (kein) Recht auf Bildung | (kein) gesicherter Zugang zu Lebensmitteln | bessere Berufschancen | persönliche Beziehungen

	Schubfaktoren	Sogfaktoren
Arbeit	*Arbeitslosigkeit*	
Bildung		
Gesellschaft		*Religionsfreiheit*
Umwelt		
Politik		
Gesundheit		
Netzwerk		

295b Review: Causal vs. Final Clauses

Watching people's actions, we often wonder what drives them. Looking more closely into their motives, you might be able to distinguish between reasons (*Gründe*) and goals (*Ziele*). German has several ways to make this distinction using structures you have already learned.

Causal Sentences	**Handlung (*action*)**	
Main clause	Suzanne **verließ** ihr Heimatland,	*Suzanne left her home country*
	Gründe (*reasons*)	
Main clause	**denn** sie **wurde** politisch verfolgt.	*because she was politically persecuted.*
Subordinate clause	**weil** sie auf bessere Chancen **hoffte**.	*because she hoped for better opportunities.*
Subordinate clause	**da** sie dort ihre Familie nicht **ernähren konnte**.	*because/since she couldn't feed her family there.*

Final Sentences	**Handlung (*action*)**	
	Suzanne **verließ** ihr Heimatland,	*Suzanne left her home country*
	Ziele (*goals*)	
Infinitive sentence with ***um … zu*** (for sentences with the same subject)	**um** ein besseres Leben in Y **zu finden**.	*in order to find a better life in Y.*
Subordinate clause with ***damit*** (for sentences with different subjects)	**damit** ihr Kind ein besseres Leben **hat**.	*so that her child would have a better life.*

295c Hier sind Schub- und Sogfaktoren am Werk. Sind die Argumente unten Gründe (= kausal: weil, da) oder Ziele (final = damit)?

Samira ist nach Liechtenstein ausgewandert,

weil | damit der Krieg in Syrien ihre Heimat zerstört hat.

In Äthiopien hat Berhane Deutsch gelernt,

weil | damit er in Aachen Ingenieurwesen studieren will.

Uwe will nächsten Monat nach Kalifornien ziehen,

weil | damit er dort als Tontechniker arbeiten wird.

Sandra plant ein Jahr lang als Au-pair in Kanada zu leben,

weil | damit sie dort ihr Französisch verbessern kann.

Feyine möchte ihre Lehre als Mechanikerin mit „sehr gut" bestehen,

weil | damit der Betrieb ihr eine feste Stelle anbietet und sie in Österreich bleiben kann.

295d **Was sind die Gründe bzw. Ziele? Beenden Sie die folgenden Sätze. Sie können frei schreiben oder die Ideen unten benutzen.**

Ist Knut nach Madagaskar ausgewandert,

weil ______________________________?

Jana sucht Arbeit in Südkorea,

damit ______________________________.

Inés und Pedro wollen ihr Land verlassen,

um ______________________________.

Es geht Sediq jetzt viel besser,

da ______________________________.

Hatice lebt nicht mehr in der Türkei,

weil ______________________________.

Ideen:

ein sicheres Leben führen können
eine Stelle als Hotelmanager*in gefunden haben
nicht mehr als Andersdenkende*r verfolgt werden
wieder mit dem*der Freund*in zusammen sein
ihre*seine Eltern aus dem Militärgefängnis entlassen werden
eine Aufenthaltsgenehmigung bekommen haben
eine lang ersehnte (*desired*) Ausbildung beginnen

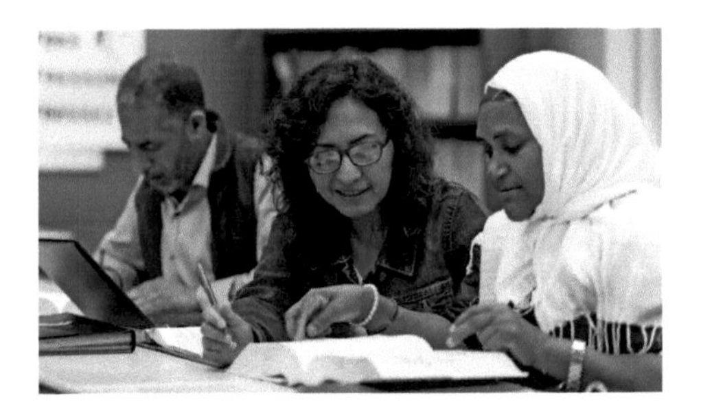

296a **Lesen Sie die drei Abschnitte über die Auswanderung und Flucht von Menschen aus deutschsprachigen Ländern in die USA zu verschiedenen Zeiten. Beantworten Sie dann die R/F-Fragen auf der nächsten Seite.**

Land und Reichtum?
Bereits im 17. Jahrhundert wanderten Menschen aus den deutschsprachigen Ländern in die USA aus. Viele der frühen Zuwander*innen waren Wirtschaftsflüchtlinge. Ein Grund für das Auswandern war zum Beispiel die wachsende Armut durch die Industrialisierung. In den USA gab es günstiges Land, das die Kolonist*innen von den vielen verschiedenen indigenen Völkern, die schon vor der Kolonisierung in Nordamerika gewohnt hatten, gewaltsam annektierten. So war das Versprechen von „freiem Land" und „vielen Ressourcen" für weiße Europäer*innen ein wichtiger Sog-Faktor.

Freiheit und Demokratie?
Im 19. Jahrhundert gab es in Europa viele revolutionäre Bewegungen. In Deutschland und Österreich scheiterte (*failed*) die Märzrevolution von 1848 und viele der enttäuschten Demokrat*innen wanderten als politische Flüchtlinge in die USA aus. Sie wurden „Forty-Eighters" genannt und siedelten vor allem in den nördlichen Staaten wie Wisconsin und Minnesota. In Briefen nach Europa kommentierten sie die Versklavung von aus Afrika verschleppten (*kidnapped*) Menschen. Manche äußerten sich kritisch, viele sahen jedoch keinen Widerspruch (*contradiction*) zwischen der Freiheit, die sie als weiße Europäer*innen in den USA erlebten, und der nicht-existenten Freiheit von Schwarzen Menschen in den USA. Viele deutschsprachige Zuwander*innen kämpften auch im Amerikanischen Bürger*innenkrieg. Durch die Siedlungsgebiete kämpften sie vor allem auf Seiten der Union, aber es gab auch ungefähr 5.000 deutschsprachige Soldaten auf Seiten der Konföderation.

Schutz vor Verfolgung?
1933 begann in Deutschland und ab 1938 auch in Österreich die systematische Diskriminierung, Verfolgung und Ermordung von Bevölkerungsgruppen wie Jüd*innen, Schwarzen Deutschen, Slaw*innen, Roma und Sinti, politischen Oppositionellen und Menschen mit Behinderung. Ungefähr 500.000 Menschen verließen zu dieser Zeit Deutschland und Österreich. 80–90 % von ihnen waren Jüd*innen. Durch eine Quotenregelung bearbeiteten die USA nur wenige der Asylanträge aus den beiden Ländern. Zwischen 1933 und 1939 fanden ungefähr 6.000 Jüd*innen in Kanada und 102.000 Jüd*innen in den USA Zuflucht. Andere Flüchtlinge wurden abgewiesen (*rejected*) und zum Teil zurück nach Europa geschickt, wie das Schiff St. Louis im Jahr 1939.

richtig	falsch	
		Die Auswanderung aus den deutschsprachigen Ländern begann im 19. Jahrhundert.
		Zwischen dem 17. und 20. Jahrhundert flohen Menschen aus ökonomischen und politischen Gründen.
		Deutschsprachige Auswander*innen kritisierten die Versklavung von Afrikaner*innen nicht.
		Deutschsprachige Auswander*innen kämpften im Amerikanischen Bürger*innenkrieg auf beiden Seiten.
		Jüd*innen fanden während des Dritten Reichs ohne Probleme Schutz in Nordamerika.

296b **Schreiben Sie jeweils einen Satz zu den Fragen. Sie können allgemein oder über die spezifische Auswanderung/ Flucht von deutschsprachigen Menschen in die USA (siehe Aktivität 296a) schreiben.**

Welche Gründe für Flucht und Auswanderung sind historisch spezifisch und welche gibt es zu verschiedenen Zeitpunkten (und eventuell auch heute noch)?

____

Welche Gründe führen zu freiwilliger Auswanderung? Welche Gründe führen zu Flucht?

____

____

296c Enriching and Specifying Nouns With Attributes

After nearly four semesters of studying German, your range of expression has most likely widened dramatically. Beyond grammatical correctness, we can now integrate more and more aspects of precision and style. One way of doing this is by expanding certain parts of speech.

In particular, nouns have great potential to be enriched or specified in many different ways. All the additional information that ascribe a quality to a noun are called attributes, and we can distinguish them by their position: left-side attributes and right-side attributes. You have encountered most of them in earlier chapters, and we will review some of them more closely in this chapter.

Please look at the various ways how you can elaborate on the noun *Geschichte* (story) in the following sentence:

Die [L] Geschichte [R] passierte angeblich vor Emils Einwanderung in die USA.	*The story supposedly took place before Emil's immigration to the U.S.*

left-side attributes:

Adjective	Die	abenteuerliche	Geschichte	*The adventurous story*
Present participle	Die	folgende	Geschichte	*The following story*
Past participle	Die	(völlig) erfundene	Geschichte	*The (completely) fabricated story*
Genitive (for names)		Emils	Geschichte	*Emil's story*

right-side attributes:

Genitive (for nouns)	Die	Geschichte	meines Urgroßvaters	*The story of my great grandfather*
Adjunct with preposition	Die	Geschichte	von Emil	*The story of Emil*
	Die	Geschichte	mit all ihren Varianten	*The story with all its variations*
Adverb	Die	Geschichte	damals	*The story back then*
Apposition	Die	Geschichte	, so unglaublich wie sie war,	*The story, as incredible as it was,*
Relative clause	Die	Geschichte	, die alle glaubten,	*The story that everybody believed*

296d **Schauen Sie sich hier Sätze aus dem Text in Aktivität 296a genauer an. Unterstrichen sind die Nomen, die von den farbig markierten Satzteilen erklärt werden. Bestimmen Sie: Um welche Art von Attribut handelt es sich bei den farbig markierten Satzelementen?**

Bereits im 17. Jahrhundert wanderten Menschen aus den deutschsprachigen Ländern in die USA aus.

Relativsatz   Partizip   Präpositionalphrase

Viele der frühen Zuwander*innen waren Wirtschaftsflüchtlinge.

Partizip   Adjektiv   Genitiv

Ein Grund für das Auswandern war zum Beispiel die wachsende Armut durch die Industrialisierung.

Relativsatz   Partizip   Apposition

… von den vielen verschiedenen indigenen Völkern, die schon vor der Kolonisierung in Nordamerika gewohnt hatten, gewaltsam annektierten.

Relativsatz   Genitiv   Präpositionalphrase

Viele deutschsprachige Zuwander*innen kämpften auch im Amerikanischen Bürger*innenkrieg.

Adjektiv   Partizip   Adverb

296e Review: Adjective Endings

The first enriching/specifying attributes that we will review are adjectives. They are left-side attributes, and both in German and English, they serve to describe, characterize, or clarify a noun.

Die Geschichte ist abenteuerlich.	*The story is adventurous.* (= predicate adjective)
Ich erzähle meine abenteuerlich**e** Geschichte.	*I am telling my adventurous story.* (= attributive adjective)
Das Ende der abenteuerlich**en** Geschichte ist klasse!	*The ending of the adventurous story is awesome!*

German adjectives change endings based on grammatical gender, case, and number of the noun. In *Impuls Deutsch 1*, you learned to determine them by asking four questions about the article preceding the adjective and the noun it is referring to:

Question 1: Is there an article before the adjective?	yes →	**Question 2:** Is the article identical to the nominative article?	yes →	**Question 3:** Is the noun singular?	yes →	**Question 4:** Does the article show gender?	yes →	**-e**
↓ no		↓ no		↓ no		↓ no		
add ending of definite article		***-en***		***-en***		**-er (*m.*)** **-es (*n.*)**		

296f **Eine Emigrationsgeschichte in die Vereinigten Staaten von Amerika. Schmücken Sie die Geschichte mit Adjektiven aus. Sie können selbst Adjektive suchen oder Vorschläge aus dem Kasten verwenden.**

geliebt (*beloved*) | lang | wenig | klein | gefürchtet (*feared*) | billig | schrecklich | verarmt (*impoverished*) | schmutzig | altmodisch | viel

1821 begann Tobias Müllers Familie, ihre ____________________ Sachen zu packen. Die Eltern Lina und Heinrich hatten beschlossen (*decided*), ihr ____________________ Heimatdorf nahe Speyer zu verlassen, denn nach dem ____________________ Krieg zwischen Preußen und Frankreich war das Land verwüstet (*devastated*). Zuerst musste die ____________________ Familie nach Antwerpen reisen und dort auf das ____________________ Überseeschiff warten. Die ____________________ Fahrt auf einem ____________________ Segelschiff war gefährlich: 25 % der Kleinkinder starben auf dieser Reise und wenn eine Person eine ____________________ Krankheit wie Masern (*measles*) hatte, wurden oft ____________________ Passagiere krank.

296g Review: Adjective Endings in the Comparative and the Superlative

Whenever an adjective precedes a noun, whether in its basic form (positive) or in comparative or superlative forms, it needs an adjective ending. For comparative and superlative, it will look like this:

Comparative adjective + *er* + **adjective ending**

Superlative adjective + *(e)st* + **adjective ending**

Please note that **adjective endings** are needed whenever comparatives and superlatives precede the noun they describe:

	Sie erzählt eine abenteuerlich**ere** Geschichte.	*She tells a more adventurous story.*
vs.	Die Geschichte ist abenteuerlicher.	*The story is more adventurous.*

An adjective in the superlative that precedes a noun does not have an ***am***, unlike freestanding adjectives.

	Ich höre die abenteuerlichs**te** Geschichte.	*I am hearing the most adventurous story.*
vs.	Die Geschichte ist **am** abenteuerlichsten.	*The story is the most adventurous.*

296h Deutsche Einwanderer*innen in Kanada. Setzen Sie entweder die Komparativ- oder Superlativform ein und ergänzen Sie das Adjektiv mit der richtigen Endung.

Ungefähr 10 % aller kanadischen Bürger*innen sagen, dass sie deutsche Vorfahren haben. Die ______________ dieser Kanadier*innen stammen aus dem deutschsprachigen Osteuropa. (viel) Im späten 19. Jahrhundert hatte Waterloo County in Ontario die ______________ Anzahl von deutschsprachigen Immigrant*innen. (hoch) Im Jahr 1854 gründeten die deutschsprachigen Siedler*innen dort die Stadt Berlin, aber diese Leute kamen aus Pennsylvania und nicht aus dem viel ______________ Deutschland. (fern) Obwohl die Einwohner*innen im kanadischen Berlin auch Englisch sprachen, blieb Deutsch bis 1916 die ______________ Sprache von beiden. (dominant) Wegen des Ersten Weltkrieges gab es immer ______________ anti-deutsche Proteste in Berlin und schließlich änderte die Stadtregierung den Namen zu Kitchener. (viel)

297a Ergänzen Sie die Sätze mit dem richtigen Wort. Versuchen Sie es zuerst ohne Hilfe. Schlagen Sie dann im zweiten Schritt die Wörter, die Sie noch nicht kennen, in einem Wörterbuch nach.

Werte | interkulturelles Lernen | Schmelztiegel | Sinnbild | Bildung | Gesellschaft

New York ist auch als ______________ bekannt, weil dort Menschen aus vielen verschiedenen Kulturen zusammenkommen. Eine Gruppe von Menschen, die unter spezifischen politischen, sozialen und ökonomischen Bedingungen zusammenlebt, ist eine ______________. Ein Synonym für ______________ ist Symbol. ______________ bedeutet, das Verhalten und die Bräuche (*customs*) einer Kultur zu beobachten, es mit den eigenen zu vergleichen und in diesem Dialog etwas Neues zu lernen. ______________ beschreiben Dinge oder Eigenschaften, die für eine Gruppe von Menschen sehr wichtig sind, wie zum Beispiel Familie, Ehrlichkeit, Freiheit etc. Alles, was eine Person in der Schule, an der Uni oder auch allgemein über das Leben lernt, ist ______________.

298a **Auswandern, einwandern, zuwandern, flüchten. Ordnen Sie die Begriffe den Definitionen zu.**

ein Zuhause in einem neuen Land suchen

Zuflucht in einem neuen Land suchen, aber danach zurückkehren

das alte Zuhause verlassen, um woanders zu leben

das alte Zuhause unfreiwillig verlassen, ein neues Zuhause suchen müssen

auswandern, emigrieren
die Auswanderung/Emigration
der*die Auswanderer*in/Emigrant*in

einwandern, zuwandern, immigrieren
die Zuwanderung/Immigration
der*die Zuwanderer*in/Immigrant*in

ins Exil gehen
das Exil
der*die Exilant*in

flüchten
die Flucht
der*die Geflüchtete (der Flüchtling)

94: Auf nach Europa

299a Review: The Present Participle as Adjective

Another left-side attribute, the participial modifier, is a "hybrid" grammatical form that is derived from a verb (participle) to describe a noun. Participial modifiers use **adjective endings** and are placed before a noun. They offer information in a nutshell in front of a noun that can also be expressed by a relative sentence after the noun.

There are two types of participles: the present participle (called *Partizip I = Partizip eins*), and the past participle (called *Partizip II = Partizip zwei*). We will review the first one here:

Creating a present participle is very easy: you take the stem of a verb and add the ending *-(e)nd*.

lesen	→	les_	→	lesend
gehen	→	geh_	→	gehend

Now you are ready to go, and you can treat your participle like an adjective by adding the same adjective endings we reviewed in the previous units.

Partizip I	Relativsatz	
eine fesselnde Geschichte	eine Geschichte, die fesselt	*a captivating story (a story that captivates)*
ein lachender Student	ein Student, der lacht	*a laughing (male) student (a (male) student who is laughing)*
– fließendes Wasser	Wasser, das fließt	*running water (water that is running)*

You can even take it a step further and add some more specifying elements in front of the participle, like adverbs, objects, or prepositional phrases.

die	lesende	Studentin	*the reading (female) student*
die	aufmerksam lesende	Studentin	*the attentively reading (female) student*
die	ständig lesende	Studentin	*the constantly reading (female) student*
die	Zeitung lesende	Studentin	*the (female) student reading a newspaper*[1]
die	in der Sonne lesende	Studentin	*the (female) student reading in the sunshine*[1]
die	schon seit einer Stunde lesende	Studentin	*the (female) student reading for an hour already*[1]
die	mit der Lupe lesende	Studentin	*the (female) student reading with the magnifier*[1]

[1] Most of the time, the extended participles in front of the noun don't translate well. In English, the information is usually put into a relative clause placed directly after the noun.

299b **Definieren Sie die folgenden Gruppen von Personen. Benutzen Sie jeweils das Partizip I für Ihre Definitionen. Achten Sie dabei auf die richtigen Adjektivendungen.**

Die Mehrzahl von jungen Menschen an einer Universität sind ____________________ Personen. (studieren)

Biolog*innen, Chemiker*innen, Geolog*innen und Physiker*innen sind ____________________

____________________ Naturwissenschaftler*innen. (über natürliche Prozesse forschen)

Berufe wie Journalist*in, Autor*in oder Werbetexter*in eignen sich am besten für ____________________

Leute. (gern schreiben)

Alle Sportarten werden von ____________________ Athlet*innen ausgeübt. (ihre Körper trainieren)

Manche Deutschland-Besucher*innen wie Ex-G.I.s, Tourist*innen oder internationale Geschäftsleute wollen nicht in ihre Heimat zurückkehren. Diese ____________________ Menschen lernen die Sprache und viele Aspekte der deutschen Kultur kennen. (in Deutschland bleiben)

300a **Audre Lorde: „black lesbian feminist mother poet warrior". Hier ist eine Liste von Dingen, die in Lordes Leben gleichzeitig passieren. Verbinden Sie die Sätze, indem Sie aus dem ersten Satz eine Nominalphrase mit Partizip I bilden, wie im Beispiel.**

Die Autorin wächst in Harlem auf. Sie erlebt dort die Great Depression.

Die in Harlem aufwachsende Autorin erlebt dort die Great Depression.

Die Autorin geht in die achte Klasse. Sie schreibt ihr erstes Gedicht.

____

Die Autorin studiert am Hunter College. Sie bekommt dort den BA.

____

Die Autorin studiert Bibliothekswissenschaft. Sie arbeitet in einer Fabrik.

____

Die Autorin schreibt Gedichte. Sie wird bekannt.

____

Die Autorin wohnt 1992 in Deutschland. Sie erlebt einen rassistischen Angriff und schreibt an Bundeskanzler Kohl.

____

Die Autorin wohnt öfters in Berlin. Sie lehrt an der Freien Universität Berlin.

____

302a Modifying Nouns With the Past Participle as Adjective

We will now look at the second type of participle: the past participle (*Partizip II*). You have previously used past participles to form the *Perfekt* (with a helping verb) and the passive voice (with *werden*).

As you know, participles are hybrids of a verb and an adjective. They are derived from a verb and are positioned before the noun they describe, making them left-side attributes. As with the present participle (*Partizip I*), you add **adjective endings** to the past participle (*Partizip II*) to make it function as a participial modifier (i.e., a special type of adjective):

malen	→ gemalt	→ das gemalt**e** Bild	*the painted picture*
schreiben	→ geschrieben	→ der geschrieben**e** Text	*the written text*
reparieren	→ _repariert	→ repariert**e** Autos	*repaired cars*

When you look at the examples above, you might notice that the participles *gemalt*, *geschrieben*, and *repariert* don't describe an "active action" but an action that was done to the picture, the text, and the cars by someone else, i.e., an "agent." Thus, the participles in the examples have a **passive meaning**. This is true for most German verbs that require a direct object (transitive verbs).

Die Künstlerin malte ein Bild.
→ Das gemalte Bild hängt jetzt in einer Galerie.

The (female) artist painted a picture.
→ *The painted picture is hanging in a gallery now.*

Der Professor korrigierte einen Text.
→ Die Studierenden lesen den korrigierten Text.

The (male) professor edited a text.
→ *The students are reading the edited text.*

As you did with the present participle (*Partizip I*), you can place any number of adverbs or prepositional phrases before the past participle (*Partizip II*) to create quite complex participial modifiers.

der	korrigierte	Text	*the edited text*
der	hastig korrigierte	Text	*the hastily edited text*
der	ohne Sorgfalt korrigierte	Text	*the text edited without care*[1]
der	vom Professor korrigierte	Text	*the text edited by the (male) professor*[1]
der	in weniger als zehn Minuten korrigierte	Text	*the text edited in less than ten minutes*[1]

[1] Most of the time, the extended participles in front of the noun don't translate well. In English, the information is usually put into a relative clause placed directly after the noun. Example: *Das von meinem Bruder erst gestern gekaufte Auto wurde heute morgen ohne Reifen auf dem Campus gefunden.* → The car, which my brother just bought yesterday, was found on campus this morning missing its tires.

302b Was sagen diese Opernsänger*innen? Fügen Sie das Partizip II mit der richtigen Adjektivendung ein.

Viele Opernsänger*innen lernen Deutsch, weil sie die ______________________ Lieder so gerne vortragen. (in dieser Sprache singen)

Die in den letzten Jahren ______________________ Opernhäuser in Deutschland sind Frankfurt, Stuttgart und Mannheim. (am höchsten bewerten)

Ein Drittel aller ______________________ Opern finden auf deutschen Bühnen statt. (weltweit aufführen)

Es gibt 115 ______________________ Opernhäuser im deutschsprachigen Raum: 80 in Deutschland, 23 in Österreich und 12 in der Schweiz. (von der Regierung jeweils stark subventionieren)

Oft singen ______________________ Opernsänger*innen auf deutschsprachigen Bühnen. (aus dem Ausland einwandern)

302c Abenteuer Auswandern. Ergänzen Sie die Sätze mit den entsprechenden Partizipien. Achten Sie dabei auf den richtigen Kasus und die Adjektivdeklination.

Viele europäische Länder suchen Fachkräfte in den ______________ Industrien. (führen; Partizip I)

In der Landessprache ______________ Geschäftstreffen sind in vielen Firmen üblich – ein weiterer Grund, die Sprache zu lernen. (führen; Partizip II)

Es gibt ______________ Programme, um Einwanderer*innen den Einstieg in das neue Leben zu erleichtern. (unterstützen; Partizip I)

Finanziell ______________ Einwanderer*innen haben es im neuen Land leichter. (unterstützen; Partizip II)

Gemeinschaftliche Feste ______________ Nachbarschaften können uns dabei helfen, schnell neue Kontakte zu knüpfen. (organisieren; Partizip I)

Ein gut ______________ Alltag hilft auch dabei, die stressige Anfangsphase zu überstehen. (organisieren; Partizip II)

Deutschland hat einen ______________ Bedarf an ausländischen Arbeitskräften. (steigen; Partizip I)

Die 2015 stark ______________ Zahl an Einwanderer*innen ist in den letzten Jahren wieder gesunken. (steigen; Partizip II)

95: Die Faszinationen mit dem „Wilden Westen"°

303a **Amerikanische Ureinwohner*innen. Lesen Sie den Text und beantworten Sie die Fragen.**

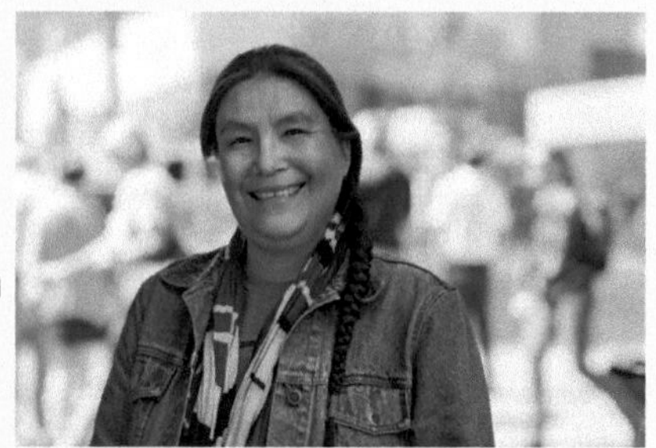

Kulturbox – Terminologie: Auf Deutsch werden die Amerikanischen Ureinwohner*innen meist als „Indianer*innen" bezeichnet. Dieser Begriff stammt aus der Kolonialzeit, weil er explizit auf Kolumbus' Ziel, nach Indien zu segeln, zurückgeht. Auch heute wird der Begriff unreflektiert von Deutschsprechenden benutzt. Obwohl sie ihn nicht als Schimpfwort meinen, gibt es einige Probleme mit dem Wort. In „Impuls Deutsch" benutzen wir ihn deshalb nur als Zitat in Anführungszeichen (*quotation marks*) und bevorzugen andere Begriffe wie „Amerikanische Ureinwohner*innen", „indigene Völker" oder einfach „Indigene". Der koloniale Begriff fasst alle verschiedenen Völker von Indigenen zusammen und macht Unterschiede unsichtbar. Außerdem führt der Begriff „Indianer*innen" auch zu einer Perspektive, die in der Vergangenheit liegt. Wenige Deutschsprechende sind sich der Tatsache bewusst, dass es auch heute noch indigene Völker mit lebendigen Kulturen gibt. Diese Dynamik und Gegenwart von Indigenen wollen wir in den Vordergrund stellen.

Warum bevorzugen wir in „Impuls Deutsch" die Begriffe „Amerikanische Ureinwohner*innen", „indigene Völker" oder „Indigene"? Kreuzen Sie alle richtigen Gründe an.

- ☐ Weil „Indianer*innen" ein kolonialer Begriff ist.
- ☐ Weil „Indianer*innen" ein Schimpfwort ist.
- ☐ Weil „Amerikanische Ureinwohner*innen" besser die Pluralität der verschiedenen Völker repräsentiert.
- ☐ Weil „Amerikanische Ureinwohner*innen" in der Gegenwart (und nicht nur in der Kolonialzeit) leben.

What do you know about Indigenous people and the naming of Indigenous groups in the U.S.? In what ways are the practices of giving names to Indigenous people different or the same for German speakers in Europe and for people in the U.S.?

____

____

____

303b **Kulturelle Appropriation. Ergänzen Sie die folgenden Sätze mit der korrekten Form des Partizip I oder II.**

„Kulturelle Appropriation" bedeutet die unreflektierte Verwendung von ____________________ Aspekten einer Minderheitenkultur, wie zum Beispiel Kleidung, Artefakten oder Praktiken. (bedeuten; Partizip; Dativ)

„Unreflektiert" heißt, dass die fremde, ____________________ Kultur nicht in ihrer vollen Komplexität gesehen wird, sondern dass einzelne „Bausteine" benutzt werden, um das eigene Leben zu bereichern oder um Spaß zu haben, zum Beispiel beim Sport oder Karneval, aber auch für spirituelle Trends. (berauben; Partizip II; Nominativ)

Die andere Kultur und die in ihr ____________________ Menschen werden durch Appropriation auf Stereotype reduziert. (leben; Partizip I; Nominativ)

Kulturelle Appropriation ____________________ Personen verstehen oft nicht, dass sie dazu beitragen, rassistische Strukturen in der Gesellschaft zu reproduzieren. (betreiben; Partizip I; Nominativ)

Indigene Menschen machen unter anderem mit dem häufig ____________________ Hashtag #mycultureisnotacostume in den sozialen Medien auf kulturelle Appropriation aufmerksam. (benutzen; Partizip II; Dativ)

305a **Kurzbiografie über den Schriftsteller Karl May. Ergänzen Sie den Text mit den Partizipien und Adjektiven und korrekten Endungen.**

Karl May wurde 1842 in einem sehr ______________ Sommer in der ______________ Kleinstadt Ernstthal geboren. (heiß; sächsisch) Seine Eltern waren ______________ Weber*innen (*weavers*), die schon drei Kinder vor Karl verloren hatten. (verarmt = *impoverished*) Aus Mangel an Vitamin A konnte der kleine Karl nicht sehen. Das ______________ Kind wurde mit vier Jahren erfolgreich behandelt. (blind) Karl May glaubte, dass seine ______________ Blindheit ihm eine Extradosis Fantasie schenkte. (kindlich) In seiner Jugend beging May ______________ Verbrechen wie Diebstahl und Identitätsbetrug (*identity theft*) und er musste deshalb öfters ins Gefängnis. (viel) Er nannte sich zum Beispiel Dr. med. Heilig und spielte einen ______________ Augenarzt. (reich) Während seiner Gefängnisstrafen konnte er viele ______________ Bücher lesen, auch über ______________ Länder (interessant; fern). So begann er ______________ Reiseerzählungen zu schreiben, ohne diese Länder aus eigener Erfahrung zu kennen. (fesselnd) Durch seine ______________ Fantasie wurde er der ______________ Schriftsteller Deutschlands. (blühend; meist verkauft)

305b **Filme über und von Indigene(n). Notieren Sie sich alle Filme (und/oder Romane) über Indigene oder über die europäischen Kolonist*innen in den USA, die Sie kennen.**

____

____

Was haben diese Filme gemeinsam? Welches Bild von Indigenen und von europäischen Kolonist*innen vermitteln sie?

____

____

____

Kennen Sie Filme und/oder Romane, die die Gegenwart der indigenen Bevölkerung in den USA beschreiben? Schreiben Sie sie auf.

____

____

Schauen Sie sich den Trailer oder einen Clip vom Film „Skins" an. Chris Eyre hat bei dem Film Regie geführt und ihn produziert. Können Sie erkennen, dass es sich hier um eine indigene Perspektive handelt? Warum (nicht)? Welches Bild von Indigenen (und Europäer*innen) vermittelt der Film? Welchen Eindruck haben Sie von dem Film?

Recherche

____

____

____

307a **David Hasselhoff und die Deutschen. Ergänzen Sie die Sätze. Formen Sie zuerst das Partizip II des Infinitivs in Klammern. Wählen Sie dann die korrekte Adjektivendung.**

Schon in den 1980ern wurde David Hasselhoff durch die von vielen _geliebte_ Serie „Knight Rider" in Deutschland bekannt. (lieben)

Gegen Ende der Serie nahm die Popularität des „The Hoff" ________________ Schauspielers ab. (nennen)

Dann aber wurde ein 1989 ________________ Song von David Hasselhoff nicht nur zum Hit, sondern auch zur Hymne des Mauerfalls. (veröffentlichen)

Hasselhoff sang das Lied in Berlin – mit der teils ________________ Mauer im Hintergrund. (abreißen)

Das ________________ Timing für die Veröffentlichung des Liedes war perfekt, denn Hasselhoff wurde über Nacht zum Star in Deutschland. (wählen)

Die oft ________________ Liebe der Deutschen zu David Hasselhoff hat sich seitdem abgekühlt, aber Fans hat der Schauspieler und Sänger in Deutschland immer noch. (zitieren)

Das weit ________________ Stereotyp, dass *alle* Deutschen David Hasselhoff kennen und nach ihm verrückt sind, stimmt allerdings nicht. (verbreiten)

309a Review: Modifying Nouns With the Genitive Case

So far, we have talked about how to give more detail to a noun using adjectives and/or participial modifiers. When we introduced the genitive case in Chapter 4, we explained that the genitive helps us express a relationship between two nouns, in which one noun is part of, is connected to, belongs to, or depends on the other noun. In this way, the genitive case provides more information about a noun in two different ways. Genitives of proper names are left-side attributes, while genitives of nouns are right-side attributes.

Genitive of proper names

As in English, the main noun (right column) takes the second position while the preceding "modifying attribute" (green column) is marked by a simple -s. Unlike English, no apostrophe is used in German, unless the name ends in -s, -ss, -ß, -x, or -z.

Annas	Band	*Anna's band*
Europas	Musikwettbewerb	*Europe's song contest*
Professor Pills	Lied	*Professor Pill's song*
Frau Mörikes	Meinung	*Ms. Mörike's opinion*
Hans'	Position	*Hans' position*

Genitive of nouns

In German genitive constructions, the main noun (which can be in the nominative, accusative, or dative form) comes first. The noun that possesses or modifies the main noun follows in the genitive case.

Das	Lied	des Professors	*The (male) professor's song*
Die	Position	der Mutter	*The mother's position*
Die	Meinungen	der Studierend**en**	*The students' opinions*

309b **Elvis in Deutschland. Ergänzen Sie die Sätze mit einem Genitivattribut. Vergessen Sie nicht, die Artikel und Adjektivendungen an den Genitiv anzupassen.**

Elvis Presley, der von vielen König ______________________ (der amerikanische Rock 'n' Roll) genannt wurde, kam 1958 in Deutschland an. Er sollte die zwei Jahre ______________________ (sein Militärdienst) im hessischen Friedberg verrichten (*to carry out, perform*). Hunderte ______________________ (deutsche Jugendliche) begrüßten ihn enthusiastisch bei seiner Ankunft in Bremerhaven. Der Sänger hatte zu diesem Zeitpunkt schon Millionen ______________________ (seine Schallplatten = *records*) verkauft. Zwei Jahre nach seiner Militärzeit sang Elvis das Lied „Wooden Heart" („Muss i denn"), in dem er Sätze ______________________ (die deutsche Sprache) verwendete.

309c **In diesem Text über die Einflüsse der amerikanischen auf die deutsche Musik fehlen viele Ergänzungen. Ergänzen Sie die Lücken und achten Sie auf den richtigen Kasus. Achtung: Das zweite Wort in Klammern bildet jeweils das Genitivattribut.**

Der Einfluss der amerikanischen Musik (der Einfluss; die amerikanische Musik) ist schon offensichtlich, wenn man sich die aktuellen Charts anschaut. An ______________________ (die Spitze; die Rangliste) stehen oft Performer*innen aus den USA. Und auch ______________________ (die Musik; viele deutsche Sänger*innen) ist von amerikanischen Vorbildern beeinflusst. Roger Cicero, der ______________________ (ein Meister; der Jazz) war, nannte ______________________ (die Swingmusik; die 40er Jahre) als großes Vorbild seiner Arbeit. Auch in ______________________ (die Welt; die elektronische Musik) sind die Einflüsse auf die deutsche Szene unverkennbar. Durch ______________________ (der Erfolg; die afroamerikanische Hip-Hop-Bewegung) entstand eine deutschsprachige Subkultur, die in den neunziger Jahren kommerziell populär wurde.

310a Modifying Nouns With Prepositional Phrases

We can also modify nouns by using prepositional phrases containing other nouns. You might remember that in spoken German, the genitive is often replaced by a prepositional phrase starting with *von*.

Genitiv	Paula benutzt gern das Auto ihr**es** Vater**s**.	*Paula likes to use her father's car.*
von + Dativ	Paula benutzt gern das Auto von ihr**em** Vater.	*Paula likes to use the car of her father.*

In both cases, the information about the father's ownership adds additional information about the car in question, so—like the genitive—the prepositional phrase *von ihrem Vater* serves as a right-side attribute to the car.

Ein	Buch	über die Revolution	*A book on the revolution*
	Fußballclubs	in Deutschland	*Soccer clubs in Germany*
Meine	Tante	aus Amerika	*My aunt from America*

310b **Musicals! Markieren Sie die präpositionalen Attribute in den folgenden Sätzen.**

Das Musical über New York hat mir ganz gut gefallen.

Ich kenne den Darsteller mit den roten Haaren nicht.

Die Handlung von „Les Misérables" basiert auf dem Roman „Die Elenden" von Victor Hugo.

In dem Musical geht es um eine Romanze zwischen zwei High School-Schüler*innen.

Die Premiere in Hamburg war gut besucht.

Ich konnte die Darsteller*innen auf dem hinteren Teil der Bühne nicht gut sehen.

Hat sie Regie für Theater oder Musiktheater studiert?

Wir sind in das Theater neben dem Schlosspark gegangen.

Er hat den Tony Award in der Kategorie „Bestes Bühnenbild" bekommen.

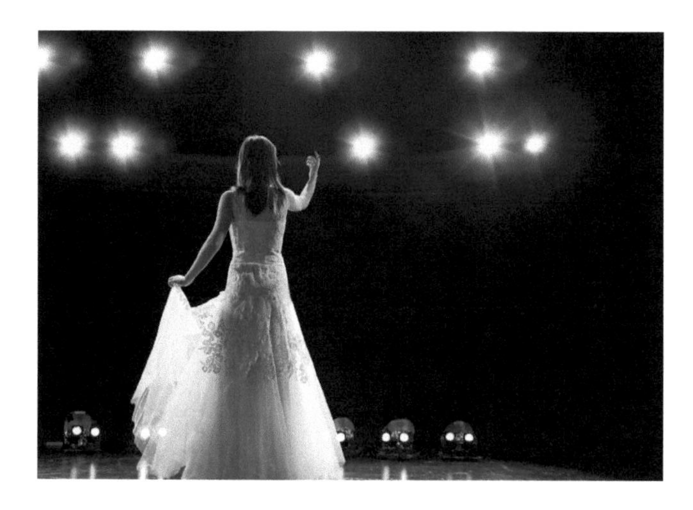

310c **Schreiben Sie drei Sätze über ein Musical, das Sie kennen, das Sie gerne sehen möchten oder in dem Sie vielleicht selbst mitgemacht haben. Benutzen Sie in jedem Satz mindestens ein präpositionales Attribut.**

____

____

____

____

____

97: Sprachliche Einflüsse aus D-A-CH-L

312a   **Reflektieren: Bei der amerikanischen Volkszählung (*U.S. Census*) im Jahr 1910 gaben 8.817.420 sogenannte „foreign-born white Americans" (Anmerkung: Dies war die offizielle Zensuskategorie) an, dass sie zu Hause Deutsch sprachen. Bei der Volkszählung 10 Jahre später war diese Zahl auf 8.164.111 gesunken. Bei der Volkszählung im Jahr 1940 wurde diese Zensuskategorie auf alle weißen Amerikaner*innen ausgeweitet. Trotz der Erweiterung dieser Kategorie gaben nur 4.949.780 Personen an, dass sie zu Hause Deutsch sprachen. Finden Sie diese Entwicklungen überraschend? Wie erklären Sie, dass zwischen 1920 und 1940 die Zahl der Personen, die angaben (*to report*) zu Hause Deutsch zu sprechen, so stark gesunken ist?**

312b In Aktivität 312a haben Sie die Zahlen der Amerikaner*innen kennengelernt, die zu Beginn des Jahrhunderts berichteten, dass sie zu Hause Deutsch gesprochen haben. Was denken Sie: Wie viele Menschen sprechen in den USA heute noch Deutsch? In welchen US-Staaten?

Recherche

___

___

___

Schauen Sie sich jetzt die MLA Sprachdaten an, indem Sie auf den ersten Link klicken, den Sie unter www.klett-usa.com/impuls2links für diese Aktivität finden. Klicken Sie auf „Language by State". In welchen Staaten gibt es die meisten Deutschsprecher*innen? Was ist interessant? Warum?

___

___

___

Besuchen Sie jetzt über den zweiten Link die MLA Language Map. Klicken Sie auf „Languages by Percentage of Speakers" und wählen Sie „Deutsch" aus. Beschreiben Sie die Karte. Was finden Sie interessant? Warum?

___

___

___

Wo wird Deutsch studiert? Wählen Sie „Enrollments and Predominant Languages" und dann „predominant language, excluding English" aus. Beschreiben Sie, was Sie sehen.

___

___

___

Wie ändern sich die Suchergebnisse, wenn Sie „predominant language, excluding English and Spanish" auswählen?

___

___

___

Schauen Sie sich die Region, in der Sie leben, genau an. Welche Sprachen werden außer Englisch und Deutsch gesprochen?

___

___

___

313a In MACHEN lernen Sie die deutschen Dialekte Pennsylvania Dutch und Texas German kennen. Wer spricht diese Sprachen und wo in Pennsylvania und Texas werden diese Variationen des Deutschen gesprochen? Machen Sie eine Online-Recherche zu den Informationen, die unten in der Tabelle fehlen.

Recherche

	Wo wird diese Sprache gesprochen?	Wie viele Sprecher*innen gibt es?	Wie kam die Sprache an diese Orte?
Pennsylvania Dutch			
Texas German			

Aussprache: Satzakzent

313b **Hören und Markieren: Hören Sie die Sätze und markieren Sie den stärksten Akzent im Satz (= Satzakzent).**

A: Was ist denn los?
B: Ich habe ein Problem mit meinem Professor.
A: Was genau ist denn vorgefallen?
B: Ich habe ein Referat gehalten. Alle fanden es richtig gut.
A: Und wo ist das Problem?
B: Mein Professor hat nicht richtig zugehört. Später hatte er keine Zeit für mich. Er hat mir dann eine schlechte Note gegeben.
A: Das gibt's doch nicht!

313c **Hören und Markieren: Hören Sie die Sätze und markieren Sie den stärksten Akzent im Satz.**

a) Ich möchte einen Termin in dieser Woche.
b) Der Termin ist am Freitag, nicht am Mittwoch.
c) Wie ist denn das passiert?
d) Wir gehen ins Kino, nicht ins Theater.

313d **Sprechen: In deutschen Sätzen oder Wortgruppen wird immer eine Silbe stärker als alle anderen betont. Die Silbe, die am stärksten betont wird, ist der Satzakzent. Er liegt normalerweise auf Sinnwörtern (Nomen, Verben, Adjektiven, Adverbien). Sprechen Sie die Sätze in Aktivität 313c laut und klopfen Sie bei dem Satzakzent auf den Tisch.**

313e **Ordnen: Wir unterscheiden zwischen Kontrast- und Demonstrativakzent. Ordnen Sie die Sätze aus Aktivität 313c zu den Kategorien.**

Kontrastakzent: Man möchte einen Gegensatz ausdrücken, z. B.: Das ist **meine** Tasche (nicht deine).

Sätze Nr. ____________________

Demonstrativakzent: Man weist auf etwas besonders deutlich hin, z. B.: Mir gefällt **diese** Tasche.

Sätze Nr. ____________________

313f **Hören und Sprechen: Hören Sie den Satz fünfmal und achten Sie auf die verschiedenen Varianten. Sprechen Sie anschließend in den verschiedenen Varianten nach.**

1) **Ich** komme morgen um acht Uhr zu dir. (nicht Christina)
2) Ich **komme** morgen um acht Uhr zu dir. (ganz sicher)
3) Ich komme **morgen** um acht Uhr zu dir. (nicht heute)
4) Ich komme morgen **um acht Uhr** zu dir. (nicht um sieben Uhr)
5) Ich komme morgen um acht Uhr zu **dir**. (nicht zu Christina)

313g **Sprechen Sie den folgenden Satz in verschiedenen Varianten.**

Ich gehe nächsten Dienstag um zehn zu meinem Professor in die Sprechstunde.

313h **Hören: Hören Sie die Sätze in zwei Versionen: neutral und emotional. Was ist anders?**

a) Das ist doch wohl die Höhe.
b) Das ist wirklich eine Frechheit!
c) So ein Quatsch!
d) Das ist ja gemein!
e) Das ist wirklich ärgerlich.
f) Das geht doch nicht!
g) Ich bin echt sauer!

Die emotionale Variante ist ☐ leiser. ☐ lauter.

Die emotionale Variante ☐ ist monotoner. ☐ hat eine größere Melodiebewegung.

98: Politik im Vergleich°

314a **Politikwörterbuch. Hier sehen Sie eine alphabetische Liste mit wichtigen Wörtern aus dem Bereich „Politik". Schreiben Sie hinter die Wörter, die Sie schon kennen, die englische Übersetzung. Schlagen Sie dann alle neuen Wörter nach.**

der*die Bundeskanzler*in ______________
der*die Bundespräsident*in ______________
die Partei ______________
die Wahl ______________
die Stimme ______________
der*die Politiker*in ______________
das Staatsoberhaupt ______________
der*die Abgeordnete ______________
die Regierung ______________
das Volk ______________
der Staat ______________
das Ministerium ______________
das Gesetz ______________
der*die Regierungschef*in ______________

314b **Wer hat wo die Macht? Es gibt unterschiedliche Regierungsformen. Erklären Sie basierend auf dem Kulturpunkt die Wörter „Monarchie", „Anarchie" und „Theokratie".**

Beispiel:
Demokratie (demos + kratie) = das Volk herrscht

Kulturpunkt

monos = eins
demos = das Volk
theos = der Gott
archie = Herrschaft/Macht
kratie = Herrschaft/Macht
ana = ohne

Worterklärungen:

Monarchie (monos + archie) = ______________

Anarchie (ana + archie) = ______________

Theokratie (theos + kratie) = ______________

314c **Ordnen Sie nun die Regierungsformen im linken Kasten in die Tabelle ein und entscheiden Sie, welches Land aus dem rechten Kasten zu welcher Regierungsform passt. Wenn Sie sich nicht sicher sind, schauen Sie im Internet nach.**

Recherche

Diktatur | direkte Demokratie | parlamentarische Demokratie | parlamentarische Monarchie | absolute Monarchie | ~~Theokratie~~ | Anarchie | präsidentielle Demokratie | konstitutionelle Monarchie

die USA | die BRD | die Schweiz | England | Belgien | die Freistadt Christiania | ~~Vatikanstaat~~ | Deutschland 1933–45 | Frankreich vor 1789

Erklärung	Regierungsform	Land
ein*e „Repräsentant*in Gottes" herrscht	*Theokratie*	*Vatikanstaat*
niemand herrscht		
eine Person „diktiert" alles		
ein*e König*in bestimmt alles		
das Volk stimmt direkt über Themen ab		
das Volk wählt ein Parlament, das Parlament entscheidet über Themen		
eine Verfassung (Konstitution) begrenzt und definiert die Macht des Königs		

der*die König*in ist offiziell die oberste Person im Land, aber das Parlament hat die Macht		
Präsident*in und Parlament werden beide direkt vom Volk gewählt		

315a Forming Adjectives With Suffixes

You can expand the range of your vocabulary miraculously once you know how to create new words out of old words. At the same time, you can change the category of words by adding certain suffixes. This process is called "derivation," and it looks very similar in English. Today, we will look at some typical suffixes that can change nouns and verbs into adjectives:

Noun	+	**Suffix**	→ **Adjective**		
der Schlaf die Hoffnung[1]	+	**-los**	schlaf**los** hoffnungs**los**	*the sleep* *the hope*	→ *sleep**less*** → *hope**less***
der Wind das Salz	+	**-ig**	wind**ig** salz**ig**	*the wind* *the salt*	→ *wind**y*** → *salt**y***
der Freund die Wissenschaft	+	**-lich**	freund**lich** wissenschaft**lich**	*the friend* *the science*	→ *friend**ly*** → *scientific*
die Partei das Kind	+	**-isch**	partei**isch** kind**isch**	*the party* *the child*	→ *partial, partisan* → *child**ish***
Verb	+	**Suffix**	→ **Adjective**		
trinken brauchen	+	**-bar**	trink**bar** brauch**bar**	*to drink* *to use*	→ *drink**able*** → *us**able***

[1] For feminine nouns that end in *-ung, -heit, -keit, -schaft, -ion*, and *-tät* you have to insert the letter -s between the noun and the suffix *-los*.

As you can see, the endings ***-los*** and ***-bar*** carry meaning (as they do in English: **-less** and **-able**), whereas the other suffixes simply transform the nouns into adjectives.

315b Wie können wir diese politischen Konzepte anders ausdrücken? Wählen Sie das jeweils richtige Adjektiv.

In den USA muss ein*e Kandidat*in für das Präsident*innenamt im Land geboren sein. Immigrant*innen können also nicht gewählt werden. Sie sind nicht ______________________. (wählbar | wahllos)

Wenn ich keine Affiliation mit einer politischen Partei habe, bin ich ______________________. (parteiisch | parteilos)

Eine Nation, die eine Demokratie als politisches System hat, ist ______________________. (demokratisch | demokratielos)

Wenn das Militär einen Coup gegen das Regime organisiert, werden die Regimepolitiker*innen ______________________. (mächtig | machtlos)

Effektive Politiker*innen versuchen, die Probleme in ihrer Gesellschaft zu lösen. Sie engagieren sich für ______________________ Probleme. (gesellschaftliche | gesellschaftslose)

315c **Bundeskanzler*in vs. Präsident*in. Hier sehen Sie eine Gegenüberstellung der Systeme in Deutschland und in den USA für die Wahl der Regierungschef*innen (*head of government*). Schauen Sie sich die Tabelle an und schreiben Sie, welche Aspekte Sie warum am interessantesten finden oder was Sie überrascht.**

	Deutschland	**USA**
Wer wählt?	Die Wähler*innen wählen den Bundestag, der Bundestag wählt den*die Bundeskanzler*in.	Die Wähler*innen stimmen für eine*n Präsidentschaftskandidat*in, das *Electoral College* wählt den*die Präsident*in.
Wie oft gibt es diese Wahl?	Alle 4 Jahre.	Alle 4 Jahre.
An welchem Tag wird gewählt?	Am Sonntag.	Am Dienstag.
Gibt es Vorwahlen?	Nein.	Ja.
Wer darf wählen?	Menschen, die mindestens 18 Jahre alt sind, die deutsche Staatsangehörigkeit besitzen und seit mindestens drei Monaten einen festen Wohnsitz in Deutschland haben.	Menschen, die mindestens 18 Jahre alt sind, die US-amerikanische Staatsangehörigkeit besitzen und sich für die Wahl haben registrieren lassen. Außerdem hat jeder Staat seine eigenen, zusätzlichen Regeln.
Wer darf nicht wählen?	Menschen, die die oben genannten Kriterien nicht erfüllen. Außerdem: Menschen, die eine schwere politische Straftat (*felony*) begangen haben; Menschen, für die eine andere Person alle wichtigen Entscheidungen fällt (z. B. Menschen mit starker Demenz).[1]	Menschen, die die oben genannten Kriterien nicht erfüllen. Außerdem: Menschen, die eine schwere Straftat begangen haben (von Staat zu Staat verschieden); Menschen mit geistiger Behinderung (*intellectual disability*) (von Staat zu Staat verschieden); Menschen, die in den US-Territorien leben.
Muss ich mich für die Wahl registrieren lassen?	Jein. Wenn man in eine neue Stadt zieht, muss man sich beim Meldeamt für Einwohner*innen als neue*r Bürger*in der Stadt registrieren lassen. Dann wird man automatisch ins Wahlregister eingetragen. Deutsche, die länger als ein halbes Jahr im Ausland leben, müssen sich ins Wahlregister eintragen lassen.	Ja.
Muss ich im Wahllokal (*polling location*) einen Ausweis vorzeigen?	Jein. Jede Person, die zur Wahl berechtigt (*eligible*) ist, bekommt eine Wahlbenachrichtigung (*polling card*) per Post zugeschickt. Wenn eine Person diese Benachrichtigung zu Hause vergisst, muss sie ihren Personalausweis oder Reisepass vorzeigen.	Das ist von Staat zu Staat unterschiedlich. In den meisten Staaten müssen die Personen aber einen Ausweis dabei haben (mit oder ohne Foto). In sechzehn Staaten kann gewählt werden, ohne sich ausweisen zu müssen (Stand 2020).
Wie werden die Stimmen verteilt – also wer gewinnt?	Jede*r Wähler*in hat zwei Stimmen: Die Erststimme geht an eine*n Abgeordnete*n (*representative*); die Zweitstimme entscheidet, wie viele Sitze eine Partei im Bundestag insgesamt bekommt (sie braucht 5 % aller Zweitstimmen, um in den Bundestag zu kommen). Der neue Bundestag wählt dann den*die neue*n Kanzler*in. Meistens ist das der*die Kanzlerkandidat*in der stärksten Partei.	Der*Die Präsidentschaftskandidat*in mit den meisten Wahlpersonen (*delegates*) – mindestens 270 – wird der*die neue Präsident*in. Das kann, muss aber nicht die Mehrheit der Wähler*innenstimmen sein.

[1] Die meisten Menschen mit psychischen Erkrankungen sowie die meisten (schwer) Kriminellen, deren Straftat nicht politisch motiviert war (z. B. Mörder*innen, Betrüger*innen etc.), dürfen also wählen.

315d **Schauen Sie sich die Tabellen zur Wahlbeteiligung (= wie viele Menschen gewählt haben) an. Mit Blick auf die Informationen aus Aktivität 315c und Ihr Vorwissen über die USA: Was könnte die unterschiedliche Wahlbeteiligung in Deutschland und den USA erklären?**

	1996	2008	2016
Wahlbeteiligung USA	49 %	58,2 %	55,7 %

	1994	2002	2017
Wahlbeteiligung Deutschland	79,0 %	79,1 %	76,2 %

____

____

____

____

315e **Die CDU: Daten und Fakten. Entscheiden Sie, ob die angegebenen Verben als Partizip I oder II in die Lücken passen.**

Die CDU ist eine ______________________________ Partei. (im Jahr 1945 in Westdeutschland gründen) Sie entstand als Gegensatz zur ______________________ Zentrumspartei. (katholisch fokussiert) Die ________________ Kraft in den jungen Jahren dieser Partei war Konrad Adenauer. (treiben) Nach der Bundestagswahl 1969 musste die CDU zum ersten Mal in die Opposition zu der ________________ ________________ Regierung gehen. (von der SPD und FDP führen) Die ________________ Säulen der Partei sind: Freiheit, Solidarität und Gerechtigkeit. (feststehen) Bei der ________________ Bundestagswahl 2005 wurde Angela Merkel zur ersten deutschen Bundeskanzlerin gewählt, der Beginn einer 16-jährigen Amtszeit. (vorziehen)

99: Sport im Vergleich

317a Modifying Nouns With Appositions

Another very creative way of "attributing" a noun is by adding an apposition to it. An apposition is a phrase after the noun it is referring to, making it a right-side attribute. It can consist of a few words or of a full-blown sentence and is usually separated by a comma from the preceding noun.

Frau Müller	, unsere Trainerin,	begleitet uns zu den Wettkämpfen.	*Ms. Müller, our coach, accompanies us to the competitions.*
Der Mann	, ein guter Schwimmer,	gewann die Goldmedaille.	*The man, a good swimmer, won the gold medal.*
Sabine	, in guter Form wie immer,	gewann das Wettrennen.	*Sabine, in good shape as usual, won the race.*
Alle	, besonders Sabine und Fatima,	trugen zu diesem Erfolg bei.	*Everyone, in particular Sabine and Fatima, contributed to this success.*
Frau Müller	als[1] ihre Trainerin	war sehr zufrieden mit ihnen.	*Ms. Müller as their coach was very satisfied with them.*

[1] *Als* is one of the few exceptions where the apposition is not separated from the preceding noun by a comma.

317b **Zwei Gespräche im Turnverein. Welche Appositionen passen hier am besten? Wählen Sie eine Apposition aus der Liste und ergänzen Sie die Sätze.**

unsere Nachbarin | also Schmetterling, Brust und Freistil | das ist was ganz Tolles | der Glückspilz (*lucky guy*)

Nadia: Wo steckt Marcel, ______________________, eigentlich? Er hat gestern beim Mehrkampf im Jugendschwimmen gewonnen, ______________________, und sollte sich heute topfit fühlen!

Tanja: Und seine Mutter, ______________________, ist wieder Übungsleiterin für die Kinderschwimmgruppe geworden.

Nadia: Ja, genau, und bei den Schwimmwettkämpfen, ______________________, hilft sie nicht nur beim Training, sondern lädt uns danach auch immer zum Pizzaessen ein.

sogar die Trainer*innen | ihr zwei Superschwimmerinnen | wie großzügig | die fünf aus Florida

Klaus: Hallo, Marina und Claudia, ______________________. Kommt ihr nächsten Monat auch mit zur Klassenskifahrt nach Brixen?

Claudia: Na klar! Wisst ihr, dass auch die internationalen Austauschschüler*innen, ______________________, mitkommen werden?

Marina: Haha, Leute aus Florida im Schnee – das sollte interessant werden. Habt ihr gehört, dass sie an ihrer Schule in St. Petersburg ein eigenes Footballteam haben? Und Baseball?

Klaus: Ja, und auch ein Schwimmteam und eine Tennismannschaft. Ihre Schule fährt diese Teams, ______________________, in einem Schulbus zu den Wettkämpfen. Die Schule finanziert auch alle Kosten für ihren Sport, ______________________.

317c **Vereinskultur in Deutschland. Ergänzen Sie die folgenden Sätze mit der passenden Apposition.**

abgekürzt e. V. | dem Land des Collegesports | speziell Kinder und Jugendliche | also in einem Klub | egal ob für Fußball, Tennis oder Leichtathletik | das heißt registrierten | darunter knapp 90.000 Sportvereine

Fast jede*r zweite Deutsche ist in einem Verein, ______________________. Vor dem Gesetz legitim ist ein Verein nur dann, wenn es sich um einen eingetragenen, ______________________, Verein handelt. Eingetragene Vereine, ______________________, gibt es für alle möglichen Interessen und Hobbys: Wandern, Umweltschutz, Karneval, Kaninchenzucht (*rabbit breeding*) und so weiter. Insgesamt gibt es rund 600.000 Vereine, ______________________, in Deutschland.

Sportvereine, ______________________, sind der Ort, wo Menschen nicht nur Freizeitspaß finden. Wenn Mitglieder, ______________________, Ambitionen haben, Profisportler*in zu werden, beginnt ihre Sportkarriere im Verein. Anders als zum Beispiel in den USA, ______________________, bereitet der Schulsport in Deutschland nicht auf eine Zukunft als Profisportler*in vor.

317d **In Aktivität 317c haben Sie einige Aspekte der Vereinskultur in Deutschland kennengelernt. Beantworten Sie jetzt die folgenden Fragen zum Thema „Vereine".**

Wie wichtig sind Vereine in Ihrem Land?

____

____

Was für Vereine gibt es? Nennen Sie mindestens drei Beispiele.

____

____

Sind oder waren Sie schon einmal Mitglied in einem Verein?

____

____

317e **Sportarten. In MACHEN werden Sie über Sportarten in unterschiedlichen Kontexten sprechen. Beantworten Sie zur Vorbereitung die folgenden Fragen in Stichpunkten.**

Welche Sportarten haben Sie in der Schule betrieben?

____

____

Welchen Sport machen Sie aktuell?

____

____

Gibt es andere Sportarten, die Sie gern ausprobieren würden?

____

____

Welche Sportarten sind besonders beliebt in Ihrem Land?

____

____

Ist Sport an Universitäten in Ihrem Land wichtig?

____

____

318a Lesen Sie zuerst den Kulturpunkt über die Organisation von Fußball in Deutschland. Besuchen Sie dann die offizielle Webseite der 2. Bundesliga (der Männer oder der Frauen) und beschreiben Sie die Situation basierend auf der aktuellen Tabelle. Benutzen Sie Strukturen mit Appositionen, wie im Beispiel. Sie können gerne übertreiben.

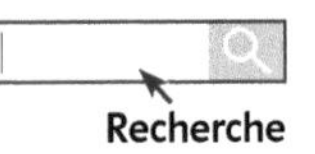

Kulturpunkt

In Deutschland ist Fußball in unterschiedliche Ligen (Klassen) eingeteilt. Die höchste Liga heißt Bundesliga oder 1. Liga. Danach kommt an zweiter Stelle die 2. Bundesliga. Eine Besonderheit ist, dass Mannschaften am Ende der Saison in eine höhere Liga aufsteigen (von der zweiten in die erste oder von der dritten in die zweite usw.) oder in eine tiefere Liga absteigen (von der ersten in die zweite oder von der zweiten in die dritte) können. Die ersten beiden Mannschaften der 2. Liga steigen automatisch in die 1. Liga auf. Die letzten zwei Mannschaften steigen in die 3. Liga ab. Es gibt auch noch Relegationsspiele. Die dritte Mannschaft in der 2. Liga spielt gegen die drittletzte Mannschaft in der 1. Liga. Die Gewinner*innen dieses Spiels spielen in der nächsten Saison in der 1. Liga. Diese Relegation gibt es auch zwischen der 2. und 3. Liga, 3. und 4. Liga etc.

Beispiele aus der 2. Bundesliga der Männer, Saison 2019–2020:
Arminia Bielefeld, allein auf dem ersten Platz, steigt in die 1. Bundesliga auf.
Bielefeld, mit 65 Toren, liegt 10 Punkte vor dem Zweiten, dem VfB Stuttgart.
Dynamo Dresden, mit nur 32 Punkten, steigt in die 3. Liga ab.

100: Bildung im Vergleich

321a In MACHEN werden Sie sich mit dem deutschen Bildungssystem beschäftigen. Reflektieren Sie jetzt über Ihren eigenen Bildungsweg und schreiben Sie Ihren „Bildungslebenslauf". Dieser tabellarische Lebenslauf soll eine Übersicht sein, wann Sie welche Schule besucht haben von Kindergarten/Kita/Vorschule *(day care/pre-school/ kindergarten)* bis heute. Machen Sie sich Notizen in Stichworten, damit Sie über diese Aspekte im Kurs sprechen können.

Alter	Schule	Lieblingsfächer	Nicht-akademische Aktivitäten	Transportmittel (zur Schule)

321b **Grundschule in deutschsprachigen Ländern. Hier sind einige Traditionen:**

die Schultüte:	Am ersten Schultag bekommen die Erstklässler*innen eine Tüte mit Geschenken.
der Schulranzen:	Das ist eine Tasche für Bücher, die auf dem Rücken getragen wird.
der Füller:	Das ist ein Schreibwerkzeug, das mit Tinte gefüllt ist.
der*die Klassensprecher*in:	Das ist ein*e Schüler*in, die dem*der Lehrer*in sagt, wenn die Klasse ein Problem hat.
der*die Schülerlots*in:	Das ist ein*e ältere*r Schüler*in oder eine erwachsene Person, die den Kindern im Verkehr hilft.
das Klassenzimmer:	In den deutschsprachigen Schulen hat nicht der*die Lehrer*in ein festes Zimmer, sondern die Klasse.

Wie ist das in Ihrer Heimat? Schreiben Sie Sätze, in denen Sie das Schulsystem in Deutschland mit dem Schulsystem in Ihrem Land vergleichen. Fügen Sie dabei Informationen von oben als Apposition hinzu.

Schultüte: *In Deutschland bekommen Schüler*innen in der 1. Klasse eine Schultüte, also eine Tüte voller Geschenke. In den USA ...*

Schulranzen: ______

Füller: ______

Klassensprecher*in: ______

Schülerlots*in: ______

Klassenzimmer: ______

321c **Hier sehen Sie einen Vergleich von Betreuungsangeboten für Vorschulkinder in Deutschland und in den USA. Wie war das bei Ihnen? Markieren Sie alle Aspekte, die Sie kennen. Schlagen Sie die fettgedruckten Wörter nach, wenn Sie sie noch nicht kennen.**

Kindergarten und Kita (Deutschland)
- Vorschulalter, die meisten Kinder sind zwischen 3 und 6 Jahre alt
- montags bis freitags
- halbtags oder ganztags
- Der **Aufenthalt** ist **locker** strukturiert, z. B.: Frühstück, Spielzeit draußen, Gruppenaktivität, spielen oder **basteln** drinnen.
- pädagogischer Fokus: vor allem soziale Kompetenzen und **Feinmotorik** entwickeln
- Es gibt eine längere **Eingewöhnung**sphase, während derer die Eltern im Kindergarten bleiben können.
- Es gibt öffentliche und private Kindergärten, inzwischen auch alternative Angebote wie Waldkindergärten, bei denen die Kinder den ganzen Tag draußen sind.
- Der Besuch ist freiwillig.
- Kosten: 0 bis ca. 350 Euro pro Monat (Die Kosten **richten sich nach** dem Einkommen der Eltern.)

Day Care (USA)
- für das gesamte Vorschulalter (ab sechs Wochen) und manchmal auch Betreuung während der Schulzeit

Pre-School (USA)
- Kinder von 3 bis 5 Jahren (zum Teil parallel zur *day care*)
- oft nur zwei oder drei Tage die Woche
- vormittags, nachmittags oder ganztags
- Der Aufenthalt ist oft stark strukturiert wie in einer Schule, vor allem bei privaten *pre-schools*. Es gibt aber auch spielorientierte *pre-schools*.
- pädagogischer Fokus: vor allem akademische Kompetenzen entwickeln
- Normalerweise gibt es keine oder nur eine kurze **Eingewöhnung**sphase.
- Es gibt öffentliche und private *pre-schools*.
- Der Besuch ist freiwillig.
- Kosten: im Durchschnitt ca. 350 bis 1.000 Dollar pro Monat (Es gibt aber auch *pre-schools*, für die die Eltern bis zu 4.000 Dollar pro Monat zahlen.)

Fragen:

Welche Aspekte eines deutschen Kindergartens oder des US-amerikanischen Vorschulsystems finden Sie am interessantesten? Was hat Sie am meisten überrascht?

Schreiben Sie zwei oder drei Sätze und erklären Sie, wie der US-amerikanische Kindergarten funktioniert. Wie alt sind die Kinder? Ist er freiwillig oder verpflichtend (*mandatory*)? Was lernen/machen die Kinder dort?

322a **In MACHEN werden Sie das Hochschulsystem in Ihrem Land mit dem in Deutschland vergleichen. Bereiten Sie die Diskussion vor, indem Sie die folgenden Fragen in Stichworten beantworten.**

Welche Schulformen gibt es in Ihrem Land?

Wann entscheidet man, ob man an einer Uni oder einem College studieren möchte?

Welche Alternativen gibt es zum Studieren?

Wie wichtig sind außerschulische Aktivitäten in der Schule?

Wie alt sind die Schulabsolvent*innen ungefähr, wenn sie an die Uni kommen?

Bezahlen Student*innen in Ihrem Land Studiengebühren? Wie viel?

Wie finanzieren junge Leute in Ihrem Land das Leben als Student*in (z. B. Arbeit, Stipendium etc.)?

323a **Universitätskulturen. Fügen Sie die richtigen Komparativ- und Superlativformen ein. Wählen Sie dafür die passenden Basisformen aus dem Kasten.**

alt | hoch | lang | viel | wenig

Die Universität Heidelberg, im Jahr 1386 gegründet, ist ______________ als die Harvard University (1636), aber die University of Oxford (1096) ist ______________.

Die École Polytechnique Fédérale Lausanne in der Schweiz ist eine berühmte Institution für Hightech-Studien und hat viele Nobelpreise (21) gewonnen. Das California Institute of Technology ist auch auf Technologie spezialisiert und hat ______________ Nobelpreise (32) als Lausanne bekommen. Aber das Massachusetts Institute of Technology (MIT) hat die ______________ Preise gewonnen (70).

Das Studieren an deutschen Universitäten kostet wenig, aber an taiwanesischen Unis kostet es noch ______________ und in Norwegen kostet es ______________.

Die Islamic Azad Universität (دانشگاه آزاد اسلامی) im Iran hat 1,5 Millionen Studierende, doch mit 1,9 Millionen Studierenden hat die türkische Anadolu Üniversitesi eine ______________ Anzahl an Studierenden.

Die ______________ Anzahl hat aber die Indira Gandhi National Open University mit 4,9 Millionen Studierenden.

Um einen Bachelorabschluss zu erlangen, studiert Dara sechs Semester (drei Jahre). Florian macht einen Masterabschluss und muss deshalb ______________ studieren (6 + 4 Semester). Kadisha macht ihren Doktor in Informatik und studiert ______________ (6 + 4 + 10 Semester).

101: Grenzüberschreitender Wissenschaftsaustausch°

324a **Der Vater der Atombombe. Im folgenden Text lernen Sie etwas über Julius Robert Oppenheimer und das Manhattan-Projekt. Schlagen Sie zuerst die fettgedruckten Wörter nach. Lesen Sie dann den Text und ordnen Sie die Sätze auf der nächsten Seite den vier Abschnitten zu.**

Der amerikanische Physiker Julius Robert Oppenheimer wird oft „Vater der Atombombe" genannt. Er war ab 1942 der Leiter des sogenannten Manhattan-Projekts. Gemeinsam mit einer Gruppe von tausenden Expert*innen **entwickelte** er die ersten amerikanischen **Kernwaffen.** ____

Dieses Projekt war ein **Wettlauf** mit der Zeit. Die USA hatten Angst, dass Deutschland unter Hitlers Herrschaft auch bald eine Atombombe **fertigstellen** würde. Aber diese Angst war unbegründet. Denn die deutschen Wissenschaftler*innen unter der Leitung von Werner Heisenberg waren in ihrer Arbeit noch nicht so weit fortgeschritten wie die Amerikaner*innen. ____

Die USA erreichten ihr Ziel vor den Deutschen. Im Juli 1945 **zündete** das Team um Oppenheimer die erste Atombombe in der Wüste New Mexicos. Die Atombombe hieß Trinity. Ihre **Sprengkraft** war mit 21.000 Tonnen enorm. Im Vergleich zu anderen konventionellen Bomben war diese Sprengkraft fast doppelt so hoch. ____

Obwohl Oppenheimer diesen Wettkampf gewann, hatte er für den Rest seines Lebens ein schlechtes Gewissen. **In Bezug auf** den erfolgreichen Test der ersten Atombombe sagte er später, dass er nur zu einem **Zerstörer** der Welt geworden war. ____

entwickeln	______________	zünden	______________
die Kernwaffen (*pl.*)	______________	die Sprengkraft	______________
der Wettlauf	______________	in Bezug auf	______________
fertigstellen	______________	der Zerstörer	______________

a) Die USA testeten vor den Deutschen eine Atombombe.
b) Viele Menschen haben an der Entwicklung der ersten Atomwaffen in den USA gearbeitet.
c) Oppenheimer hat den Rest seines Lebens bereut (*regret*), die Atombombe gebaut zu haben.
d) Die Wissenschaftler*innen in Deutschland lagen mit der Konstruktion einer Atombombe hinter den Wissenschaftler*innen des Manhattan-Projekts zurück.

326a **Der niederländische Kulturwissenschaftler Geert Hofstede hat sich viel mit interkultureller Kommunikation beschäftigt. Er machte in den 1960er und 70er Jahren eine empirische Studie mit Mitarbeiter*innen der Firma IBM, die aus über 60 verschiedenen Ländern kamen. Danach fasste er die Ergebnisse in erst vier, inzwischen sechs Kulturdimensionen zusammen: Machtdistanz, Kollektivismus/Individualismus, Maskulinität/Femininität, Unsicherheitsvermeidung (*uncertainty avoidance*), Langzeitorientierung/Kurzzeitorientierung und Genuss (*indulgence*)/Zurückhaltung (*restraint*). Bestimmen Sie Ihre Position auf den Skalen unten, um sich selbst in diesen Dimensionen zu platzieren.**

Alle Menschen in einer Institution sind gleich, alle treffen Entscheidungen gemeinsam.	Es gibt eine klare Hierarchie, der*die Chef*in entscheidet.
Die Gruppe ist wichtiger als das Individuum, Kooperation ist wichtiger als Wettbewerb.	Das Individuum ist wichtiger als die Gruppe, Wettbewerb macht alle besser.
Frauen und Männer haben die exakt gleichen Rollen, beide gehen arbeiten und machen gleich viel im Haushalt.	Frauen und Männer haben klar unterschiedliche Rollen.
Ich habe Angst vor Unsicherheit oder unbekannten Situationen. Regeln sind nützlich.	Ich mag keine Regeln und habe kein Problem mit Unsicherheit.
Traditionen sind wichtig. Lösungen sollten für lange Zeit gut sein.	Neuerungen sind gut. Lösungen müssen jetzt funktionieren.
Ich sehe der Zukunft eher pessimistisch entgegen. Ich lebe, um zu arbeiten.	Ich sehe der Zukunft eher optimistisch entgegen. Ich arbeite, um zu leben.

102: Impulse für Ihr Leben

327a  **Schauen Sie sich noch einmal in MACHEN alle Kapitel von „Impuls Deutsch 2" an. Was waren Ihre Lieblingseinheiten? Was haben Sie darin über die deutschsprachigen Länder gelernt? Was haben Sie über andere Disziplinen gelernt? Und was haben Sie über sich selbst und Ihre eigene Kultur gelernt? Schreiben Sie über mindestens fünf Einheiten, die Sie besonders interessant fanden. Erklären Sie auch, warum Sie diese Einheiten besonders spannend, informativ oder kurzweilig fanden. In MACHEN werden Sie mit anderen Studierenden darüber sprechen.**

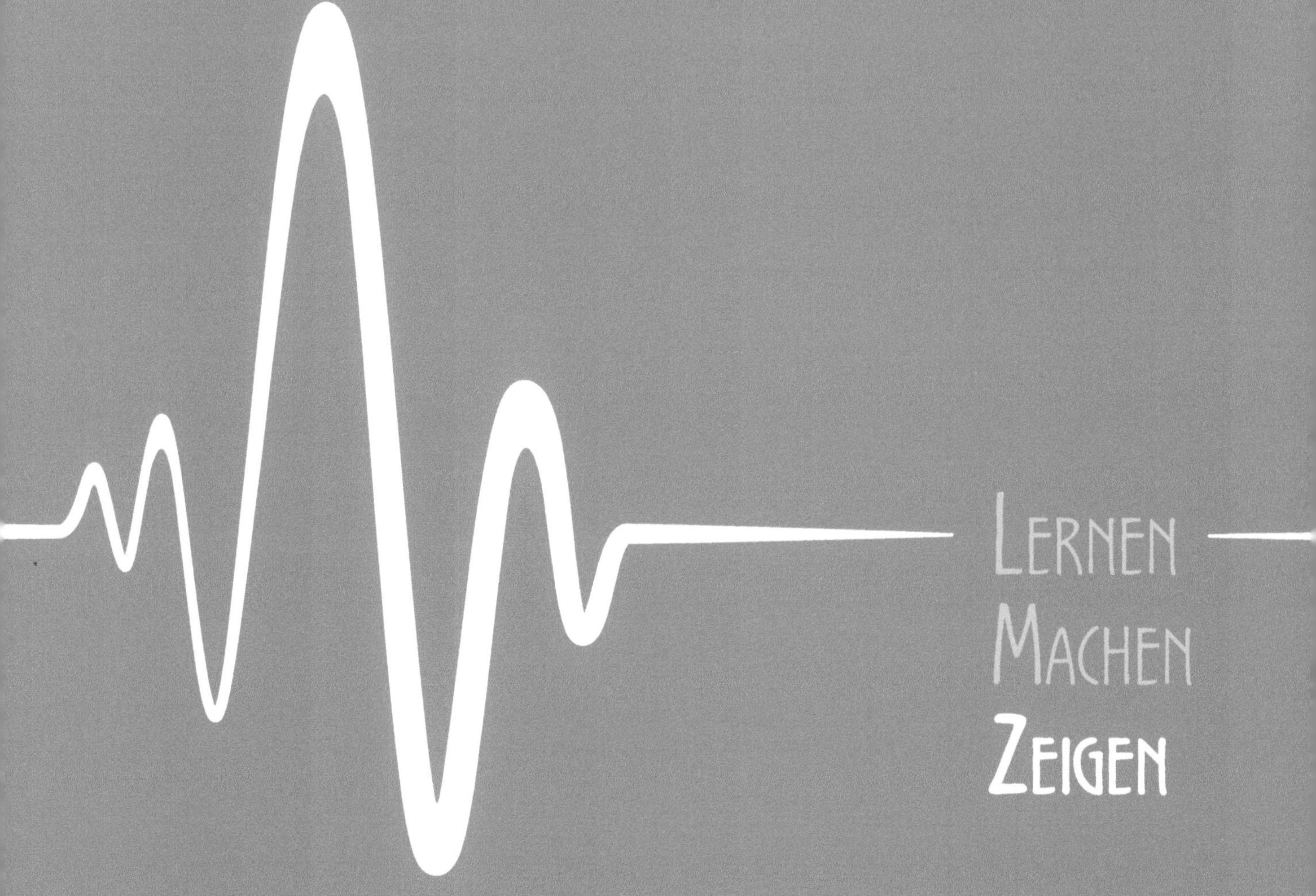
Lernen
Machen
Zeigen

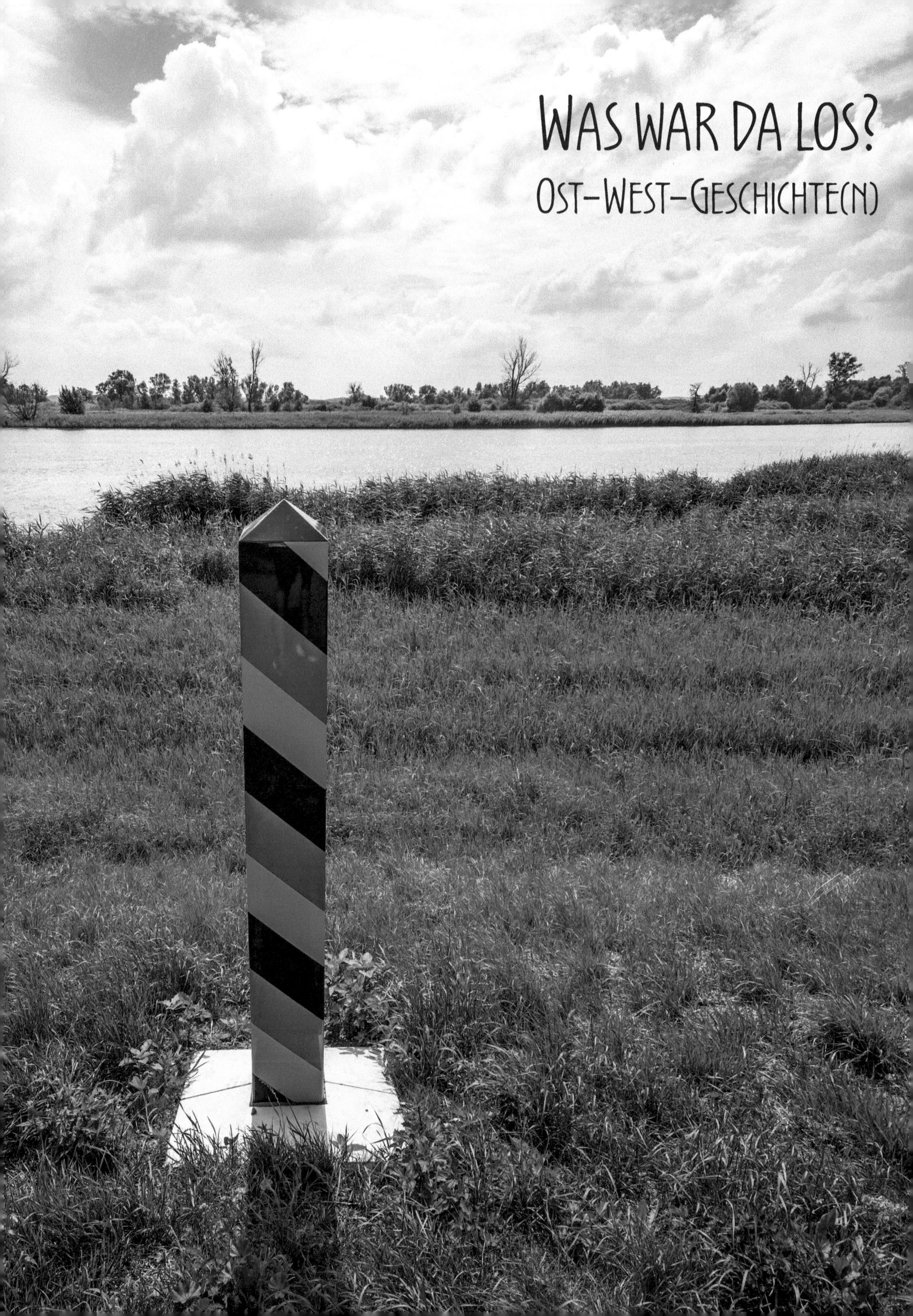

Was war da los?

Ost-West-Geschichte(n)

0: WILLKOMMEN (ZURÜCK)

1a 

Erzähl mal: Wer bin ich? Stellen Sie sich vor. Nehmen Sie ein kurzes Video auf (z. B. mit Ihrem Handy, am Computer etc.) und beantworten Sie 12–15 Fragen, mindestens drei pro Block:

Wie heißen Sie? Woher kommen Sie?
Wie alt sind Sie?
Was studieren Sie? Was essen Sie gerne?
Was trinken Sie gerne?
Welche internationale Küche finden Sie am besten?
Wie heißen die Hauptstädte von Deutschland, der Schweiz und Österreich?
Welche Stadt würden Sie am liebsten besuchen?
Wann haben Sie Geburtstag?

Was ist Ihre Handynummer?
Was sind Ihre Hobbys?
Was machen Sie nicht gern?
Welchen Beruf wollen Sie haben?
Wie wohnen Sie, hier an der Uni und in Ihrem Heimatort? (z. B. mit einem*einer Mitbewohner*in, bei den Großeltern …)
Was ist Ihr Umfeld? Mit wem verbringen Sie Ihre Zeit?
Wann stehen Sie an Wochentagen auf?
Was ziehen Sie normalerweise an, wenn Sie zur Uni gehen?
Wie sieht ein typischer Tag bei Ihnen aus?
Was ist Ihr Lieblingswetter? (Benutzen Sie Celsius für die Temperatur.)

Kennen Sie deutsche Maler*innen? Welche?
Welche Feiertage feiern Sie?
Vor welchen Naturkatastrophen haben Sie Angst?
Welche gibt es da, wo Sie wohnen?
Welches Obst und welches Gemüse essen Sie gern?
Wie heißt Ihr Lieblingsrestaurant?
Versuchen Sie, gesund zu leben? Wenn ja, wie?
Kennen Sie Chemikalien, die ihren eigenen deutschen Namen haben?
Halten Sie eine bestimmte Diät? (vegetarisch, vegan, koscher …)
Wie wohnen Sie in Ihrem Heimatort? (in einer Wohnung, in einem Reihenhaus …)
Welche Form von Architektur gefällt Ihnen? (Romanik, Barock …) Warum?

Was machen Sie an der Uni?
Machen Sie Sport? Wenn ja, welchen?
Finden Sie es wichtig, woher die Produkte kommen, die Sie kaufen?
Recyceln Sie? Warum (nicht)? Und wenn ja, was?
Was wissen Sie über die Mülltrennung in europäischen Ländern?
Was ist Ihre Lieblingsgeschichte oder Ihr Lieblingsbuch?
Was mussten Sie als Kind im Haushalt machen?
Würden Sie gerne nach Wien fahren? Warum (nicht)?
Welche deutschen Bundesländer kennen Sie?
Wie sieht Ihr Traumauto aus?

4g **Lisa spricht mit ihrer Psychotherapeutin über ihre Pläne. Welche Präpositionen und Artikel fehlen hier noch? Wählen Sie „im" oder „in der", „am" oder „um".**

Therapeutin: Hallo, wir haben uns ja __________ letzten Monat gar nicht gesehen, weil du im Urlaub warst. Hattest du Spaß?

Lisa: Ja, mein Urlaub hat viel Spaß gemacht! __________ Montag letzte Woche war ich noch in den Schweizer Alpen zum Skilaufen. Wir sind erst __________ Dienstag nach Hause gekommen.

Therapeutin: Und wie geht es dir heute?

Lisa: Es geht mir jetzt viel besser. Zum Beispiel kann ich __________ Nacht sehr gut schlafen. Und __________ Morgen fühle ich mich prima. Nur __________ Abend bin ich dann müde und gestresst. Ich habe __________ Nachmittag immer zu viel zu tun. __________ 16 Uhr habe ich jeden Tag ein Meeting mit meinen Kollegen und Kolleginnen.

Therapeutin: Kannst du vielleicht __________ 15 Uhr eine kleine Pause machen und einen Tee trinken? Am besten gehst du auch __________ Vormittag, vielleicht __________ elf Uhr, in einen dunklen Raum und meditierst.

Lisa: Gute Idee! Ich werde es versuchen. Leider fahre ich __________ Juni mit meiner Chefin zu unserer Firma in Pirmasens, da werde ich keine Zeit für Pausen haben.

Therapeutin: Was machst du dann stattdessen?

Lisa: Ich werde __________ Abend einfach früher ins Bett gehen und ein entspannendes Buch lesen. __________ 22 Uhr schlafe ich dann ein und bekomme acht Stunden Schlaf.

Therapeutin: Das klingt gut. Hast du auch schon Pläne für deine psychische Gesundheit fürs nächste Jahr?

Lisa: Also, __________ neuen Jahr werde ich auf jeden Fall einmal __________ Monat in die Therapie kommen. Am besten ist immer der Mittwoch, denn das ist mein freier Tag __________ Woche. Und am besten ist es __________ 13 Uhr, sodass ich lange schlafen kann. Und __________ Wochenende treffe ich mich oft mit meinen Freundinnen und Freunden aus der Gruppentherapie.

4h **Sie lernen für einen Test etwas über wichtige deutsche Ereignisse. Beginnen Sie mit dem Datum.**

Am 17.09.1179 ist Hildegard von Bingen in Bingen gestorben.
Hildegard von Bingen ist in Bingen gestorben. (US-Datum: 9/17/1179)

____
Martin Luther hat 95 Thesen an die Wittenberger Kirche genagelt. (US-Datum: 10/31/1517)

____
Dorothea Erxleben ist die erste deutsche Ärztin geworden. (US-Datum: 6/12/1762)

____
Wilhelm I. von Preußen hat die deutsche Kaiserkrone bekommen. (US-Datum: 1/18/1871)

____
Deutschland war kein Kaiserreich mehr. (US-Datum: 11/9/1918)

Lesen Sie Ihre Antworten laut vor.

Dorothea Christiane Erxleben (1715–1762), eine Pionierin des Frauenstudiums

4i **Wann ist das passiert? Kombinieren Sie das historische Ereignis und die Jahreszahl.**

Was?	**Wann?**
Karl der Große ist Kaiser geworden.	800
Das Oktoberfest hat begonnen.	1810
Gottfried Daimler hat das erste Auto konstruiert.	1886
Albert Einstein hat die Relativitätstheorie formuliert.	1905
Die Nonne Berta Hummel hat die erste Hummel-Figur verkauft.	1935
Der millionste VW ist vom Band gerollt.	1955
~~Die DDR hat die Mauer in Berlin gebaut.~~	~~1961~~
Ost- und Westdeutschland kamen wieder zusammen.	1990
Nena hat ihren Hit „Neunundneunzig Luftballons" gesungen.	1995

__________ ist Karl der Große Kaiser geworden. Das Oktoberfest hat __________ begonnen. Gottfried Daimler hat das erste Auto __________ konstruiert. __________ hat Albert Einstein die Relativitätstheorie formuliert. Die Nonne Berta Hummel hat die erste Hummel-Figur __________ verkauft. Der millionste VW ist __________ vom Band gerollt. (Im Jahr) 1961 hat die DDR die Mauer in Berlin gebaut. Ost- und Westdeutschland kamen __________ wieder zusammen. __________ hat Nena ihren Hit „Neunundneunzig Luftballons" gesungen.

4j **Verstanden? Sie hören ein paar Informationen zu ausgewählten Ereignissen der Geschichte der deutsch-deutschen Teilung. Schreiben Sie für jedes Ereignis das Datum (entweder Jahr oder genaues Datum), das Sie hören, mit der richtigen temporalen Praposition: „am" oder „im".**

Das Ende des Zweiten Weltkriegs: Im Jahr 1945

Die Gründung der Bundesrepublik Deutschland: __________

Die Gründung der Deutschen Demokratischen Republik: __________

Der Beginn des Mauerbaus: __________

Der Warschauer Kniefall: __________

Erich Honecker wird SED-Vorsitzender: __________

Der Fall der Mauer: __________

5a **Sortieren Sie die Stichworte. Was gehört zur BRD, was zur DDR?**

soziale Marktwirtschaft	Hauptstadt: Ostberlin	eine Partei (SED)
Gründung am 07.10.1949	Bundesländer	Planwirtschaft
Bezirke	mehrere Parteien	Gründung am 23.05.1949
Hauptstadt: Bonn	Staatsratsvorsitzende*r (Generalsekretär*in)	Bundespräsident*in und Bundeskanzler*in

Deutsche Demokratische Republik	**Bundesrepublik Deutschland**
__________	__________
__________	__________
__________	__________
__________	__________
__________	__________
__________	__________

5b **Beschriften Sie:**

Fahne der ______________________

Fahne der ______________________

5c **Zugehört: Folge 1 – Vorstellung. Hören Sie das Gespräch zwischen Nicole Coleman und Stine Eckert, zwei Professorinnen aus Detroit, und kreuzen Sie an: Was ist gleich und was ist anders in ihren Geschichten?**

	gleich	unterschiedlich
Beruf		
Ort, an dem sie arbeiten		
Unterrichtsfächer (*subjects*)		
Geburtsjahr		
Geburtsort/Geburtsland		
Wohnort der Familien		

2: Ost-West-Perspektiven zum 17.06.1953

8b **Verstanden? Sie hören Aussagen über die Aufstände vom 17. Juni 1953. Entscheiden Sie: Stammt die Aussage aus den DDR- oder BRD-Medien?**

BRD	DDR	
		Aussage 1
		Aussage 2
		Aussage 3
		Aussage 4

10a **Reflektieren: How do we know what is truth when it comes to history? Comment on any or all of these questions.**

Media and history books often differ in the way they explain the same event. How, then, do we know what is fact and what is an interpretation or exaggeration? How have history books shaped your views? How different might your view of the past be if you had read a history book from a feminist or a Mexican standpoint, for example?

You can also consider the following: Who do we commemorate? What kind of perspective do we reinforce with memorials, bank notes, holidays, etc.? Some of them are obviously contestable—but why?

And lastly, the words we use to describe an event have a profound impact on how we see that event. Just think of the connotation of words such as riot, protest, rebellion, and demonstration. Some of these are rather neutral, others positive, and others negative. You may be able to think of concrete examples where these words were used to paint a certain picture of an event. What comes to mind?

3: GETEILTES BERLIN

11a **Reisefreiheit? Nur mit dem richtigen Pass! Beantworten Sie die Fragen zu den Bildern. Vergrößern Sie sie mit Klett Augmented.**

In welchen Ländern ist diese Person gewesen? An den Stempeln können Sie sehen, dass diese Reisen alle VOR dem Fall der Mauer waren. Was glauben Sie: Welchen deutschen Pass hat diese Person wohl gehabt? Welche Länder auf diesen Stempeln lagen westlich bzw. östlich der Mauer?

____

____

____

____

____

Diese Person musste/durfte oft über die Transitstrecken durch die DDR fahren. Welche Grenzübertritte hat er*sie benutzt? Schauen Sie auf einer Landkarte von damals nach. Wie ist diese Person jeweils durch die DDR gereist? Mit dem Auto, mit der Bahn …? Sie können auf jedem Transitvisum das Datum sehen. Was ist die Zahl dahinter? Tipp: Die DDR wollte, dass man auf dem direkten Weg ohne lange Pausen – und mit Tempo 100 – durch das Land fuhr. Was sehen Sie noch auf jedem Stempel?

____

____

____

____

____

12g **Gabryell erzählt von seiner Kindheit. Schreiben Sie die schwachen Verben und die Modalverben im Präteritum. Achtung: Einige Modalverben haben spezielle Formen!**

Hallo, ich heiße Gabryell. Als Kind __________ (wohnen) ich in Częstochowa, einer Stadt in Polen. Meine Familie __________ (leben) in einer Wohnung in der Innenstadt. Mama __________ (arbeiten) damals als Tanzlehrerin und Papa __________ (unterrichten) Deutsch. Mit meiner Mutter __________ (einkaufen) meine kleine Schwester Krystyna und ich jeden Freitag auf dem Wochenmarkt _____. Damals war Krystyna noch taub – sie __________ (hören) uns nicht. Wir alle __________ (lernen) deshalb Gebärdensprache und __________ (kommunizieren) so miteinander. Als meine Schwester sechs Jahre alt war, __________ (informieren) sich unsere Eltern über eine Operation für Gehörlose. Mein Vater __________ (telefonieren) sehr oft mit einem Arzt aus Innsbruck namens Hochmair. Die Professor*innen Erwin Hochmair und Ingeborg Hochmair-Desoyer __________ (entwickeln) das erste Cochlea-Implantat der Welt. Meine Eltern __________ (besuchen) zusammen mit Krystyna die Hochmair-Klinik in Innsbruck. Als sie alle drei nach einem Monat zurück __________ (kommen), __________ (können) Krystyna mich hören! Danach __________ (sollen) sie das Sprechen viel üben. Sie __________ (wollen) auch unbedingt tanzen lernen – und sie hat wirklich großes Talent! Nach dem Fall der Berliner Mauer __________ (arbeiten) meine Eltern an einer Schule in Würzburg. Und jetzt wohnen wir alle in Deutschland.

12h **Verstanden? Sie hören Informationen über Opfer der Berliner Mauer, also Menschen, die direkt oder indirekt wegen der Mauer gestorben sind oder getötet wurden. Füllen Sie die Tabelle aus.**

Kategorie	Anzahl
Insgesamt (alle zusammen)	
	101 Personen
Menschen aus Ost und West, die nicht fliehen wollten	
DDR-Grenzsoldat*innen	

12i **Reflektieren: Was bedeutete es, Berliner*in zu sein? John F. Kennedy gave his famous "Ich bin ein Berliner" speech in 1963. The shortened quote leaves out much of what he was getting at. Because he didn't mean that he himself was a Berliner but what it symbolized to be a Berliner in 1963, during the Cold War and after the wall had been built. Read the complete quote from his speech and answer the question: Was meinte JFK mit dem Satz „Ich bin ein Berliner"? Was könnte man heute stattdessen sagen?**

Two thousand years ago the proudest boast was "Civis Romanus sum" [I am a Roman citizen]. Today, in the world of freedom, the proudest boast is "Ich bin ein Berliner."

13e **Warum wollte Tante Irmtraut nicht aus der DDR fliehen? Ergänzen Sie die Verbformen im Präteritum.**

Lieber Erich,

du ______________ (fragen) in deinem letzten Brief, warum ich 1960 die DDR nicht verlassen ______________ (wollen). Du weißt sicher, dass ich damals noch nicht verheiratet ____________ (sein). Mein Freund ______________ (heißen) Karl-Heinz. Ich ______________ (gehen) noch in die Schule. Jeden Morgen ______________ (kommen) Karl-Heinz zu meiner Haustür und wartete auf mich. Wir ______________ (halten) uns an der Hand und ______________ (laufen) zusammen zur Schule. Das Leben ______________ (sein) so schön! Von der Politik ______________ (lassen) wir uns nicht erschrecken. Es ______________ (geben) keine Warnungen in der Zeitung. Aber dann ______________ (schreiben) Karl-Heinz mir einen Brief. Er ______________ (wollen) fliehen, aber ich ______________ (haben) keine Ahnung. Und dann war er eines Tages weg und ich ______________ (bleiben) alleine zurück. Der Westen ______________ (scheinen) mir brutal und dunkel, denn er hatte mir meinen Freund genommen …

Liebe Grüße

deine Tante Irmtraut

13f **Verstanden? Sie hören über die Flucht der Familie Holzapfel aus der DDR. Wie sind die Holzapfels geflohen? Kreuzen Sie die richtigen Antworten an.**

Warum wollte die Familie Holzapfel aus der DDR fliehen?

- ☐ Vater Heinz Holzapfel wollte nicht weiter für die DDR-Regierung als Ingenieur arbeiten.
- ☐ Die Holzapfels wollten fliehen, weil viele andere Menschen aus ihrer Familie geflohen waren.
- ☐ Sie wollten fliehen, weil die Eltern von der DDR frustriert waren.

Warum wählte die Familie das Haus der Ministerien als Startpunkt für ihre Flucht?

- ☐ Das Haus der Ministerien wurde streng bewacht und war deshalb ein sicherer Fluchtort.
- ☐ Das Haus der Ministerien hatte eine direkte Verbindung zur Mauer durch eine Sicherheitsbrücke.
- ☐ Das Haus der Ministerien war sehr hoch und stand direkt gegenüber vom Westberliner Sektor.

13g **Karl-Heinz erinnert sich. Ergänzen Sie den Text mit den Verben aus dem Kasten. Benutzen Sie das Präteritum.**

anfangen | haben | verlieren | tragen | aussehen | fallen | geben | bekommen | lesen | anbieten | wollen

Vor vielen Jahren, noch vor dem Bau der Mauer, ________________ ich eine junge Freundin namens Irmtraut. Sie ________________ immer eine schwarze Schleife im Haar. Sie ________________ so schön ________________ mit ihren roten Haaren! An ihrem 14. Geburtstag ________________ ich ihr ein Buch von Thomas Mann. Von ihr ________________ ich auch ein Geschenk: ein Foto. Ich habe dieses Bild immer noch.

Als ich 16 Jahre alt wurde, ________________ ich in der Zeitung, dass man jungen Männern in Westberlin Arbeit ________________. Ich ________________ ________________, von einem neuen Leben zu träumen. Aber Irmtraut ________________ nicht mit mir träumen. Sie ________________ von einer Fantasie in eine andere. Ich wusste, ich musste mich entscheiden, Irmtraut oder meinen Traum. Und so ________________ ich meine Freundin.

13h **Fluchtgeschichten. Während der Zeit der DDR sind nicht nur Menschen von Ostberlin nach Westberlin geflüchtet, sondern auch über die innerdeutsche Grenze. Hier lernen Sie so eine Geschichte kennen. Lesen Sie die Geschichte und markieren Sie unten alle Aussagen, die korrekt sind.**

Ingo Bethke ist der älteste von drei Brüdern gewesen, die aus der DDR geflohen sind. Die Eltern sind dem Regime in der DDR gegenüber loyal gewesen: Der Vater hat im Innenministerium als Major gearbeitet, die Mutter als Oberstleutnantin. Das hat Ingo geholfen, seinen Militärdienst an der Grenze in Mecklenburg zu machen, und er hat viel über die Sicherheitsmaßnahmen gelernt. Nach seiner Zeit im Militär hat er als Müllfahrer gearbeitet. Dann ist er am 22. Mai 1975 mit einem Seitenschneider (*wire cutting pliers*), einem Holzstück und einer Luftmatratze im Kofferraum zur Grenze gefahren. Einen halben Kilometer vor der Elbe hat Ingo ein Loch in den Grenzzaun geschnitten. Danach ist er durch das Minenfeld gegangen. Vorsichtig hat er mit dem Holzstück die Erde nach den Minen abgeklopft (*to tap*). Es hat keine Explosion gegeben und er hat es bis zum Fluss geschafft. Er hat die Luftmatratze aufgeblasen und ist ins Wasser gesprungen. Nach 200 Metern ist er endlich in Niedersachsen, im Westen, angekommen.

- Ingo war der einzige Bruder, der aus der DDR geflohen ist.
- Ingos Eltern haben gegen das DDR-Regime gekämpft.
- Nach dem Militär hat Ingo als Müllfahrer gearbeitet.
- Bei seiner Flucht ist Ingo über den Grenzzaun geklettert.
- Ingo musste durch ein Minenfeld gehen. Zum Glück gab es keine Explosion.
- Ingo ist mit einem selbstgebauten Boot über den Fluss in den Westen gefahren.

13i **Schreiben Sie die Geschichte im Präteritum auf.**

*Ingo Bethke **war** der älteste von drei Brüdern, die aus der DDR **flohen**.*

13j **Reflektieren: Fliehen oder bleiben? Sie haben Szenarien kennengelernt, warum Menschen fliehen oder bleiben. Reflektieren Sie darüber schriftlich.**

Wer wollte vielleicht bleiben und warum? Reflektieren Sie darüber, was Sie im täglichen Leben machen und brauchen und wo es das gibt. Überlegen Sie auch, in welchen Bereichen eine Grenze vielleicht Probleme bereiten kann (Studium, Reisen, Beruf, politische Aktionen ...). Schreiben Sie Ihre Ideen möglichst auf Deutsch auf, Sie können aber einzelne Wörter oder Teile von Sätzen auf Englisch schreiben, wenn Ihnen das deutsche Wort nicht einfällt oder Sie bestimmte Formulierungen und Ausdrücke, die Sie noch nicht kennen, benutzen möchten.

4: Kindheit im Osten und Westen

14g **Verstanden? Ein Diktat. Sie hören einen Text über die Jugendweihe in der DDR dreimal.**

Erstes Hören (normale Geschwindigkeit): Hören Sie nur zu, ohne Notizen zu machen.
Zweites Hören (langsam mit Pausen): Schreiben Sie so viel wie möglich von der Passage auf.
Drittes Hören (langsam ohne Pausen): Überarbeiten Sie, was Sie geschrieben haben.

Wiederholen Sie die Sequenz so oft, bis Sie die komplette Textpassage aufgeschrieben haben.

____

____

____

____

____

____

____

____

____

____

____

____

14h **Nesrin und Shiyan sprechen über ihre Kindheit. Welche Satzverbindungen fehlen noch? Ergänzen Sie „wenn", „als", „während" oder „bevor". Es gibt für einige Sätze mehrere Möglichkeiten.**

Nesrin: Wusstest du immer, was für Geschenke du bekommst, ____________ du sie an deinem Geburtstag ausgepackt hast?

Shiyan: Eine Zeit lang ja. Ich habe immer in den Kleiderschrank meiner Eltern geschaut, ____________ meine Mutter einkaufen war und ich danach nicht in die Taschen gucken durfte.

Nesrin: Warum im Kleiderschrank?

Shiyan: Meine Mutter hat dort immer Geschenke versteckt, ____________ ich klein war. Und ____________ sie auf der Arbeit war, habe ich im Schrank nachgesehen. Wenn ich ein Geschenk gefunden habe, habe ich es mir angesehen und es schnell zurückgelegt, ____________ meine Mutter nach Hause kam. Aber irgendwann hat sie etwas gemerkt und ein neues Versteck für die Geschenke gefunden, ____________ ich in der Schule war.

14i **Erzählen Sie die Geschichte eines Kindes aus der DDR, das in einer Jugendorganisation ist. Verwenden Sie „wenn", „als", „während" und „bevor", so oft Sie können.**

Beispiel: Als ich in der ersten Klasse war, durfte ich … Wenn man bei den Jungen Pionieren war …

____

____

____

____

15c **Das Magazin Stern hat im Jahr 2003 eine große Umfrage bei forsa in Auftrag gegeben und gefragt, wer die größten Idole der Deutschen sind. In der Tabelle sehen Sie die Top 40. Beantworten Sie unten die Fragen.**

Rang	Name	Gesamt	West	Ost
1	meine Mutter	35,00 %	33,60 %	41,30 %
2	Mutter Teresa	34,90 %	36,60 %	25,20 %
3	mein Vater	32,50 %	31,70 %	36,00 %
4	Nelson Mandela	31,70 %	32,90 %	23,60 %
5	Michail Gorbatschow	31,10 %	29,00 %	38,50 %
6	Albert Schweitzer	30,90 %	31,70 %	27,10 %
7	Mahatma Gandhi	30,40 %	33,20 %	21,30 %
8	Martin Luther King	28,10 %	29,20 %	22,80 %
9	Albert Einstein	28,00 %	27,00 %	31,40 %
10	Jesus Christus	26,90 %	30,20 %	10,00 %
11	Günther Jauch	25,30 %	23,60 %	32,60 %
12	Dalai Lama	24,90 %	27,50 %	15,60 %
13	Oskar Schindler	24,50 %	26,20 %	18,30 %
14	John F. Kennedy	23,30 %	22,70 %	25,50 %
15	Anne Frank	20,70 %	21,20 %	18,50 %
16	Karlheinz Böhm	20,50 %	22,30 %	13,30 %
17	Martin Luther	20,20 %	21,00 %	16,70 %
18	Hans Dietrich Genscher	20,20 %	16,60 %	36,90 %
19	Willy Brandt	20,10 %	18,10 %	30,90 %
20	Helmut Schmidt	20,10 %	19,10 %	26,30 %

Rang	Name	Gesamt	West	Ost
21	Michael Schumacher	19,50 %	19,60 %	19,00 %
22	Konrad Adenauer	18,80 %	19,80 %	12,80 %
23	Graf von Stauffenberg	18,80 %	17,60 %	22,80 %
24	Herbert Grönemeyer	18,70 %	17,30 %	23,40 %
25	Richard von Weizsäcker	18,70 %	16,60 %	26,20 %
26	Regine Hildebrandt	18,10 %	13,40 %	37,50 %
27	Sophie & Hans Scholl	18,00 %	19,20 %	13,60 %
28	Peter Ustinov	17,70 %	19,10 %	12,30 %
29	Sean Connery	17,40 %	16,70 %	20,40 %
30	Königin Silvia von Schweden	17,00 %	17,10 %	16,40 %
31	Astrid Lindgren	16,90 %	19,10 %	6,70 %
32	ein*e Freund*in	16,90 %	15,10 %	22,70 %
33	Kofi Annan	16,10 %	18,10 %	6,50 %
34	Muhammad Ali	16,00 %	15,70 %	16,90 %
35	Leonardo da Vinci	15,90 %	15,30 %	18,40 %
36	Beatles	15,80 %	15,00 %	19,10 %
37	Johann Wolfgang von Goethe	15,50 %	14,50 %	19,50 %
38	Wolfgang Amadeus Mozart	15,50 %	14,80 %	18,30 %
39	Heinz Rühmann	14,50 %	14,30 %	15,90 %
40	Marie Curie	14,50 %	14,20 %	15,70 %

Quelle: Stern.de nach einer forsa-Umfrage im Auftrag von STERN

Welche Personen aus den Top 40 kennen Sie? Markieren Sie sie in der Tabelle.

Bei welchen Personen gibt es den größten Unterschied zwischen Ost und West?

Person: ______________ Unterschied in Prozent: ______________

Person: ______________ Unterschied in Prozent: ______________

Person: ______________ Unterschied in Prozent: ______________

Welches Ergebnis hat Sie am meisten überrascht? Warum? Schreiben Sie drei Sätze darüber.

____

____

____

15d Verstanden? Steffen erzählt vom Lieblingshelden aus seiner Kindheit. Hören Sie die Aufnahme zweimal und notieren Sie sich möglichst viele Details. Machen Sie sich nur Stichworte und schreiben Sie keine ganzen Sätze.

____

____

____

____

15e Schreiben Sie mit den Informationen aus Aktivität 15d einen kurzen Text über Steffens Lieblingshelden.

Steffens Held war ...

____

____

____

____

5: „Zwischen uns die Mauer"

18e „Zwischen uns die Mauer": Die Zukunft von Katja und Markus. Was denken Sie: Wie entwickelt sich die Beziehung von Katja und Markus weiter? Sammeln Sie ein paar Ideen in Stichworten.

____

____

____

____

18f Verstanden? Am 22. November antwortet Katja auf den Brief von Markus, den Sie in MACHEN gelesen haben. Leider war sie sehr traurig und ihre Tränen haben ein paar Wörter verwischt. Hören Sie zu und tragen Sie die fehlenden Wörter in die Lücken ein.

Lieber Markus,

okay, ich geb's zu. Ich hab auch irgendwie auf deinen Brief ________________, lässt sich halt nicht ändern. Aber ich hab 'nen Horror davor, zu viel an dich zu ________________, zu viel rumzuträumen – das macht mich ________________.

Als ich deinen ________________ von den zusammengewachsenen, eng stehenden Bäumen ________________ habe, gab mir das ein blödes ________________. Ich will ich bleiben und den anderen ________________ sich selber sein lassen, und der andere soll ________________ können, wenn er mag, und ich will gehen können, wenn ich mag.

Genauso wenig wie ich Sonnenstrahlen oder ________________ oder Wolken oder den Mond besitzen will, will ich die Gefühle eines anderen Menschen ________________.

Deine Katja

Quelle: Katja Hildebrand, „Zwischen uns die Mauer", Thienemann-Esslinger Verlag (vereinfacht)

6: Ampelmann – Eine Ost-West-Geschichte°

21b Reflektieren: Ampelmännchen-Soziologie. Sie haben in MACHEN gelernt, dass Ampelmännchen besonders sicher sind, wenn sie freundlich wirken und wenn sie möglichst groß sind, damit viel Licht durch sie scheint. Aber die Sicherheit ist nicht immer alles. Es gibt auch soziologische Gründe für bestimmte Ampelmännchen. In Mainz gibt es zum Beispiel die Mainzelmännchen als Ampelmännchen, das sind Trickfilmfiguren. Und in Leipzig gibt es seit 2011 Ampelmädchen. Vielleicht erinnern Sie sich noch daran, dass es in Wien Ampelpärchen gibt, darunter auch lesbische und schwule Ampelpärchen. Wie finden Sie das? Sollte es einheitliche Ampelmännchen geben? Oder sollte es auch bei Ampelmännchen Gleichberechtigung geben, z. B. durch Ampelmännchen und Ampelmädchen?

7: Chancengleichheit?

Kulturpunkt: Queer in Deutschland

"Hold on a second: …

… what were the experiences of LGBTQ+ people like in divided Germany?" From the end of World War II and the initial division of Germany into East and West in 1949 until the fall of the Berlin Wall and German Reunification in 1990, LGBTQ+ people in East and West Germany had experiences that mirrored each other in some ways and differed in others. Both East and West Germany inherited an earlier German law that criminalized male homosexuality, Paragraph 175. This law had been in place since 1871, but it was intensified and made easier to enforce by the Nazis. A mere glance could trigger police action. Approximately 100,000 men were arrested for violating this law under the Nazis; 10,000–15,000 were sent to concentration camps. Paragraph 175 was repealed in East Germany in 1968 and in West Germany in 1969. Although the law was repealed, gay men and lesbians still faced social discrimination for many years afterward.

In West Germany, lesbians and gay men faced prejudice in many aspects of their lives. Before the anti-gay laws were repealed, homosexual activity was illegal. Targets of Nazi persecution were still considered criminals after the war. The influence of Christian churches was also strong in West Germany, and many religious figures supported enforcing the anti-gay law and preventing advances in gay rights. There were, however, many places for queer people to meet, especially in large cities. After decriminalization, multiple organizations were founded so that activists could work for queer equality. There were also many publications for lesbians and gay men, some of which were smuggled into East Germany.

In East Germany, homosexuality was a different kind of taboo. Citizens had limited ability to gather for unsanctioned political or social causes, and the government was always concerned that gender or sexual expression could lead to disruptive demonstrations and illegal activity (like spying for West Germany or the United States). Although the socialist country's policies technically accepted everyone who was willing to work for the common good, in actuality homosexuality and non-conforming gender could be considered forms of individualism. Even after decriminalization, lesbians and gay men were targeted for surveillance by the Ministry for State Security, the Stasi, which aimed to protect the nation from what it saw as a disruptive threat. Large cities, like East Berlin, had some bars and social spots where lesbians and gay men could meet.

After the fall of the Berlin Wall in 1989 and German Reunification in 1990, the country's laws were unified and Paragraph 175 was conclusively removed from the German criminal code. In the decades since Reunification, the German government has passed laws to expunge the criminal convictions of those affected by Paragraph 175, both under the Nazis and after World War II, and has instituted a plan to provide compensation to the individuals who were prosecuted.

Reflektieren: Choose one of the assignments below.

Compare what you just learned about LGBTQ+ people in East and West Germany with what you know about the LGBTQ2S+ movement in the United States. Where do you see similarities? Where do you see differences? You can also research the legal background for the U.S. if you are not familiar with it before writing your response.

In the text, you learn that East Germany opposed same sex relations because they could be seen as a sign of individualism. Explain what that means and how you feel about this different kind of opposition to LGBTQ+ rights.

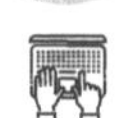

Reflektieren: Gender Inequality. Der Gender Inequality-Index von den Vereinten Nationen rankt Länder nach dem Level von Gleichberechtigung. Der Index misst die Lücke zwischen Männern und Frauen in drei Bereichen: Gesundheit, Teilhabe in der Politik (*empowerment*) und im Wirtschaftsleben (*labor market*).

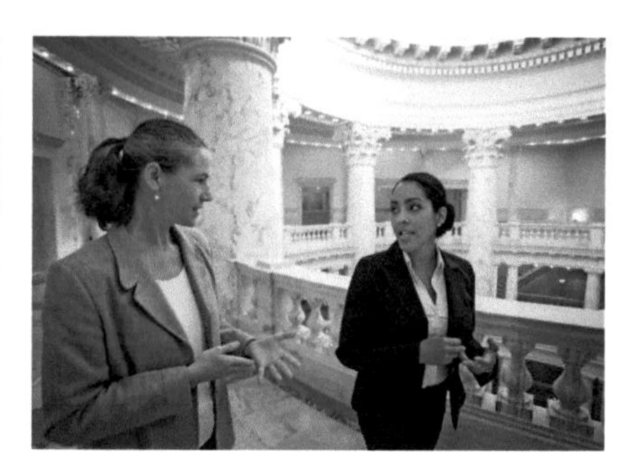

Reflektieren Sie, warum diese Kategorien mit Gleichberechtigung zu tun haben. Verstehen Sie, warum die UNO diese Dimensionen wählt? Wie kategorisieren Sie die DDR und die BRD zwischen 1949 und 1989 – welches Land hatte wahrscheinlich den besseren Rang und warum? Was glauben Sie: Wo befinden sich die USA auf dem Index? Warum?

Wenn Sie möchten, können Sie auch auf der UN-Webseite, die Sie unter www.klett-usa.com/impuls2links finden, mehr über den Index lesen und auch sehen, wie Deutschland heute abschneidet (und auch die USA und andere Länder). Sie können das auch gerne kommentieren. Schreiben Sie Ihre Gedanken möglichst auf Deutsch auf, aber Sie dürfen auch etwas auf Englisch schreiben, damit Sie alle Ihre Gedanken ausdrücken können.

Verstanden? Unten sehen Sie eine Statistik zum Frauenanteil von allen Erwerbstätigen (Arbeiter*innen) in der DDR. Hören Sie gut zu und entscheiden Sie, ob die Aussagen richtig oder falsch sind.

Jahr	Beschäftigte insgesamt	davon Frauen	Frauenanteil %
1950	7.196.000	2.880.000	40,0
1960	7.686.000	3.456.000	45,0
1970	7.769.000	3.750.000	48,3
1980	8.225.000	4.106.000	49,9
1989	8.547.000	4.178.000	48,9

Quelle: Bundesministerium für Familie, Senioren, Frauen und Jugend (2015)

richtig falsch

Aussage 1

Aussage 2

Aussage 3

Aussage 4

26a **Gendergerechte Sprache. Die Rentnerin Marlies Krämer verklagte (*sued*) 2017 ihre Bank. Warum? Die 80-jährige Feministin will auf Formularen und in Briefen als „Kundin" und „Sparerin" angeredet werden, nicht als „Kunde" und „Sparer". Im März 2018 scheiterte (*failed*) ihre Klage zum zweiten Mal. Aufgeben will Krämer aber nicht.**

Jahrzehntelang war Marlies Krämer Hausfrau und Mutter. Ihr Mann starb früh und sie musste ihre vier Kinder alleine großziehen. Erst im Alter von 50 Jahren begann Krämer ein Soziologiestudium. Das hat ihr die Augen für die gesellschaftliche Benachteiligung von Frauen geöffnet. Seitdem sieht sie sich selbst als Feministin.

Marlies Krämer hat zwei Thesen. Die erste lautet: „Mit der sprachlichen Ausgrenzung beginnt die patriarchale Ausbeutung von Frauen." Und die zweite: „Die feminine Sprache ist der Schlüssel zur Gleichberechtigung."

Für ihren Kampf vor Gericht hat Krämer viele positive, aber auch negative Reaktionen erhalten. Ein Kritikpunkt ist, dass es größere Probleme beim Thema „Gleichberechtigung" gibt, als dass eine Bank feminine Formen auf Formularen oder in Briefen benutzt. Krämers Kommentar dazu: „Sprache ist unser höchstes Kulturgut, aber wir Frauen kommen darin nicht vor."

Marlies Krämer will nicht aufgeben. Wenn es sein muss, geht sie mit ihrer Klage bis vor den Europäischen Gerichtshof für Menschenrechte.

Quelle der direkten Zitate: SZ.de vom 13.03.2018

Was denken Sie über Krämers Thesen? Ist eine Gruppe von Menschen nur dann ein gleichberechtigter Teil der Gesellschaft, wenn eine Sprachgemeinschaft sie in der Sprache bzw. der Grammatik berücksichtigt? Übersetzen Sie, wenn nötig, zuerst die Thesen ins Englische.

____

____

____

____

____

____

____

____

____

8: Vertrags- und Gastarbeit in der DDR und BRD

28c **Verstanden? Ein bisschen Mathematik. Hören Sie zu und schreiben Sie die Fragen auf. Beantworten Sie danach die Fragen.**

Frage 1: ______________________________

Antwort 1: ______________________________

Frage 2: ______________________________

Antwort 2: ______________________________

Frage 3: ______________________________

Antwort 3: ______________________________

Frage 4: ______________________________

Antwort 4: ______________________________

Frage 5: ______________________________

Antwort 5: ______________________________

29a **Reflektieren: When commenting about the guest worker program, author Max Frisch famously said: "Wir riefen Arbeitskräfte, und es kamen Menschen." How do you interpret this statement? What could Frisch have meant? Also reflect on the terms *Gastarbeiter*innen* and *Vertragsarbeiter*innen*. What connotations do these terms have?**

29b **Verstanden? In MACHEN haben Sie etwas über den Film „Almanya" gelernt. Jetzt hören Sie eine Kurzbiografie der Regisseurin von „Almanya", Yasemin Şamdereli. Hören Sie gut zu und beantworten Sie die Fragen.**

Welche zwei Informationen über Yasemin Şamdereli sind nicht korrekt?

- Sie ist auch eine Autorin, die Romane schreibt.
- Sie ist in Dortmund aufgewachsen.
- Sie macht Filme, hat aber Theater studiert.

Was ist Şamderelis Verbindung zur Türkei?

- Sie hat in der Türkei Film studiert.
- Alle ihre Filme spielen in der Türkei.
- Sie hat familiäre Verbindungen zur Türkei.

Was erfahren Sie über Şamderelis Schwester Nesrin?

- Nesrin hat einen Preis für den Film „Almanya" gewonnen.
- Nesrin ist auch Filmemacherin wie ihre Schwester.
- Yasemin und Nesrin planen, in der Zukunft ihren ersten Film gemeinsam zu produzieren.

9: Die Wende

30h **Schnelle Ausreise aus Karl-Marx-Stadt! Knut und sein Lebensgefährte Sven hörten im Radio, dass die Grenze offen ist. Was machten sie? Verbinden Sie die Satzteile, die logisch zusammenpassen.**

- Knut und Sven lernten sich 1983 kennen,
- Weil sie ihren Familien nicht wehtun wollten,
- Sie legten schnell Kleidung in einen Koffer,
- Die BRD-Perspektive über Homosexualität war ihnen fremd,
- Sie hatten sich sehr beeilt,
- Sie hatten an der Demonstration in der Stadt teilgenommen,
- Zuerst hatten sie ihren Trabi vollgetankt,

- denn sie befürchteten eine Grenzschließung.
- bevor sie die Nachricht im Radio hörten.
- hatten sie nie über Ausreisepläne gesprochen.
- als sie im Zug nach Ungarn reisten.
- aber in der DDR hatten sie Toleranz gekannt.
- dann fuhren sie zur Grenze.
- denn sie wollten Reformen und mehr Freiheit.

31a **Reflektieren: Kennen Sie weitere historische Ereignisse, die sehr emotional waren? Glauben Sie, dass Emotionen gut oder schlecht für Politik sind? Oder denken Sie, dass Emotionen für die Politik keine Rolle spielen? Schreiben Sie möglichst auf Deutsch, Sie können aber auch Englisch benutzen.**

31b **Lesen Sie den Text zur Wiedervereinigung und beantworten Sie die Fragen.**

Am 15.11.1989, sechs Tage nachdem die DDR die Mauer geöffnet hatte, sprach Gorbatschow von einer Wiedervereinigung. Auch noch im November schlug der neue DDR-Ministerpräsident Modrow eine Vertragsgemeinschaft vor und Bundeskanzler Helmut Kohl stellte einen 10-Punkte-Plan vor. Nachdem vorher bei den Montagsdemonstrationen die Demonstrant*innen „Wir sind das Volk!" gerufen hatten, hörte man im Dezember zum ersten Mal den Ruf „Wir sind ein Volk!".

Nachdem Kohl und Modrow sich am 19.12.1989 getroffen hatten, konnten DDR- und BRD-Bürger*innen ab dem 24.12.1989 ohne Visum ins jeweils andere Land reisen.

Im Januar begannen die Verhandlungen über eine Vertragsgemeinschaft. Ab Februar sprachen die beiden Seiten über eine Währungsunion, also gleiches Geld, und gemeinsamen Handel.

Nachdem im März die ersten freien, demokratischen Wahlen stattgefunden hatten, wurde Lothar de Maizière am 12.04.1990 neuer Ministerpräsident der DDR.

Im Mai begannen die 2+4 Verhandlungen: 2 waren die DDR und die BRD und 4 waren die vier Alliierten, also die USA, Großbritannien, Frankreich und die Sowjetunion. Da es davor nie einen Friedensvertrag gegeben hatte, waren die BRD und die DDR immer noch nicht voll souverän und die Alliierten mussten zustimmen.

Am 01.07.1990 trat die Wirtschafts-, Währungs- und Sozialunion zwischen der BRD und der DDR in Kraft. Nach vielen Verhandlungen mit den Alliierten, gab es grünes Licht für eine Wiedervereinigung. Am 23.08.1990 stimmte das ostdeutsche Parlament mit 294 zu 62 Stimmen für einen Beitritt zur BRD.

Nachdem die Alliierten zugestimmt hatten, traten die fünf ostdeutschen Bundesländer am 03.10.1990 der BRD bei. Am 02.12.1990 gab es die ersten gesamtdeutschen Bundestagswahlen.

richtig	falsch	
		Die Demonstrant*innen riefen „Wir sind ein Volk!".
		DDR-Bürger*innen brauchten ein Visum, um in die BRD zu reisen.
		Im Januar begannen die Verhandlungen zwischen der DDR und der BRD.
		Die SED bestimmte im April einen neuen Ministerpräsidenten für die DDR.
		Die DDR und die BRD verhandelten alleine über die Einheit.
		Das ostdeutsche Parlament stimmte für den Beitritt zur BRD.
		Am 2. Dezember fand die Wiedervereinigung statt.

31c **Aus zwei mach eins. In einem Land kann es nur eine Flagge, nur eine Nationalhymne, nur eine Hauptstadt und nur eine Verfassung geben. Recherchieren Sie fünf Minuten lang über alles, was Sie zu diesen Themen finden.**

Recherche

Flagge der DDR (Was bedeutete sie?)
Flagge der BRD (Woher kam sie historisch?)
Nationalhymne der DDR (Wer hat sie geschrieben? Wie klingt sie? Wie ist der Text?)
Nationalhymne der BRD (Wer hat sie geschrieben? Wie klingt sie? Wie ist der Text? Was ist die Geschichte?)

Welche Hymne und Flagge gibt es heute in der BRD: die der BRD oder DDR? Wie finden Sie das?

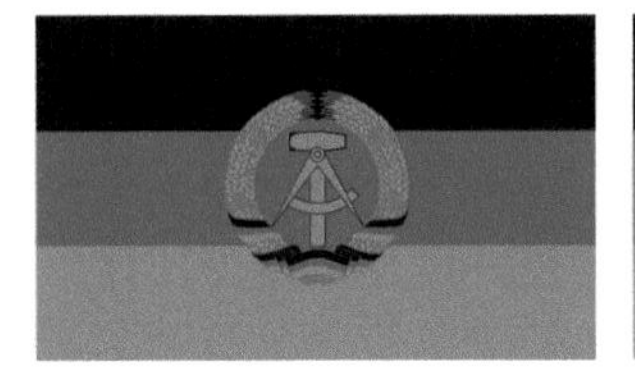

___

___

___

___

31d Verstanden? Zahlen und Fakten zu „25 Jahre Deutsche Einheit". Im Jahr 2014 gab es eine Umfrage des Sozialwissenschaftlichen Forschungszentrums Berlin-Brandenburg zum Stand der Deutschen Einheit. Was denken Menschen im Osten und Westen Deutschlands zum Status der Deutschen Einheit? Hören Sie zu und füllen Sie die Tabelle aus.

Frage/Aussage	Osten	Westen
Sind Sie insgesamt zufrieden mit Ihrem Leben im wiedervereinigten Deutschland?		
Die Einheit bringt mehr Vor- als Nachteile.		
Es gibt noch sehr große Unterschiede zwischen dem Osten und dem Westen Deutschlands.		
Freiheit und Demokratie sehe ich als wichtige Grundwerte (*core value*).		86 % / 68 %
Ich fühle mich als richtige*r Bundesbürger*in.		

32b Zugehört: Folge 4 – Wiedervereinigung persönlich. Die beiden Professorinnen unterhalten sich über den Fall der Mauer, die Wiedervereinigung und darüber, was diese Ereignisse für sie persönlich bedeute(te)n. Hören Sie zu und beantworten Sie dann die Fragen.

Können sich beide Frauen an den Tag, an dem die Mauer fiel, erinnern? Warum (nicht)?

____

____

Wie hat der Fall der Mauer das Leben der beiden verändert?

Stine Eckert: ______________________________

Nicole Coleman: ______________________________

10: Einheit?°

35b Verstanden? In MACHEN haben Sie den Anfang des Gedichts „grenzenlos und unverschämt – ein gedicht gegen die deutsche sch-einheit" von May Ayim gelesen. Unten finden Sie das Ende des Gedichts. Hören Sie nun das komplette Gedicht und füllen Sie die Lücken aus.

ich werde

noch einen ______________ weitergehen und

noch einen schritt

____

und wiederkehren

wann

ich ______________

____

ich will

______________ und unverschämt

bleiben

Quelle: May Ayim, „grenzenlos und unverschämt. ein gedicht gegen die deutsche sch-einheit", Orlanda Verlag

37d **Verstanden? Es gibt viele Varianten, wie man auf „Danke" antwortet. Sie hören nun drei Mini-Dialoge und sollen dann die Fragen beantworten.**

Maria bedankt sich bei Ebru für ihre Hilfe bei den Hausaufgaben. Wie reagiert Ebru darauf?

- Sie sagt, dass Maria sich nicht bedanken muss, weil sie Freundinnen sind.
- Sie sagt, dass es kein Problem für sie ist, weil sie gern Mathe macht.
- Sie sagt, dass Maria ihr bei den Hausaufgaben für Englisch helfen kann.

Oli bedankt sich bei Mia dafür, dass sie ihm von ihrer Kindheit erzählt hat. Was antwortet ihm Mia?

- Sie sagt, dass er sich nicht bedanken muss, weil sie gerne über ihre Kindheit in der DDR spricht.
- Sie sagt, dass es schon okay ist, obwohl sie sich nicht gern an diese Zeit erinnert.
- Sie sagt, dass sie es gern gemacht hat, weil er ihr auch schon viel aus seiner Kindheit erzählt hat.

Tori bedankt sich bei Jörn für das Geschenk. Was sagt Jörn?

- Er sagt, dass er ihr das Geschenk gern gegeben hat, weil Tori seine beste Freundin ist.
- Er sagt, dass sie sich nicht bedanken muss, weil es nur ein kleines Geschenk ist.
- Er sagt, dass er gerne Geschenke macht und Toris Freude besser als ein Dankeschön ist.

38e **Zugehört: Folge 6 – Identitätsgeschichten. Hören Sie zu und notieren Sie sich, wie der ostdeutsche und westdeutsche Hintergrund die Identität der beiden Frauen jeweils bestimmt. Stichpunkte reichen, es müssen keine ganzen Sätze sein.**

38f **Reflektieren: Denken Sie darüber nach, inwiefern Ihre eigene Geschichte etwas mit Ihrer Identität zu tun hat und verweisen Sie dabei auf das, was Sie in Aktivität 38e gehört haben (z. B. Ich kann gut verstehen, dass ... Ich kenne das auch, dass ... Ich verstehe nicht, warum ...). Schreiben Sie Ihren Text möglichst auf Deutsch, aber Sie können auch englische Wörter oder Redemittel benutzen, wenn Sie das deutsche Wort nicht kennen oder eine englische Formulierung besonders gut passt.**

40b **Ostalgie: eine Nostalgie für die DDR und ihre Produkte. Lesen Sie den kurzen Text und beantworten Sie die Fragen.**

Manche kritisierten den Film „Good Bye, Lenin!" für die Ostalgie, die darin vorkommt. Ostalgie ist ein Phänomen, das seit den frühen 1990er Jahren eine Nostalgie für den Osten und die alten DDR-Produkte beschreibt. So sucht Alex zum Beispiel im Supermarkt nach Spreewald-Gurken, Mokka Fix und Fillinchen, findet sie aber nicht, weil man sie durch Westprodukte ersetzt hatte. Er findet deshalb alte Gläser von Spreewald-Gurken, entfernt die Etiketten und klebt sie auf Gewürzgurken aus den Niederlanden. Seine Mutter merkt es nicht, weil Nostalgie oft emotional ist und es mehr um den Namen als um den Geschmack geht. Eine andere Art, wie Ostalgie im Film zum Tragen kommt, ist die Inkorporation von Sigmund Jähn. Der ehemalige Kosmonaut war immer Alex' Idol. Deshalb macht er ihn in seinen falschen Nachrichten zum Staatsratsvorsitzenden.

Seit wann gibt es das Phänomen der Ostalgie? Und was ist Ostalgie?

___

___

Was ist bei Ostalgie oft wichtiger als die Produkte? Wo sieht man das im Film „Good Bye, Lenin!"?

___

___

In MACHEN haben Sie etwas zum Thema „Erinnerungskultur" gelesen. Reflektieren Sie über die folgenden zwei Fragen: Ist es ein Problem, wenn man sich an die DDR *nur* als Diktatur erinnert?

___

___

___

Ist es ein Problem, wenn sie ostalgisch erinnert wird? Was wäre eine adäquate Erinnerungsform?

___

___

___

40c **Verstanden? Julian muss einen Aufsatz an der Uni über die Filme „Good Bye, Lenin!" und „Das Leben der Anderen" schreiben. Er spricht mit Nathan über den Aufsatz. Kreuzen Sie die richtigen Antworten an.**

Was denkt Nathan über Julians Idee, im Aufsatz die Darstellungen des Lebens in der DDR zu vergleichen?

- ☐ Nathan findet das Thema langweilig, weil die Filme sehr ähnlich sind.
- ☐ Nathan findet das Thema interessant, aber er denkt, dass es zu breit ist.
- ☐ Nathan findet, dass dieses Thema den Hauptpunkt der Filme ignoriert.

Welches Thema schlägt Nathan Julian vor?

- ☐ Ein Vergleich des Lebens von Künstler*innen und „normalen" Bürger*innen.
- ☐ Die Rolle der Künstler*innen im Sozialismus.
- ☐ Das Alltagsleben in der DDR.

Was ist der Fokus des Films „Das Leben der Anderen"?

- ☐ Die Konsequenzen des repressiven DDR-Regimes auf die Arbeit von Künstler*innen.
- ☐ Die wichtige Bedeutung von Familienbeziehungen unter einem repressiven Regime.
- ☐ Die Beziehung von Staat und Religion in der DDR.

42a **Erzähl mal: Nehmen Sie ein kurzes Video (z. B. mit Ihrem Handy oder am Computer) auf und beantworten Sie die Fragen.**

Was ist in den letzten Wochen/Monaten in Ihrem Leben und/oder Ihrem Land passiert? (Erzählen Sie im Perfekt.)

Was wussten Sie vor diesem Kapitel über die Geschichte von Ost- und Westdeutschland? (Ich wusste, dass …)

Was wissen Sie jetzt über die Geschichte von Ost- und Westdeutschland? Berichten Sie über zwei oder drei Ereignisse im Präteritum.

Was hat Sie überrascht?

42b **Self-Assessment**

You now get a chance to reflect on the many things you have learned throughout the chapter. Carefully read through the "Can-Do Statements" below, and ask yourself if you can perform all of these tasks. It might be helpful for each of the statements to actually practice the communicative scenario. Once you are confident that you are able to perform a task, check the respective box on the left side.

- I can ask and answer questions about meaningful events and people in the recent past.
- I can describe authentic historical images and make assumptions about their meaning.
- I can understand and summarize the main ideas and a few supporting facts from texts about historical events.
- I can contrast ideological viewpoints presented in texts about historical events.
- I can ask for and provide information about specific historical events.
- I can understand a straight-forward description, such as one of the architecture of the Berlin Wall.
- I can exchange biographical information on historical figures.
- I can visualize core information from texts through diagrams, drawings, etc.
- I can use my language to plan a presentation in a group.
- I can answer questions about, and express my views on, longer literary texts, poems, and movie trailers.
- I can narrate events from the past in the *Präteritum* tense using strong, weak, and mixed verbs.
- I can read the dates of events using ordinal numbers and the temporal prepositions *am*, *im*, and *um*.
- I can form temporal clauses with the conjunctions *wenn/als* and *bevor/während*.
- I can talk about the distant past using the *Plusquamperfekt* tense and temporal phrases with the conjunction *nachdem*.
- I can talk about events in a structured way using the temporal prepositions *vor*, *nach*, *von … bis*, and *seit*.

- I am familiar with important dates and events of German post-war history.
- I am familiar with how school shapes how we talk about historical events of divided Germany.
- I am familiar with stories about people's attempts to escape from the GDR.
- I am familiar with youth organizations in East and West Germany and their social role.
- I am familiar with questions of gender equality in East and West Germany.
- I am familiar with the guest and contract worker programs in the GDR and FRG.

Wer würde sich trauen?

Achterbahnen und anderer Nervenkitzel

KULTURPUNKT: KIRMES

"Hold on a second: Do Germans …

… really dig out bones and dance around a tree?" Not usually, no, and most Germans won't have ever heard about this custom, either. While the *Münchner Oktoberfest* has become an internationally renowned festival with millions of visitors each year, all over Germany you'll find similar, usually much smaller, *Volksfeste* (folk fairs) with their own homegrown traditions.

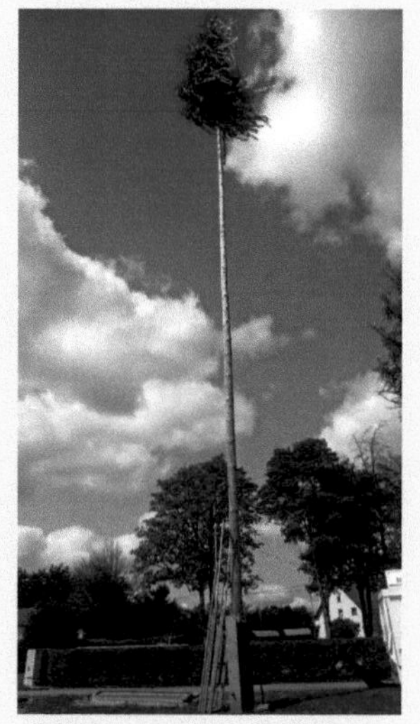

Giescheider *Kirmesbaum* (*Kirmes* tree), consisting of a long thin trunk and a colorfully decorated conifer on top, in 2019.

I grew up in the Eifel, a rural region in western Germany and eastern Belgium. From June to November, each weekend a different town or village celebrates *Kirmes*, which is a regional term for *Kirchweih* or *Kirchweihfest*. According to the name, people celebrate the dedication day of the local church. In other German speaking regions, you might hear names like *Chilbi*, *Kirtag*, *Kerwe*, or *Kirb*. The church's birthday is less religious than it sounds, though, and it's mostly a huge get together with dance music, lots of alcohol, and nowadays also fun rides like carousels.

Although the Eifeler are probably as proud as many people of their local traditions, they are well aware that some of their traditions are a bit weird. In my eyes that's definitely the case for the above mentioned *Kirmesknochen* (*Kirmes* bone). My sources suggest the *Kirmesknochen* has Germanic roots, but the custom is obviously not that old. As a figurative personification of *Kirmes*, it might symbolize the culinary indulgences that came with the festival. Anyhow, it is the lead character in the rather comical theatrical rituals that start off the celebrations and eventually end them. In my village, it's still up to the young men, who have traditionally organized the *Kirmes* festivities, to put on the show. Beforehand, they hide a cleaned ham bone with the current year written on it. After mass on the first day of *Kirmes*, and accompanied by a brass-band, two men start looking for the bone and dig some smaller holes. Eventually, they find it, tie it to a stick between them, and dance around to the music to celebrate the beginning of *Kirmes*. After a few days of partying, *Kirmes* dies and is carried to its grave: people mourn heavily at its funeral when the *Kirmesknochen* is laid to rest.

43k **Reflektieren: What do you think of these traditions? What might their purpose be for the local community? Did you grow up with traditions that were "normal" to you but which other people might find weird? Do you know any "traditions" that were invented recently? If you don't have an example from your own experience, research a local tradition from your home country or one of the German-speaking countries. Describe it, and reflect on it.**

43l **Das Volksfest als Kulisse (*set*). Es gibt viele Filme und Serien, deren Handlung auf einem Volksfest, in einem Zirkus oder einem Themenpark spielt. Wählen Sie einen Film oder eine Serie und untersuchen Sie, wie das Volksfest, der Zirkus oder der Themenpark als Kulisse funktioniert.**

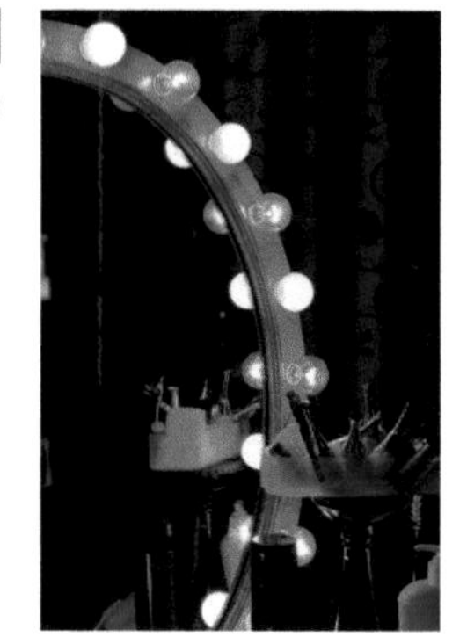

Beispiele:
„Dumbo" (1941, 2019)
„Carnivàle" (2003-2005)
„Final Destination 3" (2006)
„American Horror Story: Freak Show" (2014-2015)
„The Greatest Showman" (2017)

Film/Serie Genre

Welche Besucher*innenattraktionen sieht man in dem Film oder der Serie? Erstellen Sie eine Liste.

Wählen Sie zwei von diesen Attraktionen und sagen Sie, warum sie für die Handlung so wichtig sind.

Wie werden die Personen in dem Film oder der Serie dargestellt, die für das Volksfest, den Zirkus oder den Themenpark arbeiten?

Würde der Film oder die Serie dieselbe Atmosphäre haben, wenn er/sie eine andere Kulisse hätte? Warum (nicht)?

44c **Verstanden? Lisa und Antonia gehen auf den Kreuznacher Jahrmarkt, ein Volksfest in Rheinland-Pfalz. Was wollen die beiden dort machen? Hören Sie gut zu und kreuzen Sie die richtigen Antworten an.**

Warum möchte Antonia auf das Volksfest gehen?

- Sie möchte endlich mal wieder Zeit mit Lisa verbringen.
- Sie macht samstags immer einen Ausflug mit Freund*innen.
- Sie möchte nach einer langen Zeit wieder Riesenrad fahren.

Mit welchen Fahrgeschäften wollen die beiden gemeinsam fahren?

- Riesenrad und Kettenkarussell
- Kettenkarussell und Wildwasserbahn
- Riesenrad und Autoscooter

Warum möchte Antonia keine Bratwurst essen?

- Sie ist seit ein paar Wochen Vegetarierin.
- Sie isst süße Speisen lieber als herzhafte (*savory*).
- Sie isst während der Fastenzeit kein Fleisch.

45a **Ein Volksfest zu besuchen, macht riesigen Spaß. Das wäre nicht möglich ohne die Menschen, die auf dem Volksfest arbeiten. Überlegen Sie, was man alles tun muss, damit das Volksfest für die Besucher*innen zu einem tollen Erlebnis wird. Die Verben im Kasten helfen Ihnen beim Formulieren von Sätzen.**

verkaufen | braten | vorbereiten | kontrollieren | sorgen für | aufbauen | aufstellen | sein

Man muss Eintrittskarten verkaufen.

46a **Schaustellerei: Wie würden Sie das machen? Beantworten Sie mindestens sechs Fragen.**

Schausteller*innen fahren viel herum. Wie würden Sie das finden?

___

Stellen Sie sich vor, Sie haben Kinder. Wie würden Sie das Leben als Schausteller*in für die Kinder schön machen?

___

Sie treffen an einem Ort jemanden, den Sie sehr nett finden. Wie würden Sie mit der Person in Kontakt bleiben?

___

Nicht alle Haustiere sind geeignet für das Reisen. Welche würden Sie haben?

___

Wie würden Sie Ihren Wohnwagen einrichten (*furnish*)?

___

Würden Sie versuchen, den Ort, wo Sie gerade sind, kennenzulernen? Warum (nicht)?

___

Wenn Sie heute einen Zirkus sehen, würden Sie gerne mitfahren?

___

Was würde Sie an diesem Wanderleben faszinieren?

___

Sie fahren also mit. Was würden Ihre Freund*innen dazu sagen?

___

Was würde Sie am meisten davon abhalten, mitzufahren?

___

15: OKTOBERFEST – DAMALS UND HEUTE°

49b **Verstanden? Das Oktoberfest 2018 in Zahlen. Wählen Sie die richtige Antwort aus.**

Besucher*innen	6,3 Millionen	3,6 Millionen	36 Millionen	63 Millionen
Liter Bier	5,7 Millionen	7,5 Millionen	7.500	5.700
Gäst*innen aus ___ Nationen	16	26	55	65
größtes Festzelt	Paulaner	Käfer	Hofbräu	Franziskaner

49c **Sie arbeiten als Assistent*in für die München Betriebs-GmbH & Co. KG, die Management-Firma hinter dem Oktoberfest. Stellen Sie sich vor, Sie wären dieses Jahr bei der Detailplanung des Oktoberfests im Koordinationsteam. Was würde Ihr Team tun, um die Planung im Vergleich zum letzten Jahr zu verbessern? Schreiben Sie Sätze im Konjunktiv II, wie im Beispiel.**

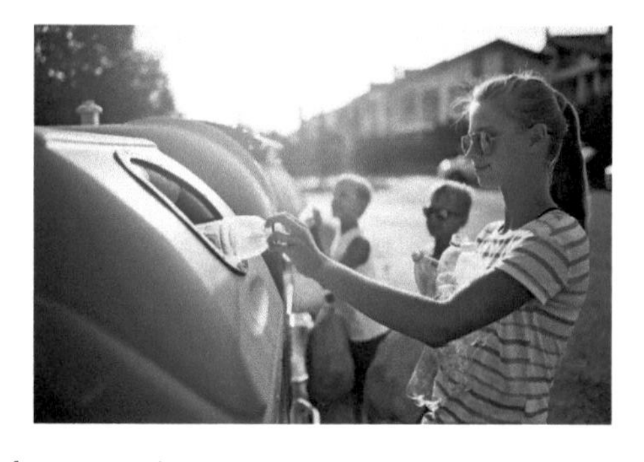

Ideen (Sie können auch Ihre eigenen Ideen benutzen.):

nicht so viel Geld für Werbung ausgeben / dürfen
die Fundobjekte schneller zurückgeben / können
den Müllarbeiter*innen höhere Löhne zahlen / sollen
mehr Recyclingcontainer aufstellen / müssen
~~mehr Erste-Hilfe-Ambulanzen anbieten / können~~
die Straßen besser reinigen / müssen

Wir könnten mehr Erste-Hilfe-Ambulanzen anbieten.

____

____

____

____

____

16: FREIZEITPARKS

53f **Ach du meine Güte! Maren und ihre Mitbewohner*innen entdecken, dass der Recyclingcontainer vor ihrem Haus zu voll ist. Ihr Müll passt nicht mehr rein. Was könnten sie jetzt machen?**

Aiko: *Wir könnten mal die Stadt anrufen.* (mal die Stadt anrufen können)

James: ______________________________ (mal unsere Nachbar*innen fragen sollen)

Marcelline: ______________________________ (mal zum nächsten Recycling-container laufen müssen)

Alireza: ______________________________ (mal noch einen Tag warten können)

Maren: ______________________________ (mal mit dem Amt telefonieren sollen)

53g **Hier lesen Sie Ratschläge. Was war das Problem?**

An deiner Stelle würde ich erstmal den größten Dreck wegräumen, die leeren Flaschen, Pizzakartons usw. Vielleicht könntest du sogar noch saugen. Aber das mit dem Teppichreiniger würde nicht mehr gehen.

Problem: ____________________

Ich würde erstmal eine Liste machen mit dem, was du nicht weißt. Dann könntest du deine Freundin fragen, sie ist doch gut in Mathe. Und du könntest dir sicher noch etwas Zeit nehmen, um die wichtigsten Punkte zu wiederholen.

Problem: ____________________

Du müsstest dich da jetzt wirklich entscheiden. Du könntest es auf die Dauer nicht immer beiden recht machen. Ein ehrliches Gespräch mit beiden kannst du jetzt nicht mehr vermeiden.

Problem: ____________________

Du solltest erstmal beschreiben, wie viele wichtige Dinge du hier machst. Dann könntest du ein paar Beispiele bringen von Aufgaben, die du richtig gut gemacht hast. Du könntest auch sagen, dass bei 2.000 Euro Miete momentan das Geld einfach nicht reicht.

Problem: ____________________

53h **Verstanden? Lukas bittet Antje um Ratschläge für seinen nächsten Besuch im Heide Park. Wählen Sie die korrekten Antworten aus.**

Warum bittet Lukas Antje um Empfehlungen für den Heide Park?

- Antje arbeitet dort und kennt den Park sehr gut.
- Antje ist Freizeitpark-Expertin und baut Holzachterbahnen.
- Antje war vor kurzem mit ihrer Familie im Heide Park.

Warum hat Antje bei ihrem Besuch im Heide Park ein T-Shirt gekauft?

- Antje wollte ein Souvenir als Erinnerung an den tollen Tag im Park.
- Antje brauchte ein neues T-Shirt, weil ihres beim Mountain-Rafting nass wurde.
- Antje wollte das T-Shirt, weil es ein Foto von ihr mit ihrer Familie beim Mountain-Rafting zeigt.

Warum empfiehlt Antje Lukas, die Piraten-Arena zu besuchen?

- Lukas ist ein großer Fan des Films „Fluch der Karibik", der ein Modell für die Piraten-Arena war.
- Lukas' Cousinen sind erst 5 und 7 Jahre alt und die Piraten-Arena ist für Kinder gedacht.
- Lukas' Cousinen fahren nicht gerne Karussell, deswegen ist die Piraten-Arena die einzige Option.

54a **Reflektieren: Theme parks and foreign cultures.**

In MACHEN, you talked about stereotypical representations of American and German culture found in theme parks around the world. What effect would you say it has on both children and adults if every theme park they go to depicts the U.S. as the Wild West, for example, and Germany as a village full of fairytale-esque *Fachwerkhäuser* (half-timber houses)? Would you expect people from different countries to react differently?

In MACHEN, you also had the chance to explain what you would do differently (or similarly) if you were the park's designer or cultural expert. Reflect on the choices you made. Did you decide to forgo stereotypical depictions altogether, did you stick with them, or did you opt for a mix of both stereotypes and cultural variety in your park concept? Explain why. What kind of visitor experience were you aiming for?

KULTURPUNKT: RUHESTÖRUNG

"Hold on a second: Why can't Germans ...

... mow their lawn on Sundays?" When we talk about pollution, we often think about air pollution—levels of nitrogen oxide in the air, for instance, that can cause trouble breathing. But noise can make us sick as well. The German government strives to reduce noise both in active and passive ways. Active ways include supporting the construction of cars and household appliances that are quieter and also using special asphalt when building streets that makes driving on them less noisy. But some noise remains, and Germans have lots of rules. In fact, there is a law, and some unwritten rules, that regulate what kind of noise can be made, and when. The law is called *Lärmschutzverordnung* (noise protection regulation), and it applies to garden tools, construction equipment, planes, and other loud vehicles. In Switzerland, *Lärmschutz* is called *Lärmsanierung*. The Swiss ministry for the environment centrally undertakes measures to prevent and regulate noise. There is no law like the *Lärmschutzverordnung* in Austria, but many laws include measures to reduce noise emission.

The German law establishes *Ruhezeiten* (quiet times) during which loud machines may not be used in residential areas. And this applies to your normal lawn mower as well. Garden tools may not be used on Sundays or on holidays at all, and during the week they cannot be used after 8 p.m. or before 7 a.m. Some particularly loud tools (such as leaf blowers, which seem to be ever-present in the U.S.) can only be used during the week and between 9 a.m. and 1 p.m. and then again between 3 and 5 p.m. That means that there is a *Mittagsruhe*, kind of like a siesta, where people should not be bothered by these loud noises. Until the 90s, and sometimes still today in smaller towns, shops are closed for *Mittagsruhe* as well. During these midday hours, kids are not usually allowed on playgrounds, either, but cities may differ in how far they go to create a *Mittagsruhe*. By the way, kids (and barking dogs) do not fall under any *Lärmschutzverordnung*, no matter how annoying people may find them. That doesn't mean that parents won't encourage them to be quiet during certain times of the day, though. In fact, to show how an upbringing can influence attitudes and behavior: When I was a kid, I was told to respect other people's *Mittagsruhe*. Therefore, I still don't call anyone between 1 and 3 p.m. or after 8 p.m.

Many neighborly arguments have to do with noise complaints (and some neighbors may not know that kids are allowed to play loudly). Some people will call the police if they hear loud music after 10 p.m. (or even earlier), and in some cities, citizens have petitioned the local government to stop outdoor activities after a certain time. Given that Germany is the country of *Biergärten* and lots of outdoor events in the summer, it can mean significant noise for people living in cities. At the same time, when people complain about noise, about *Lärmbelästigung* (noise disruption), they can also stop some fun events. That was the case in the city of Bonn, for example. Two people sued the city for *Lärmbelästigung*, and the city had to stop the *Klangwelle* (sound wave), a multimedia art installation that combined water and sound for ten days each summer. Some people might say that these two people went a little too far.

55a **Reflektieren: What do you think about these rules? Do they make sense to you? Are you ever bothered by noise? Or have you been at the receiving end of a noise complaint? You can either write about your take on how Germans deal with noise, or speak about your own experiences here.**

56e **Höflicher, bitte! Schreiben Sie diese sehr direkten Sätze in höfliche Bitten um. Benutzen Sie dafür die korrekte Form von „hätte", „möchte", „könnte" oder „würde". Es gibt immer mehr als eine richtige Antwort.**

Ich will ein Ei. *Ich hätte gern ein Ei.* ODER *Ich möchte gern ein Ei.*

Mach das Fenster auf! ______________________

Geben Sie mir Ihre Telefonnummer. ______________________

Macht die Musik aus! ______________________

Sprechen Sie lauter! ______________________

56f **In MACHEN haben Sie sich mit dem Thema „Bürger*innenbegehren“ beschäftigt. Formulieren Sie zur Wiederholung fünf höfliche Bitten, die man in einer Petition finden oder beim Sammeln von Unterschriften hören könnte. Verwenden Sie für alle Sätze das formelle „Sie“.**

~~den Abbau von Braunkohle verbieten~~
gegen die Abholzung stimmen
Geld zum Schutz von Bienen spenden
die Petition unterschreiben
den Ausbau des Parks stoppen
zu unserer Demonstration kommen

Könnten Sie bitte den Abbau von Braunkohle verbieten?

____

____

____

____

____

56g **Verstanden? Im Jahr 2018 hat Europa-Park-Gründer Roland Mack angekündigt, dass es Pläne gibt, den Europa-Park mit einer Seilbahn über den Rhein direkt mit Frankreich zu verbinden, um Menschen den Zugang zum Park zu erleichtern. Es gibt viele gute Gründe für die Bahn, aber auch viele Kritikpunkte. Hören Sie gut zu und notieren Sie in der Tabelle, welche Pro- und Contra-Meinungen es gibt.**

Pro-Meinungen	Contra-Meinungen
Punkt 1:	Punkt 1:
Punkt 2:	Punkt 2:
Punkt 3:	Punkt 3:
Punkt 4:	Punkt 4:
Punkt 5:	Punkt 5:

56h **In Aktivität 56g haben Sie Argumente für und gegen den Bau einer Seilbahn vom Europa-Park nach Frankreich gehört. Jetzt sollen Sie eine Petition für eine der beiden Seiten schreiben, also entweder pro oder contra Seilbahn. Ihre Petition soll sehr höflich formuliert sein. Benutzen Sie daher die Konjunktiv II-Formen aus der Grammatik in 56a in LERNEN. Nutzen Sie die Argumente aus 56g und formulieren Sie eine höfliche, aber deutliche Petition.**

Titel der Petition: ______________________________

Was ist das Ziel der Petition: ______________________________

An wen schreiben Sie die Petition: ______________________________

Text der Petition mit Argumenten aus 56g:

____

____

____

____

____

____

____

18: „Penny Pepper: Alarm auf der Achterbahn"°

60b **Wer ist der*die Taschendieb*in? Lesen Sie weiter, um herauszufinden, wer der*die Taschendieb*in ist. Beantworten Sie dann auch die Fragen.**

Der Affe ist jetzt von der Pommesbude über einen Zweig auf einen Kastanienbaum geklettert und wer saß darunter?

DER BLÖDE MALER

→ Der immer Kinder ignoriert!

Im Moment hat er aber nicht gemalt, sondern den Affen gestreichelt. Wir haben es genau gesehen, weil wir hinter dem Baum standen. Mitten in ein paar matschigen Pommes. Örks! → Ida hat sie trotzdem hungrig angestarrt.

UND DANN HABEN WIR ES GESEHEN:

Der kleine AFFE hat dem Maler die GELDBÖRSE von *Konrad* gegeben!

Dann hat der Maler die Geldbörse von Konrad aufgemacht und das Gesicht verzogen. »Läppische zehn Euro«, hat er gemurmelt. »Lohnt sich ja kaum.« Und dann hat er die GELDBÖRSE achtlos in eine große Sporttasche gestopft.

DA WAREN GANZ, GANZ, VIELE GELDBÖRSEN DRIN!

UND EINE DAVON ...

WAR:

MEINE!

Und in dem Moment wurde ich so wütend! Sooooooo WÜTEND!

Quelle: Ulrike Rylance, „Penny Pepper: Alarm auf der Achterbahn", dtv junior

Beantworten Sie die folgenden Fragen im Präsens.

Wer hat die Geldbörse von Konrad? Was macht diese Figur mit der Geldbörse?

____

Was bedeuten die Wörter „läppisch" und „lohnen"? Suchen Sie die Bedeutung in einem Wörterbuch und schreiben Sie dann für jedes Wort einen neuen Satz, in dem Sie das Wort korrekt benutzen.

läppisch: ____

____

lohnen: ____

____

Wie reagiert der Maler, als er Konrads Geldbörse öffnet? ____

____

Was sieht Penny in der großen Sporttasche des Malers? Wie reagiert sie? ____

____

60c **Sie kennen nur einen kleinen Teil der „Penny Pepper"-Geschichte. Wie ist Ihre Reaktion? Würden Sie gern das ganze Buch lesen? Warum (nicht)? Was denken Sie: Warum würden Kinder das Buch gern lesen? Schreiben Sie ein paar Sätze.**

____

____

____

____

60d **Reflektieren: You may have realized that Penny and her friends suspected people based on stereotypes and prejudices, in terms of ethnic identities, for example. Go back to MACHEN to see why Penny and her friends picked their suspects. Which of those reasons do(n't) you find problematic and why? Do you see any connections to the way crime is dealt with in the real world?**

60e **Verstanden? Sie hören drei kurze Aussagen von Jugendlichen, die gerade „Penny Pepper – Alarm auf der Achterbahn" gelesen haben. Hören Sie gut zu und beantworten Sie die Fragen.**

Warum war „Alarm auf der Achterbahn" Julias Lieblingsbuch in der „Penny Pepper"-Serie?

- In „Alarm auf der Achterbahn" hat es lange gedauert, bis klar war, wer der Verbrecher ist. Das war spannend.
- Sie geht selbst gern auf den Rummel und konnte sich daher mit den Orten im Buch identifizieren.
- Sie fand es toll, dass die Freundinnen gemeinsam den Verbrecher gefunden haben.

Wie fand Michel „Alarm auf der Achterbahn" im Vergleich zu anderen „Penny Pepper"-Büchern?

- „Alarm auf der Achterbahn" war sein Lieblingsbuch, weil die Geschichte viele spannende Teile hatte.
- Er fand „Alarm auf der Achterbahn" nicht gut, weil es zu wenig spannende Elemente gab.
- Er fand „Alarm auf der Achterbahn" in Ordnung, weil er das Buch schnell lesen konnte.

Was hat Max in „Alarm auf der Achterbahn" am besten gefallen?

- Max mochte am meisten, dass die Geschichte von Anfang bis Ende spannend war.
- Max fand die Illustrationen am besten.
- „Alarm auf der Achterbahn" war sein erstes „Penny Pepper"-Buch und er fand die Kombination aus Text und Illustrationen am besten.

63e **Gestern war Markus sehr faul und lag den ganzen Tag im Bett. Was hätte er alles machen sollen oder müssen?**

Markus ____________ seine Hausaufgaben machen ____________.

Er ____________ seine Eltern anrufen ____________.

Er ____________ auch eine E-Mail an seine Oma schreiben ____________.

Gestern ____________ er einkaufen ____________.

Seine Rechnungen ____________ er bezahlen ____________.

Ebenso ____________ er seine schmutzige Wäsche waschen ____________.

Ach, Markus! Du ____________ deinen Tag besser gestalten ____________.

63f **Werner Stengels Konstruktionsprinzipien haben Achterbahnen innoviert. Wie wäre die Fahrt ohne die Innovationen gewesen?**

Das Herzlinienprinzip: Durch diese Innovation orientieren sich Stengels Ingenieur*innen an der Rotation vom Herz – nicht von den Füßen! – der mitfahrenden Person. Deshalb beginnt eine extreme Rechtskurve mit einer minimalen Linkskurve.

⇒ Durch das Herzlinienprinzip konnten Achterbahnen extreme Kurven haben.

Ohne das Herzlinienprinzip hätten Achterbahnen keine extremen Kurven haben können.

Das Herzlinienprinzip: Die Idee ist, wenig Stress und Bewegung in der Herzregion zu produzieren. Das optimiert den Fahrkomfort.

⇒ Durch das Herzlinienprinzip mussten Mitfahrende weniger Stress in der Herzregion fühlen.

____

Das Klothoide-Prinzip: Bevor die Achterbahn sehr schnell zu fahren beginnt, gibt es eine große, langsame Kurve, die dann kleiner und kleiner wird, wie eine Spirale.

⇒ Durch den Spiraleffekt gab es ein viel kleineres Risiko für ein Schleudertrauma (*whiplash*).

____

Der Stengel Dive: Diese Innovation ist eine Rotationskurve, in der ein*e Mitfahrer*in für ein paar Sekunden glaubt, dass er*sie aus dem Wagen fallen wird.

⇒ Durch den Stengel Dive hatten Mitfahrende schockierende Fallillusionen.

____

Herzlinienprinzip

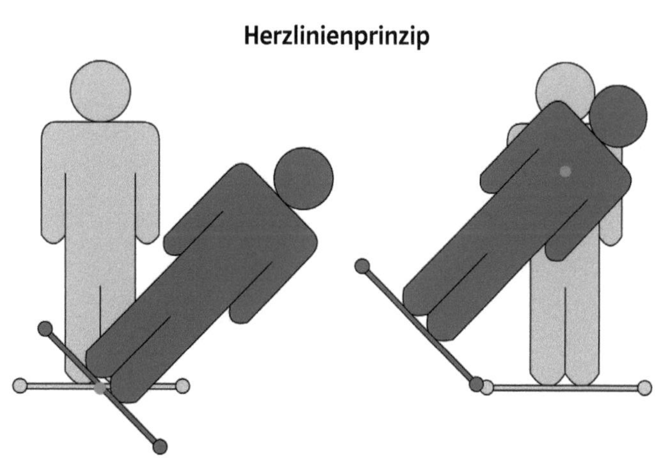

Weg, den der Kopf zurücklegt bei Drehung um die Schienenmitte

Weg, den der Kopf zurücklegt bei Drehung um die Herzlinie

64a **Achterbahnhersteller. In MACHEN haben Sie bereits verschiedene Achterbahnhersteller kennengelernt, wie zum Beispiel Intamin Amusement Rides. Gehen Sie nun auf die Webseite von zwei Achterbahnherstellern und sammeln Sie weitere Informationen. Ergänzen Sie die Steckbriefe.**

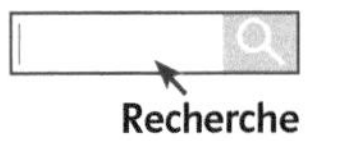

Recherche

I)	II)
Name und Standort des Herstellers:	Name und Standort des Herstellers:
Welche anderen Dinge außer Achterbahnen werden hier produziert?	Welche anderen Dinge außer Achterbahnen werden hier produziert?
Welches Produkt finden Sie besonders interessant oder überraschend? Warum?	Welches Produkt finden Sie besonders interessant oder überraschend? Warum?
Welche Achterbahn von diesem Hersteller finden Sie besonders toll? Warum?	Welche Achterbahn von diesem Hersteller finden Sie besonders toll? Warum?

64b  **Verstanden? Sie lernen jetzt mehr über die Geschichte von Intamin, eine wichtige Firma in der Freizeitparkindustrie. Hören Sie gut zu und beantworten Sie die Fragen.**

Wie hat sich die Firma Intamin vom Anfang der Firma bis heute verändert?

- Am Anfang produzierte das Unternehmen nur Kettenkarussells, aber seit 2012 baut es auch Achterbahnen.
- Am Anfang war die Firma in einer kleinen Wohnung und heute hat sie mehrere Hundert Mitarbeiter*innen.
- Anfangs hatte die Firma mit ihren Achterbahnen keinen Erfolg, aber das hat sich im Jahr 1994 geändert.

Was war an „Eurostar" besonders?

- „Eurostar" war die erste River-Rapids-Bahn der Welt.
- „Eurostar" wurde von einem Expert*innenteam aus Menschen aus 90 europäischen Ländern entwickelt.
- „Eurostar" war ein Inverted Coaster, den man mit 90 Trucks transportieren konnte.

Welche Eigenschaften haben die neuen Antriebssysteme, die die Firma Intamin in den 2000er Jahren entwickelt hat?

- Diese Antriebssysteme sind energieeffizienter als die alten.
- Diese Antriebssysteme funktionieren mit 100 % Solarenergie.
- Die Antriebssysteme erlauben den Mitfahrenden, mit einer App die Geschwindigkeit zu steuern.

65a Kurioses aus Liechtenstein. In MACHEN haben Sie Daten und Fakten über Liechtenstein recherchiert. Hier lesen Sie sechs ungewöhnliche Informationen über den viertkleinsten Staat Europas.

1) Liechtenstein hat weder Autobahnen noch einen eigenen Flughafen.

2) Das allgemeine Frauenwahlrecht gibt es in Liechtenstein erst seit 1984.

3) Mehr als fünfzig Prozent aller Erwerbstätigen (also Menschen, die eine Arbeit haben) sind Pendler*innen. Sie wohnen nicht in Liechtenstein, arbeiten aber dort.

4) Liechtenstein ist das einzige Land, das vollständig in den Alpen liegt. Mehr noch, es besteht zu 70 % aus Bergen!

5) Seit 2014 werden keine Babys mehr in Liechtenstein geboren – zumindest nicht offiziell im Krankenhaus. In diesem Jahr wurde die Geburtsstation im Landesspital Vaduz geschlossen. Seitdem kommen die meisten Liechtensteiner Babys in Grabs in der Schweiz zur Welt.

6) Für ein Musikvideo wollte der Rapper Snoop Dogg 2010 ganz Liechtenstein mieten. Nein, nicht nur einen besonderen Ort in Liechtenstein – das komplette Land! Am Ende kam es aber nicht dazu. Snoop Doggs Management gab der Regierung von Liechtenstein nicht genug Zeit, um diese ungewöhnliche Bitte zu realisieren.

Ich finde Info Nr. _____ besonders lustig, weil ______________________________

____

Ich finde Info Nr. _____ besonders überraschend, weil ______________________________

____

Ich finde Info Nr. _____ besonders verrückt, weil ______________________________

____

65b **Liechtenstein: Wussten Sie das schon? Setzen Sie die Hilfsverben für das Perfekt (haben, sein), Plusquamperfekt (hatten, waren) und den Konjunktiv II der Vergangenheit (hätten, wären) ein. Achten Sie auf die Konjugation.**

hat | hatte | hätte

Bevor Liechtenstein von 1815 bis 1866 zum Deutschen Bund gehhört _hat_, _hatte_ es im Mittelalter zum Heiligen Römischen Reich gehört. Wenn Österreich den Ersten Weltkrieg gewonnen hätte, _hätte_ es zu Österreich gehört.

hatten | haben | hätten

Bis 1984 __________ die Liechtensteiner Frauen kein Wahlrecht gehabt. Zwischen 1971 und 1983 __________ sie das kommunale Wahlrecht (in den Städten) gehabt. Aber die Liechtensteinerinnen __________ das Wahlrecht gerne schon viel früher gehabt.

wäre | war | hätte | ist

Nachdem Vaduz schon 1175 eine kleine Stadt geworden __________, __________ sie zwischen 1342 und 1500 eine Grafschaft (*earldom*) geworden. Wenn Liechtenstein eine größere Hauptstadt gewollt __________, __________ die Stadt Schaan die Hauptstadt geworden.

hatte | wäre | hat | hätte

Bevor es im Mittelalter in Liechtenstein mehrere Burgen gegeben __________, __________ es dort antike römische Villen gegeben. Wenn Liechtenstein reicher gewesen __________, __________ es dort auch Barockpaläste gegeben.

ist | wäre | war

Nachdem Liechtenstein im Ersten Weltkrieg neutral geblieben __________, __________ es auch im Zweiten Weltkrieg neutral geblieben. Es __________ gerne auch im Deutschen Bund neutral geblieben.

70f **Achterbahnen: Ein Faktencheck. Ergänzen Sie die richtigen Adjektivendungen – und lernen Sie nebenbei noch mehr über Achterbahnen.**

Eine Achterbahn ist ein beliebt______ Fahrgeschäft auf einer Kirmes oder in einem Vergnügungspark. Bei einer Achterbahn fahren mehrere Wagen auf Schienen. Die Wagen können bei manchen Achterbahnen unter den metallen_____ Schienen hängen. Die Schienen sind auf einem Gerüst befestigt. Die Gerüste können verschieden hoch sein. Manche Achterbahnen haben auch krass_______ Loopings oder Schrauben.

Schon im 17. Jahrhundert gab es in Russland im kalt______ Winter Bahnen, die man zum Spaß benutzte. Sie hatten aber keine Schienen, sondern eine vereist______ Bahn, auf der die Menschen mit „Schlitten" aus Eisblöcken heruntergerutscht sind. Darum waren das noch keine richtig_______ Achterbahnen. Später, im 19. Jahrhundert, gab es in Frankreich die erst_______ Achterbahnen. In Paris gab es 1817 zwei Achterbahnen aus Holz. Erst viel später entstanden die schnell_______ Stahlachterbahnen, wie man sie heute kennt.

Die höchst______ Achterbahn der Welt ist „Kingda Ka" mit 139 Metern und sie steht in den USA. Die längst______ Achterbahn ist „Steel Dragon 2000" in Japan. Sie ist 2.479 Meter lang. Die schnellst______ Achterbahn der Welt ist die „Formula Rossa" in den Vereinigten Arabischen Emiraten. Die Wagen fahren mit einer unglaublich______ Geschwindigkeit von 240 Kilometern pro Stunde.

Quelle: Klexikon (vereinfacht)

70g **Und Sie? Sie kennen nun acht verschiedene Arten von Achterbahnen und können auch unterschiedliche Stationen und Elemente einer Achterbahnfahrt benennen (siehe Aktivität 70e). Beantworten Sie die folgenden Fragen in jeweils 2–3 Sätzen.**

Mit welchem Typ von Achterbahn würden Sie gerne fahren? Warum?

____

____

Was glauben Sie, welcher Typ von Achterbahn würde Ihnen keinen Spaß machen? Warum?

____

____

Welche Station oder welches Element einer Achterbahnfahrt gefällt Ihnen am besten? Warum?

____

____

Welche Station oder welches Element mögen Sie nicht so gerne? Warum?

____

____

70h  **Verstanden? Meral erzählt ihrer Freundin Sina am Telefon von ihrem Besuch im Freizeitpark. Hören Sie gut zu und kreuzen Sie die richtigen Antworten an.**

Warum ist Meral dreimal mit der Achterbahn „Blue Fire" gefahren?

- Es gab wenige Leute im Park und man musste bei „Blue Fire" nicht in der Schlange warten.
- „Blue Fire" ist eine schnelle Achterbahn und Meral mag schnelle Achterbahnen am liebsten.
- Es war Merals Geburtstag und bei „Blue Fire" darf man am Geburtstag kostenlos fahren.

Warum ist Meral nicht mit der Wasserachterbahn „Poseidon" gefahren?

- Es war an dem Tag sehr kalt und sie hatte Angst, nass zu werden.
- Sie wollte lieber ein Stück von Shakespeare im Globe Theatre anschauen.
- Die Leute mussten für „Poseidon" zu lange in der Sonne warten.

Welchen Park möchte Sina gerne besuchen und warum?

- Sie möchte gerne Disneyworld in Florida besuchen, weil sie ein großer Disney-Fan ist.
- Sie möchte gern den Europa-Park besuchen, weil ihr Bruder in Freiburg studiert.
- Sie möchte gern Six Flags in New Jersey besuchen, weil sie dort auch ihre Cousine besuchen könnte.

72b **Ein Brief an die Parkleitung. In MACHEN haben Sie mit den anderen Kursteilnehmer*innen darüber gesprochen, wie ein Park für alle aussehen könnte oder sollte. Stellen Sie sich vor, Sie schreiben einen Brief an die Leitung von Ihrem Lieblingspark. Sagen Sie, was der Park besser machen könnte, um für alle zugänglicher zu sein. Seien Sie dabei höflich.**

Beispiele: Ich denke, das könnte man besser machen. / Sie könnten zum Beispiel … / Wäre es möglich, dass … ?

Sehr geehrte Parkleitung,

Mit freundlichen Grüßen

72c  **Reflektieren: In MACHEN, you learned and talked about ideas to make parks more accessible for all people. Reflect on how parks define accessibility. What accommodations are being made? What is missing? Reflect on your visits to theme parks: Do you get the sense that designers think about matters of representation and consider the accessibility of their parks and specific rides in the design process? Or does it seem like representation and accessibility has always been an afterthought? Why do you think that? Give specific examples. If you have never thought about questions of representation and accessibility while visiting a theme park, think about the reasons why. Do you want to pay attention next time? Why (not)?**

22: Geprüfte Sicherheit°

73d **Lesen Sie die Sätze und schreiben Sie die Wahrscheinlichkeiten und Häufigkeiten in Kurzform wie im Beispiel.**

In den großen Parks gibt es ca. 300 Millionen Besucher*innen pro Jahr.

*300 Millionen Besucher*innen/Jahr*

In Freizeitparks in den USA gibt es pro Jahr ca. 4.400 Verletzungen.

___

Die Wahrscheinlichkeit für einen Unfall in einem Freizeitpark ist eins zu fünfundsiebzigtausend.

___

Der Europa-Park hat ca. 14.000 Besucher*innen pro Tag.

___

Die Wahrscheinlichkeit, im Europa-Park mit einer Holzachterbahn zu fahren, ist eins zu fünfzehn.

___

76b **Verstanden? Die durcheinandergeratene Checkliste. Unten sehen Sie eine TÜV-Checkliste für eine Achterbahn. Aber die Schritte sind nicht in der richtigen Reihenfolge. Hören Sie zu und nummerieren Sie die Schritte.**

___ Die Haltebügel kontrollieren.

___ Alle Schrauben festziehen.

___ Elektronische Systeme überprüfen.

___ Kaputte Teile austauschen.

___ Die Kette vom Aufzug ölen.

1 Den Bauplan genau studieren.

23: Hobbys und Berufe für Adrenalin-Junkies

80a **Verstanden? Hören Sie die Informationen zu David Lamas Biografie und kreuzen Sie die richtigen Antworten an.**

Wo und wann wurde David Lama geboren?

- am 14.03.1990 in St. Gallen
- am 04.09.1990 in Regensburg
- am 04.08.1990 in Innsbruck

Woher kommen seine Eltern?

- aus Österreich und Nepal
- aus der Schweiz und Thailand
- aus Frankreich und der Türkei

Was war David Lama von Beruf?

- David Lama war ein renommierter Alpin-Ökologe.
- David Lama arbeitete als Bergführer in Nepal.
- David Lama war ein erfolgreicher Sportkletterer.

Was waren Highlights seiner Karriere?

- Er begann das Klettern mit 5 Jahren und gewann schon mit 9 Jahren den Junior-Cup.
- 2019 kletterte er ohne Begleitung auf den Lunag Ri in Nepal.
- Er begann zu klettern, bevor er zu sprechen begann.

Wie ist David Lama gestorben?

- Er starb an einer chronischen Lungenkrankheit.
- Er wurde mit zwei anderen Kletterern von einer Lawine überrascht.
- Er starb bei einem Skiunfall im Banff National Park.

80b **Steh auf und flieg. In Aktivität 80c sehen Sie einen Auszug aus einem Interview mit der Extremsportlerin Susanne Böhme. Sie erzählt von ihrem schweren Unfall, wie sich ihr Leben verändert hat, und warum sie den Extremsport nicht aufgegeben hat. Bevor Sie den Text lesen, schlagen Sie die englische Bedeutung für die folgenden Wörter online nach.**

auskommen	______________	der Fallschirm	______________
der Felsen	______________	gestalten	______________
die Kante	______________		
die Krücke	______________		
querschnittgelähmt	______________		
jemandem etwas raten	______________		
die Vorstellung	______________		
sich auf etwas einlassen	______________		
der Sprung	______________		

Susanne Böhmes erster Sprung nach dem Unfall (2013)

80c **Lesen Sie nun den Text und beantworten Sie dann die Fragen.**

Susanne Böhme hat sich beim Basejumpen schwer verletzt. Sie ist querschnittgelähmt. Im Interview spricht sie darüber, warum sie trotzdem noch aus Flugzeugen springt und was sie ihrem Sohn rät, wenn er eines Tages basejumpen will.

Sie sind Ende 2012 beim Basejumpen mit einem Felsen kollidiert und seitdem querschnittgelähmt. Im Sommer sind Sie zum ersten Mal wieder mit einem Wingsuit aus dem Flugzeug gesprungen. Ist Ihnen eine Katastrophe nicht genug?
Aus einem Flugzeug zu springen, ist viel ungefährlicher als von Felsen, Brücken oder Gebäuden, wie man es beim Basejumpen macht. Das Risiko, das ich jetzt eingehe, ist ungefähr so hoch wie beim Motorradfahren. Das kann man auch kritisch sehen. Aber es ist nicht mein Lebensziel, es jedem recht zu machen. Niemand wird damit glücklich, das eigene Leben nach den Vorstellungen anderer Leute zu gestalten.

Vor Ihrem Unfall wollten Sie mit dem Basejumpen eigentlich schon aufhören.
Ja, weil ich eine Familie gründen wollte, was wir dann nach meiner Verletzung auch gemacht haben. Das hätte für mich nicht zusammengepasst. Jetzt habe ich ein Kind und weiß, dass mir das Basejumpen nicht mehr das Gleiche geben würde. Ich könnte nicht mehr mit freiem Kopf an der Kante stehen, wenn zu Hause mein Kind sitzt.

Sie haben im Krankenhaus Mentaltraining gemacht, sich also vorgestellt, dass Sie Ihre Beine bewegen. Wie kommt man darauf?
In unserem Sport hat man so verdammt wenig richtige Trainingszeit. An einem guten Tag kommt man vielleicht auf fünf bis zehn Sprünge, da hat man zehn Minuten Trainingszeit. Das reicht nicht. Deswegen haben wir uns sehr viel mit mentalem Training beschäftigt, das hilft wirklich enorm. Inzwischen gibt es sogar eine Studie, die zeigt, dass mentales Training essentiell ist. Ich kann heute mit Krücken wieder ganz gut laufen. Wenn man sich das Laufen nicht mal vorstellt, verlernt man es ganz.

Wie sieht Ihr Alltag heute aus?
Ich arbeite weiter in meiner eigenen Werkstatt als Fallschirmtechnikerin, früher war ich auch Fallschirmlehrerin. Wenn es sein muss, komme ich den ganzen Tag ohne Rollstuhl aus. Alles geht langsamer, aber es geht. Und ich feiere jeden kleinen Schritt: zum ersten Mal an ein hohes Regal kommen, zum ersten Mal den Rollstuhl in den Kofferraum packen und bis zum Fahrersitz laufen. Das sind Höhepunkte, die wahnsinnig viel Lebensqualität bringen. Mein Ziel ist es, nächstes Jahr nur noch einen Wanderstock zu brauchen.

Sie haben 2014 einen Sohn bekommen. Wenn er eines Tages basejumpen will: Was sagen Sie?
Tja. Ich kann es ihm schlecht verbieten. Er sagt schon: ‚Mama, ich auch hop, hop.' Aber ich will ihn so erziehen, dass er sich viele Gedanken darüber macht, sich das richtige Equipment holt und auch weiß, auf was er sich einlässt. Aber das brauche ich ihm nicht groß zu erklären. Das sieht er ja jeden Tag.

Quelle: faz.net (gekürzt und vereinfacht)

Susanne Böhme ist querschnittgelähmt, weil

- sie mit einem Fallschirm aus einem Flugzeug gesprungen ist.
- sie beim Basejumpen einen schweren Unfall hatte.

Basejumping ist gefährlicher als ein Sprung aus einem Flugzeug,

- sagt sie.
- sagt sie nicht.

Sie macht jetzt kein Basejumping mehr, weil

- sie nach ihrem Unfall Angst davor hat.
- sie ein Kind hat.

Susanne Böhme kann

- nichts ohne den Rollstuhl machen.
- mit ein wenig Hilfe schon wieder relativ gut laufen.

Böhme im Wingsuit mit Rollstuhl

Wenn ihr Sohn eines Tages auch Basejumping machen möchte,

- erlaubt sie es ihm, wenn er gut vorbereitet ist.
- wird sie es ihm verbieten.

Beantworten Sie die folgenden Fragen in 1–2 Sätzen.

Womit vergleicht Susanne Böhme das Risiko, das man eingeht, wenn man mit einem Wingsuit aus einem Flugzeug springt?

____

____

____

Was für eine Therapie hat ihr dabei geholfen, wieder laufen zu lernen?

____

____

____

Wie mobil ist Susanne Böhme jetzt?

____

____

____

24: Angst – Psyche und Körper

82f **Reflektieren Option A: In LERNEN, you heard a text about the processes in our body that occur when we are anxious, scared, or frightened. Reflect now on what it means when such fears and anxieties become chronic and permanent. What are the consequences of living in a state of permanent fear and anxiety? Also, how do you explain the fact that more and more people suffer from chronic forms of fear and anxiety?**

Reflektieren Option B: Sometimes people don't want to admit their fears and anxieties. Reflect on why people might want to downplay these emotions. What societal pressures force people to be "fearless"?

82g **Wie würden Sie reagieren? Wählen Sie ein passendes Verb und beenden Sie den Satz.**

küssen | schenken | fliegen | geben | organisieren | ~~gewinnen~~

Wenn ich in der Lotterie *gewinnen würde, würde ich eine Weltreise machen.*

Wenn man mir ein Haus in der Karibik ______________________.

Wenn ich wie ein Vogel ______________________.

Wenn meine Familie mir eine Überraschungsparty ______________________.

Wenn du mich ______________________.

Wenn ihr mir einen Job ______________________.

84a **Verstanden? Welche Ausreden hat Nick, um nicht mit den unterschiedlichen Fahrgeschäften zu fahren? Hören Sie gut zu und kreuzen Sie die richtigen Antworten an.**

Warum möchte Nick nicht mit der Holzachterbahn fahren?

- Nick findet Holzachterbahnen zu instabil.
- Nick findet Holzachterbahnen zu laut.
- Nick findet Holzachterbahnen nicht umweltfreundlich.

Warum möchte Nick nicht mit der Geisterbahn fahren?

- Nick möchte nicht mit der Geisterbahn fahren, weil er Angst im Dunkeln hat.
- Nick möchte nicht mit der Geisterbahn fahren, weil diese zu viel Geld kostet.
- Nick möchte nicht mit der Geisterbahn fahren, weil man dort zu lange warten muss.

Warum möchte Nick nicht mit dem Wasser-Rafting fahren?

- Nick hat Angst, dass sein neues T-Shirt nass wird.
- Das Wasser-Rafting wird neu gebaut und ist heute geschlossen.
- Das Wasser-Rafting ist für jüngere Kinder gedacht und Nick fühlt sich zu alt.

25: Das Leben ist eine Achterbahn

85c **Was würdest du machen, wenn ... ?**

Was würdest du machen, wenn du morgen einen freien Tag hättest?

Dann würde ich endlich mal auf die Kirmes gehen.

Was würdest du machen, wenn ein Zirkus in die Stadt kommen würde?

____

Was würdest du sagen, wenn der Zirkusdirektor dir einen Job anbieten würde?

____

Was würdest du machen, wenn man neben deinem Haus einen Freizeitpark bauen würde?

____

Was würdest du denken, wenn deine Freundin deine SMS nicht mehr beantworten würde?

____

Was würdest du machen, wenn du im Lotto gewonnen hättest?

____

Was würdest du machen, wenn du Angst vor dem Achterbahnfahren hättest?

____

Was würdest du machen, damit dein*e Professor*in nicht merkt, dass du die Grammatikregeln nicht gelernt hast?

____

88b **Verstanden? Sie hören nun einen weiteren Teil des Interviews mit Karl Völker[1] aus MACHEN. Hören Sie gut zu und füllen Sie die Lücken aus. Beantworten Sie dann die Fragen auf der nächsten Seite.**

DFK: Was war eigentlich das ____________ für Sie in der Zeit? Die Armut, die ____________, die Obdachlosigkeit oder einer von denen zu sein, die einfach nicht mehr dazugehören zu der Welt, zu der Sie vorher gehörten?

Völker: Ich glaube, das war eine ____________ aus diesen drei Punkten. Es tut natürlich unheimlich weh, dass man auf einmal nicht mehr dabei ist. Vor allen Dingen, dass man nicht mehr die Sachen machen kann, die man gern gemacht hat, wie zum Beispiel, ein ____________ ____________ ______ ____________, das man sich dann eben nicht mehr kaufen kann; oder eine gute Zeitung zu lesen, die man sich dann ____________ ____________ kann in dem Augenblick. Es liegt natürlich auch daran, zu dieser „Gruppe der Obdachlosen" zu gehören, obwohl sie absolut nicht ____________ ist. Das ist jetzt nicht so, wie das viele Leute im Kopf haben. Der alte Mann, der einen Einkaufswagen durch die Gegend schiebt – das ist nur ein ____________ der Obdachlosen. Der größte Teil ist nicht ____________. Die sind einfach ganz unauffällig. Das war natürlich ganz schlimm, und vor allen Dingen hat mir einfach ein ____________ gefehlt, ein Schutzraum, ein Ort, wo man sich zurückziehen kann. Man hat überhaupt keine ____________, wenn man auf der Straße lebt.

Quelle: Deutschlandfunk Kultur (vereinfacht) [1] Name von der Redaktion geändert.

Fragen:

Was konnte sich Karl Völker nicht mehr leisten, als er obdachlos war?

____

____

Wie beschreibt Karl Völker die „Gruppe der Obdachlosen"?

____

____

Was hat Karl Völker am meisten gefehlt? Warum ist so ein Ort wichtig?

____

____

88c **Den Burnout verhindern! Was könnte man machen?**

Dies sind die häufigsten Ursachen eines Burnouts:

zu viel bürokratische Arbeit
zu viele Arbeitsstunden
Mangel an Respekt
das Gefühl, nutzlos zu sein
die Firma nimmt den Profit wichtiger als die Kund*innen
keinen Respekt von den Kund*innen zu bekommen
zu wenig zu verdienen
wenig selbst entscheiden zu können

Mitarbeiter*innen mit Burnout machen weniger und schlechtere Arbeit als erholte. Was können Sie als gute*r Manager*in machen, damit Ihre Mitarbeiter*innen durch die Ursachen oben keinen Burnout bekommen?

____

____

____

____

88d **Burnout im Vergleich: Mehr als zweimal so viele Ärzt*innen sind in den USA burned-out als in der BRD.**

Eine Umfrage unter deutschen und amerikanischen Ärzt*innen hat gezeigt:

	USA	**BRD**
burned-out	27%	12%
zu viel Bürokratie	56%	52%
keine Autonomie	22%	10%
zunehmende Computerisierung	25%	18%
Mehr bezahlter Urlaub würde helfen.	22%	16%
Ich suche keine professionelle Hilfe, weil ich Angst habe, man hört davon.	18%	10%
Ich besuche eine*n Therapeut*in als Hilfe.	27%	46%
Mein religiöser Glaube hilft mir.	69%	52%
Ich habe 5 bis 6 Wochen Urlaub.	12%	40%

Quelle: medscape.com

Welche Probleme präsentiert die Statistik? Haben Sie Ideen für Lösungen? Beschreiben Sie das Problem und eine mögliche Lösung, wie in dem Beispiel. Wählen Sie vier Punkte aus der Statistik.

Beispiel:
Wenig Urlaub ist nicht gut für die Gesundheit. Man sollte den amerikanischen Ärzt*innen mehr Urlaubstage geben.

26: Projekt 2 – Ein Exposé°

89a **Erzähl mal: Nehmen Sie ein kurzes Video auf (z. B. mit Ihrem Handy oder am Computer) und beantworten Sie die Fragen.**

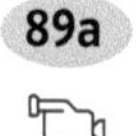

Mögen Sie Freizeitparks? Warum (nicht)?
Falls Sie Freizeitparks mögen: Was sind Ihre Lieblingsattraktionen/-achterbahnen?

Wie finden Sie extreme Hobbys und Sportarten? Was würden Sie machen? Was würden Sie nicht machen? Haben Sie Kriterien? (z. B.: Ich würde xyz machen, wenn …)

Was würden Sie jetzt machen, wenn Sie nicht an den Hausaufgaben arbeiten würden?

Denken Sie an das letzte Jahr: Gibt es etwas, das Sie gerne anders gemacht hätten? Warum? (z. B.: Ich hätte gern öfter mit meiner Familie telefoniert, weil ich sie vermisse.)

89b Self-Assessment

You now get a chance to reflect on the many things you have learned throughout the chapter. Carefully read through the "Can-Do Statements" below, and ask yourself if you can perform all of these tasks. It might be helpful for each of the statements to actually practice the communicative scenario. Once you are confident that you are able to perform a task, check the respective box on the left side.

- I can ask and answers questions about personal preferences, such as preferred rides and attractions in theme parks.
- I can give a presentation about the design of different theme park rides.
- I can read and understand the main plot elements of a fictional crime story.
- I can critically reflect on how fictional stories employ stereotypes in their depictions of different cultures.
- I can use my language to research information necessary to plan a trip to Germany.
- I can express how I would react in a scary situation and have a simple conversation about things one can be afraid of.
- I can ask and answer questions about the representation of different cultures in theme parks around the world and reflect critically about cultural stereotypes inherent in such *Themenwelten*.
- I can collect arguments for and against the expansion of theme parks, including hypothetical observations about the impact such expansions would have on neighboring communities.
- I can express the ups and downs of my life and state what I could have done differently.
- I can formulate polite requests within the context of debates about the environmental impact of theme parks.
- I can understand a simple recording of a person's biography and bring statements about the person's life into the correct order.
- I can understand the main points presented in non-fictional texts about topics such as accidents in theme parks.
- I can make comments of (dis)approval and suggestions using the subjunctive II mood with regular and modal verbs.
- I can express irreal wishes using the *Wenn … doch/nur* and *Hätte … doch* subjunctive II structures.
- I can talk about hypothetical situations in the past using the subjunctive II mood in the past tense.
- I can comfortably use adjective endings across cases and in their base (positive), comparative, and superlative forms.
- I can form conditional sentences with *wenn* in the subjunctive II mood.

- I am familiar with *Schaustellerei* as a profession, as well as the pros and cons of such a lifestyle.
- I am familiar with the historical roots, facts and figures, and traditional customs of *Oktoberfest* in Munich and can critically reflect on the cultural stereotypes implicit to *Oktoberfest* culture.
- I am familiar with the history and physics of roller coasters.
- I am familiar with the accessibility of German theme parks and how they could be improved to make parks more accessible.
- I am familiar with the country of Liechtenstein: its history, culture, and economy.

Wie wird das gemacht?

Die Schweiz als Herstellerin von Qualitätsprodukten

27: (PRODUKT-)GEOGRAFIE DER SCHWEIZ°

92a **Verstanden? Die Geschichte des Schweizer Taschenmessers. Hören Sie gut zu und ergänzen Sie die fehlenden Informationen.**

hergestellt | Sackmesser | unterscheidet | Outdoor-Aktivitäten | achtzig | gekauft | Wandern | Offiziersmesser | Werkzeuge | Taschenmesser | Schere

Das Schweizer Taschenmesser ist eines der bekanntesten ______________________ weltweit. Es wird manchmal Schweizer ______________________ oder auch ______________________ genannt. Ein Schweizer Taschenmesser ______________________ sich von anderen Taschenmessern, weil es nicht nur eine Klinge, also das Messer, hat. Es enthält auch andere ______________________: zum Beispiel einen Flaschenöffner, eine ______________________ und viele andere Dinge. Das Schweizer Taschenmesser mit den meisten Elementen hat über ______________________ unterschiedliche Werkzeuge. Die Menschen benutzen ihr Schweizer Taschenmesser oft für ______________________ wie Campen oder ______________________. Das Schweizer Taschenmesser im Original wurde von den Firmen Victorinox und Wenger ______________________. Im Jahr 2005 hat Victorinox die Firma Wenger ______________________.

92b **Verstanden? Aus welchen Kantonen kommen diese Erfindungen? Und in welchem Teil der Schweiz liegt der Kanton? Hören Sie gut zu und notieren Sie die Informationen.**

Erfindung	Kanton	Lage
Helvetica Schrift		
Alufolie		
Toblerone		
Mineralwasser mit Kohlensäure		

28: GESCHICHTE(N) DER SCHWEIZ

94e **Meilensteine. In MACHEN haben Sie Meilensteine in der Geschichte der Schweiz kennengelernt. Formulieren Sie nun vier Meilensteine in der Geschichte <u>Ihres Landes</u>. Beschreiben Sie die Meilensteine in wenigen Stichworten.**

Beispiele (für Deutschland): 1918 Frauenwahlrecht, 1990 Wiedervereinigung Ost- und Westdeutschland

Mein Land: ______________________

Jahr	Meilenstein

Reflektieren: The "Tell" story is an important part of Swiss national identity. Are there any such stories in your country that play an important role in people's understanding of their and the country's identity?

 Kulturpunkt: Schweizer Banken

"Hold on a second: Why is Switzerland …

kind of like the Cayman Islands?" The short answer is because of the Swiss banks and bank secrecy that allowed people to avoid paying taxes. But it is more complicated than that, so let's start at the beginning; with the Swiss banking system.

The Swiss banking industry has a great reputation worldwide largely due to the political and economic stability of the small country. Its main focus is wealth management, and its strategies build on conservative investment. About 6% of all employees within Switzerland work for the banking industry. The whole financial sector of Switzerland (this includes insurance companies) contributes more than 10% of its gross value, which is a share of well above 5% of Switzerland's GDP. Banks might therefore be up there with chocolate, clocks, and cheese when it comes to Swiss quality (products).

The famous Swiss banking secrecy dates back to the early 1700s. It was written into federal law in 1934. Since then, there have been a few scandals related to banking secrecy that led to its abolishment as we knew it in 2018. The main impetus for changing the law was that Switzerland wanted to get rid of its reputation as a paradise for tax evasion. With the amendment, Switzerland automatically exchanges finance data with other countries (among them all EU member states and the United States). This change will certainly have an impact on quite a few celebrities in the German-speaking countries who have Cayman-style accounts, which are anonymous. In German, these anonymous accounts are called *Nummernkonto* because the name of the owner is hidden and the account is only identified by a number. Before this amendment, people could hide their assets, which has now become impossible.

Nummernkonto accounts weren't just convenient for rich people trying to hide their assets, but also for other criminal activities such as money laundering. Criminals and dictators also used Swiss banking secrecy to keep their shady business running. Nazis, in fact, hid stolen gold, money, and art in Switzerland. Nazis as well as their victims used Swiss banks. As a neighbor to Germany and Austria, Switzerland and its neutrality led many Jews fleeing the Holocaust to deposit money and valuables in Swiss accounts. Survivors or the heirs of victims often had a difficult time recovering their money after the war. Many of these accounts lay dormant without anyone being able to claim their family's money. In the 1990s, this issue was brought to global attention. Eventually, the World Jewish Congress worked together with Swiss banks to identify accounts of victims of the Nazis. In this process, more than 50,000 accounts were found that had probably belonged to Jewish victims of the Holocaust, all in all about 35 million Swiss Francs. Swiss bankers settled a class-action lawsuit in the United States in 1998 for more than $1.25 billion for the victims and their heirs.

While the scandal surrounding the role of Swiss banks during the Holocaust may have discredited the banks, it did not move Swiss banking from its global top spot. It is too early to say how the new law will impact Switzerland's financial sector. Politically, it will likely strengthen its reputation.

Reflektieren: Write about the questions below.

- Did you know anything about Swiss banks?
- What did you know, and how did you know about it?
- Do you think the new law will significantly change the Swiss banking industry? And if so, for the better or for the worse? If not, why not?
- Why do you think the Swiss were able to keep this industry of anonymous bank accounts going for so long?

29: Globales Genf – Auf der Suche nach Fortschritt

97c **Viele Grüße aus Genf! Sie verbringen ein langes Wochenende in Genf und schreiben eine Postkarte an Ihre Familie oder an Freund*innen. Verwenden Sie Informationen aus Ihrer Präsentation über den perfekten Tag in Genf. Was haben Sie schon gemacht und gesehen? Wie war das Wetter bisher? Schreiben Sie die Karte im Perfekt.**

Hallo ______________________,

Liebe Grüße

____

97d **Verstanden? Hören Sie zu und beantworten Sie die Fragen über das Museum für moderne und zeitgenössische Kunst (MAMCO) in Genf.**

Wann wurde das MAMCO eröffnet?

- Das MAMCO wurde schon 1973 eröffnet und ist seitdem sehr beliebt.
- Die Planung für das MAMCO begann 1973, aber eröffnet wurde das Museum erst 1994.
- Das Museum wurde 1999 eröffnet.

Warum ist die Zahl 21 signifikant für die Geschichte des MAMCO? (2 richtige Antworten)

- Das Museum wurde erst 21 Jahre nach Beginn der Planung eröffnet.
- Die Exponate sind auf drei Stockwerken mit insgesamt 21 Räumen chronologisch ausgestellt.
- Der erste Direktor des Museums war 21 Jahre der Leiter des Museums.

Wie sind die Stockwerke im Museum angeordnet?

- Es gibt drei Stockwerke und jedes ist chronologisch einem Jahrzehnt gewidmet (1980er, 1990er, 2000er).
- Die Stockwerke beginnen unten mit der Gegenwart und enden im dritten Stock mit den 1960/1970ern.
- Auf allen Stockwerken ist die Kunst thematisch geordnet und es gibt Werke von 1960–2000.

98f **In der Genfer Innenstadt. Beantworten Sie die Fragen.**

Auf der Pont de la Machine fangen Amateurfischer*innen Fische.

Was ist das Subjekt im Aktivsatz? Amateurfischer*innen ⇒ Wir eliminieren dieses Subjekt im Passivsatz.

Was ist das Akkusativobjekt? Fische

Was ist das Partizip vom Verb? gefangen

Was ist der neue Passivsatz? Auf der Pont de la Machine werden Fische gefangen.

Zwei Architekten aus Zürich bauen ein neues Museum in Genf.

Was ist das Subjekt im Aktivsatz? ________ ⇒ Wir eliminieren dieses Subjekt im Passivsatz.

Was ist das Akkusativobjekt? ________

Was ist das Partizip vom Verb? ________

Was ist der neue Passivsatz? ________

35.000 Menschen feiern LGBTQ+-Rechte in der Geneva Pride Parade.

Was ist das Subjekt im Aktivsatz? ________ ⇒ Wir eliminieren dieses Subjekt im Passivsatz.

Was ist das Akkusativobjekt? ________

Was ist das Partizip vom Verb? ________

Was ist der neue Passivsatz? ________

Circa 1.800 Sportler*innen laufen jeden Mai den Genf-Marathon.

Was ist das Subjekt im Aktivsatz? ________ ⇒ Wir eliminieren dieses Subjekt im Passivsatz.

Was ist das Akkusativobjekt? ________

Was ist das Partizip vom Verb? ________

Was ist der neue Passivsatz? ________

98g **Was machen Suzette und Nikita im Genfer Umland? Schreiben Sie die Sätze vom Aktiv ins Passiv oder vom Passiv ins Aktiv um.**

Aktiv:	**Passiv:**
Sie rudern ein Boot auf dem Genfer See.	Ein Boot wird auf dem Genfer See gerudert.
________	Die französische Stadt Annecy wird fotografiert.
Sie sehen das Schloss Bellerive.	________
Sie nehmen den Panorama-Express nach Gruyères.	________
________	Die Städte Lausanne und Montreux werden besucht.
Sie erleben den Mont Blanc (den höchsten Alpenberg).	________

In den Alpen

Schwan am Genfersee-Damm, Lausanne

99a **In MACHEN haben Sie Fabiola Gianotti, die Generaldirektorin von CERN, kennengelernt. Schauen Sie sich nun die Statistik „Frauen und Männer in der akademischen Laufbahn in der Schweiz und in Europa" an und beschreiben Sie sie.**

Frauen und Männer in der akademischen Laufbahn, in der Schweiz und in Europa (EU-28), 2016

In % am Total jedes Abschnitts

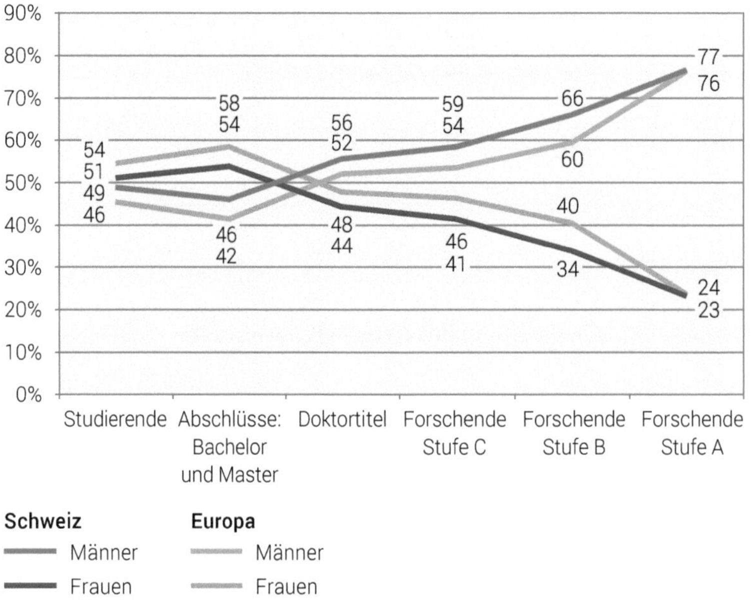

90%
80%
70%
60%
50%
40%
30%
20%
10%
0%

Studierende: 54, 51, 49, 46
Abschlüsse: Bachelor und Master: 58, 54, 46, 42
Doktortitel: 56, 52, 48, 44
Forschende Stufe C: 59, 54, 46, 41
Forschende Stufe B: 66, 60, 40, 34
Forschende Stufe A: 77, 76, 24, 23

Schweiz
Männer
Frauen

Europa
Männer
Frauen

Quellen: BFS – SIUS, Forschung und Entwicklung (F+E) in den Hochschulen; Europäische Kommission – She Figures 2018

Beispiele:

In Europa werden 76 % aller Forschungsjobs in der Stufe A[1] von Männern und nur 24 % von Frauen besetzt.
In der Schweiz werden 45 % aller Studienplätze an Männer vergeben.

[1] Stufe A = die höchste Forschungsposition in der Schweiz

99b **Schauen Sie sich noch einmal die Statistik aus Aktivität 99a an. Welche Trends können Sie sehen? In welchen Teilen der akademischen Karriere werden Frauen am meisten benachteiligt? Finden Sie online ähnliche Statistiken für Ihr Land oder Ihren Bundesstaat. Sind die Ergebnisse ähnlich? Wo gibt es Unterschiede?**

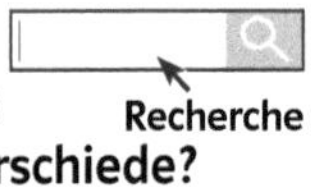

Recherche

30: Wie werden Schweizer Uhren hergestellt?°

100a **Reflektieren: How is your attitude towards time shaped by both technology (cell phones, computers) but also social media and the speed of the world we live in? Do you think that these technologies have had a positive or negative impact on how we use and experience time?**

101a **Die Schweizer Uhrenindustrie. Lesen Sie die Sätze und beantworten Sie die Fragen.**

Zum Zeitmessen braucht man eine Uhr.

Was ist das Akkusativobjekt? *eine Uhr* Was ist das Partizip vom Verb? *gebraucht*

Passivsatz: *Zum Zeitmessen wird eine Uhr gebraucht.*

Man baut Uhren meistens aus Stahl.

Was ist das Akkusativobjekt? ______ Was ist das Partizip vom Verb? ______

Passivsatz: ______

Man misst die kürzeste Zeit in Nanosekunden.

Was ist das Akkusativobjekt? ______ Was ist das Partizip vom Verb? ______

Passivsatz: ______

Für eine akkurate Zeitinformation braucht man den Sekundenzeiger.

Was ist das Akkusativobjekt? ______ Was ist das Partizip vom Verb? ______

Passivsatz: ______

101b **Was habe ich gelernt? Schauen Sie sich in MACHEN noch einmal die Aktivitäten 100, 101 und 102 an. Schreiben Sie nun vier Sätze zum Thema „(Schweizer) Uhren und Zeit". Benutzen Sie mindestens dreimal das Passiv.**

In der Schweiz werden Qualitätsuhren hergestellt. oder *In der Schweiz produziert man Qualitätsuhren.*

______

______

______

______

101c **Reflektieren: Wie nachhaltig ist das Herstellen von Uhren? WWF Schweiz untersuchte 2018 die Goldbeschaffung (*sourcing of gold*) der Schweizer Uhrenhersteller. Nur wenige Uhrenproduzent*innen publizieren ihre Beschaffung von Gold. Jetzt soll dies geändert und besser kontrolliert werden. Das Ziel ist „fairmined" Gold. Einige Uhren- und Schmuckhersteller möchten 100 % nachhaltig mit Recycled Gold produzieren. Unter www.klett-usa.com/impuls2links finden Sie den Link zu dieser Übung. Welche Schweizer Uhrenhersteller werden am schlechtesten platziert? Was finden Sie interessant an dieser Grafik?**

Recherche

101d **Verstanden? Sie hören einen kurzen Text über den Schweizer Unternehmer Nicolas G. Hayek, einen der bekanntesten Vertreter der Schweizer Uhrenbranche. Kreuzen Sie die richtigen Antworten an.**

Warum steckte die Schweizer Uhrenindustrie in den frühen 1980er Jahren in einer Krise?

- Uhrenanbieter aus anderen Ländern hatten es geschafft, preiswertere Qualitätsuhren zu produzieren.
- Viele Länder, wie die USA, erhoben hohe Zölle (*tariffs*) auf Schweizer Uhren.
- Ein instabiler Währungsmarkt machte die Herstellung und die Distribution von Schweizer Uhren zu teuer.

Wie hat Nicolas G. Hayek auf diese Krise reagiert?

- Er hat eine neue Produktlinie von teuren Qualitätsuhren entwickelt, um den High-End-Markt zu bedienen.
- Er hat ein Konzept für eine elektronische Qualitätsuhr entwickelt, die nicht zu teuer war.
- Er hat begonnen, seine Uhren im Ausland zu produzieren, um Produktionskosten zu sparen.

Was waren zwei Gründe dafür, dass die Swatch so erfolgreich war?

- Hayek schaffte ein hippes Produkt, indem er das Design von Künstler*innen entwickeln ließ.
- Hayek schaffte es, dass viele Stars die Uhren trugen. Das war gute Werbung.
- Er benutzte Plastik- statt Aluminiumgehäuse. Dadurch waren die Uhren preisgünstiger.

31: Das Filmfestival in Locarno

106a **Was ist ein guter Film? In MACHEN haben Sie mit anderen Kursteilnehmer*innen darüber gesprochen, welche Kriterien einen guten Film ausmachen. Fassen Sie sie zusammen. Schreiben Sie mindestens einen Satz im Passiv.**

Was sind Ihre individuellen Top 3-Kriterien für einen guten Film?

Welche fünf Kriterien haben Sie in Ihrer Gruppe gewählt?

Welchen Film hat Ihre Gruppe gewählt, der in allen fünf Punkten sehr gut war? Warum dieser Film?

107b **Verstanden? Sie hören eine Kurzbiografie der Filmemacherin Petra Volpe. Notieren Sie die Informationen.**

Name:

Alter:

Geburtsort (Kanton):

Beruf:

Studienfach und -ort 1:

Studienfach und -ort 2:

Bekannteste Filme:

32: DEMOKRATIE – MIT ODER OHNE FRAUEN?

108c **Schweizerinnen, die alle kennen sollten. Schreiben Sie die Sätze über wichtige Persönlichkeiten der Schweizer Geschichte vom Aktiv Präteritum ins Passiv Präteritum um.**

Die Märtyrerin Wiborada († 926) rettete die Bücher des Klosters St. Gallen.

Die Bücher des Klosters St. Gallen wurden von der Märtyrerin Wiborada gerettet.

Die Fürstäbtissin Elisabeth von Wetzikon (1235–1298) leitete die Geschäfte der Stadt Zürich.

____

Die Bestseller-Autorin Johanna Spyri (1827–1901) erschuf (Infinitiv: erschaffen) die bekannte Romanfigur Heidi.

____

Die erste Schweizer Ärztin Marie Heim-Vögtlin (1845–1916) gründete das Zürcher Frauenspital mit.

____

Die erste Schweizer Juristin Emilie Kempin-Spyri (1853–1901) forderte ein neues, inklusives Anwaltsgesetz.

____

109c **Verstanden? Sie hören Informationen über den Einfluss (*influence*) der Stimme von Frauen bei Wahlen und Abstimmungen in der Schweiz. Wählen Sie die richtigen Antworten.**

Was haben Forschende über das Abstimmungsverhalten von Frauen und Männern in der Schweiz herausgefunden?

- Männer und Frauen stimmen bei 10 % aller Abstimmungen fast gleich ab.
- Frauen haben eine 10 % höhere Wahlbeteiligung, das heißt, prozentual stimmen mehr Frauen als Männer ab.
- Bei circa 90 % aller Abstimmungen gibt es keinen signifikanten Unterschied zwischen Männern und Frauen.

Bei welchen Abstimmungsthemen gibt es den signifikantesten Unterschied zwischen Männern und Frauen?

- Den größten Unterschied gibt es bei Themen, die Frauen direkt betreffen.
- Den größten Unterschied gibt es bei Themen, die Männer direkt betreffen.
- Den größten Unterschied gibt es bei Themen, die eine der beiden Gruppen direkt betreffen.

Bei welchen der folgenden Themen gab es signifikante Unterschiede?

- Kindesmissbrauch
- Diskriminierung
- Steuersenkungen

109d **Recherchieren: Suchen Sie online nach Informationen über die Schweizer Politikerin Min Li Marti. Wer ist Min Li Marti? Wo wohnt sie, was hat sie studiert und was macht sie jetzt? Finden Sie so viele Informationen wie möglich und schreiben Sie eine Kurzbiografie.**

Recherche

____

____

____

____

____

____

____

110a  **Reflektieren: Can one still call a country a democracy when certain parts of the population (e.g. women, ethnic minorities, or poor people) are either excluded entirely from political participation, or when their political participation is stifled systematically through political and social measures (voter ID laws, gerrymandering, etc.)? Why do many countries not have 'democracy' and see western democracy as weak and, when imposed on other countries, as a kind of neo-colonialism?**

33: PHARMAZENTRUM BASEL

111d **Symptome und Behandlungsoptionen. Was kann/muss/soll da gemacht werden?**

ein gebrochenes Bein / vergipsen / müssen

Ein gebrochenes Bein muss vergipst werden.

eine kranke Lunge / röntgen / können

gegen Masern / impfen / sollen

kaputte Zähne / ziehen / müssen

ein entzündeter Blinddarm (*appendix*) / operieren / sollen

111e **Damals und heute. Was kann heute medizinisch anders gemacht werden? Benutzen Sie Passiv im Präteritum für die „damals"-Sätze und Passiv Präsens für die „heute"-Sätze.**

Damals: vor 200 Jahren	**Heute**
eine schwer verletzte Hand / amputieren müssen	nähen können
Eine schwer verletzte Hand musste amputiert werden.	*Sie kann genäht werden.*
Patient*innen / mit unsauberen Instrumenten operieren dürfen	steril operieren müssen
Krebs (*m.*) / nicht heilen können	oft durch Radiotherapie heilen können
Patient*innen / durch Aderlass[1] / behandeln sollen	Blut / zur Untersuchung abnehmen dürfen

[1] *blood-letting*

111f **Das Passiv mit Modalverben. Setzen Sie die erste Hälfte der folgenden Sätze ins Passiv.**

Man kann Arzneimittel einnehmen, wenn man krank ist.

Arzneimittel können eingenommen werden, wenn man krank ist.

Man sollte Arzneimittel immer testen, bevor man sie verkaufen darf.

___

Man muss Forschung betreiben, damit man Krankheiten besser verstehen kann.

___

Man muss neue Technologien entwickeln, um gefährliche Krankheiten besser zu verstehen.

___

Man kann pflanzliche Medikamente benutzen, wenn man keine starken Chemikalien einnehmen möchte.

___

111g **Verstanden? Tina hat starke Magenschmerzen und fragt Jörn nach Medikamenten. Hören Sie das Gespräch und beantworten Sie die Fragen.**

Was ist Iberogast?

- Es ist ein pflanzliches Mittel gegen Magenschmerzen.
- Es ist ein Mix aus Wasser und Kräutern, der gegen Magenschmerzen hilft.
- Es ist ein Schmerzmittel, das vor allem gegen Magenkrämpfe hilft.

Warum möchte Tina Iberogast nicht einnehmen?

- Tina hat Angst, dass ihre Magenschmerzen dadurch noch schlimmer werden.
- Sie glaubt nicht, dass pflanzliche Mittel wirklich effektiv sind.
- Tina kennt die aktiven Wirkstoffe von Iberogast nicht und vertraut dem Medikament deshalb nicht.

Wie reagiert Jörn darauf, dass Tina Iberogast nicht einnehmen möchte?

- Er erklärt ihr, dass pflanzliche Mittel genauso effektiv sind wie andere Medikamente.
- Er erklärt ihr, dass natürliche Optionen weniger gefährlich für den Körper sind.
- Er möchte nicht für Tina zur Apotheke gehen.

⊙ Kulturpunkt: Drei-Länder-Grenzverkehr

"Hold on a second: Why do so many Swiss people …

… buy their groceries in Germany?" The medieval town of Basel is situated on the big bend of the Rhine river where the borders of Switzerland, Germany, and France meet. The University of Basel was already founded by 1460 and it is one of the oldest universities in the world. Famous scholars from all over Europe such as Erasmus of Rotterdam and Friedrich Nietzsche taught here. The town has developed into a modern city with a conglomerate of global, pharmaceutical, and chemical industries that offer work for scientists, developers, business specialists, and highly trained workers. Thousands of them commute daily from Germany and France to work in Basel and vice versa. Yet fewer Swiss cross the border to work in France and Germany, but many opt to live there because it is considerably cheaper than in Switzerland. Switzerland—not a member of the EU—is part of the Schengen Area, in which internal border controls have largely been abolished. Switzerland has its own very stable and strong currency, the Swiss Franc or CHF. Salaries and wages are higher in Switzerland than in other European countries. However, the cost of living is lower and goods are cheaper in the EU than in notoriously expensive Switzerland. This fact causes the so-called *Einkaufstourismus*. By the thousands, the Swiss go shopping abroad, especially on weekends. They spend more than 1 billion CHF annually in stores and shopping centers that have popped up along the borders. Many Swiss shoppers take the *grenzenlose Tram 8* from Basel to the German border town Weil am Rhein. The streetcar route—mostly financed by the Swiss, with a small contribution by Weil am Rhein—was opened in 2014. The phenomenon of *Einkaufstourismus* occurs also in Ticino, Geneva, and Kreuzlingen, which is connected by a bridge over the Rhine with the German town of Konstanz. The *Drei-Länder-Grenzverkehr* around Basel is best symbolized by the airport Basel-Mulhouse-Freiburg on French soil, which is only minutes away from the Basel City center, 40 km from Mulhouse, and 70 km from Freiburg. The Basel Airport in France is easier to access for many Swiss than the large airport in Zurich or in Frankfurt for the Germans. The city of Basel has three train stations; however, the *Basel Badischer Bahnhof* is operated by the Deutsche Bahn. The border towns and villages also share a lively cultural exchange, with French and German being equal languages of communication.

112b **Reflektieren: Write about the questions below.**

- The author of the text describes the so-called *Einkaufstourismus* in rather positive terms. Can you also think of any negative aspects or consequences, both for Switzerland (and the Swiss people) and Germany (and the Germans)?
- In what ways, do you think, does this free movement of people and goods across three borders affect the way in which the residents in this area see themselves? Do you think they are more or less inclined to identify with more than one country?
- What does this example tell you about national (political) borders?
- In the course of the corona pandemic, European countries closed their national borders and went back to border controls for some months. What does this tell you about national (political) borders?

34: Lärmverschmutzung in transkultureller Perspektive°

118a **Reflektieren: Definieren Sie, was Stille für Sie bedeutet. Wo können Sie im Alltag Stille finden? Was machen Sie, wenn Sie Stille brauchen?**

118b Verstanden? Auch in Kunst und Literatur geht es oft um das Thema „Lärm und Stille". Hier sehen Sie ein Gedicht von Johann Wolfgang von Goethe. Es heißt „Meeresstille". Hören Sie gut zu und ergänzen Sie die fehlenden Wörter. Beantworten Sie danach die Fragen.

Tiefe Stille herrscht im ________________,
________________ Regung ruht das Meer,
Und bekümmert ________________ der Schiffer
Glatte Fläche ringsumher.
Keine ________________ von keiner ________________!
Todesstille fürchterlich!
In der ungeheuern
Reget keine ________________ sich.

Was bedeuten diese Wörter? Benutzen Sie ein Wörterbuch:

die Regung: ________________
bekümmert: ________________
die Fläche: ________________
die Todesstille: ________________
ungeheuer: ________________

Wie ist die Stimmung/Atmosphäre in dem Gedicht? Wie finden Sie das Gedicht?

____

35: Schweizer Käse

119f Reflektieren: In recent years, more and more people across the globe have adopted a vegan lifestyle. While no official surveys exist, it is estimated that in Switzerland roughly 3% of the population are vegans; in the U.S. it is even higher at an estimated 6%. You have learned a lot about the history, culture, and science of cheese making in Switzerland. Why do you think more and more people forego dairy, and thus cheese, in their diets? What could the consequences be for people who produce cheese, especially small independent cheesemakers? What steps could they take to respond to this trend?

119g Verstanden? Sie hören einen Text über eine Schaukäserei in Emmental. Sie hören den Text dreimal. Beim zweiten Mal hören Sie ihn mit Pausen. Schreiben Sie den Text so auf, wie Sie ihn hören.

____

121a **Nachhaltigkeit (und Probleme damit) bei der Käseherstellung. In LERNEN und MACHEN haben Sie viel über die Traditionen und Produktionsprozesse von Schweizer Käse erfahren. Jetzt lesen Sie einen Text zum Thema „Nachhaltigkeit bei der Käseherstellung". Beantworten Sie die Fragen.**

Bei der Käseherstellung werden alle Beiprodukte wiederverwertet. Die flüssige, grünliche Molke (*whey*) wird bei der Käseherstellung abgepumpt und zentrifugiert (entrahmt). Sie dient als Tierfutter (*animal feed*) oder wird weiterverarbeitet, z. B. zu Molkedrinks oder Molkenpulver. Molkenpulver wird zum Beispiel für Protein-Shakes aber auch als Tierfutter verwendet. In Spas werden auch Molkebäder angeboten.

Artgerechte Tierhaltung (*species appropriate husbandry*) und eine umweltschonende, nachhaltige Nutzung des Bodens sind wichtig, wie auch die effiziente Nutzung von Ressourcen. Etwa 10 Liter Wasser werden benötigt, um 1 Liter Milch zu produzieren und weitere 3–4 Liter Wasser bei der Verarbeitung von 1 Liter Milch bei der Käseherstellung. Die Energie auf Bauernhöfen und Käsereien wird immer mehr von erneuerbaren Energiequellen gewonnen, z. B. Solaranlagen auf den Dächern.

Was wird mit den Beiprodukten bei der Käseherstellung gemacht? Geben Sie Beispiele aus dem Text.

____

____

Im Text gibt es Informationen zur Wassernutzung bei der Käseherstellung. Wie viel Wasser wird bei der Käseherstellung benötigt? Finden Sie, dass diese Nutzung nachhaltig (*sustainable*) und effizient ist? Warum (nicht)?

____

____

Welche Technologien benutzen Bauernhöfe und Käsereien, um Energie zu gewinnen?

____

____

36: Formvollendete Schokolade

122b **Hier sehen Sie die acht wichtigsten Kakaoproduzenten: die Elfenbeinküste, Ghana, Indonesien, Nigeria, Kamerun, Brasilien, Ecuador, Mexiko. Dies sind einige Länder, in denen die meiste Schokolade produziert und konsumiert wird: die USA, Deutschland, die Schweiz, Belgien, Österreich, Kanada, Großbritannien, Norwegen. Malen Sie die Länder, in denen Kakao produziert wird, rot an und die Länder, in denen viel Schokolade produziert und konsumiert wird, blau.**

122c **Reflektieren in vier Schritten:**

Part 1) What do you notice about the visualization in activity 122b? What is your initial reaction to it? Why?

Part 2) Now think about and reflect on reasons for the difference between North and South. Why do those who grow the most cocoa beans eat less chocolate than people in Europe and North America? Here are some starting points: What role might temperature play if you think about the melting point of chocolate or the climatic conditions that the cocoa tree needs? What role might dietary habits play? What about the cultural and economic significance of cocoa and chocolate in the countries in red and blue? What about standards of living? What role does the history of European colonialism play? Etc.

Part 3) Fair trade projects are growing in numbers, yet cocoa farmers are still thought to be among the poorest people in the world, child labor and slavery on cocoa farms are an alarming problem. Can you think of realistic ways to make the North's chocolate consumption more sustainable?

Part 4) Do you have a different attitude towards the visualization now? Why (not)? Would you say that chocolate is a luxury product? Why (not)?

122d **Verstanden? Im Hörtext lernen Sie das ghanaische Start-up-Unternehmen '57Chocolate der beiden Schwestern Kimberly und Priscilla Addison kennen. Hören Sie zu und beantworten Sie die Fragen.**

Welche Rolle spielt die Schokoladenproduktion in Ghana?

- Ghana ist der zweitgrößte Schokoladenproduzent der Welt und Schokolade ist dort sehr beliebt.
- Ghanaische Schokolade ist eher eine Seltenheit, obwohl Ghana ein großer Kakaoproduzent ist.
- Die Schokoladenproduktion in Ghana ist teuer, weil man den Rohstoff Kakao importieren muss.

Was ist charakteristisch für die Schokolade von '57Chocolate?

- Sie imitiert Schweizer Schokolade, weil die Gründerinnen das Schokoladenhandwerk in Genf gelernt haben.
- Ihre Schokolade hat einen relativ hohen Kakaoanteil und wenig Zucker.
- Die Schokolade kann nur direkt im Geschäft der Schwestern gekauft werden.

Warum heißt das Unternehmen '57Chocolate?

- 57 ist eine Hommage an ihre Eltern, die 57 Jahre lang verheiratet waren, als die Firma gegründet wurde.
- Die Schokolade hat immer 57 % Kakaoanteil. Das soll mit dem Namen ausgedrückt werden.
- Im Jahr 1957 wurde Ghana unabhängig. Der Name zeigt, dass es ghanaische Schokolade ist.

124g **Welche Beispiele für geometrische Körper und Flächen im Alltag kennen Sie? Nennen Sie drei.**

Ein Fußballfeld ist ein Rechteck. / Ein Fußballfeld ist rechteckig.

124h **Formschön. Beschreiben Sie das Bild mit mindestens fünf Sätzen. Benutzen Sie viele Begriffe aus der Geometrie.**

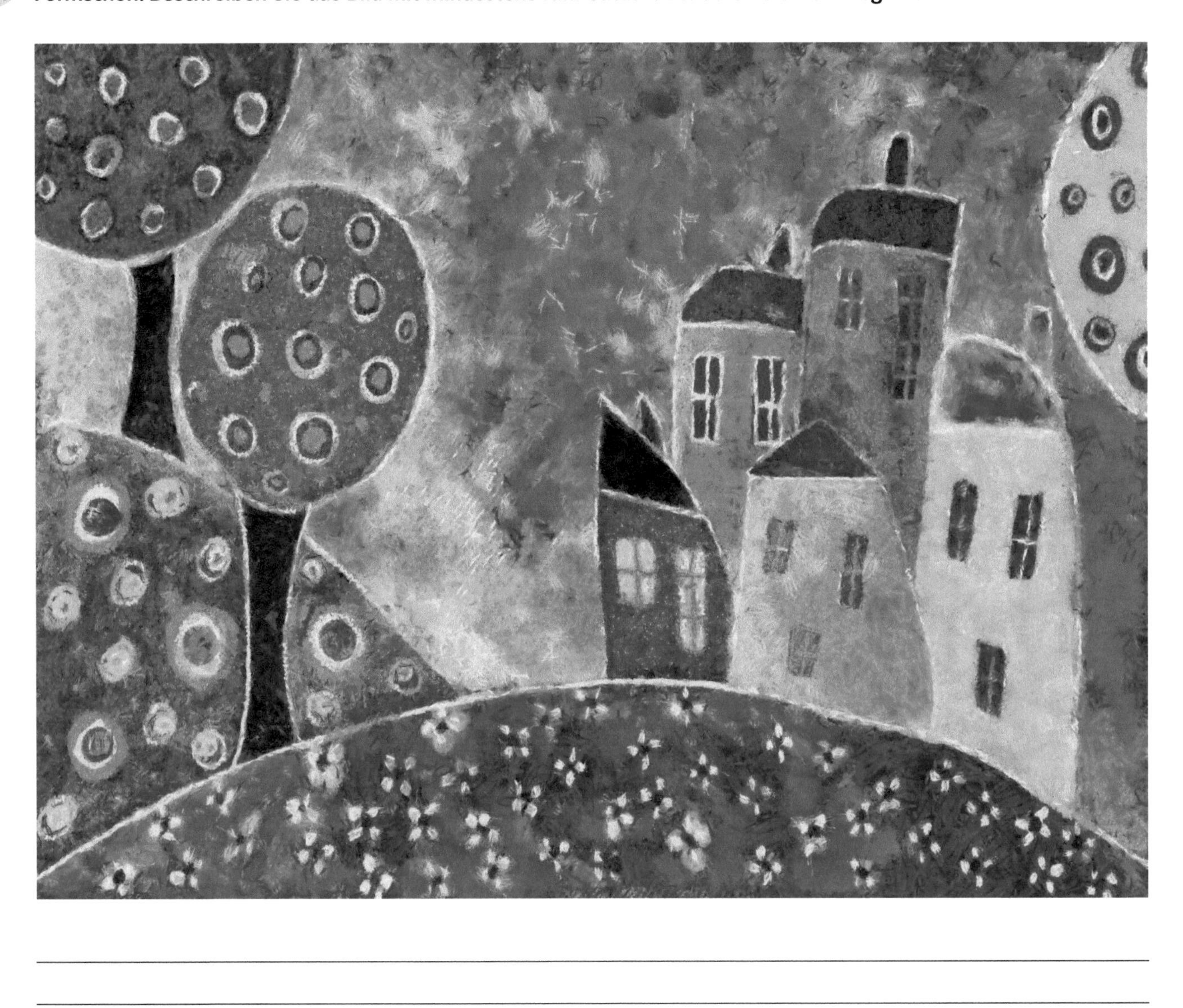

____

____

____

____

____

____

37: Die vielsprachige Schweiz

128e **Verstanden? Sie hören nun ein paar Formulierungen und Wörter auf Schwyzerdütsch. Geben Sie an, in welcher Reihenfolge Sie diese hören.**

	Wie gaht's dir?		Ich wohne i de Schwiz.		Chönnte Sie mir hälfe?
	Guete Morge!		Grüezi!	*1*	Möchtisch mit miar en Kaffi go trinka?

38: Produktmarketing in vier Sprachen°

130a **Produktpräsentationen. Im Unterricht haben die anderen Kursteilnehmer*innen verschiedene Marketingkonzepte vorgestellt. Welche Präsentation fanden Sie besonders überzeugend und warum?**

Welches Produkt wurde präsentiert?

Was kann mit diesem Produkt gemacht werden?

Wie sah die Werbung aus, die die Gruppe für dieses Produkt konzipiert hat? Wurden Slogans benutzt?

Warum hat Ihnen diese Produktpräsentation am besten gefallen?

130b **Verstanden? Janne und Torben unterhalten sich über das Sprachenlernen. Hören Sie gut zu und kreuzen Sie die richtigen Antworten an.**

Wie viele Sprachen sprechen Janne und Torben?

- Torben ist bilingual und Janne spricht drei Sprachen.
- Beide lernen gerade ihre vierte Sprache.
- Torben spricht mehr Sprachen als Janne.

Warum möchte Janne mit Torben Norwegisch sprechen?

- Sie geht in einer Woche für ein Auslandssemester nach Norwegen und möchte das Sprechen üben.
- Sie hat eine norwegische Austauschstudentin kennengelernt und möchte ein paar Sätze lernen.
- Sie hat bald eine mündliche Norwegischprüfung an der Uni und möchte das Sprechen üben.

Warum lernt Torben momentan Arabisch?

- Er macht das aus persönlichen Gründen, weil er möglichst viele Sprachen beherrschen möchte.
- Er möchte ein Praktikum bei einer humanitären Organisation in Marokko machen.
- Er möchte später in seinem Beruf in so vielen Sprachen wie möglich mit Menschen kommunizieren können.

39: PRODUZIERT AUF RÄTOROMANISCH

131b **Sprachen, die aussterben. Rätoromanisch ist nur eine von vielen Sprachen, die bedroht sind. In einigen Jahrzehnten (oder noch früher) werden sie von niemandem mehr gesprochen werden. Benutzen Sie die Webseite „UNESCO Atlas of the World's Languages in Danger" und finden Sie eine bedrohte Sprache aus Deutschland, Österreich, der Schweiz oder den USA. Beantworten Sie dann unten die Fragen über die Sprache, die Sie gewählt haben.**

Recherche

Wie heißt die Sprache?

____

Wo wird diese Sprache gesprochen?

____

Wie viele Menschen sprechen diese Sprache?

____

Ist diese Sprache eine Amtssprache (offizielle Sprache) in dem Land?

____

131c **Reflektieren: Sie haben in MACHEN gesehen, dass viele kleine Sprachen bedroht sind und oft verschwinden. Englisch wird immer mehr zur Lingua franca. Warum ist es (nicht) wichtig, dass wir kleine Sprachen schützen? Denken Sie an interne und externe Faktoren und Akteur*innen. Welche Vorteile hat Mehrsprachigkeit (Multilingualismus)? Reflektieren Sie auf Deutsch und/oder Englisch.**

134a **Verstanden? Hören Sie die Informationen über die Biografie von Arno Camenisch und beantworten Sie die Fragen.**

Wo ist Arno Camenisch als Schriftsteller erfolgreich?

- ☐ Camenisch ist vor allem im Schweizer Kanton Graubünden erfolgreich.
- ☐ Seine größten Erfolge hat er in Russland gefeiert. Er hat viele Fans in Moskau.
- ☐ Er ist als Schriftsteller weltweit erfolgreich und daher in vielen Ländern bekannt.

In welchen Sprachen sind Camenischs Werke zu lesen?

- ☐ Camenischs Bücher sind alle auf Deutsch und auf Rätoromanisch erschienen.
- ☐ Camenisch schreibt Romane auf Deutsch, Lyrik auf Rätoromanisch und Theaterstücke auf Englisch.
- ☐ Camenischs Werke wurden in mehr als 20 Sprachen übersetzt. Er selbst schreibt zweisprachig.

Wie waren die Reaktionen auf Camenischs Roman „Sez Ner"?

- ☐ Literaturkritiker*innen kritisierten, dass die einfache Sprache wenig Emotionen zeigt.
- ☐ Literaturkritiker*innen lobten Camenisch für seine ausdrucksstarken Beschreibungen der Schweizer Natur.
- ☐ Literaturkritiker*innen hofften auf einen Roman, der mehr in der Tradition des Naturalismus ist.

40: Projekt 3 – Eine Produktvorstellung°

135a **Erzähl mal: Nehmen Sie ein kurzes Video auf (z. B. mit Ihrem Handy oder am Computer) und beantworten Sie die Fragen.**

Welches Produkt benutzen Sie täglich? Warum ist dieses Produkt wichtig für Sie?

Wissen Sie, wo das Produkt hergestellt wird? Wird es auch in anderen Ländern verkauft oder nur in Ihrem Land? Welche bekannten Produkte wurden in Ihrer Region erfunden und/oder produziert?

Welche Sprachen werden in Ihrer Region oder in Ihrem Land gesprochen? Sprechen Sie mehr als eine Sprache?

135b **Self-Assessment**

You now get a chance to reflect on the many things you have learned throughout the chapter. Carefully read through the "Can-Do Statements" below, and ask yourself if you can perform all of these tasks. It might be helpful for each of the statements to actually practice the communicative scenario. Once you are confident that you are able to perform a task, check the respective box on the left side.

- I can describe the geographical location of the Swiss cantons using cardinal directions.
- I can ask and answer questions about major events from Swiss history.
- I can have a conversation about major Swiss industries, easily understand spoken information and answer questions about Swiss companies.
- I can follow written and spoken instructions describing production processes for products such as Swiss watches, chocolate, and pharmaceuticals.
- I can have simple conversations about topics of personal interest, such as my opinion on noise pollution.
- I can use my language to research and talk about things I can do in different Swiss cities, such as Locarno, Geneva, and Basel.
- I can understand the main viewpoints of and a few supporting facts about political topics such as gender inequality.
- I can ask and answer questions about historical aspects of Swiss and other European film festivals.
- I can have a simple conversation about current voting rights issues from an intercultural perspective.
- I can formulate and express arguments for the benefits of bi- or multilingualism.
- I can understand the details of movie trailers and give presentations about films I like.
- I can give a presentation based on factual information I have researched online about a variety of intercultural topics.
- I can use the passive voice to make statements that focus on processes and actions rather than agents.
- I can use the passive voice in different tenses, with or without prepositional phrases indicating the action's agent.
- I can use modal verbs in the passive voice in different tenses.
- I can use the impersonal passive with *es* for sentences with intrasitive verbs that do not take a direct object in active sentences.

- I am familiar with major Swiss inventions and their inventors.
- I am familiar with Swiss campaigns for and against women's suffrage.
- I am familiar with Swiss multilingualism and its role in the educational system as well as in product marketing.
- I am familiar with small languages and what can be done to save them from going extinct.

Wie leben wir nachhaltig?

Kommunikation für die Zukunft unseres Planeten

41: Was ist Nachhaltigkeit?

137i **Eine Studierendengruppe in Augsburg möchte ihre Uni-Mensa zu einem Infopoint für Nachhaltigkeit machen. Ergänzen Sie im Dialog die Relativpronomen im Nominativ.**

Dayyan: Kauft die Mensa viele Produkte, *die* aus dem fairen Handel kommen?

Gabi: Ich kenne jemanden, ________ in der Mensa-Verwaltung arbeitet. Soll ich ihn fragen?

Shixin: Ja, unbedingt. Können wir auch ein Poster über die Geschichte von Nachhaltigkeit machen? Es ist doch interessant, dass es ein Deutscher war, ________ das Prinzip zuerst formuliert hat.

Markus: Aber ist das denn wichtig? Produktiver ist vielleicht, wenn wir alle, ________ noch nicht viel über Chancengleichheit wissen, informieren.

Dayyan: Wir müssen also den fairen Handel und Chancengleichheit thematisieren. Nachhaltigkeit ist ein Konzept, ________ nur dann funktioniert, wenn die ganze Welt involviert ist.

Gabi: Genau. Es ist ein Handeln, ________ global ist, weil Klimawandel und Umweltzerstörung die ganze Welt betreffen.

137j **Diskussionsforum zum Thema „Nachhaltigkeit“: Schreiben Sie einen kurzen Kommentar zu Sebastians Forumsbeitrag. Orientieren Sie sich am Beispiel und benutzen Sie mindestens einen Relativsatz. Benutzen Sie Nomen wie „Aspekt“, „Seite“, „Problem“, „Sache“ und Verben wie „verbessern“, „regeln“, „lösen“, „(un)wichtig sein“.**

Seb2004

Hi! Wir behandeln gerade das Thema „Nachhaltigkeit“ an unserer Schule und haben verschiedene Kategorien kennengelernt: „soziale Nachhaltigkeit“, „ökologische Nachhaltigkeit“ und „ökonomische Nachhaltigkeit“. Wir haben dabei vor allem über Deutschland gesprochen. Aber mich würde interessieren, wie das in eurem Land aussieht. Danke für eure Antworten!

arnoXYZ

Hallo Seb2004! Ich komme aus Utrecht in den Niederlanden. Bei uns ist Nachhaltigkeit auch ein großes Thema. Wir fahren zum Beispiel viel Fahrrad und die Stadt hat ein großes Fahrrad-Parkhaus gebaut. Jetzt haben wir nicht nur tolle Radwege, sondern auch Platz zum Parken. Das ist ein Aspekt, der zu der Kategorie „ökologische Nachhaltigkeit“ passt, oder? Das regelt mein Land wirklich ganz gut, finde ich. Andere Probleme müssen wir noch lösen.

____

____

____

____

____

____

____

138c **Verstanden? Hören Sie die Kritik zum Thema „Fast Fashion" und beantworten Sie die Fragen.**

Wie sind die Bedingungen bei der Produktion von Fast Fashion?

- Die Arbeiter*innen bekommen zwar Pausen, aber sie müssen oft Überstunden machen.
- Die Herstellerfirmen von Fast Fashion kontrollieren die Produktionsbedingungen regelmäßig.
- Die Kleidung wird unter schlechten Bedingungen produziert und die Arbeiter*innen bekommen wenig Geld.

Warum hat Fast Fashion negative Auswirkungen auf die Ozeane?

- Fast Fashion wird aus Asien mit Schiffen nach Europa und Nordamerika gebracht. Das verschmutzt die Meere.
- Fast Fashion ist fast immer aus Polyester. Von unserer Kleidung gelangen Plastikpartikel ins Wasser.
- Die Firmen, die Fast Fashion produzieren, leiten ihr Abwasser in Flüsse. So gelangt Schmutz in die Meere.

Wie nachhaltig ist Fast Fashion?

- Menschen kaufen mehr Kleidung, weil Fast Fashion billig ist. Das führt zu einer nachhaltigen Wirtschaft.
- Menschen kaufen viel billige Kleidung und werfen mehr Kleidung weg. Das produziert viel Müll.
- Fast Fashion ist genauso nachhaltig wie andere Kleidung.

138d **Reflektieren: What is Fast Fashion? What are your experiences with it? Do you feel inclined to follow Fast Fashion trends, i.e., exchanging most or all of your closet's content each year? Why (not)? Also, what do you think are the biggest challenges when trying to switch from a large wardrobe of inexpensive clothes to a selection of a few items that are organic and sustainable? Think about social, cultural, practical, and other aspects.**

42: Klimawandel°

139b **Klimawandel im Film. Das Thema „Klimawandel" wird regelmäßig in Filmen behandelt. Wählen Sie einen solchen Film und analysieren Sie ihn mithilfe der folgenden Fragen. Wenn Sie keinen Film dieser Art kennen, nutzen Sie eine Zusammenfassung für Ihre Antworten.**

Beispiele:
„Soylent Green" (1973) „Waterworld" (1995) „The Day After Tomorrow" (2004)
„Arctic Tale" (2007) „Snowpiercer" (2013) „Geostorm" (2017)

Film: ____________________

Welche Folgen hat der Klimawandel für die Erde im Film?

____

____

Wie gehen die Menschen mit den extremen Folgen des Klimawandels um oder wie haben sie sich anpasst (*adapted*)?

____

____

Wer ist der*die Protagonist*in im Film? Was will er*sie erreichen?

____

____

Wie endet der Film?

____

____

Wie werden die Folgen des Klimawandels im Film gezeigt? Was denken Sie darüber: Sind sie realistisch oder übertrieben (*exaggerated*)? Warum?

____

____

139c **Verstanden? Zwei Freundinnen unterhalten sich über Klimawandel und die Fridays for Future-Demonstrationen. Kreuzen Sie die richtigen Antworten an.**

Was denkt Naja über die Fridays for Future-Demonstrationen?

- Sie wünscht sich, dass sich noch mehr Jugendliche engagieren würden.
- Sie findet es super, dass vor allem Jugendliche sich so für die Umwelt einsetzen.
- Sie versteht nicht, warum diese Bewegung nicht früher begonnen hat.

Warum macht die Fridays for Future-Bewegung sie auch traurig?

- Sie findet es schade, dass die Kinder durch die Demonstrationen so viel Schulunterricht verpassen.
- Sie findet es schade, dass Jugendliche sich mehr Sorgen um die Umwelt als um die Politik machen.
- Sie findet es schade, dass sich Politiker*innen nicht mehr Sorgen um die Umwelt machen.

141b **Klimawandel in den sozialen Medien. Ihre Freund*innen schreiben in einem sozialen Netzwerk. Lesen Sie den Post und wählen Sie rechts eine Reaktion.**

Pony Marony
2. Februar 2020

Ich merk' nichts von Klimaerwärmung. Heute Morgen -10° C und 15 cm Neuschnee. #winterishere

Ihre Reaktion:

 12 8 Kommentare

Babs Fernandez Pony Marony Voll das coole Foto! Viel Spaß im Schnee! 

Pierre Jürgens Ein schönes Foto ist es. Aber Klima hat bekanntlich nichts mit Wetter zu tun.

Uli Nguyen #mansplaining

Pierre Jürgens Uli Nguyen Ich find's wichtig, dass wir beim Thema Klimawandel bei den Fakten bleiben.

Uli Nguyen Deine Besserwisserei gehört hier aber nicht hin!

Sharon Heller Beruhigt euch mal. Ist doch ein interessantes Thema. Im Übrigen hab' ich da demletzt 'nen Artikel im Spiegel drüber gelesen: Es gibt wohl 'ne neue Studie von der ETH Zürich. Da zeigen sie, dass man im täglichen Weltwetter doch schon Spuren vom Klimawandel sehen kann.

Pierre Jürgens Sharon Heller Teil mal den Link, bitte.

141c **Schreiben Sie jetzt eine Antwort zu den Posts in Aktivität 141b und teilen Sie darin einen Link zum Thema „Klimawandel".**

____

____

____

____

____

141d **Reflektieren: Climate Change on Social Media. In activity 141c you reacted to a thread on a social media platform that turned into a discussion on climate change and whether it was appropriate or not to direct the discussion in this direction. Do you discuss topics like climate change on social media? Why (not)? What opportunities and pitfalls do these platforms provide?**

43: Ich in der Umwelt

143g **Nominativ, Akkusativ oder Dativ? Uli spricht mit seiner Freundin Kai. Setzen Sie den passenden bestimmten oder unbestimmten Artikel im richtigen Kasus ein.**

Uli: Ich bin echt genervt!

Kai: Warum? Was ist passiert? Hast du ________ schlechte Note für deine SoWi-Hausaufgabe bekommen?

Uli: Nein, nicht wirklich. In meinem Text erkläre ich, was ________ ökologischer Fußabdruck ist. Du weißt schon, wie viele Ressourcen wir verschwenden. Und ________ Fantasie-Person ist meine Zuhörerin. Ich habe ________ Fantasie-Person genommen, damit ________ Problem etwas persönlicher wird.

Kai: Das ist ________ klare Botschaft, finde ich. Obwohl ich nicht weiß, was du mit Fantasie-Person meinst.

Uli: Frau Maier auch nicht. Sie sagt, ich soll besser ________ Erde als Zuhörerin nehmen.

Kai: Das ist doch eine super Idee! Es ist ja ________ Natur, die unter unserem Verhalten leidet.

143h **Welche Relativpronomen im Akkusativ passen hier?**

Umweltbewusste Leute sind Personen, für ________ das Motto lautet: „Gut leben, statt viel haben!"

Waren ohne Verpackung zu kaufen? Das ist eine Methode, durch ________ sich Abfall vermeiden lässt.

Fahrradfahren und Zufußgehen ersetzen giftiges Benzin, für ________ wir auch noch viel Geld bezahlen müssen.

Autos und Motorräder sind Transportmethoden, ohne ________ man in einer Stadt gut leben kann.

Umweltverschmutzung ist ein Problem, auf ________ wir aufmerksam machen müssen.

Viele Leute sind auf eine vegetarische Ernährung umgestiegen, für ________ es tolle Rezepte gibt.

143i **Vervollständigen Sie die Sätze. Geben Sie in Klammern an, ob das Relativpronomen im Akkusativ oder im Nominativ steht.**

Fleisch und Wurst sind Lebensmittel, die *viele Deutsche gern essen. (Akk.)*

Milch, Käse und Eier sind Produkte, die ______________________________.

Biolebensmittel sind Lebensmittel, die ______________________________.

Wohnfläche ist die Fläche, die ______________________________.

20 °C ist die Temperatur, die ______________________________.

Mein Fußabdruck ist der Abdruck, den ______________________________.

Das Flugzeug ist ein Transportmittel, das ______________________________.

Restmüll ist der Müll, der ______________________________.

143j **Lesen Sie die drei Texte und entscheiden Sie: Welcher Text ist für Sie persönlich am interessantesten?**

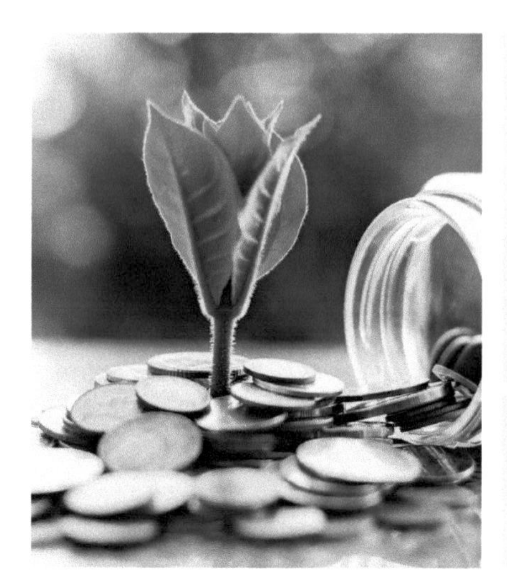

Text 1: Beim Duschen verbraucht ein normaler Duschkopf 14 bis 16 l pro Minute. Der Wassersparduschkopf verbraucht nicht nur weniger, sondern signalisiert auch, wenn zu viel Wasser benutzt wird. Nach 50 l Wasser, die durch die Dusche laufen, blinkt sie rot.

Text 2: Über Webseiten wie atmosfair können Sie berechnen, wie viel CO_2 Ihr Flug verursacht hat. Es wird ein Preis berechnet (z.B. 260 Euro für drei Personen für Hin- und Rückflug Detroit-Frankfurt) und Sie können dieses Geld dann an ein Klimaschutzprojekt spenden.

Text 3: Ein gut isoliertes Haus reduziert den ökologischen Fußabdruck immens. Dafür werden gute Fenster gebraucht. Wenn Sie gute Fenster haben, müssen Sie weniger heizen. Schüco verspricht, dass man 750 l Heizöl pro Jahr pro Haus sparen kann, was zwei Tonnen CO_2 entspricht.

Ich finde Text ______ am interessantesten.

Beantworten Sie die folgenden Fragen zu diesem Text: Worum geht es? Wie ermöglicht es das Produkt oder die Dienstleistung einer Person, umweltfreundlicher zu leben? Wie finden Sie die Idee? Sehen Sie auch Probleme bei dieser Idee? Wenn ja, welche?

____

____

____

____

____

____

143k **Verstanden? Zwei Freunde unterhalten sich über ihre Essgewohnheiten und inwiefern die Wahl von Lebensmitteln auch mit Umweltschutz zu tun hat. Beantworten Sie die Fragen.**

Warum hat Peter sich dafür entschieden, Vegetarier zu werden?

- Er hatte Angst, dass Fleisch nicht gut für ihn war, und wollte sich gesünder ernähren.
- Er wollte nicht, dass wegen seiner Essgewohnheiten Tiere sterben müssen.
- Er hat gesehen, wie Tiere getötet werden, und das hat ihm Angst gemacht.

Was ist für Peter die Verbindung von Nachhaltigkeit und Ernährungsweise?

- Peter glaubt, dass nur eine vegetarische Ernährung richtig nachhaltig sein kann.
- Peter denkt, dass tierische Produkte okay sind, wenn sie lokal gekauft werden.
- Peter denkt, dass man lokale Produkte kaufen soll, um lange Transportwege zu vermeiden.

Was denkt Tibor über das Thema „Nachhaltigkeit"?

- Für ihn ist es am wichtigsten zu wissen, woher sein Essen kommt.
- Er stimmt Peter zu, dass Menschen sich idealerweise alle vegan ernähren sollten.
- Es ist ihm nicht so wichtig, dass Tiere gut behandelt werden, so lange er gutes Essen bekommt.

144e **Wie viel Fleisch isst du? – Ein Interview. Machen Sie mit drei Personen ein kurzes Interview zum Thema „Fleischkonsum". Stellen Sie die zwei vorgegebenen Fragen und überlegen Sie sich drei eigene. Wenn Sie das Interview nicht auf Deutsch führen können, dürfen Sie auch eine andere Sprache benutzen. Schreiben Sie Ihre Auswertung aber auf Deutsch. Tipp: Ja/Nein-Fragen sind keine guten Interviewfragen. Stellen Sie offene Fragen, auf die Sie die Antwort nicht im Internet finden können.**

Ihre Fragen auf Deutsch

Wie viel Fleisch isst du in der Woche?

Wie würdest du es finden, wenn der Staat den Fleischkonsum mehr regulieren würde – zum Beispiel durch höhere Preise oder bessere Informationen auf Labels und Verpackungen?

____

____

____

Ihre Auswertung auf Deutsch: Schreiben Sie zu jeder Person, welche Antwort oder welchen Aspekt Sie am interessantesten fanden.

Person 1: ______________________________

____

Person 2: ______________________________

____

Person 3: ______________________________

____

44: „Die Wolke"

147c **Welche Auswirkungen haben Katastrophen wie ein atomarer Unfall auf zwischenmenschliche Beziehungen? Auch darum geht es im Buch „Die Wolke". Achten Sie auf die Präpositionen und Verben. Setzen Sie den passenden bestimmten oder unbestimmten Artikel im Nominativ, Akkusativ oder Dativ ein.**

„Die Wolke" erzählt __________ Geschichte eines atomaren Unfalls. Aber in __________ Geschichte geht es um viel mehr als __________ Unfall in einem Atomkraftwerk. Durch __________ Unfall wird __________ Leben der Hauptfiguren stark beeinflusst. __________ Roman erzählt auch die Liebesgeschichte zwischen Janna-Berta und Elmar. Hier wird __________ Frage gestellt, wie __________ Beziehung und Liebe Menschen bei __________ Herausforderungen einer Krisensituation helfen können. Aber es geht nicht nur um __________ Beziehung zwischen Janna-Berta und Elmar. Zum Beispiel erfahren wir schon sehr früh, wie wichtig __________ Familie für Janna-Berta ist. Nach __________ Unfall im Atomkraftwerk möchte sie sofort wissen, wie es ihrer Mutter geht.

148f **Janna-Bertas und Ulis Flucht. Nach dem atomaren Unfall müssen Janna-Berta und Uli wegen der gefährlichen Strahlung (*radiation*) schnell die Stadt verlassen. Sie wollen in die Stadt Bad Hersfeld gehen, weil es von dort aus einen Zug nach Hamburg gibt. Aber auf dem Weg nach Bad Hersfeld passiert etwas Schreckliches, weil Uli zu schnell einen Berg mit seinem Fahrrad hinunter fährt. Lesen Sie den Textabschnitt und suchen Sie die Wörter, die Sie noch nicht kennen, in einem Wörterbuch. Beantworten Sie dann unten die Fragen.**

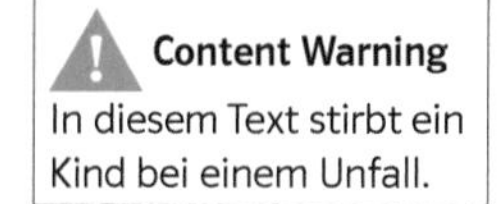

Schon fliegt er kopfüber vom Rad. Er fällt hinunter auf den breiten Weg. Ein Auto kommt in hoher Geschwindigkeit. „Uli!" Der Autofahrer bremst nicht. Janna-Berta hört einen Schlag. Das Auto rast weiter. Entsetzt steht Janna-Berta auf dem Bahndamm. Dort unten liegt Uli. Nicht weit von ihm sein Teddy. Daneben das Fahrrad. Das Vorderrad dreht sich noch. Janna-Berta stürzt hinunter zu ihm. Seine Hand ist ganz warm.
Sie hockt neben Uli mitten auf dem Weg. Kein Auto kann vorbeifahren. Hinter ihr wird wütend gehupt. Ein Mann und eine Frau kommen zu ihr hin. Die Frau zieht Janna-Berta hoch. „Steig ein", sagt der Mann. „Wir nehmen dich mit. Die Kinder rücken zusammen." „Uli muss mit", sagt Janna-Berta. „Uli?", fragt die Frau. „Du meinst …" „Er ist mein Bruder", schreit Janna-Berta. „Du kannst ihm nicht mehr helfen", sagt der Mann leise.

Quelle: Gudrun Pausewang, „Die Wolke", Alinea Verlag

Was passiert mit Uli?

___

Wie reagiert Janna-Berta? Was macht sie?

___

Janna-Berta sagt „Uli muss mit", worauf der Mann antwortet: „Du kannst ihm nicht mehr helfen." Beschreiben Sie, welche Gedanken in diesem Moment durch Janna-Bertas Kopf gehen.

___

___

___

148g **Hier sehen Sie das Cover des Buchs „Die Wolke". Sie hören eine Beschreibung des Covers. Hören Sie gut zu und ergänzen Sie die Lücken mit den fehlenden Wörtern.**

1) Auf dem Cover ist unten der ________ in Weiß zu sehen.
2) Dahinter sieht man eine violette Landschaft. Es gibt ein paar ________, aber der Rest der Landschaft ist abgestorben, wie ________.
3) Im Zentrum des Covers ist eine junge ________, aber nur ihr ________ ist sichtbar.
4) Im Vordergrund ist vor der Abbildung der Frau das Zeichen für ________ Strahlung. Im Hintergrund kommt Rauch aus einem ________.
5) Die Stimmung auf dem Cover ist dunkel, fast apokalyptisch. Die ________ sind teilweise hell, teilweise düster (*dim*). Es gibt also einen ________ zwischen der oberen und der unteren Hälfte des Covers. Das radioaktive Zeichen ist sehr ________ und verleiht dem Cover eine negative, dystopische ________.

148h Auf dem Cover in Aktivität 148g sind vier Elemente mit Kreisen markiert. Ordnen Sie die Elemente den Textabschnitten zu und schreiben Sie die passenden Nummer (1–4) in die Kreise.

148i Sie haben Teile aus dem Buch gelesen und den Trailer des Films „Die Wolke" gesehen. Finden Sie, das Cover passt gut zu der Geschichte? Schreiben Sie Gründe, warum Sie es (nicht) gut finden.

____

____

148j Als der Roman 1987 erschien, gab es noch keine Smartphones. Stellen Sie sich vor, es hätte sie schon gegeben. Schreiben Sie eine Nachricht, die Janna-Berta nach der atomaren Katastrophe an eine Person aus Ihrer Familie oder Ihrem Freundeskreis schickt.

148k  Reflektieren: „Die Wolke" ist ein Jugendroman über eine atomare Katastrophe. Der Roman erschien nach der Nuklearkatastrophe in Tschernobyl. Auch der atomare Unfall in Fukushima hatte in Deutschland große politische und kulturelle Konsequenzen. 2010 hatte Angela Merkels Regierung angekündigt, Atomkraftwerke länger laufen zu lassen. Aber nach Fukushima erklärte sie einen sofortigen Ausstieg aus der Atomenergie. Atomenergie und Atomausstieg sind also in der deutschen Kultur sehr präsent und spielen eine wichtige Rolle. Beantworten Sie ein paar der Fragen auf Deutsch oder Englisch:

Wie ist das in Ihrem Land? Gibt es dort eine Diskussion über die Endlagerung (*final storage*) von Atommüll? Gab es schon einmal eine Katastrophe wie in Tschernobyl oder Fukushima und wie waren die Reaktionen darauf? Hat eine ähnliche Katastrophe zu einer Debatte über Atomkraft geführt? Was glauben Sie: Warum (nicht)? Gibt es eventuell auch Literatur oder Filme, die sich mit dem Thema beschäftigen? Auf welche Weise? Und welche Haltung (*attitude*) haben Sie selbst zu Atomenergie? Glauben Sie, dass Sie anders denken würden, wenn Sie in Deutschland aufgewachsen wären?

45: Umweltbewegungen

150f **Die Arbeit der Bürger*innen in der Oberasbacher Umweltschutz-Initiative. Nominativ, Akkusativ, Dativ oder Genitiv? Achten Sie auf die Präpositionen und Verben und setzen Sie den passenden bestimmten oder unbestimmten Artikel im richtigen Kasus ein.**

Gestern haben sich wieder viele engagierte Bürger*innen im Oberasbacher Rathaus getroffen. Sie verfolgten ________ gemeinsames Ziel: Sie wollen ________ Bau der Plastikwarenfirma Koppersheim in ihrer Stadt verhindern. Koppersheim will ein großes Stück Land in der Nähe ________ Oberasbacher Stadtwaldes kaufen. Wirtschaftlich ist ________ neue Firma in ________ Stadt natürlich hilfreich, denn dann gibt es mehr Jobs. Deshalb ist ________ Bevölkerung auch geteilter Meinung. Einige von ________ Leuten wollen mehr Arbeitsplätze, aber die meisten sind gegen ________ Arbeitgeber, der mit Plastik arbeitet, also mit ________ nicht nachhaltigen Rohstoff.

150g **Recherchieren und Schreiben: Gab oder gibt es in Ihrem Land eine Anti-Atomkraft-Bewegung? Recherchieren Sie online und schreiben Sie fünf Fakten in ganzen Sätzen auf.**

Recherche

____

____

____

____

150h **Im Wald. Ergänzen Sie die korrekten Genitivendungen, wenn nötig.**

Die Ringe ein_____ Baum_____ zeigen das jeweilige Alter an.

Die Tiere d_____ Wald_____ leben im Rhythmus d_____ Natur_____ .

Die bevorzugte Nahrung d_____ Eichhörnchen_____ (*pl.*) sind Nüsse, Samen und Früchte.

In Mitteleuropa sind der Sommer und der Herbst als Saison d_____ Pilze_____ bekannt.

Wenn die Bäume besonders eng (*close*) stehen, können nur wenige Strahlen d_____ Sonne_____ den Waldboden erreichen.

151c **Schreiben Sie 4–5 Sätze zu den Informationen über die Grüne Partei Ihres Landes, über die Sie im Unterricht recherchiert haben.**

____

____

____

____

Kulturpunkt: Streiken fürs Klima

"Hold on a second: …

… why do kids strike on Fridays?" In August 2018, then 15-year-old Greta Thunberg began her school strike. She sat in front of the Swedish parliament for three weeks, demanding action to stop the effects of climate change. When she returned to school, she continued her strike on Fridays and coined the hashtag and consequently the movement Fridays for Future (FFF). This became a global movement, with millions participating in strikes and marches for climate justice.

In Germany, Austria, and Switzerland, there are also FFF groups. The main German initiator is Luisa Neubauer, a 22-year-old university student. She has organized strikes in Berlin with tens of thousands of participants, including the climate strike in September 2019, which saw more than 1 million Germans take to the streets in many cities across the country. The main demands of the movement in the German-speaking countries align with other groups in Europe and the world: a reduction of the greenhouse gases (to net zero in Germany and Switzerland), abandoning coal as an energy source (Germany and Austria), subsidies for alternative and renewable energy sources (Germany), and explicitly climate justice to make sure that the next generation will have a planet to live on (Switzerland).

Many politicians have supported the movement, while other groups have formed that reinforce the student movement, such as Parents for Future and Scientists for Future. At the same time, those who are afraid to lose their privileges, as well as those who deny climate change and its consequences, have pushed back against the movement. This pushback is particularly apparent in toxic social media campaigns against Thunberg and other climate activists.

In Germany, pushback comes disguised as a legal debate: here, some have argued that students who are on strike violate *Schulpflicht* (compulsory education) and have threatened repercussions for those who don't go to school. In some *Bundesländer*, however, schools and governments have been more understanding by acknowledging that the students' strikes could be seen as project-based learning.

The movement's main success has been that climate change has become a topic of social attention, not just one for politics. *Klimajugend* (climate youth) was coined the word of the year 2019 in Switzerland, and the opposite word *Klimahysterie* (climate hysteria), denoting the attempt of the opposition to paint the students as unreasonable and dramatic, was the German *Unwort* (most unnecessary word) in 2019.

152a **Reflektieren: Write about the questions below.**

- What has the climate movement been like in your country/community?
- Have you participated in it or would you like to participate? Why (not)?
- Why do you think that there is so much vitriol in the debate about climate change and the movements to act for climate justice?
- Do you know of other instances when students are called "dramatic" for standing up for social justice causes?

152b **Verstanden? In Aktivität 139c haben Sie im Dialog von zwei Freundinnen erfahren, wie Jugendliche sich für die Umwelt engagieren. Jetzt lernen Sie mehr über Fridays for Future in Deutschland und wie die Gruppe organisiert ist. Hören Sie gut zu und füllen Sie die Lücken aus.**

Die ____________________ Fridays for Future spielt seit 2018 auch in Deutschland eine große ____________________. Es gibt mehrere hundert ____________________ Ortsgruppen verteilt in allen 16 Bundesländern. Damit die Bewegung auch überregional ____________________ arbeiten kann, gibt es unterschiedliche Arbeitsgruppen. Jede ____________________ hat bestimmte Aufgaben, die alle helfen sollen, die Ortsgruppen im ganzen ____________________ besser zu vernetzen. Es gibt zum Beispiel Arbeitsgruppen zu den Themen „Finanzen", „Grafik" oder „E-Mail". Fridays for Future hat einige Forderungen an die ____________________ gestellt. Am wichtigsten ist wahrscheinlich die Einhaltung der ____________________ des Pariser Abkommens aus dem Jahr 2016.

46: Deutschland, grünes Vorbild°

155a  **Verstanden? Nora und Jarne unterhalten sich darüber, was sie tun, um nachhaltiger zu leben. Entscheiden Sie, was die richtigen Antworten sind.**

Wo geht Jarne einkaufen?

- Er ist gerade auf dem Weg zu Aldi, um dort einzukaufen.
- Er möchte in einem neuen Laden einkaufen, den Nora empfohlen hat.
- Er ist auf dem Weg zu einem neuen Laden, wo alles unverpackt verkauft wird.

Was ist das Ziel von Unverpackt?

- Unverpackt will, dass Menschen weniger einkaufen, weil sie nur kleine Packungen kaufen können.
- Unverpackt will Müll von Verpackungen vermeiden, um die Umwelt zu schützen.
- Unverpackt will alle tierischen Produkte wie Fisch oder Fleisch abschaffen, weil das nachhaltiger ist.

47: Deutschland, grünes Vorbild?

156h  **Reflektieren: In MACHEN haben Sie gelernt, dass Deutschland nicht in allen Aspekten ein grünes Vorbild ist. Wie ist das in Ihrem Heimatland? Welche Dinge zum Thema „Umweltschutz und Nachhaltigkeit" funktionieren gut? Wo gibt es Defizite? Was könnte Ihr Heimatland besser machen?**

Kulturpunkt: Umweltfreundlich Deutsch

"Hold on a second: …

… what's up with the idea of environmentalism as something particularly German?" A well-known stereotype about Germans is that they are *umweltfreundlich*, environmentally friendly. It's not just a stereotype that others have about Germans (a heterostereotype) but also one that Germans have about themselves (an autostereotype). While there are a lot of environment-focused policies and conventions in Germany, there are nonetheless also "unfriendly" behaviors Germans exhibit toward the environment. Whether positive or negative, stereotypes group together individual behaviors in ways that erase differences.

Whenever people believe in an autostereotype and are perhaps even proud of it, they can make it a measure of belonging to their group. If being environmentally conscious were something particularly German, then conversely, some Germans might assume that all others are less environmentally friendly. Perhaps some of you have encountered this sentiment when traveling or studying in Germany. Someone might have gone to great lengths to explain how to recycle, for instance, maybe even assuming that you've never heard of it. And the German recycling system can get complicated, so even Germans sometimes need help with all those detailed rules! Nonetheless, the assumption that anyone who didn't grow up in Germany doesn't know about environmentalism is, of course, wrong. And if knowing how to recycle in Germany is considered a condition of belonging, then environmentalism becomes a way to exclude those who don't pass this test.

We have talked before about the fact that "incorrect" recycling behavior can lead to neighborly strife (*Impuls Deutsch 1*, chapter 5, unit 63). While we focused on the absurdity of such arguments between neighbors then, it becomes less funny if it fuels racism and prejudice. In the context of the so-called "refugee crisis" around 2015, for instance, when many refugees and asylum seekers arrived in Germany, they were offered not just language and culture courses, but also *Umweltbildung*, or environmental education. These programs emphasized that Germans consider environmentalism a central cultural value, but they implicitly also assumed that none of the new arrivals knew anything about it or thought that it was important.

Consider the perspective of a refugee: many immediate needs like food, shelter, health, safety, and communication will understandably rank before *Umweltfreundlichkeit*, but that does not mean that they do not care. Not knowing how to recycle in Germany is not a sign of indifference toward the planet; recycling is simply one of many things to be learned. What most refugees do know first hand is how to live with very limited resources, an important environmental skill.

Indeed, it seems as if the actual goal of environmentalism, protecting the planet, gets lost somewhere between recycling drills and national pride. This goes to show that even something positive like environmentalism can become a tool of exclusion and prejudice when it's viewed as the particular concern of a certain national group.

You can read more about this topic in the article you will find under the link for this *Kulturpunkt* on www.klett-usa.com/impuls2links.

156i **Reflektieren: Answer the questions below.**

- What kinds of stereotypes exist about your culture? What is untrue about them?
- Can you think of a positive value in your culture that can become a tool for excluding others?
- How can you identify stereotypes about others in your own thinking?

156j **Die Erderwärmung. Ergänzen Sie bei den folgenden Sätzen die fehlenden Relativpronomen im Genitiv.**

Das Thema meiner Präsentation ist die Erderwärmung. Wir können die Folgen der Erderwärmung schon spüren.

Das Thema meiner Präsentation ist die Erderwärmung, *deren* Folgen wir schon spüren können.

Erderwärmung ist ein großes Thema für Jugendliche. Wir müssen die Angst der Jugendlichen ernst nehmen.

Erderwärmung ist ein großes Thema für Jugendliche, __________ Angst wir ernst nehmen müssen.

Die Menschen leben auf einem Planeten. Die Ressourcen des Planeten sind begrenzt.

Die Menschen leben auf einem Planeten, __________ Ressourcen begrenzt sind.

Das Klima wird sich in den kommenden Jahren noch weiter verändern. Der Wandel des Klimas ist unbestreitbar.

Das Klima, __________ Wandel unbestreitbar ist, wird sich in den kommenden Jahren noch weiter verändern.

156k **In Aktivität 156 in MACHEN haben Sie gelernt, dass Deutschland in einigen Dingen kein grünes Vorbild ist. Formulieren Sie drei Fragen an Deutschland und an die Deutschen, die sich auf die Informationen in 156 beziehen.**

Warum wird Fleisch von der Regierung nicht weniger subventioniert?

____

____

____

156l **Der Atomausstieg und seine Folgen: Lesen Sie den kurzen Text und beantworten Sie die R/F-Fragen auf der nächsten Seite.**

In Deutschland wird der Atomausstieg weitestgehend als etwas Positives porträtiert. In kulturellen und medialen Diskursen wird Atomenergie als etwas Gefährliches dargestellt, vor allem wegen der Gefahren bei atomaren Unfällen. Es wird auch oft über das Problem gesprochen, dass atomarer Müll nicht sicher gelagert werden kann. Aber was bedeutet der Atomausstieg für die Energieerzeugung in Deutschland? Bei dieser Frage wird oft ignoriert, dass Deutschland schon seit Jahren an Braun- und Steinkohle festhält. Und wie die Proteste im Hambacher Forst gezeigt haben, wollen große Energiefirmen sogar noch mehr Kohle abbauen. Viele Menschen haben im Hambacher Forst protestiert, um das Abholzen von Bäumen für den klimaschädlichen Kohleabbau zu stoppen.

richtig falsch

- Die meisten Deutschen sehen den Atomausstieg als etwas Negatives.
- Eine Kritik an Atomenergie ist, dass man den Atommüll nicht sicher lagern kann.
- Nach dem Atomausstieg benutzt Deutschland nur erneuerbare Energien, keine Kohle.
- Viele Menschen haben im Hambacher Forst gegen Atomenergie protestiert.

156m Schauen Sie sich das Diagramm an. Wie hat sich die Nutzung der unterschiedlichen Energiequellen entwickelt? Beantworten Sie die Fragen.

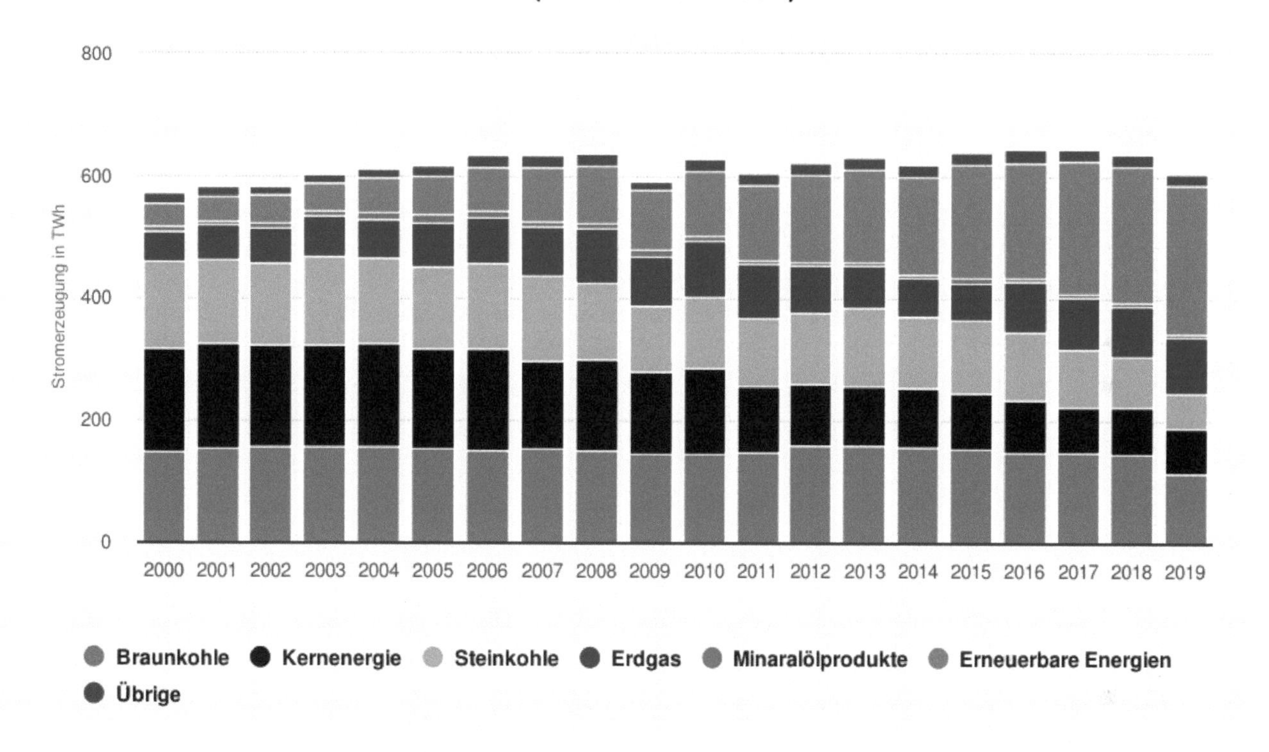

Quellen
BDEW; Statistisches Bundesamt; AGEB; BMWi; ZSW; Statistik der Kohlenwirtschaft

Weitere Informationen:
Deutschland

Welche Energiequellen werden in der Statistik genannt?

____

Welche Energiequellen haben in den Jahren zwischen 2000 und 2019 am meisten zugenommen?

____

Welche Energiequellen haben in den Jahren zwischen 2000 und 2019 am meisten abgenommen?

____

Welche Energiequellen sind relativ gleich geblieben?

____

156n Reflektieren: Was sagt die Statistik in Aktivität 156m über Deutschlands Ziel, bis 2050 CO_2-neutral zu sein? Ist die Entwicklung der Energiequellen nachhaltig?

157k **Wie können wir die CO_2-Bilanz verbessern? Schreiben Sie Appelle. Benutzen Sie Relativpronomen im Genitiv und die 2. Person Plural, wie im Beispiel.**

Bio-Fleisch | Fleisch aus der Massenproduktion kaufen (CO_2-Ausstoß, niedriger)

Kauft Bio-Fleisch, dessen CO_2-Ausstoß niedriger ist!

ein langsames Auto | ein schnelles Auto fahren (CO_2-Ausstoß, niedriger)

Plastikverpackung | Papierverpackung benutzen (Lebensdauer auf der Müllhalde, kürzer)

Glasflaschen | Plastikflaschen kaufen (Lebensdauer, länger)

Milchprodukte | vegane Produkte konsumieren (Wasserverbrauch, geringer)

Gemüse | Fleisch essen (Landverbrauch, geringer)

158a **Verstanden? Deutschland sieht sich oft als Vorbild, wenn es um nachhaltiges Verhalten geht. Aber wie nachhaltig leben die Deutschen tatsächlich im Vergleich zu anderen Ländern? Hier hören Sie ein paar Zahlen zu den Treibhausgasemissionen pro Person in verschiedenen europäischen Ländern. Ergänzen Sie die fehlenden Informationen.**

Platz	Land	Tonnen Treibhausgas
1	Liechtenstein	
2		5,5
3	Rumänien	
5	Schweiz, Kroatien	
9		7,3
13		8,8
15	Österreich	
20		11,3

48: Kommunikation

159g **Verstanden? Sie hören vier Aussagen. Entscheiden Sie, welcher Appell zu welcher Aussage passt.**

Appell:

Koch bitte nächstes Mal etwas anderes.

Bitte erklär mir diese Aufgabe.

1 Ruf mich mal wieder an, bitte.

Bitte schalte die Heizung an.

160a **Das Vier-Seiten-Modell: Eine Übung. Lesen Sie die Nachricht und formulieren Sie für die drei offenen Ebenen einen Satz aus der Perspektive der empfangenden Person. Für Appell, Selbstaussage und Beziehung gibt es keine „richtigen" Antworten. Es kommt darauf an, wie Sie diese Nachricht interpretieren.**

Nachricht: Oh, es gibt heute wieder Spaghetti Bolognese?

Sachinhalt: ______________________________

Appell: ______________________________

Selbstaussage: ______________________________

Beziehung: *Du weißt doch, dass ich Spaghetti Bolognese nicht gern esse. Warum kochst du sie denn?*

160b **Reflektieren: Gab es in Ihrem Leben schon einmal Situationen, in denen es Kommunikationsprobleme gab? Geben Sie ein Beispiel. Können Sie die Situation mit dem Vier-Seiten-Modell erklären?**

160c **Sie haben viel über verbale Kommunikation und Missverständnisse beim Kommunizieren gelernt. Aber es gibt natürlich auch nonverbale Formen der Kommunikation. Der Kommunikationswissenschaftler Paul Watzlawick hat in einem Axiom formuliert: „Man kann nicht nicht kommunizieren." Also auch wenn man nichts sagt, kommuniziert man. Unten sehen Sie vier Fotos. Überlegen Sie, was die Personen auf diesen Fotos durch nonverbale Elemente (Mimik, Gestik, Körperhaltung) kommunizieren. Schreiben Sie sich für jedes Foto ein paar Informationen in Stichworten (Adjektive, Nomen oder Verben) auf, die das beschreiben, was kommuniziert wird.**

Was wird hier nonverbal kommuniziert?

Was wird hier nonverbal kommuniziert?

Was wird hier nonverbal kommuniziert?

Was wird hier nonverbal kommuniziert?

160d **Schauen Sie sich die folgenden Handzeichen an und schreiben Sie, was diese Zeichen in Ihrer Kultur nonverbal kommunizieren.**

In meiner Kultur:

____

In Japan:
Geld

In Brasilien:
wie ein Mittelfinger in den USA

In meiner Kultur:

____

Im Iran:
wie ein Mittelfinger in den USA

In ASL:
die Zahl 10

In meiner Kultur:

____

In Griechenland:
wie ein Mittelfinger in den USA

In Mexiko:
Hallo!

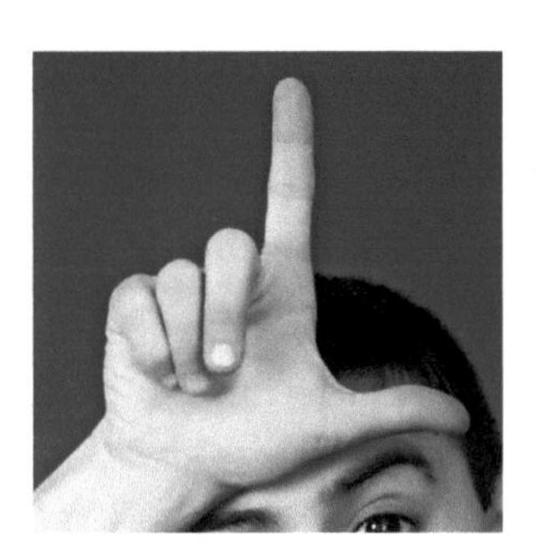

In meiner Kultur:

____

In China:
die Zahl 8

162g **Reflektieren: Was ist die Botschaft des Liedes „Welt der Wunder" von Marteria? Wie finden Sie das Lied? Kennen Sie Lieder mit einer ähnlichen Botschaft? Beschreiben Sie sie.**

49: Was bewegt zu nachhaltigem Handeln?

164f **Ein Gedankenfluss. Ergänzen Sie die bestimmten Artikel im richtigen Kasus. Achten Sie dabei auf die Präposition.**

Was motiviert Menschen, etwas gegen ________ Klimawandel (*m.*) zu tun? Ist es wegen ________ steigenden Meeresspiegels (*m.*) und ________ anderen Folgen (*pl.*) des Klimawandels? Oder machen die Menschen trotz ________ Probleme (*pl.*) nichts dagegen, weil sie statt ________ Lösungen (*pl.*) immer nur noch mehr Probleme sehen? Warten sie darauf, mit ________ anderen Menschen (*pl.*) aktiv zu werden? Wenn sie auf ________ anderen (*pl.*) warten[1], kann es natürlich zu spät werden. Wegen ________ hohen Kosten (*pl.*) warten viele Länder vielleicht auf[1] ________ anderen Länder (*pl.*), um selbst die Kosten zu vermeiden. Ist es dann unfair für ________ Länder (*pl.*), die zuerst etwas gegen ________ Klimawandel (*m.*) gemacht haben? Oder ist es für sie eher eine Chance, weil nachhaltiges Handeln immer besser ist? Zusätzlich kompliziert ist es dadurch, dass oft arme Länder wegen ________ Klimawandels (*m.*) größere Probleme mit ________ Kosten (*pl.*) haben. Trotz ________ Unterschiede (*pl.*) zwischen ________ Ländern (*pl.*) – oder gerade wegen ________ Unterschiede (*pl.*) zwischen ________ Regionen (*pl.*) – sollten wir dieses globale Problem mit ________ anderen Ländern (*pl.*) zusammen, also global, angehen.

[1] warten auf + *Akk.*

165a **Schreiben Sie über die preisgekrönte Titelseite der Bild-Zeitung, die Sie in MACHEN kennengelernt haben – wieso, weshalb, warum? Nutzen Sie „wegen" + Genitiv.**

Warum hat die Boulevardzeitung Bild im Jahr 2007 einen European Newspaper Award gewonnen? (ihre Titelseite)

Wegen ihrer Titelseite.

Wieso war diese Titelseite so dramatisch? (die visuellen Effekte)

____

Warum fanden die Leser*innen die Titelseite so faszinierend? (der Appell)

____

Weshalb ist die Sprache auf der Titelseite so schockierend? (die starken Wörter)

____

Warum nahmen die Journalist*innen Wörter wie „stirbt" und „Gefahr"? (das Katastrophenszenario)

____

Aus welchem Grund ist der letzte Satz („Und an allem ist nur der Mensch schuld") rot? (die Warnung an uns)

____

165b **Verstanden? Hier hören Sie vier Schlagzeilen aus den Medien zum Thema „Umwelt und Nachhaltigkeit". Schreiben Sie die fehlenden Wörter in die Lücken.**

Unser ______________ stirbt. Und wir ______________ dabei nur ______________.

Wir müssen etwas gegen die ______________ tun.

Die Erde ______________. Die Meeresspiegel ______________.
Wir sind dem Ende nah.

Fünf ______________, was wir alle für die ______________ tun können.

165c **In Aktivität 165b haben Sie vier Schlagzeilen gehört. Welche der vier Schlagzeilen motiviert Ihrer Meinung nach die Menschen am meisten zu nachhaltigem Handeln?**

Die effektivste Schlagzeile ist Nummer ________, weil ______________________________

____

____

166c **Reflektieren: In MACHEN haben Sie vier Beispiele für Nachhaltigkeitskommunikation kennengelernt. Wie hat Ihnen das Vier-Seiten-Modell dabei geholfen, über die Intention der Nachhaltigkeitskommunikation nachzudenken? Warum ist es wichtig, bei den Themen „Nachhaltigkeit" und „Klimawandel" die Funktionen und Strategien von Kommunikation zu analysieren?**

166d **Benutzen Sie Relativsätze, um alle Zusatzinformationen in den Hauptsatz zu integrieren.**

Hauptsatz: Firmen holen sich Rat, um Anzeigen effektiver zu gestalten.

Zusatzinformationen: Die Firmen (*pl.*) möchten Produkte verkaufen.
Fachleute bieten Rat (*m.*) an.
Die Botschaft der Anzeigen (*pl.*) ist besonders wichtig.

____

____

Hauptsatz: Was bewegt Menschen dazu, Gutes für die Umwelt und den Planeten zu tun?

Zusatzinformationen: Nachhaltiges Handeln ist den Menschen (*pl.*) egal.
Viele Leute schaden der Umwelt (*f.*) durch ihre rücksichtslosen Handlungen.
Die Zukunft des Planeten (*m.*) ist bedroht.

____

____

50: Nachhaltigkeit im Uni-Alltag°

167b **Meine Ressourcen: Zusammenfassung. In MACHEN haben Sie Ihre Antworten mit den Antworten einer anderen Person verglichen und dabei überlegt, was Sie anders machen möchten. Fassen Sie zusammen, was gesagt wurde. Beantworten Sie dafür die folgenden Fragen.**

Welche Ressource managen Sie am besten? Warum?

Ich manage die Ressource ______________ am besten.

____

____

Welche Ressource managen Sie am schlechtesten? Warum?

____

____

____

Was möchten Sie anders machen?

____

____

____

Hatte die andere Person im Kurs andere oder ähnliche Antworten? Vergleichen Sie.

____

____

____

168b **Meine Ziele: Nachbearbeitung. In MACHEN haben Sie Ihre Ziele als Student*in für die nächsten sechs Monate vorgestellt. Wählen Sie eines dieser Ziele und brechen Sie es in kleinere Schritte herunter, sodass der Weg dorthin einfacher wird. Folgen Sie dem Beispiel.**

Ziel: *Ich will besser schlafen.*	Ziel: ______
Schritt 1: *Gesundheit: Esse ich zu viel vorm Schlafen? Nehme ich Medikamente ein, die meine innere Ruhe stören könnten? Vielleicht Check-up beim Arzt.*	Schritt 1: ______
Schritt 2: *Den nächsten Tag schon abends planen: Was muss ich morgen tun? Was darf ich nicht vergessen? Andere Gedanken aufschreiben.*	Schritt 2: ______
Schritt 3: *Eine entspannte Atmosphäre vorm Schlafen herstellen: ruhige Musik, keine grellen Lichter, keine E-Mails oder Social Media, vielleicht Meditation.*	Schritt 3: ______

169b **Organisationen auf meinem Campus. Im Kurs haben Sie und die anderen Kursteilnehmer*innen Organisationen vorgestellt, die es auf dem Campus und auch in der Stadt gibt, wo Studierende Hilfe finden können. Beantworten Sie die folgenden Fragen.**

Welche Organisationen, die im Kurs vorgestellt wurden, kannten Sie schon?

______

______

Welche Organisationen kannten Sie noch nicht? Was machen diese Organisationen?

______

______

Glauben Sie, dass Sie eine von diesen Organisationen in der Zukunft aufsuchen werden? Wenn ja, welche ist das?

______

______

______

Welche Angebote, die es noch nicht gibt, würden Sie gerne auf dem Campus oder in der Stadt sehen?

______

______

______

170a  **Reflektieren: Managing my resources sustainably: opportunities and limits. You have now thought about and discussed the way you manage your time, money, and health; what works well and what does not work so well; and what you would like to change. Summarize in a few sentences what it is that you would like to do better and then answer the following questions:**

- Do you see yourself realizing the changes you are envisioning?
- What are practical resources you are planning on making use of, e.g., organizations on campus?
- Are there things you would like to change but do not think you can? If you answered the previous question with 'no': can you think of reasons why the life circumstances of other students might keep them from managing their resources more sustainably?
- Lastly, in which situations would you say we can or should cut ourselves some slack when it comes to our resource management?

170b  **Verstanden? Haben diese Personen eine nachhaltige Work-Life-Balance? Hören Sie gut zu und entscheiden Sie.**

ja	nein	
		Holger
		Namika
		Tina
		Jarne

51: Projekt 4 – Eine Kommunikationsstrategie°

171a  **Reflektieren: In MACHEN, your group developed a communication strategy that is meant to promote sustainable behavior within your region. Describe your strategy in a few sentences. How would you go about implementing your project in your community, e.g., the university or the city/town? How effective do you think it would be and why? Which aspects of the strategy would be most crucial for its success? Would you add anything that your group has not listed?**

171b 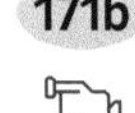 **Erzähl mal: Nehmen Sie ein kurzes Video (z.B. mit Ihrem Handy oder am Computer) auf und beantworten Sie die Fragen.**

Machen Sie etwas für die Umwelt?

Wie könnten Sie nachhaltiger handeln?

Wer könnte Ihnen dabei helfen?

Hatten Sie schon einmal ein Problem, weil es ein Missverständnis gab?

Was ist passiert?

Was war der Konflikt?

171c Self-Assessment

You now get a chance to reflect on the many things you have learned throughout the chapter. Carefully read through the "Can-Do Statements" below, and ask yourself if you can perform all of these tasks. It might be helpful for each of the statements to actually practice the communicative scenario. Once you are confident that you are able to perform a task, check the respective box on the left side.

- I can ask and answer questions about the definition, causes, and effects of climate change.
- I can compare viewpoints about environmental activism with classmates and have conversations about my own carbon footprint.
- I can understand key information related to sustainability and match it to visual and textual descriptors.
- I can understand information about an innovative product or project and why it reduces carbon emissions.
- I can answer questions about key information in informational texts about topics such as anti-nuclear energy movements.
- I can identify and describe fictional characters' emotional responses.
- I can talk about events that have had a strong impact on my life.
- I can use my language to identify and communicate strategies to achieve a better work-life-balance.
- I can create textual and visual artifacts that encourage people in my life to act more sustainably.
- I can give a presentation on topics I have researched, such as Green parties in different countries.
- I can use my language to exchange information that I have researched online.
- I can deal with the ambiguity inherent in interpersonal communication.
- I can use relative clauses in the nominative, accusative, dative, and genitive case, and with prepositions to elaborate on noun phrases.
- I can use idiomatic phrases to describe charts and tables.
- I can use the genitive case both with proper nouns and regular nouns to express possession.
- I can distinguish between genitive and the *von* plus dative construction to express possession.
- I can use masculine nouns that follow the n-declension in the accusative, dative, and genitive case.

- I am familiar with historical aspects of the German Green Party.
- I am familiar with the ramifications of climate change for wildlife and innovative German projects that promote sustainability.
- I am familiar with Friedemann Schulz von Thun's "four-sides" communication model.
- I am familiar with issues of sustainability in the fashion industry.

WER SIND WIR?
DEUTSCH IM PLURAL

52: PROMINENTE

172a **In MACHEN haben Sie Informationen über eine prominente Person kurz präsentiert. Schauen Sie sich noch einmal das Foto der Person an und beschreiben Sie sie mit sechs Wörtern.**

z. B.: Angelique Kerber: jung, blond, Sportlerin …

Name: ______________________

Wörter: ______________________ ______________________ ______________________

______________________ ______________________ ______________________

172b **Was glauben Sie: Wie würde sich die Person, die Sie in Aktivität 172a beschrieben haben, selbst beschreiben? Denken Sie, dass die Person mit Ihrer Beschreibung zufrieden wäre? Warum (nicht)?**

172c **Verstanden? Zwei Freundinnen, Miri und Sonja, unterhalten sich über berühmte Deutsche. Wählen Sie die richtigen Antworten aus.**

Warum mag Miri Sibel Kekilli?

- Sibel Kekilli spielt in „Game of Thrones" und Miri ist ein großer „Game of Thrones"-Fan.
- Sibel Kekilli ist die Hauptdarstellerin in Miris deutschem Lieblingsfilm.
- Miri hat Sibel Kekilli einmal persönlich kennengelernt.

Warum heiratet Sibel im Film „Gegen die Wand" einen Alkoholiker?

- Sie möchte ihm in seinem schwierigen Leben helfen.
- Der Mann ist ihr Ex-Freund und sie kann sich nicht von ihm trennen.
- Die Ehe ist eine Scheinehe, damit ihre Eltern denken, dass sie mit einem Türken verheiratet ist.

Hat der Film ein Happy End?

- Ja, denn die Liebe von Sibel und ihrem Mann ist stärker als ihre Probleme.
- Nein, weil die Eltern herausfinden, dass die Ehe nicht echt ist.
- Miri erzählt Sonja nicht, ob es ein Happy End gibt.

53: WOHER KOMMEN WIR?

173I **Migrationshintergründe in Deutschland. Welcher Artikel ist richtig?**

Die meisten Einwander*innen in Deutschland (67%) kommen aus (die | den) Ländern Europas, inklusive der Türkei.

Rund 1,5 Millionen Menschen haben (einen | einem) türkischen Pass, aber viele sind auch deutsche Bürger*innen.

Im Jahr 2018 lebten fast 10 Millionen Menschen ohne (einen | einer) deutschen Pass in Deutschland.

Von (diese | diesen) 10 Millionen Nicht-Deutschen sind aber 1,5 Millionen in Deutschland geboren.

Diese Personen haben (keine | keiner) eigene Migrationserfahrung.

Mindestens 61% aller Migrant*innen aus dem Ausland haben (die | der) deutsche Sprache aktiv gelernt.

173m **Personalpronomen im Nominativ und Akkusativ. Ergänzen Sie die Gespräche in der Mensa.**

Kannst _du_ mir die Nummer von Iris geben? – Tut mir leid, __________ kenne die Nummer auch nicht. Siehst du den Mann mit dem roten Pullover? Kennst du __________? – Nein, ich habe __________ noch nie gesehen.

Das ist Tobias. __________ waren Kommilitonen während unserer Studienzeit.

Wer ist diese Studentin? Ich habe __________ noch nie in unserem Kurs gesehen.

Paolo und Uma! Könnte ich __________ bitte kurz sprechen? (informell)

173n **Personalpronomen im Dativ. Ergänzen Sie.**

Wie geht es _dir_? – Gut, danke. Und __________, Hannah?

Guten Tag, Herr Schneider. Kann ich __________ einen Kaffee bringen?

Leo hat nächste Woche Geburtstag. Ich glaube, ich schenke __________ einen Gutschein.

Meine Schwester ist erst fünf. Zu Hause helfe ich __________, an die Keksdose ganz oben im Regal zu kommen.

Die Studierenden sind nervös, weil die Professorin __________ heute den Test zurückgibt.

173o **Lesen Sie den Text und entscheiden Sie: Was ist richtig?**

Kulturpunkt

In Germany, the German word for race, *Rasse*, is today intrinsically linked to Nazi ideology and the discriminatory racial hierarchy the Nazis used to justify persecution and murder. The Nazis didn't invent the term nor the political implications of categorizing people according to biological race constructions (scientists had developed racist theories before to justify colonialism and the oppression of people of color worldwide), but during the Third Reich, these theories reached a deadly climax and became the foundation for systemic mass murder. Germans, therefore, use the word today in a biological sense solely for animals and not for people. Because of the taboo, however, Germans have had a hard time acknowledging that race is a social category that continues to lead to everyday racism. Not using a word doesn't make the concept behind it (racism) disappear; on the contrary, it makes the victims of racism even more invisible. Talking about "xenophobia" or *Fremdenfeindlichkeit* (literally, hostility towards foreigners) instead reinforces racism. It deletes the structural dimension of racism and continues to exclude those who are perceived as foreigners from the German nation. Scholarly work has therefore begun to use the English term "race" in German texts, as this refers to the social (and not biological) construction of race. We will do this in *Impuls Deutsch* as well to be able to talk about the category and its real consequences for people of color. The latter, by the way, is also an English phrase that you will find in scholarly texts written in German. We also follow the convention of writing *Schwarz* with a capital S (this refers to the sociopolitical self-definition of Black people and not to the color) and *weiß* with a lower case w (this is a category of analysis introduced by Black scholars and not the self-definition of white people) because that is how German scholars of color (Noah Sow, for example) spell the words to mark their differing political implications.

Im Deutschen benutzen wir das Wort „Rasse" für Menschen nicht, weil:

- es keine „Rassen" gibt.
- die Nazis es für ihre Ideologie benutzt haben.

Stattdessen:

- sprechen wir nicht darüber.
- benutzen wir das englische Wort *race*.

174b **Blickpunkt: Anton Wilhelm Amo. Identifizieren Sie die Informationen für die fettgedruckten Wörter.**

Er war wahrscheinlich der erste afrikanische Student an einer europäischen Uni. _a_

Dort hat er studiert. _____

Das hat er studiert. _____

Das hat er geschrieben. _____

Das konnte er sprechen/schreiben. _____

Dort (3 Städte) hat er unterrichtet. _____

So wird er in Deutschland geehrt. _____

a) ~~Anton Wilhelm Amo~~
b) in Halle, Wittenberg und Jena
c) Philosophie und Rechtswissenschaften
d) an der Universität Halle und an der Universität Wittenberg
e) Deutsch, Griechisch, Französisch, Hebräisch, Niederländisch, Latein
f) vier Schriften, z. B. über die rechtliche Situation Schwarzer Menschen in Europa
g) Anton-Wilhelm-Amo-Preis der Uni Halle-Wittenberg für Studierende in Wittenberg

175b **Verstanden? In MACHEN haben Sie das Konzept der Superdiversität kennengelernt. Sie hören nun ein paar Beispiele für die Superdiversität Deutschlands. Tragen Sie in der Tabelle die richtigen Informationen, Zahlen oder Prozente ein.**

Bevölkerung Deutschlands	83 Millionen
Moscheen	
Synagogen	
christliche Kirchen	
Wie viel Fleisch essen Deutsche durchschnittlich im Jahr pro Person?	
Anzahl Vegetarier*innen	
Anzahl Veganer*innen	

Wie viel Prozent des Westniveaus verdienen Menschen in Ostdeutschland?	
Anzahl Singles	
Anzahl verheirateter Menschen	
Anzahl gleichgeschlechtlicher Ehen	
Alleinerziehende Eltern	

175c **Sie haben gelernt, dass Identitäten verschiedene Komponenten und Dimensionen haben. Schreiben Sie Ihren Namen in den großen Kreis. In die kleinen Kreise schreiben Sie dann Begriffe und Gruppen, durch die Sie sich selbst definieren würden, also Beschreibungen, die für Ihre individuelle Identität wichtig sind. Sie können auch Kreise leer lassen.**

Beispiele: Lateinamerikanerin, Mann, lesbisch, Vater, Sportlerin, Schwester, religiös, Student, Veganer …

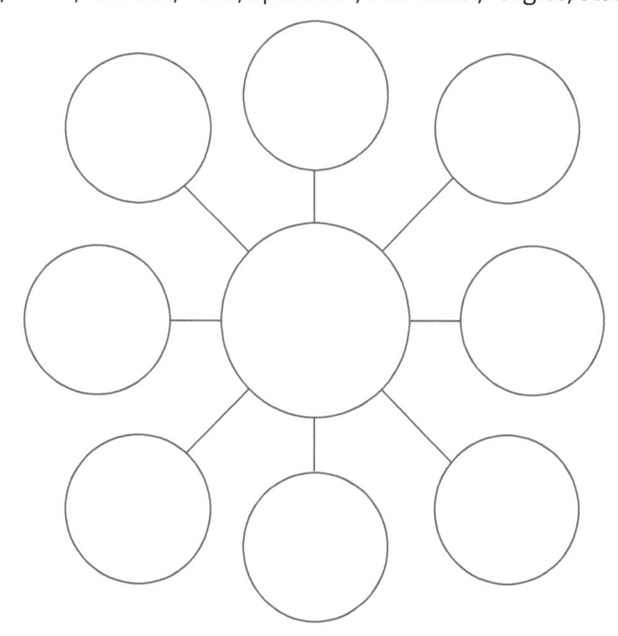

175d **Beantworten Sie die Fragen zu den Begriffen, die Sie in Aktivität 175c in die kleinen Kreise geschrieben haben.**

Erzählen Sie von einer Situation, in der Sie sich wohlgefühlt haben, weil Sie zu einer der Gruppen in 175c gehören.

____

____

Erzählen Sie von einer Situation, in der es unangenehm war, dass ein Element aus 175c Teil Ihrer Identität war/ist.

____

____

Was haben Menschen schon fälschlicherweise über Sie gedacht, weil Sie einer Gruppe angehören?

Beispiel: Ich bin Atheistin. Manche Menschen denken deshalb, dass ich unmoralisch bin. Aber das stimmt nicht.

____

____

____

54: DIASPORA

176a **Blickpunkt: Sawsan Chebli. Ergänzen Sie den Text mit den Informationen aus dem Steckbrief.**

Name:	Sawsan Chebli
Geburtstag:	26.07.1978
Zuhause:	Berlin
Eltern:	Deutsche (vormals staatenlose Palästinenser*innen)
dt. Staatsbürgerschaft:	1993
Studium:	Politikwissenschaft an der Freien Universität Berlin
Partei:	SPD
berufliche Laufbahn:	2010–2014 Referentin für interkulturelle Angelegenheiten Jan. 2014–Dez. 2016 Stellvertretende Sprecherin des Auswärtigen Amtes seit Dez. 2016 Bevollmächtigte des Landes Berlin beim Bund und Staatssekretärin für Bürgerschaftliches Engagement und Internationales in Berlin

__________ wurde am __________ geboren. Ihre Eltern waren __________. Sie bekamen in Deutschland Asyl und haben jetzt die __________ Staatsbürgerschaft. Chebli lernte erst in der Schule Deutsch. Im Jahr __________ wurde sie deutsche Staatsbürgerin. Sie studierte __________ an der __________. Sie ist eine __________-Politikerin und arbeitet heute als __________ in __________. Chebli ist Muslima und engagiert sich gegen Rassismus, Antisemitismus und Sexismus.

178e **Sie haben in MACHEN einiges über Ariel und seine Interessen erfahren. Er möchte ein Profil auf einer jüdischen Dating-Webseite erstellen. Helfen Sie ihm dabei.**

Ariel_156

16525688455

Mann sucht ____________

Aus: ____________

Alter: ____________

Über mich:

____

____

____

____

____

____

178f **Ariel erwähnt eine Meschugge-Party. Recherchieren Sie online und schreiben Sie ein paar Sätze: Was sind Meschugge-Partys? Wo gibt es sie? Würden Sie zu einer Meschugge-Party gehen? Warum (nicht)?**

Recherche

____

____

____

Kulturpunkt: Jüdisches Leben in Deutschland

"Hold on a second: ...

... who are Jewish Germans?" Today, Jewish Germans—whether they define themselves as culturally, religiously, or ethnically Jewish—are a diverse group with a variety of backgrounds. Some have lived in Germany for many centuries or generations, while the families of others were displaced from all across Europe during World War II and settled in Germany in the aftermath. But the Jewish community in postwar Germany kept shrinking, until the reunification in 1990.

After the Cold War, the German government eased the process of immigrating or returning to Germany for Jews from the former Soviet Union. They are known as Jewish quota refugees (*Kontingentflüchtlinge*), referring to the fixed number or quota of refugees admitted under this regulation. In the Soviet Union, being Jewish was considered a nationality, and Jewish cultural and religious life was suppressed, just like in the GDR. Today, Germans tend to treat Jewish identity as a religion, but ethnic heritage also factored into the category of the *Kontingentflüchtling*, since people would qualify as Jewish if they had a Jewish parent. Some Jewish Americans whose families fled Nazi Germany also (re)acquired German citizenship in the early 2000s, since new rules eased the process.

With the influx of *Kontingentflüchtlinge* into the German Jewish community, Jewish cultural and religious life experienced revitalization and growth but also change, with some synagogues becoming predominantly Russian-speaking environments and others insisting on stricter rules regarding who counted as Jewish. Not all *Kontingentflüchtlinge* reconnected with their Jewish heritage, since many had lost all cultural and religious ties. In the book *Russendisko*, for instance, Wladimir Kaminer writes humorous stories about finding out what his Jewish heritage might mean when he was moving to Germany as a young adult. He also put on popular *Russendisko* parties in the early 2000s in Berlin, where he played Russian music and played with Russian stereotypes.

In recent years, a lot of young Israelis have moved to Germany, especially Berlin. One of them, DJ Aviv Netter, has started *Meschugge Partys*, playing Jewish and Israeli music in clubs across Germany and attracting a predominantly LGBTQ+ audience, both Jewish and non-Jewish. Jewish life in Germany today has many facets, and a lot of non-Jewish Germans take great interest in the relatively small community. Many authors, such as Lena Gorelik and Olga Grjasnowa, have captured large audiences with their books about what it means to be Jewish in Germany for a generation that does not want their future to be defined only by the past.

178g  **Reflektieren: Religion, Kultur oder Biologie? What makes a person Jewish is a complex question that might be answered differently by individuals. Is it religious practice, cultural traditions, ethnic heritage, a feeling of belonging, or something else? According to Jewish law (called *Halakha*), anyone born to a Jewish mother is Jewish, whether they know of their ancestry or not. More recently, Reform Judaism has been accepting Jewish fathers as equally valid. Non-Jewish individuals can also undergo a religious conversion to Judaism, usually after taking classes at a temple and learning some Hebrew. But here is where it gets complicated: a person born in the Jewish community who converts to another religion will still be considered Jewish. That's why there are descriptions like a JewBu, a Jewish Buddhist.**

Do you know of other groups that define themselves based on heritage? What is heritage, and what kinds of heritage matter to you? Which aspects of your own identity do you attribute to your ancestry? You are welcome to write as much in German as you can or write in English.

178h **Verstanden? Cedric interviewt Jamal für ein Portrait in der Campus-Zeitung ihrer Uni. Hören Sie das Interview und beantworten Sie die Fragen.**

Warum ist Jamal nach Deutschland gekommen?

- Sie ist nach Deutschland gekommen, um Informatik zu studieren.
- Sie ist mit ihrer Familie aus Syrien nach Deutschland geflüchtet.
- Sie ist zu ihrer Familie nach Deutschland gezogen.

Was war für Jamal am Anfang in Deutschland am schwierigsten?

- Sie fand es schwierig, sich zu entscheiden, ob Deutschland oder Syrien ihre Heimat ist.
- Sie fand es schwierig, neue Beziehungen aufzubauen.
- Sie fand es schwierig, die deutsche Sprache zu lernen.

Wie definiert Jamal Heimat?

- Heimat ist für Jamal das Land, in dem sie lebt.
- Sie definiert Heimat als das Land, in dem sie geboren wurde.
- Für sie ist Heimat eine Kombination aus Sprachen und Beziehungen.

55: WAS ERZÄHLT UNSERE DNA?°

182b  **Blickpunkt: Mario Götze. Lesen Sie den Text und reflektieren Sie unten über die Fragen. Sie können Ihre Ideen auf Deutsch, Englisch oder in beiden Sprachen schreiben.**

Mario Götze war Patrick Owomoyelas Kollege beim BVB Dortmund und auch in der deutschen Nationalmannschaft. Er wurde 1992 geboren. Besonders bekannt ist Götze, weil er das Siegtor bei der WM 2014 gegen Argentinien schoss.

Vor seinem DNA-Test sagte Götze, dass er wahrscheinlich „fast 100 % deutsch" sei. Er wurde aber von dem Test sehr überrascht. Es zeigte sich, dass Götzes DNA tatsächlich zu fast 60 % mit der von Nord- und Westeuropäer*innen übereinstimmte, aber auch 12 % mit England, ungefähr 10 % mit Italien und noch 8,7 % mit Nordafrika.

Götze und die anderen BVB-Spieler, die den Test gemacht haben, überlegen: Sind wir wirklich deutsch? Reflektieren Sie darüber, was diese Frage impliziert und inwiefern Götzes Ergebnisse z. B. diese Identitätsfrage komplizierter und komplexer machen.

Sie können auch allgemeiner über diese Fragen nachdenken: Warum machen Menschen DNA-Tests? Was erhoffen sie sich davon? Was ist Ihre persönliche Meinung zu dem Thema? Können uns DNA-Tests dabei helfen, etwas über unsere eigene Identität zu erfahren? Wird unsere Identität nur von uns selbst oder auch von anderen für uns entschieden? Ist Identität nur individuell, nur sozial oder beides?

182c **Verstanden? Drei Personen sprechen über DNA-Tests. Hören Sie gut zu und beantworten Sie die Fragen.**

Was ist Timos Einstellung zu DNA-Tests?

- Er möchte einen DNA-Test machen, weil er sich sehr für seine Familiengeschichte interessiert.
- Er will Forschungsinstitute unterstützen und macht deshalb einen DNA-Test.
- Er hat Angst, dass seine persönlichen DNA-Daten verkauft werden, und macht deshalb keinen Test.

Warum ist Nika gegen DNA-Tests?

- Sie hat Angst, dass die Mitarbeiter*innen der Testfirma zu viel über sie wissen.
- Sie hat Angst, dass die Ergebnisse von DNA-Tests für Diskriminierung benutzt werden.
- Sie möchte nicht, dass ihre DNA-Informationen für die Forschung verwendet werden.

Warum findet Martha die negativen Argumente von Timo und Nika nicht stark genug?

- Martha denkt, dass ihre DNA-Informationen für niemanden interessant sind.
- Martha teilt gerne private Informationen mit anderen Menschen.
- Martha findet es super, dass man mit einem DNA-Test mehr über die eigene Geschichte erfahren kann.

56: Ein Krieg gegen Heterogenität und seine Folgen

184g **Blickpunkt: Hans J. Massaquoi. Schwarze Deutsche im Dritten Reich: Recherchieren Sie online (Texte, Videos etc.) und beantworten Sie die folgenden Fragen zu Hans J. Massaquoi in Stichpunkten.**

Recherche

Von wann bis wann hat Hans J. Massaquoi gelebt? ______________________

Wie hießen seine Eltern und wer war sein Großvater? ______________________

Was war Massaquois Einstellung (*attitude*) zur Hitlerjugend, als er ein kleiner Junge war?

____

Welche Erfahrungen mit Rassismus machte Massaquoi in Nazi-Deutschland? (Nennen Sie zwei Beispiele.)

____

____

Warum waren die Sportler Joe Louis und Jesse Owens wichtig für den jungen Massaquoi?

____

Wer hat Massaquoi und seiner Mutter geholfen, sich gegen Ende des Zweiten Weltkriegs vor den Nazis zu verstecken?

____

In welches Land ist Massaquoi 1948 immigriert? ______________________

Was war Massaquoi als Erwachsener von Beruf? ______________________

185c **Verstanden? Jüdische Menschen nach dem Zweiten Weltkrieg. Hören Sie gut zu und ordnen Sie die Satzenden (Buchstaben) den Satzanfängen zu.**

Während 1933 noch mehr als eine halbe Million jüdischer Menschen in Deutschland wohnten, e

Etwa 15.000 von ihnen waren deutsche Jüd*innen, _____

Nach dem Krieg emigrierten viele Jüd*innen, _____

Viele Jüd*innen gingen in die Sowjetische Besatzungszone zurück, _____

Aber der Antifaschismus in der DDR hatte zur Folge, _____

Seit 1991 nimmt Deutschland Jüd*innen und deren Angehörige aus der ehemaligen Sowjetunion auf; _____

Durch die „Kontingentflüchtlinge" _____

Seit 2005 gibt es wieder einen leichten Rückgang jüdischer Mitbürger*innen in Deutschland, _____

a) ... wuchsen die jüdischen Gemeinden in Deutschland auf circa 100.000 Mitglieder an und insgesamt gab es in den 90er Jahren knapp 250.000 jüdische Menschen in Deutschland.

b) ... weil sie sich durch die antifaschistische Staatsdoktrin in der späteren DDR willkommen geheißen fühlten.

c) ... die restlichen waren sogenannte „Displaced Persons", also jüdische Menschen aus anderen Ländern.

d) ... auch weil antisemitische Vorfälle in den letzten Jahren wieder zugenommen haben.

e) ... waren es 1946 nur noch etwa 74.000.

f) ... die Aufnahme dieser sogenannten „Kontingentflüchtlinge" sollte ein Signal historischer Verantwortung sein.

g) ... dass die Auseinandersetzung mit dem Holocaust in der DDR eher eine untergeordnete (*subordinate*) Rolle gespielt hat und jüdische Menschen wieder vom Staat unterdrückt wurden, so wie viele andere Gruppen auch.

h) ... vor allem nach Palästina oder in die USA.

185d **Schauen Sie sich noch einmal die Sätze in Aktivität 185c an und entscheiden Sie, ob die Aussagen unten richtig oder falsch sind.**

richtig	falsch	
		Nach dem Zweiten Weltkrieg wohnten ca. 59.000 Jüd*innen aus anderen Ländern in Deutschland.
		Aufgrund der politischen Ideale der DDR gingen jüdische Menschen nach dem Krieg nicht in die Sowjetische Besatzungszone.
		Die DDR hat sich aktiv mit dem Holocaust auseinandergesetzt (*dealt with*).
		Jüdische Menschen können sich heute in Deutschland sicher fühlen.

57: MADGERMANES

187b **Verstanden? In MACHEN haben Sie das Kulturschockmodell kennengelernt. Ehsan erzählt seiner Freundin über seine Erfahrungen mit Kulturschock. Kreuzen Sie hier die richtigen Antworten an.**

Welche Rolle spielt das Thema „Kulturschock" für Ehsan in der Schauspielerei und im wirklichen Leben?

- Für Ehsan ist Kulturschock nur ein Thema auf der Bühne.
- Für Ehsan inspiriert die Lebenserfahrung die Schauspielkunst.
- Für Ehsan müssen Leben und Schauspiel getrennt werden.

Wie und wann hat Ehsan die Erfahrung eines Kulturschocks gemacht?

- Ehsan hat vor allem am Anfang damit Erfahrung gemacht, nachdem er nach Deutschland kam.
- Ehsan hat diese Erfahrungen immer ignoriert und sich der neuen Kultur angepasst.
- Ehsan hat Kulturschock als nichts Großes erlebt, sondern als eine Vielzahl kleiner kultureller Unterschiede.

Wie denkt Ehsan über das Erfahren von kulturellen Unterschieden?

- Er denkt jetzt, dass es ein bereicherndes (*enriching*) Element in seinem Leben ist.
- Er denkt jetzt, dass es schwere emotionale Arbeit ist.
- Er denkt schon immer, dass es etwas Positives ist.

187c **Reflektieren: Haben Sie selbst schon einmal einen Kulturschock erlebt? Wenn nicht, kennen Sie jemanden, der Erfahrung damit gemacht hat? Interviewen Sie jemanden und berichten Sie hier.**

187d **Blickpunkt: Lucia Engombe. Lesen Sie den Text und entscheiden Sie, welche Aussagen richtig oder falsch sind.**

Afrikaner*innen, zum Beispiel aus Mosambik und Angola, kamen als Vertragsarbeiter*innen in die DDR. Auch ungefähr 400 namibische Kinder wurden in die DDR gebracht und wuchsen dort auf. Eine von ihnen war Lucia Engombe, die 1972 geboren wurde. Lucias Vater war im Widerstand (*resistance*) gegen die südafrikanische Regierung in Namibia. Deshalb musste die Familie fliehen. Sie gingen erst nach Sambia. Von dort wurde Lucia 1979 in die DDR gebracht, wo sie bis 1990 blieb. Nach der Wende, als auch Namibia unabhängig wurde, kam sie zurück nach Namibia, wo sie beim NBC (*Namibian Broadcasting Corporation*) arbeitet. Ihre Erfahrungen hat sie in dem Buch „Kind Nr. 95: Meine deutsch-afrikanische Odyssee" beschrieben.

richtig	falsch	
		Lucia Engombe wurde in Sambia geboren.
		Engombes Vater war gegen die südafrikanische Regierung.
		Engombe lebt heute in Deutschland.

187e **Recherchieren Sie Informationen über namibische Kinder in der DDR. Schreiben Sie 2–3 Sätze darüber.**

Recherche

188i **Glauben Sie, dass die namibischen Kinder ähnliche Erfahrungen wie die Madgermanes gemacht haben – sowohl in der DDR als auch nach ihrer Rückkehr nach Afrika? Warum (nicht)?**

____

____

____

____

188j **Was möchten Sie noch über die Madgermanes wissen? Formulieren Sie fünf Fragen.**

____

____

____

____

____

188k **Nomen und Pronomen im Dativ und Akkusativ. Schreiben Sie die Sätze viermal.**

Nom.: die Autorin (*f.*) Akk.: ein Roman (*m.*) Dat.: die Redakteurin (*f.*) Verb: geben

Akk.-Nomen + Dat.-Nomen: *Die Autorin gibt der Redakteurin einen Roman.*

Akk.-Pronomen + Dat.-Nomen: *Die Autorin gibt ihn der Redakteurin.*

Akk.-Nomen + Dat.-Pronomen: ______________________________

Akk.-Pronomen + Dat.-Pronomen: ______________________________

Nom.: der Redakteur (*m.*) Akk.: der Roman (*m.*) Dat.: der Verlag (*m.*) Verb: senden

Akk.-Nomen + Dat.-Nomen: ______________________________

Akk.-Pronomen + Dat.-Nomen: ______________________________

Akk.-Nomen + Dat.-Pronomen: ______________________________

Akk.-Pronomen + Dat.-Pronomen: ______________________________

Nom.: der Verlag (*m.*) Akk.: die Autorin (*f.*) Dat.: das Publikum (*n.*) Verb: vorstellen

Akk.-Nomen + Dat.-Nomen: ______________________________

Akk.-Pronomen + Dat.-Nomen: ______________________________

Akk.-Nomen + Dat.-Pronomen: ______________________________

Akk.-Pronomen + Dat.-Pronomen: ______________________________

58: Grenz-Identitäten°

190b **Blickpunkt: Elyas M'Barek. Lesen Sie die Kurzbiografie und schreiben Sie die Buchstaben der fettgedruckten Informationen zu den passenden Kategorien.**

Elyas M'Barek wurde am **(a) 29.05.1982** geboren. Er hat einen österreichischen Pass und ist in **(b) München** zu Hause. Er ist **(c) Schauspieler und Synchronsprecher.** Seine erste Rolle hatte er in der TV-Comedy-Serie „Türkisch für Anfänger". In der Comedy-Serie ging es um eine deutsch-türkische Familie und die Dekonstruktion von Stereotypen. Für diese Rolle bekam er den **(d) Deutschen Fernsehpreis.** Auch seine Kinofilm-Trilogie **(e) „Fack ju Göhte"**, in der er den Protagonisten Zeki Müller spielte, kam beim Publikum sehr gut an. Er wurde dafür mit mehreren Preisen ausgezeichnet und der erste Teil war mit 5,6 Millionen Kinobesucher*innen der erfolgreichste deutsche Film im Jahr 2013.

☐ Erfolg im TV ☐ Zuhause ☐ Beruf ☐ bekannte Filme ☐ Geburtstag

190c **In den beiden Statistiken unten sehen Sie Zahlen zu Menschen, die mit anderer Staatsangehörigkeit in Österreich leben, und zu Österreicher*innen, die in einem anderen Land leben. Interpretieren Sie diese Statistiken mit Blick auf Grenzen, Grenzverkehr und eine Europäischen Union „ohne Grenzen". Schreiben Sie 4–5 Sätze darüber.**

Ausländische Menschen nach Nationalitäten in Österreich, 01.01.2020:

Rang	Nationalität	Zahl der Personen[1]
1	Deutschland	199.993
2	Rumänien	123.459
3	Serbien	122.115
4	Türkei	117.607
5	Bosnien-Herzegowina	96.583
6	Ungarn	87.516
7	Kroatien	83.596
8	Polen	64.429
9	Syrien	51.502
10	Afghanistan	43.654
11	Slowakei	43.621

[1] Gezählt werden hier nur Personen, die nicht die österreichische Staatsangehörigkeit haben.

Österreicher*innen im Ausland insgesamt, 01.07.2019: 579.700 Personen

Land	Zahl der Personen[2]
Deutschland	257.000
Schweiz	65.000
Vereinigtes Königreich	33.000
USA	30.500
Australien	20.000
Spanien	12.000
Brasilien	10.000
Südafrika	10.000

[2] Diese Zahlen schließen nicht die Personen ein, die die österreichische Staatsangehörigkeit aufgegeben und eine neue Staatsangehörigkeit angenommen haben.

Quelle: Bundesanstalt Statistik Österreich

191c Sie hören einen diktierten Text über die gemeinsame Bewerbung der Städte Görlitz und Zgorzelec, die am Fluss Neiße liegen, zur EU-Kulturhauptstadt. Sie hören das Diktat dreimal mit unterschiedlichen Pausen. Schreiben Sie den Text auf, genauso wie Sie ihn hören.

____

____

____

____

____

____

____

____

____

59: Flucht, Ankunft, Kunst

193c **Blickpunkt: Hiwa K. Lesen Sie die Kurzbiografie und beantworten Sie die Fragen.**

Hiwa K ist ein Künstler, der 1975 im kurdischen Teil des Iraks geboren ist. In seiner Kunst kreiert er Videos, Skulpturen und Performances, die seine eigene Biografie mit Anekdoten seiner Familie und seiner Freund*innen zusammenbringen. Die Hauptgeschichten, mit denen sich seine Kunst beschäftigt, sind wichtige Themen unserer Zeit: Krieg, Migration, die Konsequenzen von Neoliberalismus und Kolonialismus. Sein Kunstwerk „When We Were Exhaling Images", das er in Kooperation mit Studierenden der Kunsthochschule Kassel konstruiert hat, und in dem er persönliche Erfahrungen von Flucht verarbeitet hat, war während der Kunstausstellung Documenta 14 im Jahr 2017 zu sehen.

Biografien haben oft ein Thema. Was ist das Thema von Hiwa Ks Kurzbiografie?

- Hiwa Ks Migrationsgeschichte
- Hiwa K als Künstler
- Hiwa K als kurdischer Iraker

Welche Informationen könnte man hinzufügen, um „Flucht und Migration" zum Thema der Biografie zu machen? Mehrere Antworten sind möglich.

- Datum, als Hiwa K den Irak verlassen hat, und Datum, als Hiwa K in Deutschland angekommen ist
- Hiwa Ks Studienfächer
- Hiwa Ks Erfahrungen als Migrant in Deutschland

Welche Informationen müsste man hinzufügen, um das Thema „Kindheit und Jugend" aufzugreifen?

- Informationen zu Kurd*innen im Irak
- Hiwa Ks Erfahrungen als Migrant in Deutschland
- wichtige Erlebnisse in Hiwa Ks Kindheit und Jugend (Schule, Freund*innen, Hobbys etc.)

193d **Relativsätze: Analysieren Sie Hiwa Ks Kurzbiografie grammatikalisch. Sie sehen hier die Relativsätze aus der Biografie noch einmal. Bestimmen Sie die Relativpronomen.**

Hiwa K ist ein Künstler, **der** 1975 im kurdischen Teil des Iraks geboren ist.

der ...
- steht für Künstler
- steht für Hiwa K
- ist Sg. Maskulinum
- ist Sg. Femininum
- ist Sg. Neutrum
- ist Plural
- ist Nominativ
- ist Akkusativ
- ist Dativ

In seiner Kunst kreiert er Videos, Skulpturen und Performances, **die** seine eigene Biografie mit Anekdoten seiner Familie und seiner Freund*innen zusammenbringen.

die ...
- steht für Kunst
- steht für Videos, Skulpturen und Performances
- ist Sg. Maskulinum
- ist Sg. Femininum
- ist Sg. Neutrum
- ist Plural
- ist Nominativ
- ist Akkusativ
- ist Dativ

Die Hauptgeschichten, **mit denen** sich seine Kunst beschäftigt, sind wichtige Themen unserer Zeit: Krieg, Migration, die Konsequenzen von Neoliberalismus und Kolonialismus.

mit denen ...
- ist Sg. Maskulinum
- ist Sg. Femininum
- ist Sg. Neutrum
- ist Plural
- ist Nominativ
- ist Akkusativ
- ist Dativ

Sein Kunstwerk „When We Were Exhaling Images", **das** er in Kooperation mit Studierenden der Kunsthochschule Kassel konstruiert hat, und **in dem** er persönliche Erfahrungen von Flucht verarbeitet hat, war während der Kunstausstellung Documenta 14 im Jahr 2017 zu sehen.

das ...
- ist Sg. Maskulinum
- ist Sg. Femininum
- ist Sg. Neutrum
- ist Plural
- ist Nominativ
- ist Akkusativ
- ist Dativ

in dem ...
- ist Sg. Maskulinum
- ist Sg. Femininum
- ist Sg. Neutrum
- ist Plural
- ist Nominativ
- ist Akkusativ
- ist Dativ

193e **Schauen Sie sich das Bild von Hiwa Ks Installation „When We Were Exhaling Images" an (Sie können es über Klett Augmented vergrößern). Beschreiben Sie es detailliert: Wie sieht das Kunstwerk aus? Versuchen Sie hier mindestens einen Relativsatz zu benutzen. Was ist die Botschaft? Kommt die Botschaft bei Ihnen an? Warum (nicht)?**

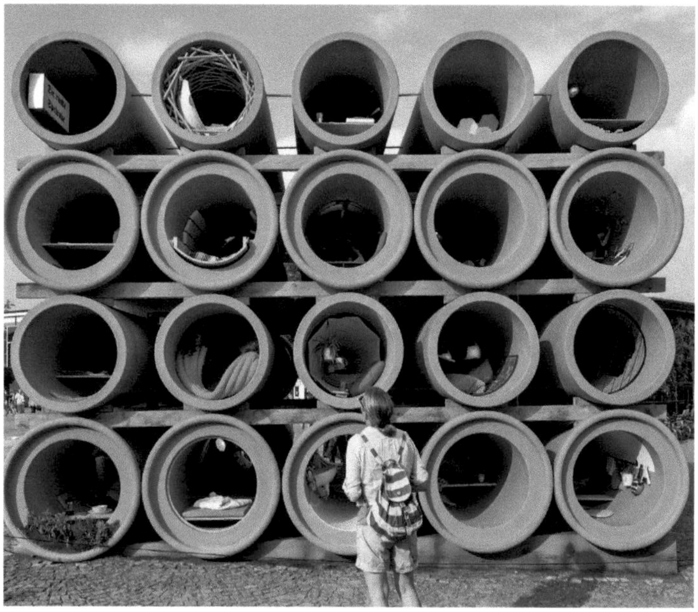

193f **Migration Experience and Art in the U.S.: *American Dirt*. Have you heard about the novel *American Dirt* by Jeanine Cummins and the controversy it has caused? The novel deals with a migration story from the perspective of a middle class Mexican woman and her son. The story is written to appeal to an American audience and for them to get an idea of the individual fates that make people leave their homes in hope for freedom and a better life. It was praised and endorsed by many people, among them Oprah Winfrey who picked it for her Book Club in early 2020. However, critics not only said that the novel is apolitical insofar as it doesn't shed light on the actual roots of forced migration; it has also been called stereotypical and opportunistically which was linked to the author's identity. Cummins, who identified as "white," also has a Puerto Rican grandmother. But she's telling a story that is not her own while other, more authentic voices exist but don't get as much attention.**

What is the role of art in the context of migration? Look at the statements and decide whether you agree or disagree. Then use your own words to express your opinion on this topic. You can either use German, English, or both.

Statements

Romane wie „American Dirt" ästhetisieren Migrationserfahrung (*migration experience*) nicht nur, sondern kommerzialisieren sie auch. Das ist unethisch.

stimme zu | stimme nicht zu | weder noch (*neither*)

Romane wie „American Dirt", die ein Mainstreampublikum erreichen (*reach a mainstream audience*), lenken mehr Aufmerksamkeit auf das Thema und helfen dabei, Migrant*innen zu humanisieren, die im öffentlichen Bewusstsein (*public awareness*) oft anonym bleiben.

stimme zu | stimme nicht zu | weder noch

Es ergibt keinen Sinn, darüber zu diskutieren, ob Autor*innen über bestimmte Themen schreiben dürfen oder nicht. Romane müssen nicht authentisch sein und die Kunstfreiheit darf nicht in Frage gestellt werden (*to question*).

stimme zu | stimme nicht zu | weder noch

Solange die Betroffenen (*those affected*) nicht zum Schweigen gebracht werden (*to be silenced*) und Raum für Selbstrepräsentation haben, stellt ein Roman wie „American Dirt" nur eine weitere Stimme in einem pluralistischen Diskurs dar.

stimme zu | stimme nicht zu | weder noch

Ihre Meinung: ______

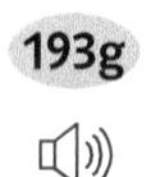

193g **Verstanden? Ein Filmkritiker spricht über den Film „Willkommen bei den Hartmanns". Hören Sie gut zu und beantworten Sie die Fragen.**

Wie thematisiert der Film das Thema „Flüchtlingskrise"?

- Durch die autobiografische Geschichte des Geflüchteten Diallo.
- In Form der Geschichte der Familie Hartmann, die einen Geflüchteten aufnimmt.
- Als Dokumentarfilm über eine Flüchtlingsfamilie.

Welche Rolle spielt Diallo für die Familie Hartmann?

- Mit der Hilfe für Diallo können die Hartmanns zeigen, dass sie moralisch gut sind.
- Um Diallo helfen zu können, muss die Familie auch ihre eigenen Probleme lösen.
- Diallo ist für die Familie nur ein Außenseiter.

Wie bewertet der Kritiker den Film?

- Er findet den Film sehr gut, weil er viele lustige Momente und eine gute Stimmung hat.
- Er findet, dass der Film das Thema „Flüchtlingskrise" zu oberflächlich und mit rassistischen Stereotypen behandelt.
- Er findet, dass eine Komödie ein gutes Genre ist, um dieses komplexe Thema darzustellen.

60: „TATORT DAF" (TEIL 1)

197b **Blickpunkt: Deutsche Krimis II – Ulrike Folkerts. Nehmen Sie den Steckbrief als Grundlage und schreiben Sie einen biografischen Text über Ulrike Folkerts. Schreiben Sie mindestens fünf Sätze. (Suchen Sie sich die Informationen aus, die Sie besonders interessant finden.)**

Name: Ulrike Folkerts
Geburtsdatum: 14.05.1961

Ausbildung

Schule:	Jacob-Grimm-Schule (Abitur)
Studium:	Theater und Musikwissenschaften nach vier Semestern abgebrochen, von 1982–1986 Schauspielerei an der Hochschule für Musik und Theater in Hannover

Berufliches

Beruf:	Schauspielerin
Rolle:	Lena Odenthal im „Tatort" (seit 1989)

Privates

Partnerin:	Katharina Schnitzler
Sport:	nahm an Gay Games und EuroGames teil
Engagement:	gegen Landminen, für Menschen mit Trisomie 21, Botschafterin von burundikids e.V., unterstützt Weißer Ring
Auszeichnungen:	Verdienstkreuz und Courage-Preis

____

____

____

____

____

____

197c **Buchauswahl: Sie haben viel über die sechs Krimis in MACHEN gelernt. Wählen Sie jetzt eines der Bücher aus. Bearbeiten Sie dafür die folgenden Schritte in der Checkliste.**

- Gehen Sie zu www.klett-usa.com/Impuls2Readers und kaufen Sie Ihr E-Book mit dem Code, den Sie auf der Seite vor dem *Preface* in MACHEN finden.
- Erstellen Sie sich einen Terminplan mit den Daten: Bis wann müssen/wollen Sie welche Seiten gelesen haben? Benutzen Sie dafür die Tabelle unten.
- Beginnen Sie mit dem Lesen des ersten Kapitels.

ID Einheit	Chiemsee	Heidelberg	Hamburg	Essen	Leipzig	Berlin
67	1-3	1-3	1-3	1-3	1-3	1-3
72	4-6	4-6	4-7	4-7	4-7	4-6
77	7-8	7-8	8-10	8-10	8-10	7-9

Important note: The reading assignments listed for units 67, 72, and 77 of *Impuls Deutsch* chapter 6 must be completed prior to that unit. For example, if your book is *Verschollen in Berlin*, you need to finish chapters 1-3 before we get to unit 67. In LERNEN for unit 67, you will answer several reading comprehension questions. Then you will discuss these chapters with other students and your professor in class (MACHEN for unit 67).

61: WAS SPRECHEN WIR?

198c **Lesen Sie den Text und beantworten Sie unten die Fragen.**

Ich bin oft ausgelacht worden
Eva I., 39 Jahre, Lehrerin, Nürnberg

Wenn ich mich zurückerinnere: Meine Erfahrung mit Dialekt ist sehr ambivalent. Einerseits habe ich mich immer sehr wohlgefühlt mit meinem Dialekt. Mein Vater hat ihn zu Hause gesprochen. Ich bin damit aufgewachsen. Und ich selbst habe ihn gern gesprochen. Aber schon bei meinem Vater konnte ich sehen: Immer wenn er beruflich mit Leuten sprach oder immer wenn wir an einem anderen Ort in Deutschland waren, hat er nur Hochdeutsch gesprochen. Dialekt, das war mehr für das Private, für zu Hause. Aber außerhalb wurde geswitcht. Ich habe auch noch genau in Erinnerung, dass ich früher oft von Bekannten ausgelacht wurde. So war ich einmal zu Besuch bei ihnen und sie haben mich permanent gehänselt (*to tease, bully*). Sie versuchten, die Worte in meinem Dialekt nachzusprechen, haben mich direkt nachgeäfft (*to mimic*) und ausgelacht. Das hat mich oft verletzt. Seitdem versuchte ich immer, meinen Dialekt möglichst zu unterdrücken (*to suppress*). Umso befreiender (*liberating*) ist es, wenn ich unter Leuten bin, die meinen Dialekt sprechen und bei denen ich sicher weiß, dass sie mich so akzeptieren, wie ich eben spreche.

Quelle: kaleidos.de (vereinfacht)

Wo sprach Evas Vater Dialekt?

- Wenn er gearbeitet hat.
- Bei Bekannten.
- Zu Hause.

Wo wechselte der Vater zu Hochdeutsch?

- Außerhalb des Hauses.
- Im Privatleben.
- Wenn er sich wohlgefühlt hat.

Wer hat sich über Eva lustig gemacht und wie?

- Ihr Vater hat sich über sie lustig gemacht, weil sie Dialekt nur zu Hause sprechen wollte.
- Freund*innen haben sich über sie lustig gemacht und haben ihre Fehler kritisiert.
- Bekannte haben sich über sie lustig gemacht, indem sie sie nachgeäfft und ausgelacht haben.

Wann fühlt sich Eva frei?

- Wenn sie zu Hause Dialekt sprechen kann.
- Wenn sie mit Leuten spricht, die auch ihren Dialekt sprechen.
- Wenn sie nicht sicher weiß, ob sie so akzeptiert wird, wie sie eben spricht.

199a **Blickpunkt: Maya Saban. Verbinden Sie jeweils die beiden Sätze zu einem Relativsatz.**

Maya Saban ist eine deutsche Sängerin. Sie wurde am 8. Oktober 1978 in Berlin geboren.

Maya Saban ist eine deutsche Sängerin, die am 8. Oktober 1978 in Berlin geboren wurde.

Sie ist die Tochter einer deutschen Jüdin und eines israelischen Juden. Sie leben in Deutschland.

Maya Saban hat das bekannte jiddische Lied „Adon Olam" auf einem großen Konzert gesungen. Als Kind sang sie das Lied auf Feiern.

Das inspirierte sie zu ihrem Projekt „Jewdyssee". In dem Projekt modernisiert sie jiddische Lieder.

199b **Finden Sie online das Lied „Adon Olam" traditionell und modern gesungen, z. B. von Maya Saban. Welche Unterschiede hören Sie? Was ist gleich oder ähnlich? Können Sie einzelne Wörter verstehen? Wie gefallen Ihnen die beiden Versionen?**

Recherche

200f **Verstanden? Tom hört, wie Marike mit ihrer Mutter telefoniert und mit ihr Dialekt spricht. Nach dem Telefonat unterhalten sich Tom und Marike. Hören Sie zu und wählen Sie die richtigen Antworten aus.**

Warum lacht Tom Marike am Anfang aus?

- Tom macht sich über alle Menschen, die Dialekt sprechen lustig, auch über seine Freundin Marike.
- Tom findet es lustig, dass Marike nur mit ihren Eltern Dialekt spricht.
- Tom findet Schwäbisch lustig.

Warum spricht Marike mit ihren Eltern Schwäbisch?

- Sie ist mit diesem Dialekt aufgewachsen und er ist ein Teil ihrer Identität.
- Marikes Eltern können kein Hochdeutsch.
- Marikes Eltern lachen Marike aus, wenn sie nicht Schwäbisch spricht.

Warum spricht Marike Hochdeutsch, wenn sie mit anderen Menschen spricht?

- Sie wurde oft für ihren Dialekt ausgelacht und das hat ihr sehr wehgetan.
- Sie kann auf Hochdeutsch ihre Emotionen besser kommunizieren.
- Mit Hochdeutsch hat sie einen neuen Teil ihrer Identität entdeckt.

62: Kulinarische Einflüsse°

201d **Blickpunkt: Ali Güngörmüs. Ali Güngörmüs ist ein berühmter Koch, der – wie Sarah Henke – mit einem Michelin-Stern ausgezeichnet wurde und auch Juror bei der Sendung „Die Küchenschlacht" ist. Finden Sie mindestens drei Informationen über seine Biografie. Schreiben Sie in ganzen Sätzen.**

Recherche

202a **Verstanden? Hören Sie gut zu. Welches Essen bestellen die Freund*innen im Restaurant? Markieren Sie die Speisen, die bestellt werden.**

Döner ohne Zwiebeln | Tiramisu | Wiener Schnitzel | Sauerbraten | Currywurst mit Pommes | Bratkartoffeln | Spaghetti Bolognese | Beilagensalat | Rindergulasch | Tofu-Curry | Veganes Gulasch | Pizza Hawaii

202b **Lassen Sie sich von den Gerichten in Aktivität 202 in MACHEN und dem Dialog in Aktivität 202a inspirieren und schreiben Sie einen kurzen Dialog im Restaurant. Welche Fragen stellt der*die Kellner*in? Was bestellen die Personen? Sie können Formulierungen aus dem Kasten und die Namen für unterschiedliche Gerichte aus Aktivität 202 in MACHEN benutzen.**

Ich hätte gern … | Haben Sie … | Ich möchte bitte … | Für mich …, bitte. | Habt ihr auch … ? | Ich probiere mal … | Ich nehme … und …, bitte. | Ich probiere mal … | Wisst ihr schon, was ihr wollt? (Weißt du schon, was du willst?) | Wollt ihr auch 'was essen? | Kann ich euch schon 'was zu trinken bringen? | Alles klar bei euch? Oder kann ich euch noch 'was bringen?

63: HEIMAT IN DER MUSIK

205d **Lese-Erinnerung und Lese-Strategien: In Einheit 67 sprechen wir über Kapitel 1–3 aus dem deutschen Krimi, den Sie momentan lesen. Wahrscheinlich haben Sie schon angefangen zu lesen; aber wenn nicht, kein Problem, denn Sie haben noch Zeit. Denken Sie an dieser Stelle einmal über die folgenden Punkte nach.**

On average, how many words per page did you have to look up in a dictionary thus far?

Number of words: ________________

Think of a sentence/passage where you did not know a word, but where the context helped you figure out the meaning of the sentence/passage. Describe (in English) the sentence/passage and how you figured out the meaning:

____

____

____

____

205e **In MACHEN haben Sie von den Künstlern in Aktivität 205 zwei Lieder gehört. Welches fanden Sie besser und warum?**

____

____

____

____

205f **Verstanden? Blickpunkt: Reyhan Şahin. Hören Sie Informationen über ihre Biografie und füllen Sie den Steckbrief aus.**

Bürgerlicher Name: ________________

Geburtstag: ________________

Künstlername: ________________

Beruf: ________________

Bekannt durch: ________________

____

____

____

206a **Im MACHEN haben Sie zwei deutsche Rapper kennengelernt, die sich mit dem Thema „Heimat" beschäftigen. Kennen Sie Musiker*innen in einem anderen Land, die auch zu einer Minderheit gehören und sich mit ähnlichen Themen in ihrer Musik beschäftigen? Worüber singen/rappen diese Künstler*innen? Wenn Sie niemanden kennen, machen Sie eine Online-Recherche.**

Recherche

____

____

____

____

____

____

206b **„Heimat“ in den sozialen Medien. Finden Sie zwei Fotos, die für Sie „Heimat“ repräsentieren. Schreiben Sie dann einen Mikroblog: Hashtags, Stichwörter oder ganze Sätze.**

Foto	Foto

______________________ ______________________

______________________ ______________________

__________ # __________ # __________ # __________

206c **Schreiben Sie, warum die Fotos, die Sie für Aktivität 206b ausgewählt haben, für Sie „Heimat“ repräsentieren.**

____

____

____

____

____

64: Projekt 5 – Eine Biografie

208a **Erzähl mal: Wählen Sie fünf Begriffe oder Bilder, die mit Ihrer eigenen Biografie und/oder Ihrem eigenen Leben zu tun haben. Nehmen Sie dazu ein kurzes Video auf (z. B. mit Ihrem Handy oder am Computer) und beantworten Sie die Fragen.**

Was bedeuten diese Begriffe und Bilder in Ihrem Leben?

Warum sind diese Dinge besonders wichtig für Ihre Identität?

Was haben sie mit Ihrer Biografie zu tun?

Denken Sie auch an die Elemente, über die Sie in Aktivität 175d geschrieben haben.

208b Self-Assessment

You now get a chance to reflect on the many things you have learned throughout the chapter. Carefully read through the "Can-Do Statements" below, and ask yourself if you can perform all of these tasks. It might be helpful for each of the statements to actually practice the communicative scenario. Once you are confident that you are able to perform a task, check the respective box on the left side.

- I can have simple conversations about celebrities I know and like and am able to explain what I like about them.
- I can give a creative presentation about a famous German person based on online research.
- I can understand the main ideas of statistics and graphics about cultural topics, such as migratory movements.
- I can exchange information about groups in diasporas and have a simple conversation about their experiences.
- I can understand personal stories dealing with questions of identity and the diaspora.
- I can understand and compare key information in texts about myths and facts about biology and race.
- I can identify essential information about discrimination, persecution, and genocide in the Third Reich.
- I can describe a linguistic map of the German Empire and a map of expulsion and compare the two.
- I can understand accounts reflecting on questions of identity in border regions.
- I can read and understand blurbs summarizing the content of crime stories.
- I can recognize words and structural patterns in *Plattdeutsch*, *Kiezdeutsch*, and Yiddish and understand their meaning.
- I can understand informational texts about intercultural issues, such as the cultural role of different food dishes.
- I can use my language to talk about how certain food dishes differ in their preparation in different countries.
- I can ask and answer questions about the concept of *Heimat* across different languages and what it means to me.
- I can distinguish German nouns in the nominative, accusative, and dative cases, and I can also replace nouns with pronouns in those cases.
- I understand basic rules about the sequencing (time-manner-place) of elements in the middle field of a German sentence.
- I understand the sequencing of accusative (direct) and dative (indirect) objects in the middle field of a German sentence.
- I can form W questions, as well as yes/no questions, around a broad range of topics.

- I am familiar with how artists engage with the topic of migration, flight, and expulsion.
- I am familiar with the socio-political connotations of non-standard German language varieties.
- I am familiar with the different phases people go through when they experience culture shock.
- I am familiar with the Madgermanes, former Mozambican contract workers in the GDR.

WIE UNTERHALTEN WIR UNS?

ALTE UND NEUE MEDIEN

65: HEUTE IM RADIOPROGRAMM

209h **Was ist passiert? Lesen Sie diesen Radiobericht über einen ungewöhnlichen Diebstahl (*theft*). Ergänzen Sie das Hilfsverb und die richtige Form des Partizips.**

Gestern ________ die Polizei in der Aachener Innenstadt einen ungewöhnlichen Dieb ________________________. (verhaften) Dieser Dieb _______ _________________________, ein Kilo Wurst im Supermarkt zu stehlen. (versuchen) Die Polizistin meinte: „Sowas ________ ich noch nie _________________________." (sehen) Warum? Nun, bei dem Dieb _______ es sich um eine Hundedame namens Frida _________________________! (handeln) Der Besitzer des Hundes ________ sich _________________________: „Ich ________ Frida nur einen Moment aus den Augen _________________________ und dann ________ sie direkt zur Fleischtheke _________________________." (entschuldigen; lassen; rennen) Ernsthafte Konsequenzen hatte der Diebstahl aber nicht für Frida, denn ihr Besitzer ________ das Kilo Wurst natürlich _________________________. (bezahlen)

211d **In Aktivität 211 in MACHEN haben Sie ein Video aufgenommen. Teilen Sie das Video mit Ihrem*Ihrer Professor*in.**

211e **„Gut gelogen?" ist eine wöchentliche Radiosendung mit Knut Pfeffer. Knut sagt etwas, das eine Lüge oder die Wahrheit sein kann. Bringen Sie die folgenden Lügenfragmente in die richtige Reihenfolge.**

Seine Mutter / seine Ex-Freundin / zur Poolparty / eingeladen / hat / .

____

von Kalifornien nach New York / Letztes Jahr / gelaufen / sind / wir / .

____

gegessen / Ich / leckeres Krokodilfleisch / habe / in einem Restaurant / .

____

schon / fünfzehn Mal / Sie / umgezogen / ist / .

____

eine Giraffe / habe / für den Kölner Zoo / gekauft / Ich / .

____

211f **Verstanden? Sie hören einen Radiobeitrag aus einer Sendung, in der der Radiomoderator Paaren bei Beziehungsproblemen hilft. Hören Sie gut zu und kreuzen Sie die richtigen Antworten an.**

Wie lange sind Anna und Natalia schon ein Paar?

- Sie hatten letzte Woche ihr erstes Date und hoffen, dass Andi ihnen hilft, ein zweites Date zu arrangieren.
- Sie sind seit fast fünf Jahren ein Paar, aber im Moment läuft ihre Beziehung nicht so gut.
- Sie sind gerade auf einem Blind Date in der Radiosendung.

Warum hat Anna die Sendung „Paare in Not" kontaktiert?

- Sie hat das Gefühl, dass Natalia ihr nicht mehr so richtig vertraut.
- Sie will die Beziehung mit Natalia beenden und braucht Andis Hilfe.
- Sie möchte Natalia einen Heiratsantrag (*marriage proposal*) machen.

Warum war Natalia in den letzten Wochen distanzierter?

- Sie hat eine Affäre mit einer anderen Person.
- Sie wird wahrscheinlich bald ihren Job verlieren und hatte Angst, Anna davon zu erzählen.
- Sie denkt, dass Anna sie betrogen (*cheated on*) hat.

211g **In Aktivität 211f hat Natalia Anna angelogen und gesagt, dass alles in Ordnung ist. Was denken Sie: Was war der Grund für Natalias Lüge? Kreuzen Sie die Gründe an, die Ihrer Meinung nach zutreffen.**

- Angst
- Scham
- Verlegenheit
- Intrige

66: PODCASTS°

212b **Deutsche Podcasts: zwei Beispiele. Unter www.klett-usa.com/impuls2links finden Sie die Links zu den Webseiten der Podcasts „Rice and Shine" und „Mensch Mutta". Besuchen Sie die Webseiten und füllen Sie die Tabelle mit den wichtigsten Fakten aus.**

Recherche

	„Rice and Shine"	„Mensch Mutta"
Sprecher*innen		
Thema/Themen		
Länge der Folgen		
zwei weitere interessante Details		

212c **Welchen der zwei Podcasts aus Aktivität 212b würden Sie lieber hören? Warum?**

____

____

____

____

____

212d **Hören Sie sich einen deutschen Podcast Ihrer Wahl an (mindestens fünf Minuten). Schreiben Sie auf: Welchen Podcast haben Sie gehört? Was war das Thema? Welche drei Wörter haben Sie verstanden / neu gelernt, die wichtig waren? Was wollen Sie noch über das Thema wissen?**

Recherche

____

____

____

212e **Verstanden? Mara und Jonathan sprechen über Podcasts. Hören Sie gut zu und kreuzen Sie die passenden Antworten an.**

Wann hört Mara Podcasts?

- ☐ Sie hört Podcasts auf dem Weg zur Arbeit im Bus.
- ☐ Sie hört Podcasts beim Trainieren im Fitnessstudio.
- ☐ Sie hört Podcasts am Sonntagmorgen beim Kaffeetrinken.

Was ist das Thema von Jonathans Lieblingspodcast?

- ☐ Jonathans Lieblingspodcast beschäftigt sich mit Fußball.
- ☐ Jonathans Lieblingspodcast ist ein Fitness- und Sportpodcast.
- ☐ Jonathans Lieblingspodcast wird von seinem Fitnessstudio produziert.

Was möchte Mara von Jonathan wissen?

- ☐ Sie möchte wissen, warum er Fußball so gut findet.
- ☐ Sie möchte wissen, ob er ihr auch andere Podcasts empfehlen kann.
- ☐ Sie möchte wissen, wann er sie wieder besuchen kann.

67: „TATORT DAF" (TEIL 2)

Bitte machen Sie die Aktivitäten, die zu dem Buch gehören, das Sie lesen.

„BÖSES ERWACHEN IN HEIDELBERG"

216d **Drei Ereignisse sind nicht geschehen. Welche? Kreisen Sie sie ein. (Kapitel 3)**

Emma nimmt am Karlsplatz die Bergbahn. | In der Bergbahn sitzen noch andere Leute. | Plötzlich glaubt Emma, der Mann mit den schwarzen Haaren sei auch in der Bergbahn. | Emma bekommt Angst. | Dann sieht sie, dass es ein anderer Mann ist. | Sie ist erleichtert und muss lachen. | Oben auf dem Berg scheint die Sonne. | Als Emma zum Schloss kommt, geht sie zuerst auf die Terrasse. | Dort hat sie einen schönen Blick auf Heidelberg und den Neckar. | Emma macht ein paar Fotos von der Stadt. | Aber dann friert sie und geht schnell ins Schloss.

216e **Wie heißt das Gegenteil? Finden Sie die passenden Wörter im Text. (Kapitel 3)**

viel	______	der Neubau	______
Person wegstoßen	______	sicher	______
sich beruhigen	______	schwitzen	______
hingehen	______	hell	______
einsteigen	______	langsam	______

„Die Lerche aus Leipzig"

215b **Was ist richtig? Kreuzen Sie an. (Kapitel 3)**

Die Hose von Udo Geißler

☐ passt gut. ☐ ist zu eng.

Udo Geißler ist

☐ zu dick. ☐ zu dünn.

Udo Geißler hat die Vase

☐ noch einmal gekauft. ☐ nicht noch einmal gekauft.

Beim Bezahlen hatte er dieses Mal

☐ ein Problem. ☐ kein Problem.

Seine Schuhe

☐ passen gut. ☐ sind zu klein.

Vor dem Auto von Udo Geißler steht ein Mann. Geißler

☐ bremst. ☐ fährt schneller.

Die Schwester von Udo Geißler heißt jetzt

☐ Geißler. ☐ Fischer.

Der Mann vor dem Auto hat

☐ schwarze Augen. ☐ blaue Augen.

216c **Was denken Sie? Schreiben Sie Ihre Antworten auf. (Kapitel 3)**

Warum passen Udo Geißler seine Schuhe nicht?

______

Wer ist der Mann mit den blauen Augen?

______

Warum sieht der Mann dieses Mal anders aus?

______

„Gefährliches Spiel in Essen"

215b **Wann war das? Notieren Sie. (Kapitel 1)**

1986 | 2001 | 1932 | 1847

Beginn des Bergbaus: ______________

Zeche Zollverein wird UNESCO-Weltkulturerbe: ______________

Zeche Zollverein ist die modernste Zeche der Welt: ______________

Ende der Kohle-Förderung: ______________

216c **Beantworten Sie die Fragen. (Kapitel 3)**

Wo wohnt Friso Breugel?

____

Wie heißt der Stadtteil von Essen, der im Text vorkommt?

____

Was, denkt Friso Breugel, ist passiert? Hat er einen Verdacht (*suspicion*)?

____

____

„Kalt erwischt in Hamburg"

216d **Was wissen Sie über Neles Exfreund? Kreuzen Sie an. (Kapitel 3)**

- ☐ Er trägt schwarze Kleidung.
- ☐ Er hat eine Tasche bei sich.
- ☐ Er trägt schwarze Schuhe.
- ☐ Er trägt einen Hut.
- ☐ Er trägt seine Sonnenbrille auch im Dunkeln.
- ☐ Er hat blonde Haare.
- ☐ Er ist sehr klein und dick.
- ☐ Er hat einen Bart.
- ☐ Er hat ein Tattoo im Gesicht.

216e **Der Dialog ist durcheinander. Wie ist die richtige Reihenfolge? (Kapitel 3)**

☐ „Oh …, Frau Brandt. Bitte kommen Sie herein. Ich habe unser Gespräch heute ganz vergessen, tut mir leid."

☐ „Hallo, Frau Brandt! Ich habe schon von Ihnen und der Reportage gehört. Klaas hat mir davon erzählt."

☐ „Frau Brandt, das ist Frau Lühders. Frau Lühders, das ist Birgit Brandt vom NDR. Sie macht eine Reportage über den Michel und seinen Trompeter."

1 „Entschuldigen Sie bitte, Pastor Dirkheide. Ich bin zu spät."

☐ „Kein Problem! Oh, Sie sind nicht allein."

☐ „Ich habe auch von Ihnen gehört."

„Verschollen in Berlin"

215c **Ergänzen Sie den Text. (Kapitel 1)**

Geschäfte | Klinik | Gebäude | Hochhaus | Büros

Hier im Norden liegen die __________________ der Humboldt Universität. In der Prachtstraße Unter den Linden gibt es viele __________________ und __________________. Das ist die Charité, unsere große __________________. Und hier im Süden sehen Sie das Sony Center, ein __________________ aus Glas und Stahl.

216d **Beantworten Sie die Fragen. (Kapitel 2)**

„Sie war also auf dem Weg." Woher weiß Jan das?

____

____

„Da stimmt was nicht!" Warum ist Jan sicher, dass etwas nicht stimmt?

____

____

„Der Schützenkönig vom Chiemsee"

215c **Welche Adjektive passen gut zu Mario? Kreuzen Sie an. (Kapitel 3)**

- [ ] intelligent
- [ ] sportlich
- [ ] böse
- [ ] __________________
- [ ] lustig
- [ ] gefährlich
- [ ] vorsichtig
- [ ] natürlich
- [ ] verrückt
- [ ] freundlich

216b **Nach dem Tod von Ludwig gibt es viele Fragen. Welche vier Fragen sind besonders wichtig? Kreuzen Sie an. (Kapitel 3)**

- [ ] Wann war Ludwig beim Schießen?
- [ ] Wer kann der*die Täter*in sein?
- [ ] Wo war Mathias vorher?
- [ ] Was ist wirklich passiert?
- [ ] Wo ist die Waffe?
- [ ] Was war das Motiv?
- [ ] Wie lange ist Ludwig schon tot?

216c **Für Kommissar Weigl gibt es zwei besonders verdächtige Personen. Notieren Sie die Namen. (Kapitel 3)**

Person 1: ____

Person 2: ____

68: NACHRICHTENMEDIEN

220f **Verstanden? Sie hören einen Ausschnitt aus einer Nachrichtensendung. Hören Sie gut zu und bringen Sie dann die Themen unten in die richtige Reihenfolge.**

- Zugverspätungen durch starken Sturm
- Das kalte Wetter in den kommenden Tagen
- Die Debatte um ein Tempolimit auf der Autobahn
- Das Treffen der Bundeskanzlerin mit der Bildungsministerin
- Die spannende Fußball-Bundesliga

220g **Lesen Sie diesen Artikel von Anfang Februar 2020 und vergleichen Sie ihn mithilfe der Tabelle mit dem Artikel aus LERNEN (Aktivität 220b). Schreiben Sie für jedes Kriterium einen Beispielsatz in die Tabelle.**

Epidemie-Alarm! Schon wieder drei neue Coronavirus-Fälle!

In einem kleinen Dorf in Bayern gab es letzte Woche drei neue Erkrankungen an dem gefährlichen Virus. Alle drei Personen arbeiteten bei der gleichen Firma. Die schloss nun komplett. Damit erhöhte sich die Zahl der Coronavirus-Infektionen um 400%. Auch die Politik bekommt langsam Panik. Das Gesundheitsministerium teilte mit, dass die drei neuen Patient*innen mit der ersten erkrankten Person Kontakt hatten. Damit war dies die erste Mensch-zu-Mensch-Infektion außerhalb von Asien. Die Bevölkerung wird immer unsicherer. Sind wir alle in Gefahr? Wie können wir uns schützen? Das Gesundheitsministerium informierte die Öffentlichkeit ausführlich über Symptome und Übertragungswege.

Aber es gibt auch gute Neuigkeiten. Forscher*innen in Australien schafften es endlich, das Virus im Labor zu reproduzieren. Die Hoffnung ist, dass sie nun im Labor einen Impfstoff entwickeln können. Damit kann eine weltweite Panik gestoppt werden.

Auch in Bremerhaven gab es vielleicht eine Infektion. Der Infizierte stand im Kontakt mit chinesischen Arbeiter*innen.

	Beispielsatz aus Artikel in LERNEN	Beispielsatz aus Artikel in ZEIGEN
Neutrale Informationen		
Analyse		
alarmierende Aussagen		
beruhigende Aussagen		

220h **Entscheiden Sie: Welcher der beiden Artikel aus den Aktivitäten 220b und 220g könnte aus einer Boulevardzeitung und welcher aus einer seriösen Zeitung stammen? Begründen Sie Ihre Meinung.**

____

____

221b **Ihre Campuszeitung hat seit ein paar Wochen auch einen Podcast. Dort werden die gleichen Nachrichten präsentiert wie in der Zeitung, aber etwas weniger seriös und in einfacher Sprache (also z. B. im Perfekt, nicht im Präteritum). Nehmen Sie Ihren Nachrichtentext mit Ihrem Handy als Audioversion auf und schicken Sie Ihre Aufnahme an Ihre*n Professor*in.**

221c **Nichts ist so alt wie die Zeitung von gestern! In dieser Einheit haben Sie einige tagesaktuelle Nachrichten vom Beginn des Jahres 2020 gelesen. Inzwischen hat sich die Welt weitergedreht. Welche Nachrichten gibt es heute? Suchen Sie in der Online-Ausgabe einer deutschsprachigen Zeitung (z. B. auf spiegel.de, zeit.de oder sueddeutsche.de) nach aktuellen Nachrichten. Notieren Sie unten zwei Schlagzeilen, die Sie wichtig finden.**

Recherche

Schlagzeile 1: ____

Schlagzeile 2: ____

69: Serienmarathon

223a **Eine Serienkritik. Lesen Sie die folgende Kritik zur deutschen Fernsehserie „Babylon Berlin". Schlagen Sie zuerst alle fettgedruckten Wörter nach. Umkreisen Sie dann alle konjugierten Verben im Präsens. Unterstreichen Sie alle anderen konjugierten Verben in einer anderen Farbe.**

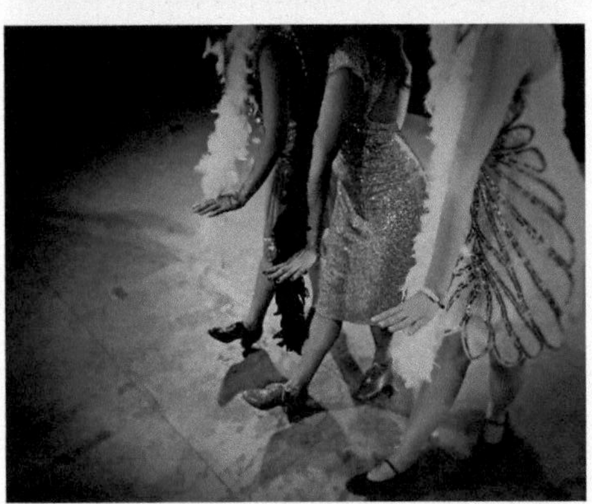

„Babylon Berlin" – opulent, aber mit wenig Herz

Bevor die erste **Staffel** von „Babylon Berlin" 2017 **ausgestrahlt** wurde, hatte sich die Krimi-Fernsehserie von Starregisseur Tom Tykwer schon einen Namen gemacht: nämlich als die teuerste deutsche Fernsehproduktion aller Zeiten. Und opulent sollte es werden, wild und dunkel, im Herzen der Weimarer Republik. Doch kann „Babylon Berlin" dieses Versprechen halten?

Die acht Folgen der ersten Staffel basieren auf dem Roman „Der kalte Fisch" von Volker Kutscher. Der Kölner **Kommissar** Gereon Rath (Volker Bruch) kommt 1929 nach Berlin, wo er einen Pornoring **entlarven** soll. Schnell gerät er ins Visier der Berliner Unterwelt, die ihn mit allen Mitteln stoppen will. Ihm zur Seite stehen Oberkommissar Bruno Wolter (Peter Kurth) sowie Charlotte Ritter (Liv Lisa Fries), die davon träumt, eines Tages Polizistin zu werden. Die **Ermittlung** findet vor der **Kulisse** des wilden Berliner Nachtlebens und politischer Unruhen statt.

Eines ist „Babylon Berlin" mit Sicherheit: ein opulentes Spektakel fürs Auge. Die Kulissen, ebenso wie die Kostüme, sind historisch akkurat und mit viel Liebe zum Detail gestaltet. Die Szenen in den Nachtclubs sind **berauschend**, die Actionszenen **atemberaubend**. Leider ist das bei der **Leistung** der Schauspieler*innen nicht immer so. Vor allem Bruch und Fries schaffen es oftmals nicht, ihren Figuren echte Gefühle – ein Herz – zu geben. Und so lassen einen selbst Gereons **Abstieg** in die Morphium**sucht** und Charlottes schreckliche Familienverhältnisse kalt.

Tykwers Neo-Noir-Produktion ist ein beeindruckendes visuelles Abenteuer für Fans von **aufwendigen** Sets und Kostümen. Eine Serie mit Figuren, die interessante Geschichten haben, ist es aber bisher nicht. Es lässt sich nur hoffen, dass vor allem Kommissar Gereon Rath in den nächsten Staffeln sympathischer **rüberkommt**.

223b **Struktur einer Kritik. Hier sehen Sie die verschiedenen Teile einer Film- und Serienkritik, aber in der falschen Reihenfolge. Lesen Sie noch einmal die Kritik aus Aktivität 223a und bringen Sie die Elemente in die richtige Reihenfolge.**

___ Die Bewertung: Hier sagen die Kritiker*innen, ob ihnen die Serie oder der Film gefallen hat und warum (nicht). Wichtige Punkte für die Kritik sind auch die Leistung der Schauspieler*innen, die Kulissen (*sets*), die Kostüme und die Musik.

1 Die Überschrift: Der Titel einer Kritik sollte das Interesse der Leser*innen wecken. Hier benutzen Kritiker*innen oft eine Frage als Überschrift oder provokante Adjektive, um einen Hinweis (*clue*) auf die Meinung der Kritik zu geben.

___ Die Einleitung: In den ersten Sätzen einer Film- oder Serienkritik werden oft Zitate oder interessante Fakten präsentiert. Auch nennen Kritiker*innen hier das Genre, den*die Regisseur*in sowie das Jahr der Veröffentlichung.

___ Der Schluss: Am Ende der Kritik sagen die Kritiker*innen ganz kurz, ob sie den Film oder die Serie empfehlen würden.

___ Die Handlung: In diesem Teil beschreiben die Kritiker*innen die Handlung und die Protagonist*innen, ohne aber zu viel zu verraten (*give away*).

223c **Eine Kritik schreiben. Wählen Sie nun eine Fernsehserie, die Sie gut kennen, und schreiben Sie eine Kritik. Folgen Sie der Struktur, wie sie in Aktivität 223b beschrieben wird. Hier sehen Sie für die Abschnitte „Handlung", „Bewertung" und „Schluss" einige nützliche Redemittel. Schlagen Sie neue Wörter nach.**

Handlung (3–4 Sätze)
- Der Film spielt in/im …
- Der Film erzählt die Geschichte von …
- Es geht um …
- Der*Die Protagonist*in / Die Hauptfigur ist …
- Er*Sie hat die Aufgabe … (zu + Infinitiv)
- Das Thema des Films wird durch … repräsentiert.
- Man sieht …

Bewertung (4–5 Sätze)
- positiv: beeindruckend, spektakulär, imposant, rasant, überzeugend, einfühlsam, sympathisch, humorvoll, opulent, berauschend, mitreißend, spannend …
- negativ: nicht sehr (positives Adjektiv), enttäuschend, langweilig, verwirrend, übertrieben, ernüchternd, herzlos, klischeehaft, unoriginell, brutal …

Schluss (2–3 Sätze)
- Alles in allem (Verb) …
- Die Serie ist sehr zu empfehlen, weil …
- Obwohl die Serie Schwächen hat, (Verb) …
- Wer Serien wie … mag, dem wird auch … gefallen.

223d **Verstanden? Samira und Nadia sprechen über ihre Lieblingsserien und planen einen Filmabend. Hören Sie gut zu und kreuzen Sie die richtigen Antworten an.**

Was sagen Samira und Nadia über die Serie „Dark"?

- Sie einigen sich darauf, „Dark" zu schauen, weil sie beide unheimliche Sendungen mögen.
- Sie schauen beide seit einer Woche „Dark".
- Sie entscheiden, dass sie „Dark" nicht gemeinsam schauen werden.

Was ist Nadias Meinung zur Serie „Transparent"?

- Sie fühlt sich als trans* Person von der Serie „Transparent" repräsentiert.
- Sie ist der Meinung, dass die trans* Figur in „Transparent" von einer trans* Person porträtiert werden sollte.
- Sie stimmt zu, mit Samira „Transparent" zu schauen.

Worauf einigen sich die beiden Freund*innen?

- Sie werden doch keinen Filmabend machen.
- Sie wollen sich nur mehr über „Transparent" unterhalten. Sie werden sich am Freitag bei Samira treffen.
- Sie werden eine Folge von „The Marvellous Mrs. Maisel" schauen.

70: „TATORT" – EINE LEIDENSCHAFT°

224b **Verstanden? In größeren Städten gibt es sogenannte „Tatort"-Kneipen, kleine Bars, wo sich Menschen treffen, um „Tatort" zu schauen. Jetzt lernen Sie eine „Tatort"-Kneipe in Berlin kennen. Hören Sie gut zu und wählen Sie die richtigen Antworten aus.**

Warum ist die Volksbar eine besondere „Tatort"-Kneipe?

- Die Gäst*innen müssen nur 5 Euro Eintritt (*admission fee*) bezahlen, um den „Tatort" schauen zu können.
- In der Volksbar finden mehr als 100 Personen Platz und es gibt bequeme Sofas.
- In der Volksbar gibt es nur alkoholfreie Getränke und man darf nicht rauchen.

Warum schauen Menschen „Tatort" in dieser Bar?

- „Tatort" wird dort auf einer großen Leinwand gezeigt.
- Man bekommt immer einen guten Platz in der Bar.
- „Tatort" wird mit Live-Musik gezeigt.

Wann hat die Volksbar geöffnet und wann nicht?

- Die Bar ist montags geschlossen.
- Die Bar hat sonntags ab 11 Uhr geöffnet.
- Die Bar hat freitags ab 17 Uhr geöffnet.

226h **Vergleichen Sie die persönlichen Geschichten der Kommissar*innen, die Sie in MACHEN in Aktivität 226 kennengelernt haben, mit Ermittler*innen in TV-Shows aus Ihrem Heimatland. Wo sehen Sie Parallelen und Unterschiede?**

____

____

226i **Gehen Sie zur ARD-Mediathek, suchen Sie sich eine Folge der Serie „Tatort" aus und schauen Sie mindestens 30 Minuten rein. (Vielleicht sind Sie auf das Ende gespannt, dann schauen Sie gerne weiter.) Schreiben Sie danach drei Sätze über Ihre Eindrücke und/oder worum es in der Folge ging.**

Recherche

____

____

____

KULTURPUNKT: SERIOUSLY FUNNY

"Hold on a second: ...

... are Germans always serious?" You learned in MACHEN that Germans love to watch *Krimis* and that, in contrast to the U.S., no comedy makes it into the list of the most watched television shows. Does that prove the stereotype that Germans really don't have a sense of humor?

We have a saying in German: *Humor ist, wem es gefällt*, which loosely translates to "humor is who likes it" and which means that people find different things funny or not funny at all. While you won't find the autostereotype in Germany that Germans are not funny, there are regions in Germany that are perceived as unfunny. The Rhineland, for example, likes to market itself as a friendly, outgoing area, where people like to celebrate and have fun (*Karneval*, for example), while Westphalia serves as the unfunny counterpart (within the same *Bundesland*). You may hear the saying that some people *gehen zum Lachen in den Keller*, meaning they "go to the basement to laugh", which reinforces such (of course, completely untrue) stereotypes.

Outside of Germany the stereotype that Germans are humorless may stem from the films that Germans are most known for: pretty heavy and serious, historical films about the Third Reich, for instance, or about the GDR. Here, we also see, however, that Germans not only use drama and tragedy to work through their recent history but also comedy with films like *Good Bye, Lenin!* There are even films now that try to look back at the Third Reich with a comical lens. A recent film, based on a book by Timur Vermes, titled *Er ist wieder da* (*Look Who's Back* in the English translation) places Hitler in today's Germany where he awakes from a coma, is seen as an impersonator, advances to a television star, and attempts to continue his racist politics. The book and film caused some controversy, also asking: what is humor allowed to do? What is satire? And can we really make fun about this part of our past (yet)?

Despite the stereotype, there is a longstanding tradition of satirical shows in Germany. One of these shows, *Mitternachtsspitzen*, has been on air since 1988 and represents a German kind of comedy that is called *politisches Kabarett*. The word is difficult to translate because it is not quite the same as cabaret, and it is also not stand-up or comedy but is rather a sophisticated form of satire, one that has been popular with Germans for a long time (both on television and on stage). There is also "comedy," which resembles American stand-up and shows that have been inspired by U.S. traditions, such as the *heute-show*, which is a little bit like John Oliver's *Last Week Tonight*. Its predecessor, *Die Wochenshow*, produced some of the most awarded comedians in German television, such as Anke Engelke, who won the German comedy prize 19 times (including several for her comedy show *Ladykracher*). Many U.S. comedy shows do well in Germany: *The Big Bang Theory* and *How I Met Your Mother* are two that drew huge audiences. There have also been remakes for popular comedy shows, such as *The Office*, which in German is called *Stromberg*. These shows may not make it on the international stage but they are ever-present on German television.

Like in any country, there is no single form of "German" humor: anyone can find something they like and can laugh about, because *Humor ist, wem's gefällt.*

226j **Reflektieren: What kind of comedy/humor do you like/dislike? Do you ever feel at odds with people you know because of the humor they or you like? Do you think humor is cultural, social, or individual/personal?**

71: INKLUSIVES FERNSEHEN TRANSNATIONAL

227g **Hypothesen über das Fernsehen. Spekulieren Sie: Was erwarten Sie in/von TV-Sendungen in der Zukunft?**

Themen: ____________________ *... werden Themen im Fernsehen sein.*

Publikum: *Das Publikum wird ...* ____________________

Sprache: ____________________

Bilder: ____________________

Quellen: ____________________

kein Thema: ____________________

228a **Reflektieren: Shows like *Queer Eye / Queer 4 You* or *RuPaul's Drag Race / Queen of Drags* create visibility for the LGBTQ+ community in mainstream media. Do you think the TV show format is a powerful platform for this kind of activism? And what are its potential limitations/problems?**

228b **Verstanden? Bei „Queer 4 You" helfen die Experten den Kandidat*innen mit einem Makeover. Jetzt hören Sie ein Gespräch zwischen Jorne und Tim, in dem es um dieses Thema geht. Wählen Sie die richtigen Antworten aus.**

Was möchte Tim an seinen Haaren verändern?

- Er möchte seine Haare kürzer schneiden.
- Er möchte mit einer neuen Haarfarbe experimentieren.
- Er möchte, dass Jorne ihm einen Vorschlag für eine neue Frisur macht.

Wie soll Jornes neue Kleidung aussehen?

- Jorne möchte ein paar dunkle Kleidungsstücke kaufen, weil das schick ist.
- Jorne möchte Kleidung, mit der er jünger aussieht, weil er sich alt fühlt.
- Jorne möchte mehr bunte Kleidungsstücke, weil seine Kleidung im Moment sehr langweilig ist.

Warum möchte Tim am Makeover-Tag Kosmetikprodukte ausprobieren?

- Er hat seinen Bart abrasiert und deswegen ist seine Haut gereizt (*irritated*).
- Er wird immer sehr schnell rot im Gesicht und möchte deswegen mit Make-up experimentieren.
- Seine Haut ist immer sehr trocken und er möchte sie besser pflegen.

72: „TATORT DAF" (TEIL 3)

Bitte machen Sie die Aktivitäten, die zu dem Buch gehören, das Sie lesen. Auf Seite 123 gibt es eine Aktivität für alle Bücher.

„BÖSES ERWACHEN IN HEIDELBERG"

231c **Was denken Sie? Beantworten Sie die Fragen. (Kapitel 4)**

Wie kommt der Unterkiefer des „Homo heidelbergensis" in Emmas Handtasche?

____

Warum möchte der Mann die Handtasche?

____

231d **Was war das? Notieren Sie. (Kapitel 5)**

die Türklinke | die Kräuter | zerdrücken | der Chili | der Schlüssel

ein Gewürz, das sehr scharf ist ________________

ein kleines Metallinstrument, mit dem man eine Tür auf- oder zuschließt ________________

Man drückt sie hinunter, um eine Tür aufzumachen. ________________

Pflanzen, mit denen man das Essen würzt ________________

klein machen ________________

„Die Lerche aus Leipzig"

232d Was wissen Sie über das frühere Leben von Udo Geißler? Kreuzen Sie an. (Kapitel 6)

- Er war Inoffizieller Mitarbeiter der Stasi.
- Seine Arbeit früher war geheim.
- Nur seine Familie hat von der Arbeit gewusst.
- Früher hat er gedacht, es ist falsch, was er tut.
- Er hat Menschen schikaniert, überwacht und gefoltert.
- Er hat gedacht, alle Dokumente mit seinem Namen sind zerstört worden.

232e Was gibt es heute in dem Museum in der Runden Ecke? Kreuzen Sie an. (Kapitel 6)

- Büros
- Waffen
- ein Café
- Tiere
- Koffer mit Kleidung
- eine Maschine zum Öffnen von Briefen
- Räume zum Befragen von Personen

„Gefährliches Spiel in Essen"

231c Was steht im Text? Notieren Sie. (Kapitel 4)

Colosseum

Heute eine Halle für ...

Margarethenhöhe

Villa Hügel

Baldeneysee

Grugapark

231d Beantworten Sie die Fragen. (Kapitel 5)

Was passiert auf der Treppe des Stadions?

Wen sieht Friso Breugel?

„KALT ERWISCHT IN HAMBURG"

231c **Finden Sie die richtige Antwort. (Kapitel 5)**

Warum kommen Nele und der Pastor nicht auf das Terminalgelände?

____

Wem gehört der Schatten, den Nele und der Pastor sehen?

____

Warum schafft es Nele ohne Probleme, Ole einen kräftigen Tritt zu geben?

____

Was denkt Nele, wo Klaas ist?

____

Wie kommen Nele und der Pastor doch auf das Terminalgelände?

____

232d **Wie heißt das Gegenteil? Finden Sie die passenden Wörter. (Kapitel 6)**

zumachen	________	hell	________
heiß	________	schnell	________
nach rechts	________	leise	________
jemand	________	flüstern	________
dünn	________	ausziehen	________

232e **Finden Sie die richtige Antwort. (Kapitel 7)**

Wo verstecken sich Nele und der Pastor?

____

Was meint der Pastor, wo Klaas ist?

____

Wen versucht der Pastor auf seinem Handy zu erreichen?

____

Wie sieht das Symbol für einen Kühlschrank aus?

____

„VERSCHOLLEN IN BERLIN"

231d **In welcher Reihenfolge fährt Jan mit dem Schiff an den Sehenswürdigkeiten vorbei? (Kapitel 5)**

☐ der Marstall	☐ Bundeskanzler*innenamt	☐ Bundespresseamt
☐ Haus der Kulturen der Welt	☐ Museumsinsel	☐ Reichstag
1 Jannowitzbrücke		

„Der Schützenkönig vom Chiemsee"

232b **Woran denkt Mathias oben auf dem Berg? Wählen Sie aus und umkreisen Sie. (Kapitel 6)**

3 = sehr intensiv; 2 = weniger intensiv; 1 = nur ein bisschen

3 2 1 Ich mag diesen Berg sehr.

3 2 1 Wo kann ich den Rucksack lassen?

3 2 1 Das war der Lieblingsberg von Vater.

3 2 1 Wer kümmert sich jetzt um meine Mutter?

3 2 1 Kann ich im Herbst studieren?

3 2 1 Die Leute sollen den Rucksack nicht finden!

3 2 1 Ich muss eine andere Möglichkeit finden.

Aktivität für alle Bücher

232x **Was finden Sie bisher in Ihrem Buch am interessantesten? Warum? Schreiben Sie 4–5 Sätze.**

____

____

____

____

____

____

____

____

233c **Verstanden? Sie hören nun einen Text aus einer weiteren Kriminalgeschichte. Achten Sie auf die Reihenfolge der Ereignisse. Was hören Sie zuerst, dann, danach, anschließend und schließlich? Schreiben Sie die Temporaladverbien in der richtigen Reihenfolge vor die Satzteile.**

__________ verkauft Hanna in der Boutique und an anderen Orten die Uhren.

__________ wird klar: Niemand außer Gerd weiß, dass die Uhren in den Paketen sind.

__________ legen Gerd und Hanna die Preise für die Uhren fest.

Zuerst kommen die Pakete per Flugzeug in Friedrichshafen an.

__________ bringt Gerd die Uhren dann gleich nach Bregenz.

Kulturpunkt: Ostdeutsche Filmproduktion

"Hold on a second: …

… what was DEFA and what was it all about?" Film production in East and West Germany started off under very different circumstances. The allied cultural administrators in the Western Zones (U.S., French, British) viewed any new beginning under German personnel as too risky (given the history of filmmaking under the Nazis), and at the same time saw the German market as a new market for their own films. Meanwhile, the Soviet Union was eager to get filmmaking going again so it could play a role in what was called the "anti-fascist, democratic renewal." It set up DEFA (*Deutsche Filmaktiengesellschaft*, "German Film Corporation") with its studio in Babelsberg near Potsdam.

The first German-made film that came out of the Western Zone was indeed made by a former Nazi filmmaker, Wolfgang Liebeneiner (he had made the "euthanasia" propaganda film *Ich klage an* in 1941). His post-war film *Liebe '47* (1949) tells the story of a self-pitying *Wehrmacht* soldier who does not feel welcomed upon his return home. In contrast, the first film produced by DEFA, *Die Mörder sind unter uns* (1946), under the director Wolfgang Staudte is also about a former *Wehrmacht* officer. This officer, however, asks uncomfortable questions about who was responsible for the war crimes committed by the *Wehrmacht* and how those who were responsible should be brought to justice.

Generally speaking, DEFA films commented on everyday life in East Germany from a perspective that did not question socialism as a whole but rather criticized socialism for not having been able to solve the problems it had promised to handle differently than capitalism. While early films such as *Irgendwo in Berlin* (1946) and *Unser täglich Brot* (1949) attempted to create enthusiasm for rebuilding the country, soon films such as *Spur der Steine* (1966) would focus on problems associated with a planned state economy.

DEFA films also played an important part in shaping how East Germans were supposed to think about who was at fault for the Nazi period (meaning: the West) and what role the Red Army played in liberating East Germany from the Hitler regime. While not outright propaganda, films such as *Ich war Neunzehn* (1968) tried to portray the Red Army soldiers as just, deliberate in dealing with their enemies, and highly educated—without mentioning any of the crimes committed by Red Army soldiers in this time period. The film *Die Abenteuer des Werner Holt* (1965) shows the learning process of a young *Wehrmacht* soldier as he moves from initial enthusiasm for the military adventures of the regime to total disgust, which leads him to turn his gun on *SS* soldiers. One can assume that his change of heart was supposed to serve as a model for those living in the East who now were charged with building a socialist state.

Beyond processing the trauma of the war and providing moral support for rebuilding the country, DEFA films soon turned to more limited subject matter such as the marital problems of couples who had married (too) young in films like *Jahrgang 45* (1966) or *Bis daß der Tod Euch scheidet* (1979). Similar films focused on the as yet not realized constitutional guarantee of equal rights of men and women. Films like *Karla* (1965), *Die Beunruhigung* (1981) or the blockbuster *Die Legende von Paul und Paula* (1972) show the difficulties women faced in balancing the demands of their jobs, their love lives, the work required in their homes, and the care for their children.

While devoting much of its efforts to depicting the everyday problems of the GDR citizens, DEFA inadvertently lost the interest of the public in its products: it seemed like movie goers preferred to be entertained rather than be confronted with these problems yet again in the movie theaters. DEFA had much greater box office successes with films directed towards a younger audience, such as film adaptations of fairy tales, animation films, even some science fiction movies, and above all Westerns. In stark contrast to Hollywood Westerns, these films (e.g. *Apachen* (1973)) show the greed and ruthlessness of the European settlers and the valiant fight of the Native Americans against them.

234c **Reflektieren: Beantworten Sie die Fragen, die Sie besonders ansprechen, auf Deutsch oder Englisch oder einer Mischung aus beiden Sprachen.**

- Compare the two first movies coming out of East and West Germany: What is similar? What is different? In what ways do they represent the new beginnings of film production in East and West?
- Which film mentioned above do you find particularly interesting and why?
- In what ways does ideology and protest against ideologies play a role in these films? Is this similar or different when you compare them to Hollywood movies?
- How does the different approach to the Western genre work with the ideology of communism/socialism? Did an East German genre of Western movies surprise you? Why (not)?

235a **Verstanden? Karina ruft ihre Mutter an, um ihr von ihren Plänen für den Tag zu erzählen, aber ihre Mutter nimmt nicht ab. Karina hinterlässt eine Sprachnachricht. Hören Sie sich diese an und beantworten Sie die Fragen.**

Warum schaut Karina im Kino den neuen Film von Quentin Tarantino an?

- Karina ist ein großer Fan von Quentin Tarantino.
- Karina hat schon als Kind immer gerne mit ihrer Mutter Tarantino-Filme gesehen.
- Karina schaut den Film nur, weil sie ihrer Freundin Tanja einen Gefallen tun möchte.

Warum freut sich Tanja auf das Essen nach dem Kino?

- Sie freut sich darauf, weil es im Restaurant DelikatEssen gutes mexikanisches Essen gibt.
- Sie freut sich darauf, weil das Restaurant DelikatEssen einer guten Freundin gehört.
- Sie freut sich darauf, weil sie zum ersten Mal die neue Freundin von Annika treffen wird.

Was möchte Karina ihrem Vater zum Geburtstag schenken?

- Sie möchte ihm einen Schal schenken, weil er Schals so gerne hat.
- Sie möchte später mit ihrer Mutter besprechen, was sie ihm schenken.
- Sie möchte ihn als Geschenk zu einem schönen Mittagessen einladen.

235b **Schauen Sie noch einmal zurück zu Aktivität 235a. Karina hat ihrer Mutter von ihrem Tag erzählt. Am nächsten Tag trifft sich die Mutter mit Karinas älterem Bruder und erzählt ihm von Karinas Tag. Versuchen Sie, sich an so viele Details wie möglich von Karinas Tag zu erinnern. Schreiben Sie dann auf, was die Mutter sagt. Benutzen Sie das Perfekt, denn die Mutter spricht über den Tag in der Vergangenheit.**

____

____

____

____

236a **Reflektieren: Sie haben gesehen, dass die Titel von US-amerikanischen Filmen oft verändert werden, wenn sie auf Deutsch geschrieben werden. Können Sie verstehen, warum die Titel für ein deutschsprachiges Publikum verändert werden? Wie erklären Sie sich, dass manche US-Filme sogar neue englische Titel bekommen? Spekulieren Sie.**

237d **Was ist Ihr Lieblingsfilm? Schauen Sie einen englischen Trailer zu dem Film, dann einen deutschen Trailer (suchen Sie online: „Filmname deutscher Trailer"). Ist der Name des Films gleich? Sind die Stimmen anders? Beschreiben Sie die Unterschiede.**

Recherche

Film: ______________________________

____

____

____

74: Tanz und Performance°

241a **Lass uns tanzen! Wählen Sie einen Tanzfilm, den Sie kennen. Wie viele Sterne würden Sie diesem Film geben? Schreiben Sie einen kurzen Kommentar (3–4 Sätze), in dem Sie Ihre Bewertung erklären. Die Wörter im Kasten helfen Ihnen dabei.**

Beispiele: „Footloose“ (1984), „Dirty Dancing“ (1987), „Billy Elliot“ (2000), „Save The Last Dance“ (2001), „Moulin Rouge“ (2001), „Chicago“ (2002), „Black Swan“ (2010), „Magic Mike“ (2012), „La La Land“ (2017)

inspirierend	der Soundtrack
spannend	gute Laune
emotional	die Filmkulisse (*set*)
lustig	die Kostüme
dramatisch	die Schauspieler*innen

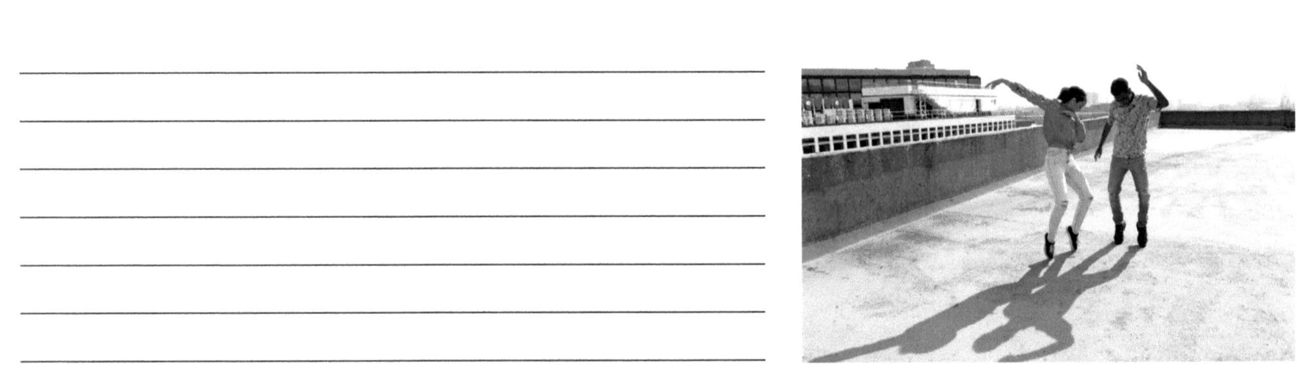

241b **Verstanden? Unten sehen Sie kurze Anleitungen für drei Tänze. Sie hören gleich Anweisungen aus einem Tanzkurs. In welcher Reihenfolge hören Sie die Anweisungen? Schreiben Sie 1–3 unten in die Kästchen. (Achtung: Sie werden die heteronormativen Bezeichnungen „Herrenschritt“ für die führende Person und „Damenschritt“ für die geführte Person hören.)**

☐ Cha Cha Cha: Eins, zwei, cha cha cha. Rück, vor, cha cha cha.

☐ Walzer: Im Quadrat. Vor, Seite, schließen. Rück, Seite, schließen.

☐ Tango: Schritt, Schritt, Wiegeschritt. Linker Fuß vor. Nach rechts und dann der Schlussschritt.

75: Postmigrantisches Theater

242e **Verstanden? Mehr Improvisation. In Aktivität 242 in MACHEN haben Sie improvisiert und einen Gegenstand beschrieben. Jetzt hören Sie einen Improvisationsmonolog von Nele. Wer oder was ist Nele? Sie können sich beim Hören Notizen machen.**

Notizen:

____

____

____

____

____

Nele ist: ______________________________

243b **In Aktivität 243 in MACHEN haben Sie Informationen zu einem Theaterstück recherchiert. Was fanden Sie an Ihrem Stück besonders faszinierend oder spannend? Warum?**

____

____

____

____

____

244b **Reflektieren: You have learned about postmigrant theater and have researched one play in more detail. Looking back at everything you have learned, what do you think is the main goal of postmigrant theater? How do these plays contribute to the cultural, social, and political discourse in Germany? Do you think theater can be a powerful vehicle of social commentary? If yes: what kind of theater? If no: why not?**

76: VIRTUELLE REALITÄTEN

245a **Verstanden? Sie hören einen Text zu dem Smartphone-Spiel „Bury me, my Love". Schreiben Sie die fehlenden Wörter in die Lücken.**

„Bury me, my Love" ist ein ____________, das die Geschichte einer jungen Syrerin erzählt, die ihre ____________ verlässt, um in Europa ____________ zu suchen. Ihr Mann Majd ist in Syrien geblieben, aber er ____________ sie über eine SMS-App. Durch die App gibt er ihr Richtungsanweisungen, damit sie hoffentlich sicher in Europa ankommt.

Die Spieler*innen nehmen in diesem Handyspiel die ____________ des Ehemanns, Majd, ein. Das Spiel ist von wahren ____________ inspiriert. Deshalb gibt es auch 20 verschiedene ____________.

„Bury me, my Love" versucht, die ____________ von Menschen auf der Flucht von Syrien nach Europa so ____________ wie möglich zu präsentieren. Es ist ein Spiel über Menschenrechte, ____________ und die schlimmen Erfahrungen, die Menschen auf der Flucht machen.

245b **Lesen Sie den Text in Aktivität 245a noch einmal. Schreiben Sie dann zwei Fragen zu dem Text und beantworten Sie sie mit Informationen aus dem Text. Beantworten Sie Frage 3 in einem oder zwei Sätzen.**

Frage 1: ______________________________

Antwort 1: ______________________________

Frage 2: ______________________________

Antwort 2: ______________________________

Frage 3: *Würden Sie „Bury me, my Love" spielen? Warum (nicht)?*

Antwort 3: ______________________________

____

245c **Reflektieren: While most video games are advertised as a form of entertainment, they can provide much more than just a means to pass the time. Which social, intellectual, or psychological benefits do you think video games can offer, depending on the type of game and genre? Think of the games you learned about in this unit. Have you experienced learning something from a video game that proved helpful in other areas of your life?**

246e **Lesen Sie den kurzen Text über Aya Jaff und entscheiden Sie, welche Informationen in die Lücken passen.**

Aya Jaff, 1995 im Nordirak geboren, __d__ und machte sich schon früh einen Namen in der Tech-Szene als Coderin. Sie beherrscht (*has mastered*) ______ und ist in Deutschland eine Ausnahme in der Tech- und Programmierszene, ______. Aber Aya Jaff ist nicht nur Programmiererin. Sie hat auch das Start-Up CoDesign-Factory, ______, gegründet und sie hat ein Buch über die Börse geschrieben. Von Forbes wurde sie als eine Person der 30unter30 ______.

a) ein innovatives Consulting-Unternehmen
b) die von weißen Männern dominiert wird
c) in der Kategorie „Leadership" gewählt
d) kam mit 2 Jahren nach Deutschland
e) mehrere Programmiersprachen, wie Java, JavaScript, Ruby oder PHP

77: „Tatort DaF" (Teil 4)

Bitte machen Sie die Aktivitäten, die zu dem Buch gehören, das Sie lesen.
Auf den Seiten 130 und 131 gibt es zwei Aktivitäten für alle Bücher.

„Böses Erwachen in Heidelberg"

249c **Was denken Sie? Beantworten Sie die Frage. (Kapitel 8)**

Warum hat Rudolf Kuhn Emma und Professor Vogt beobachtet?

____

____

____

„Die Lerche aus Leipzig"

249c **Was wissen Sie über das frühere Leben von René Hartmann? Was ist richtig? Kreuzen Sie an. (Kapitel 8)**

- ☐ Hartmann hat in der Schule einen politischen Aufsatz geschrieben. Deshalb hatte er Probleme mit der Stasi.
- ☐ Geißler hat die Familie von René Hartmann überwacht.
- ☐ Hartmann hat Medizin studiert. Aber er hat die Prüfung nicht geschafft.
- ☐ Hartmann hat nicht gut für die Prüfung gelernt.
- ☐ Hartmann hat als Arzt gearbeitet.
- ☐ Hartmann war im Gefängnis.

„Gefährliches Spiel in Essen"

250b **Finden Sie die richtige Antwort. (Kapitel 10)**

Was feiern die drei Männer?

____

Warum lachen sie über die Nachricht aus dem Radio?

____

„Kalt erwischt in Hamburg"

250b **Sie kennen nun alle Figuren. Was passt zu wem? Einmal passt die Beschreibung auch zu zwei Figuren.**

Klaas Hansen | Hendrik Dirkheide | Nele Lühders | Brigit Brandt | Ole Wilken

______________	Er ist zuverlässig und pünktlich.
______________	Er hat ein Messer.
______________	Sie ist nervös und aufgeregt.
______________	Er liebt seine Freundin.
______________	Sie ist viel unterwegs und muss viel arbeiten.
______________	Er spielt Trompete.
______________	Er trägt eine Sonnenbrille, auch wenn es dunkel ist.
______________	Er*Sie hat Angst um Klaas.
______________	Er ist ein guter Freund von Klaas.
______________	Er liebt Trompetenmusik.
______________	Sie arbeitet für das Fernsehen.
______________	Er arbeitet in einer Kirche.
______________	Er arbeitet im Hamburger Hafen.
______________	Er muss fast jeden Tag zweimal auf einen Turm steigen.
______________	Sie hat einen Kurs in Selbstverteidigung gemacht.
______________	Sie hilft bei der Suche nach Klaas.
______________	Er hat Klaas entführt.

„Verschollen in Berlin"

250b **Finden Sie die richtige Antwort. (Kapitel 8)**

Warum fährt Maja nicht mit dem Personenaufzug?

____

In welchem Stockwerk liegt die Verwaltung?

____

Wo hat Maja den Umschlag abgegeben?

____

Wer hat Maja angerufen?

____

Wen wollte Maja anrufen?

____

Wie fahren Maja und Jan hinunter?

____

„Der Schützenkönig vom Chiemsee"

249c **Mathias muss jetzt alles genau erzählen. Wie ist die richtige Reihenfolge. (Kapitel 7)**

- Da liegt ein Rucksack und ich packe alles hinein.
- In der anderen Hand hat er den Brief.
- 1 Ich suche Vater und finde ihn.
- Ich weiß: Ich muss etwas tun – für unsere Familie.
- Ich sehe das Blut an seinem Kopf.
- Die Pistole und der Brief müssen weg. Ich sehe sofort: Das ist Selbstmord!
- Er hat die Pistole in der Hand.

250a **Was meint der Pfarrer? Welches Geheimnis nimmt Ludwig mit ins Grab? (Kapitel 8)**

Die Wahrheit über ____.

Aktivitäten für alle Bücher

250x **Sie haben nun die Geschichte zu Ende gelesen. Welche Figur hat Ihnen am meisten gefallen / hat Sie am meisten beeindruckt? Warum?**

____

____

____

____

____

250y **Wie fanden Sie das Buch? Empfehlen Sie es einer anderen Person, die Deutsch lernt? Warum (nicht)? Schreiben Sie 4–5 Sätze.**

____

____

____

____

____

78: „Yolocaust"°

252a **Verstanden? Sie hören einen Radiobeitrag aus einer Sendung mit Expert*innen für soziale Themen. Wählen Sie die richtigen Antworten aus.**

Worüber spricht Professorin Jones im Radiointerview?

- Sie spricht über die Psychologie von Social Media-Sucht.
- Sie spricht über ihr Buch zum Thema „Selbstdarstellung in den sozialen Medien".
- Sie spricht über ihre Erfahrung als Social Media-Managerin.

Woher kam die Inspiration für die Forschung von Professorin Jones?

- Die Inspiration kam von der Beobachtung, dass Menschen ihre Erlebnisse zwanghaft dokumentieren.
- Die Inspiration kam von der Kontroverse um das „Yolocaust"-Projekt in Berlin.
- Die Inspiration kam von Diskussionen bei einer Konferenz in England.

Was sagt Professorin Jones über die Menschen, die sich konstant in sozialen Medien darstellen?

- Sie sagt, dass Menschen bei der Selbstdarstellung schlechte Intentionen haben.
- Sie sagt, dass Menschen sich nicht die Frage stellen, ob ihr Verhalten moralisch problematisch ist.
- Sie sagt, dass alle sozialen Medien verboten werden sollen, weil die meisten Menschen keine Selbstkontrolle haben.

252b **Reflektieren: Now reflect some more about the questions raised in activity 252a. Namely, when people share their life in public through images on social media, are there any limits as to when and where pictures can be taken? How do you decide if it is appropriate to take pictures and share them online? Do you think people in different countries have different answers to these questions?**

79: Projekt 6 – Ein Medienbeitrag°

254a **Erzähl mal: Nehmen Sie ein kurzes Video auf (z. B. mit Ihrem Handy oder am Computer) und beantworten Sie die Fragen.**

Vergangenheit: Was haben Sie in den letzten Wochen in den Nachrichten gesehen oder gelesen? Was war das Thema? Was ist passiert? Geben Sie Details.

Gegenwart: Was ist ihre Lieblingsserie oder ihr Lieblingsbuch? Warum finden Sie die Serie oder das Buch gut? Erzählen Sie von der Handlung und den Figuren.

Zukunft: Wie wird das Fernsehen der Zukunft (Ihrer Meinung nach) aussehen? Welches Format wird es haben? Welche Serien und/oder Filme wird es geben? Was wird anders sein?

254b Self-Assessment

You now get a chance to reflect on the many things you have learned throughout the chapter. Carefully read through the "Can-Do Statements" below, and ask yourself if you can perform all of these tasks. It might be helpful for each of the statements to actually practice the communicative scenario. Once you are confident that you are able to perform a task, check the respective box on the left side.

- ☐ I can understand excerpts from a radio interview and identify the major points that were discussed.
- ☐ I can have simple conversations about past experiences and elaborate on them when asked by others.
- ☐ I can express my opinion about podcasts and state which podcasts I (don't) enjoy listening to.
- ☐ I can give a presentation based on a structured outline of ideas, such as a storyboard for a podcast.
- ☐ I can talk about what news outlets I frequent and why, and reflect about the outlets' political positions.
- ☐ I can ask and answer questions about news articles that deal with past events.
- ☐ I can write about current events on my campus.
- ☐ I can have simple extemporaneous conversations about my favorite TV shows and express why I like them.
- ☐ I can understand and compare information about progressive and traditional TV shows in Germany and the U.S.
- ☐ I can plan a trip to the movie theater and present my plans to others.
- ☐ I can understand the main content and some details of plays based on short plot descriptions.
- ☐ I can ask and answer questions about my own and others' interest in computer games.
- ☐ I can read a crime story (graded reader) independently over a period of multiple weeks.
- ☐ I can summarize the plot of fictional texts and talk about the most important events of the story.
- ☐ I can make predictions about how a fictional story might develop based on what has happened thus far.
- ☐ I can talk and write about events in the past, present, and future and seamlessly move between different tenses.
- ☐ I can express purpose with *um ... zu* clauses.
- ☐ I can use temporal adverbs to connect sentences logically both in speaking and writing.

- ☐ I am familiar with different German news outlets and their ideological orientation in comparison to U.S. media.
- ☐ I am familiar with queer representation in German and American TV shows.
- ☐ I am familiar with the cultural significance of different dances, as well as their cultural and geographic origins.
- ☐ I am familiar with the role of AR in computer gaming.
- ☐ I am familiar with the ethical limits and pitfalls of social media.

Wofür/Wogegen sind wir?

Protest, Widerstand, Mitbestimmung

80: Unsere Stimmen auf dem Campus

255e **„Für" oder „gegen"? Schreiben Sie die passende Präposition in die Lücken.**

Mein Bruder und ich engagieren uns ___für___ den Umweltschutz.

Letzten Monat haben wir __________ die Benutzung von Plastikpartikeln in Kosmetik und Cremes protestiert.

Wir interessieren uns auch __________ einen plastikfreien Lifestyle.

Momentan mache ich meinen Bachelor im Fach Erneuerbare Energien, aber mein Bruder hat sich erst mal __________ die Uni entschieden.

Er macht ein freiwilliges ökologisches Jahr, denn er will direkt vor Ort __________ den Umweltschutz kämpfen.

256e **Beenden Sie den Satz zweimal, indem Sie jeweils die Wörter in die richtige Reihenfolge bringen.**

Ich demonstriere heute gegen Plastikbeutel, | 2018 wurden in Deutschland noch zwei Milliarden davon benutzt

weil: ______________________________

denn: ______________________________

Nächste Woche fahren wir nach Buir, | wir nehmen an der Protestaktion für den Hambacher Forst teil

da: ______________________________

denn: ______________________________

256f **Welche Sätze aus Aktivität 256e kann man alternativ mit der zweiten Hälfte nach dem Komma beginnen? Schreiben Sie sie auf.**

____

____

____

257a **Verstanden? Sie hören einen Dialog zwischen zwei Freundinnen, die auf dem Campus über kontroverse Meinungen sprechen. Kreuzen Sie die richtigen Antworten an.**

Warum sind Miriam und Ronja der Meinung, dass es an der Uni keine Noten für ihre Kurse geben sollte?

- ☐ Sie denken das, weil die Angst um gute Noten schlecht für das Lernen ist.
- ☐ Sie denken das, weil gute Noten nicht automatisch bedeuten, dass Studierende die Inhalte verstanden haben.
- ☐ Sie denken das, weil Noten kein detailliertes Feedback geben.

Warum wünscht sich Miriam, dass Alkohol auf dem Campus erlaubt ist?

- ☐ Sie findet, dass Alkohol zum Leben an der Uni gehört.
- ☐ Sie findet, dass ein Verbot das Trinken noch interessanter macht.
- ☐ Sie denkt, dass Studierende verantwortungsvoller trinken würden, wenn es kein Tabu wäre.

Warum nimmt Ronja oft an Demonstrationen teil?

- ☐ Sie findet es wichtig, ihre Meinung auszudrücken.
- ☐ Sie möchte, dass die Universität weiß, was den Studierenden wichtig ist.
- ☐ Sie nimmt an Demonstrationen teil, da es ihr Spaß macht.

257b **Zurück zu Aktivität 257 in MACHEN und zu Ihrem Campus: Welche politische(n), soziale(n) oder ökologische(n) Gruppe(n) unterstützen Sie? Warum engagieren Sie sich für diese Gruppe(n)? Was möchte jede Gruppe erreichen oder wogegen kämpft sie? Wie unterstützen Sie die Gruppe(n)? Schreiben Sie einen kurzen Text dazu.**

______

______

______

______

______

______

257c **Herbert Grönemeyer ist ein sehr erfolgreicher Musiker aus dem deutschsprachigen Raum. In seinem Lied „Jetzt oder nie" (1984) beklagte Grönemeyer, dass Menschen aus Angst nichts gegen Ohnmacht tun. Suchen Sie das Lied online. Hören Sie es sich an und notieren Sie, was Menschen alles mit sich machen lassen.**

Recherche

Sie lassen sich fotografieren, sie ...

______

257d **Reflektieren: Ist Grönemeyers Kritik auch heute noch gültig? Hören Sie sich das Lied aus Aktivität 257c noch einmal an und reflektieren Sie: Welche Themen werden Ihrer Meinung nach heutzutage immer noch mit dem Lied angesprochen? Denken Sie an heutige Probleme und Herausforderungen.**

81: KARNEVAL KONTROVERS

258e **Fastelovend – Karneval – Fasching – Fasnet: Das Leben ist ernst, lasst uns feiern. Wie Halloween oder Mardi Gras hat die deutsche Fastnacht in all ihren regionalen Variationen oft einen ernsten Hintergrund (zum Beispiel: patriarchalische Strukturen auf den Kopf stellen, das Ende einer Krankheitswelle oder des Winters feiern ...). Schauen Sie sich die Übersicht über regionale Unterschiede an und wählen Sie auf der nächsten Seite die richtigen Wörter für die Lücken. Sie müssen hier nicht jedes Wort verstehen, um einen generellen Eindruck zu bekommen.**

	Rheinland	Bayern	Schwaben, Schweiz
Name und Etymologie	**Fastelovend** = der Abend vor dem Anfang der Fastenzeit (*Lent*), also vor Aschermittwoch **Karneval** aus dem Lateinischen = *carne* (Fleisch) + *vale* (Tschüss!)	**Fasching** = Fastenschank = der letzte Tag, an dem es alkoholische Getränke in Schänken (historischer Name für Bars/ Tavernen) gibt	**Fastnacht/Fasnet** = die Nacht vor der Fastenzeit
zeitlicher Ablauf	• **Donnerstag**: Weiberfastnacht, das Patriarchat hat Pause, jetzt beginnt der Straßenkarneval • **Sonntag:** Schull- und Veedelszöch = Umzüge (*parades*) von Schulen und Stadtteilen • **Montag:** Rosenmontag, der größte Umzug	• **Donnerstag:** Unsinniger Donnerstag, die Welt steht Kopf (= Es ist viel los!) (siehe auch: Weiberfastnacht) • **Dienstag:** die Närr*innen regieren die Straßen	• **6. Januar:** die Kostüme werden fertig gemacht • **Schmotziger Dunschtig,** der Donnerstag vor Aschermittwoch: der letzte Tag zum Backen und Schlachten (*slaughtering*) vor der Fastenzeit (schmotzig = fettig)
Besonderheiten	• **Weiberfastnacht:** das Krawattenabschneiden • **Nubbelverbrennung:** als Sündenbock (*scapegoat*) wird eine Strohpuppe (*strawdoll*) verbrannt (*burn*) • Der Karneval hat immer ein **Motto**, z.B. 2020: „Et Hätz schleiht em Veedel" (Das Herz schlägt (*beat*) im Viertel = Stadtteil).	• **Fasnatziestag:** in Oberstaufen wird an das Pestjahr 1635 erinnert; der Butz putzt mit einem Reisigbesen (*brushwood broom*) Straßen und Häuser • **Fischzug** am Aschermittwoch: ein sogenannter Heischebrauch, d.h., verkleidete Menschen sammeln Essen und Geld	• **Fasnetsküchle:** werden am schmotzigen Donnerstag gebacken, es ist ein frittiertes (*deep-fried*) Gebäck • **Lichtmess** (2. Februar): die Menschen kritisieren in Gedichten Ereignisse und Menschen

In Bayern sagt man ______________________ (Karneval | Fasching | Fastnacht), aber im Rheinland ______________________ (Karneval | Fasching | Fastnacht). ______________________ (Fastelovend und Fastnacht | Fasching und Fastnacht) heißen „Abend und Nacht vor der Fastenzeit". Der ______________________ (Donnerstag | Samstag | Montag) ist in allen drei Regionen ein spezieller Tag. Im Rheinland heißt dieser Tag ______________________ (Weiberfastnacht | Rosenmontag). Das Wort „______________________" (Schank | schmotzig | vale) heißt nicht dreckig, sondern fettig und dabei geht es um das frittierte Gebäck, das vor der Fastenzeit gegessen wird. In Schwaben heißt dieses Gebäck „______________________" (Donut | Fasnetsküchle | Mutzemandel). Am ______________________ (Weiberfastnacht | Rosenmontag | Lichtmess) finden im Rheinland die größten Umzüge statt, zum Beispiel in Köln und Düsseldorf. Es gibt auch viele Traditionen. Zum Beispiel putzt in Oberstaufen der ______________________ (Nubbel | Butz) die Straßen und Häuser und beim ______________________ (Krawattenabschneiden | Fischzug) wird Essen gesammelt. In allen Regionen ist am ______________________ (Mardi Gras | Aschermittwoch) alles vorbei und die Fastenzeit beginnt.

KULTURPUNKT: KÖLLE

"Hold on a second: Why...

... do all these *Karneval* bands sing so much about *Kölle*?" Whether you are from Cologne or not, whether you even like the city or not, should you ever find yourself in Cologne during *Karneval*, you will most likely profess your undying love for the city. Why is that? Because as soon as you learn to sing the songs, it is hard to avoid. On their website, the city of Cologne identified the 22 *Karneval* songs that you need to know. Among those, eight mention *Kölle/Colonia* (dialect and Latin name for the city of Cologne, *Köln* in standard German), *kölsch* (adjective for Cologne), or a part of the city in the title, and six more reference the city in the chorus. And that's just a sample. But even beyond that, there are so many references, such as *Kölle* is "my heart" (*ming hätz*), "my city" (*ming Stadt*), and "a feeling" (*e Jeföhl*), that you could easily say that most *Karneval* songs are love songs, but for a city instead of a person.

Such a sentiment will possibly remind you of what we have said before about *Heimat*, which means an emotional attachment to a place—and, of course, there are lots of songs that actually use the word *Heimat*. You may also remember that *Heimat* can be experienced as exclusionary. *Heimat* and the regional patriotism expressed in these songs sometimes do indeed exclude others, such as when a song stresses that you have to be born in Cologne to have this strong bond. Other songs, however, very explicitly frame *Kölle* as a multicultural place (e.g. "Viva Colonia") and one in which all *Jeck*innen* (Karneval revelers) can come together. One of the most famous bands, the Bläck Fööss (Naked Feet), sings about *Unser Stammbaum* (our family tree). They list those who have come to Cologne—Romans in Caesar's times, the French under Napoleon, labor migrants from Italy, Greece, and Turkey, and people of different religious backgrounds—and conclude that many people have come to Cologne who are now at home there and speak a common language (*Kölsch).* In this song, these different people who all brought something with them enriched the city and made it what it is now.

And while not everyone may really speak the same language, meaning the local dialect *Kölsch*, for some strange reason every *Jeck*in* can sing it with fervor.

259c **Reflektieren: Listen to one of these songs: "Unser Stammbaum" (Bläck Fööss), "Stadt mit K" (Kasalla), "Hey Kölle! Du bes e Jeföhl" (De Höhner), "Dat es Heimat" (De Räuber). Describe your impressions: What does it sound like? What kind of emotions does the music evoke? Find the lyrics of the song and read along while you listen a second time: What is the song about? What do you understand of the dialect? Do the text and music go together in creating emotions?**

Recherche

259d Verstanden? Drei Kölner Karnevalsvereine. Hören Sie zu und schreiben Sie die Informationen in die Tabelle.

Person	Verein	Jahr	Besonderheit
Marie	Kammerkätzchen und Kammerdiener		
Rudi			
Michael			

260c **In kleinen Städten gestalten nicht nur Vereine, sondern auch die Mitarbeiter*innen einer Firma oder Institution einen Karnevalswagen für den Karnevalszug. Hier sind wir beim Gruppentreffen der Mitarbeiter*innen von der Sparkasse in Geroldsberg. Ergänzen Sie die Lücken mit den richtigen Wörtern aus dem Kasten. Benutzen Sie die Verben im Präsens.**

sprechen über | arbeiten an | informieren über | sich freuen über | sich ärgern über | diskutieren über (2x)

Die Mitarbeiter*innen der Sparkasse in Geroldsberg treffen sich jeden Mittwoch nach der Arbeit, um ihren Karnevalswagen zu planen. Heute ____________________ sie aber nicht nur __________ ihren Mottowagen, sondern sie ____________________ auch __________ die lokale Politik. Drei von ihnen ____________________ __________ sehr __________ die Politik der Geroldsberger Bürgermeisterin, Anke Emden. Sie wollen die Bürger*innen in ihrer Stadt __________ die politischen Entscheidungen (*decisions*) von Frau Emden ____________________. Aber vier Mitarbeiter*innen ____________________ __________ __________ Frau Emdens Politik, weil sie jetzt freie Parkplätze direkt hinter der Sparkasse bekommen. Alle Mitarbeiter*innen ____________________ bis lange in die Nacht __________ ihren Karnevalswagen. Sie ____________________ aktiv __________ einem Kompromiss: Sie wollen am Ende einen satirischen Karnevalswagen über die Finanzprobleme von Geroldsberg gestalten.

260d **Unser Karnevalswagen. In Aktivität 260 in MACHEN haben Sie mit Ihrer Gruppe einen eigenen Karnevalswagen entworfen. Beschreiben Sie Ihren Wagen. Beantworten Sie dazu die folgenden Fragen.**

Welches Thema hat Ihr Wagen?

____

Was brauchen Sie für den Wagen?

____

____

Wogegen protestiert Ihr Wagen? Worüber informiert er?

____

____

Welcher Wagen der anderen Gruppen hat Ihnen am besten gefallen? Warum?

____

____

Ein Karnevalswagen in Nürnberg
Illustration aus dem 19. Jahrhundert

82: Widerstand im Dritten Reich

261d **Beantworten Sie die folgenden Fragen des Reporters in ganzen Sätzen.**

Haben Sie schon einmal furchtbar mit einer Person gestritten? Warum?

____

____

Wann haben Sie sich zuletzt über etwas oder jemanden beschwert? Warum?

____

____

Wem helfen Sie regelmäßig? Wobei?

____

Wie gut können Sie Ihre Freund*innen zu spontanen Aktionen überreden?

____

262e **Die anderen Personen in der Weißen Rose. Welche Konnektoren fehlen hier? Ergänzen Sie die Lücken mit den passenden Konnektoren aus dem Kasten.**

aber | oder | sondern | und

Sophie und Hans Scholl sind die bekanntesten Mitglieder der studentischen Widerstandsgruppe Weiße Rose, ____________ es gab noch andere Leute in der Gruppe, die mit ihnen gegen die Nazis kämpften. Nicht nur Studierende, ____________ auch Professor Kurt Huber waren in der Gruppe aktiv. Die Basis der Anti-Nazi-Proteste war nicht so sehr politisch, ____________ eher philosophisch und christlich. Viele Mitglieder waren katholisch ____________ besuchten die Religionskurse von Pater Adolf Eisele aus der Mission Weiße Väter. Die Mitglieder der Weißen Rose schrieben keine Broschüren, ____________ Flugblätter. Der Buchhändler Josef Söhngen war auch gegen die Nazi-Ideologie ____________ ließ die Gruppe in seine Räume, wo sie die Flugblätter versteckten. Die Weiße Rose hatte ihren Ursprung in München, ____________ es gab auch andere Weiße Rosen in Hamburg und Berlin.

262f **Widerstand in Film und Kunst. Finden Sie einen Film, eine Serie oder ein Kunstwerk, in der/dem das Thema „Widerstand im Dritten Reich" eine zentrale Rolle spielt. Machen Sie sich Notizen zu wichtigen Informationen: Jahr der Veröffentlichung, Regisseur*in/Künstler*in, Handlung/Thema etc.**

Recherche

____

____

____

____

____

____

262g Verstanden? Moshe hört im Zug einen Podcast zum Thema „Widerstand im Dritten Reich". Hören Sie mit und kreuzen Sie die richtigen Antworten an.

Was charakterisierte den Widerstand im Dritten Reich?

- Es gab sehr wenige Widerstandsgruppen.
- Es gab nur passiven Widerstand.
- Widerständler*innen kamen aus allen sozialen Schichten.

Wie hießen zwei sehr bekannte Widerstandsgruppen?

- Rote Kapelle
- Grünes Schiff
- Kreisauer Kreis

Wer war Martin Niemöller?

- Er war ein aktiver Widerständler der studentischen Widerstandsgruppe Weiße Rose.
- Er war eine Hauptfigur des kirchlichen Widerstands und Mitbegründer der Bekennenden Kirche.
- Er war ein Gegner der Kirche und glaubte nur an säkularen Widerstand.

262h **Widerstand im Dritten Reich. Widerstand gegen das Nazi-Regime kam aus ganz unterschiedlichen sozialen Gruppierungen. Die folgenden Abschnitte geben Ihnen dafür Beispiele. Lesen Sie die Absätze und ergänzen Sie die folgenden Wörter in den Überschriften: „Ziviler", „Militärischer", „Intellektueller", „Politischer".**

__________________ Widerstand
Nachdem Hitler im Januar 1933 Reichskanzler wurde, formierte sich in den kommunistischen (KPD) und sozialdemokratischen Parteien (SPD) offener Widerstand. Das Regime verfolgte ihre Anhänger*innen und brachte viele von ihnen in Konzentrationslager. Bereits im Juni 1933 waren beide Parteien verboten. Deshalb gingen viele Kommunist*innen ins Exil, um dort am antifaschistischen Widerstand weiterzuarbeiten.

__________________ Widerstand
In den Jahren 1938 und 1939 nahm Großbritannien knapp 10.000 jüdische Kinder aus Deutschland auf. Es waren vor allem jüdische Organisationen, die in Deutschland, Österreich, Polen und der Tschechoslowakei die Kindertransporte nach Großbritannien organisierten. Heute immer noch bekannt ist auch die Studierendengruppe Weiße Rose, die in Flugblättern zum Widerstand gegen den Nationalsozialismus aufrief.

__________________ Widerstand
Viele Soldaten protestierten gegen den Vernichtungskrieg im Osten. Die Wehrmachtsoffiziere von Stauffenberg, Olbricht und von Tresckow arbeiteten mit zivilen Widerstandsgruppen zusammen, um den Sturz des NS-Regimes zu planen. Am 20. Juli 1944 verübten sie ein Attentat (*assassination attempt*) auf Hitler, das ihnen aber nicht gelang (*didn't succeed*). Nach der Aktion wurden etwa 700 Menschen von der Gestapo festgenommen; 200 von ihnen wurden hingerichtet (*executed*) oder auf andere Weise ums Leben gebracht (*killed*).

__________________ Widerstand
Der Kreisauer Kreis war eine Gruppe, die Pläne für eine sozialpolitische Neuordnung (*rearrangement*) der Gesellschaft machte. Mitglieder und Freund*innen dieses Kreises kamen aus dem Bürgertum, dem Adel und auch der Arbeiter*innenbewegung. Die Gruppe wollte keinen autoritären Staat, sondern eine Gesellschaft, die „von unten" aufgebaut werden sollte. Der Staat sollte dabei dem Individuum so viel Freiheit wie möglich lassen.

263a **Reflektieren: In this unit, you have discovered that there are many places in Germany named after Sophie and Hans Scholl. Why, do you think, is there such an emphasis on the public commemoration of these resistance fighters? That is, which larger purpose does this commemoration in the public sphere serve?**

83: Die 68er – Jugend protestiert°

266c **Verstanden? Wer war Benno Ohnesorg? Hören Sie gut zu und beantworten Sie die Fragen.**

Warum haben die Studierenden 1967 gegen den Besuch des persischen Schahs demonstriert?

- Sie haben demonstriert, weil es im Iran viele Verletzungen von Menschenrechten gab.
- Sie haben demonstriert, weil der Schah in der Vergangenheit negativ über Westberlin gesprochen hatte.
- Sie haben demonstriert, weil der Besuch des Schahs zu viel Geld kostete.

Wann/Warum wurde Benno Ohnesorg von einem Polizisten angeschossen?

- Er wurde angeschossen, als er versuchte, den Polizisten zu schlagen.
- Er wurde angeschossen, als die Gewalt zwischen der Polizei und den Demonstrierenden eskalierte.
- Er wurde angeschossen, weil der Polizist ein persönliches Problem mit Ohnesorg hatte.

Was passierte mit dem Polizisten, der auf Ohnesorg geschossen hatte?

- Er wurde für seine Tat zu fünf Jahren Gefängnis verurteilt.
- Er bekam keine Strafe und wurde freigesprochen.
- Er hat sich bei der Familie von Benno Ohnesorg entschuldigt.

266d **1968: USA und BRD Teil 1 – Sit-Ins waren in dieser Zeit in der BRD und den USA beliebte Protestformen. Hier sehen Sie Bilder aus Berkeley und aus Berlin. Was denken Sie: Was ist wo? Warum? Was ist auf den beiden Bildern anders und/oder gleich?**

266e **1968: USA und BRD Teil 2 – Wählen Sie eine der folgenden beiden Recherche-Aufgaben:**

Option 1: Recherchieren Sie die Gegner und Ziele der 68er in der BRD und den USA. Was war gleich und was war anders? Beispiele, wonach man suchen kann: der Vietnam-Krieg, die Atomwaffen, die patriarchalische Gesellschaft, die Redefreiheit an den Unis, alternative Lebensstile etc.

Option 2: Suchen Sie zwei Liedtexte online („To Bobby" von Joan Baez und „Wenn die Nacht am tiefsten …" von Ton Steine Scherben) und vergleichen Sie sie. Beide sind aus dem Jahr 1972. Welche Themen sind gleich, welche anders? Wer sind „wir", wer ist „ich"? Wer sind die „anderen"? Wie unterscheidet sich der Ton (optimistisch, resignierend …)? Geht es vorwärts oder rückwärts? Und wer gewinnt? Welche Worte kommen in beiden Texten vor (z. B. „schwer"/ *heavy*, „Nacht"/*night*)? Was assoziieren Sie mit diesen Worten?

Option: ____

____

____

____

____

____

____

____

____

____

⊙ Kulturpunkt: Protestieren für den Frieden

"Hold on a second: what kind of protest …

… (could have) happened in East Germany?" After the foundation of the two German states in 1949 along the dividing line between the Western Allies and the Soviet Union, states soon aligned with military organizations that emerged after World War II. In 1955, the Federal Republic of Germany became a member of the North Atlantic Treaty Organization and the German Democratic Republic a member of the Warsaw Pact. There had already been considerable resistance then in both parts of the country against the re-militarization of the country that had started two world wars and which had pledged that this would never happen again in the intermediate post-war period. While wars in former colonies (in Africa, Asia, and Latin America) kept peace movements active from the 60s to the 70s. However, a new form of activism emerged with a qualitative new round in the global arms race when the U.S. started planning the stationing of intermediate range nuclear missiles (Pershing II and Cruise Missiles) and the Soviet Union the stationing of a similar type, the SS-20. What seemed particularly concerning for European countries on both sides of the Iron Curtain was that hard-line Cold War politicians in the East and West (Leonid Breshnev and Juri Andropov in the USSR and Ronald Reagan in the U.S.) were considering "limited" and "winnable" nuclear wars that in all likelihood would be fought on (Central) European ground. In this sense, the peace movements emerging in the late 70s and early 80s in the FRG and GDR had a strong pull towards combining forces, as the threat posed by these new weapon systems would make victims of (and be limited to) anyone within the range of these missiles, irrespective of political alignments. Previously, nuclear weapons had been assumed to assure "mutual destruction" and thus keep a "balance of terror."

In the GDR, the peace movement often originated in and revolved around protestant churches, as the church and state in the GDR had mostly kept out of each other's business for as long as neither side caused trouble for the other. But of course, the fledgling independent peace movement was facing the same measures of repression as any other oppositional movement in East Germany. The movement did not just single out the arms race but also criticized the militarization of aspects of everyday life, such as paramilitary exercises put on by various state youth organizations and the teaching of military related subjects in school (*Wehrkunde*).

Means of communication are essential for movements such as this, but communicating was made especially hard by the way the government limited access to these means: typewriters had to be registered, photocopiers were unavailable to the public, and even carbon paper was hard to come by. In many cases, activists would resort to copying flyers by hand. You had to assume that your phones were tapped and that your apartments were bugged. Nevertheless, the movement was able to lay the groundwork for the much bigger movement that eventually led up to reunification. Regarding contact with similar organizations in the West, this relied on daring individuals that would be willing to smuggle materials across the border. One of the main activities supporting the independent peace movement in the East involved increasing Western awareness of incarcerated dissidents from the GDR and in some cases, by way of public pressure, managing to get them released. One of the most ingenious moves of the independent peace movement was its choice of a symbol. The logo quotes the Bible, and at the same time, the image looks like a monument that the Soviet Union had given to the UN in 1959 and still stands on the grounds of the UN in New York City today. In addition, people would sew the cloth emblems onto their parkas, thereby avoiding the ban on politically outspoken buttons.

266f **Reflektieren: Answer some of the following questions.**

Recherche

- Did you know anything about the peaceful movements in the East? Why was it so much more difficult for people in the East to organize protests? What does this knowledge do for your understanding of the Cold War and the people who lived on both sides of the Iron Curtain?
- Find the symbol *Schwerter zu Pflugscharen* online. Have you ever seen it before? What does it represent for you?
- Have you heard of other creative ways in which people protest or stand up for their rights?

84: Automatisierung – Protestieren oder mitbestimmen?

269b **Arbeitskampf und Mitbestimmung: Die Gewerkschaften im deutschsprachigen Raum. Lesen Sie den Text und achten Sie darauf, was die Aufgaben von Gewerkschaften sind und mit welchen Mitteln sie sie wahrnehmen. Entscheiden Sie dann, welche Aussagen richtig oder falsch sind.**

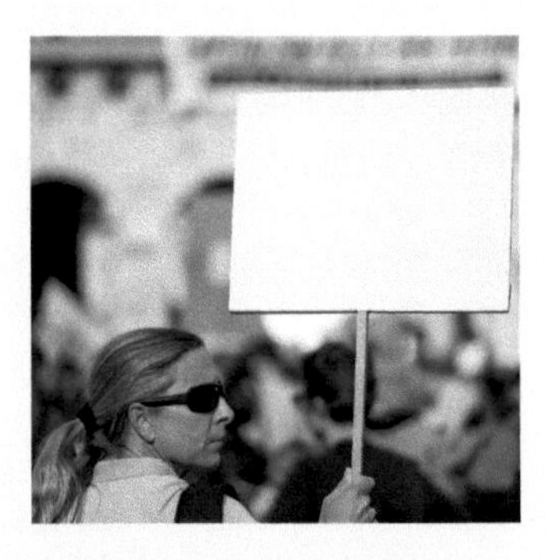

Die Gewerkschaften sind aus der Arbeiter*innenbewegung im 19. Jahrhundert entstanden. Eine Gewerkschaft vertritt die Interessen von Arbeitnehmer*innen. Es gibt verschiedene Gewerkschaften für bestimmte Branchen. Die größte deutsche Gewerkschaft IG Metall vertritt zum Beispiel Arbeitnehmer*innen in der verarbeitenden[1] Industrie. Sie hat über 2,2 Millionen Mitglieder. Und die Gewerkschaft Verdi mit 2 Millionen Mitgliedern ist für die Dienstleistungsbranche[2]. Gewerkschaften arbeiten zum Beispiel für höhere Löhne, bessere Arbeitsbedingungen (durch Tarifverträge) und mehr Mitbestimmung. Über die Gewerkschaften können Arbeitnehmer*innen in ihren Unternehmen mitbestimmen, weil die Gewerkschaften in Aufsichtsräten[3] sitzen.

Den Arbeitskampf führen Gewerkschaften vor allem durch Streik. In Deutschland wird aber recht wenig gestreikt. Pro Jahr gehen in Deutschland ungefähr 16 Arbeitstage verloren, in den USA sind es 10, in Kanada 117 und Frankreich liegt an der Spitze mit 150 Streiktagen.

Der Deutsche Gewerkschaftsbund sagt von sich, dass durch die Gewerkschaften alle deutschen Arbeitnehmer*innen wichtige Rechte und Vorteile haben: gute Löhne, garantierten Urlaub, Acht-Stunden-Tag und Fünf-Tage-Woche, freies Wochenende, Bezahlung auch bei Krankheit, Kündigungsschutz[4] und soziale Sicherheit.

[1] verarbeiten – *to process*
[2] die Dienstleistungsbranche – *service industry*
[3] der Aufsichtsrat – *board of directors*
[4] der Kündigungsschutz – *protection against unfair dismissal*

richtig	falsch	
		Eine Gewerkschaft vertritt Unternehmen.
		Die größte deutsche Gewerkschaft hat über 2 Millionen Mitglieder.
		Gewerkschaften schließen Tarifverträge.
		Gewerkschaften können nicht mitbestimmen.
		In Deutschland wird im internationalen Vergleich viel gestreikt.
		Gewerkschaften haben in Deutschland viel erreicht, z. B. gute Arbeitsbedingungen.

269c **Beantworten Sie jetzt diese Fragen. Sie finden die Antworten auch im Text von Aktivität 269b.**

Was sind die Aufgaben von Gewerkschaften?

____

____

Welche Mittel haben Gewerkschaften, um ihre Ziele zu erreichen?

____

____

Was haben Gewerkschaften in Deutschland erreicht?

____

____

269d **Reflektieren: Viele Menschen sorgen sich um die Automatisierung. Denken Sie darüber nach, warum die Automatisierung bedrohlich erscheinen kann. Gleichzeitig versprechen Roboter auch Hilfe bei der Arbeit. Welche Arten von Arbeit sollten/können Roboter machen? Welche Arbeiten sollten weiterhin von Menschen gemacht werden? Warum? Glauben Sie, Gewerkschaften können dabei helfen, diesen Prozess positiv zu gestalten?**

269e **Verstanden? Nina und Mario unterhalten sich über das Thema „Automatisierung und künstliche Intelligenz (KI)". Kreuzen Sie die richtigen Antworten an.**

Was denkt Mario über die Automatisierung von Produktionsprozessen?

- Er findet Automatisierung gut, weil sie die Produktionsprozesse effizienter macht.
- Er hat Angst vor einer weiteren Automatisierung, weil er seinen Job nicht verlieren möchte.
- Er denkt, dass Menschen immer gebraucht werden, auch wenn viele Prozesse automatisiert werden.

Welche Rolle spielt Automatisierung bei Ninas Arbeit in der Architekturfirma?

- In ihrem Beruf bringt automatisierte Produktion neue Möglichkeiten für effizientes und günstigeres Bauen.
- In ihrem Beruf gibt es Grenzen dabei, was automatisierte Prozesse machen können.
- In ihrem Beruf haben die Menschen kein Interesse an Automatisierung.

In welchem Punkt sind Mario und Nina einer Meinung?

- Beide finden, dass Firmen selbst entscheiden sollen, ob sie Arbeitsplätze durch automatisierte Prozesse ersetzen.
- Beide finden, dass Gewerkschaften dafür sorgen müssen, dass Arbeitsplätze in Zukunft geschützt werden.
- Beide finden, dass die Automatisierung zu einer besseren Work-Life-Balance führen wird.

270g **„Da"- und „wo"-Komposita. Welche Satzpaare passen zusammen? Verbinden Sie.**

Heiko interessiert sich sehr für Roboter.
Worum kümmert sich dein Service-Roboter?
Womit beschäftigt sich die Autofirma Honda auch?
Die Firma wartet auf ihren neuen Industrieroboter.
Leonardo Da Vinci entwarf einen mechanischen Ritter.
Manche Roboter haben Sensoren.

Wir wollen auch so einen Roboter und warten darauf!
Damit wollte er die Welt verbessern.
Dadurch können sie sehen und hören.
Marion interessiert sich auch dafür.
Sie beschäftigt sich mit humanoiden Robotern.
Um Hausarbeit, wie z. B. Staubsaugen.

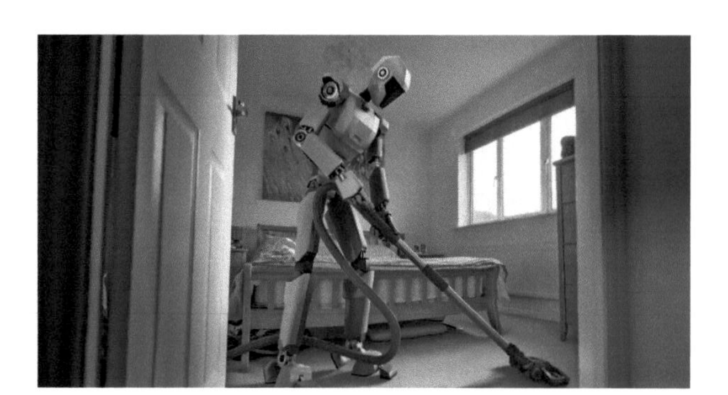

85: STREET ART

271f **Street Art in Ihrer Umgebung: Sie kennen sicherlich Beispiele von Street Art und haben auch in Ihrer Umgebung schon einmal Street Art gesehen. Skizzieren Sie ein Beispiel, geben Sie dem Werk einen Titel und beschreiben Sie es kurz: Wo haben Sie es gesehen? Was ist darauf zu sehen? Wie finden Sie das Werk? Ist das Kunst? Warum (nicht)? Ist es für/gegen etwas? Benutzen Sie Vokabeln aus dieser Einheit.**

Titel: __________

Wo? ______________________________

____

Was? ______________________________

____

____

Wie gefällt es? ______________________________

____

Kunst? ______________________________

____

271g **Reaktionen in einem Kunstmuseum. Schreiben Sie die Sätze zu Ende. Der zweite Satz wird dabei zu einem Nebensatz.**

Ich finde nicht, dass …	Diese Montage würde gut in unser Wohnzimmer passen.
Benny hat neulich gelesen, dass …	Gute Fotos können mit einem Handy gemacht werden.
Soledad, meinst du nicht auch, dass …	Dieses Bild ist schlecht gemalt.
Manche Kunstkritiker*innen behaupten, dass …	Diese Künstlerin hat ihre erste Skulptur für 100 EUR verkauft.
Bei moralischer Kunst ist es wichtig, dass …	Sie kritisiert politische oder soziale Probleme.

____

____

____

____

____

____

____

____

____

272a **Reflektieren: Wem gehört der öffentliche Raum? Choose one of these two sets of questions:**

In LERNEN you read that many street art artists want to "reclaim the streets." In your opinion, who gets to shape and design public spaces and who doesn't? Do you think street art artists can make communities or cities unique and more liveable? Why (not)? What role do street art and graffiti play in your community?

In MACHEN, you discussed whether or not street art and graffiti should be (il)legal. Why do you think that public space should (not) be regulated when it comes to street art? Why do you agree or disagree with the following quote by Banksy: "Graffiti is one of the few tools you have if you have almost nothing. As a voice of the voiceless, graffiti becomes an important translation inquiry."

273a **Verstanden? Sie hören eine kurze Audio-Tour zu drei Street Art-Gemälden in Berlin. Hören Sie gut zu und ergänzen Sie die Lücken.**

Willkommen bei unserer ____________ Street Art-Tour durch Berlin. Heute ____________ wir drei beeindruckende Straßenkunstgemälde kennen. In Kreuzberg ____________ man in der Wilhelmstraße 7 das Gemälde „Elephant Playing With a Balloon" von Jadore Tong. Es zeigt den ____________ eines Elefanten, der mit geblümten Mustern verziert ist. In seinem Rüssel ____________ er einen Luftballon, der die ____________ der Erdkugel hat.

Direkt nebenan an der ____________ zum Bezirk Mitte in der Heinrich-Heine-Straße befindet sich „Unter der Hand" des Frankfurter ____________ CASE. Dieses ____________ zeigt eine fotorealistische Abbildung zweier ____________, die sich teilweise überlappen. Bei genauerer Betrachtung sehen wir, ____________ die Hände sowohl kräftig als auch verletzt aussehen.

Ein Street Art-Gemälde mit Kultstatus befindet sich in der ____________ des Kottbusser Tors: „Astronaut Kosmonaut" des ____________ Künstlers Victor Ash. Es zeigt einen schwebenden ____________ in einer Größe von 22 x 14 Metern. Das Bild ____________ die Spannung zwischen dem Westen und dem Osten während des ____________ ____________, aber auch den Wunsch nach Freiheit.

273b **Suchen Sie online die drei Street Art-Gemälde aus Aktivität 273a. Welches Gemälde gefällt Ihnen am besten? Warum? Geben Sie mindestens drei Gründe an und benutzen Sie dabei „weil"-Sätze.**

Recherche

____

____

____

____

86: Mit Möhren gegen koloniale Spuren

275c **Spuren der Kolonialzeit. In seinem Lied „Spuren der Kolonialzeit" spricht Rapper Matondo über die Problematik von Straßennamen in Deutschland, die an die Kolonialzeit erinnern. Schauen Sie sich online das offizielle Musikvideo an. Beantworten Sie die Fragen in Stichpunkten.**

Recherche

Wo stehen Matondo und die anderen Leute? (Achten Sie auf das Schild im Hintergrund.)

____

Welche offiziellen Straßennamen sehen Sie im Video?

____

____

Welche neuen Namen wollen die Menschen im Video den Straßen geben?

____

____

Das Video zeigt ein paar Fotos aus der Kolonialzeit. Was können Sie auf diesen Fotos sehen?

____

____

275d **Verstanden? Auch Namibia hat Straßen, die nach deutschen Kolonist*innen benannt waren, umbenannt. Hören Sie gut zu und kreuzen Sie die richtigen Antworten an.**

Was passierte im Jahr 2015?

- ☐ Im Jahr 2015 begannen die Gespräche zwischen Namibia und Deutschland zur Aufarbeitung des Genozids.
- ☐ Im Jahr 2015 entschuldigte sich die Bundeskanzlerin für den Genozid an Nama und Herero.
- ☐ Im Jahr 2015 gab es einen neuen Dokumentarfilm über den deutschen Kolonialismus.

Warum gab es in Namibia Widerstand gegen eine Straße, die nach Lothar von Trotha benannt war?

- ☐ Lothar von Trotta war ein General, der versucht hat, ein modernes Straßensystem in Namibia zu etablieren.
- ☐ Lothar von Trotta war ein General, der die Straße gebaut und dabei viele Häuser zerstört hat.
- ☐ Lothar von Trotta war ein General, der die Vernichtung der Nama und Herero befohlen hat.

Was ist seit 2016 mit den Straßen in Namibia passiert, die nach deutschen Kolonist*innen benannt waren?

- ☐ Die alten Namen wurden entfernt und durch Namen namibischer Politiker*innen ersetzt.
- ☐ Die alten Namen wurden entfernt und durch Namen namibischer Aktivist*innen und Freiheitskämpfer*innen ersetzt.
- ☐ Die alten Namen wurden entfernt und durch leere Schilder ersetzt.

277b **Struwwelpeter und die schwarzen Buben. Das Buch „Struwwelpeter" von Heinrich Hoffmann, das 1845 zum ersten Mal gedruckt wurde, enthält eine Reihe von illustrierten Geschichten. Diese Geschichten erzählen von Kindern, die sich schlecht benehmen (*behave*), und dafür bestraft (*punished*) werden oder sogar sterben. „Die Geschichte von den schwarzen Buben" reagiert auf den Rassismus der Zeit. Sie soll Toleranz vermitteln, reproduziert dabei aber rassistische Denkweisen. Lesen Sie den deutschen Text und die englische Übersetzung. Lesen Sie dann die Aussagen unten und notieren Sie, in welcher Zeile diese rassistischen Aspekte oder Handlungen im Originaltext und in der Übersetzung zu finden sind.**

1 Es ging spazieren vor dem Tor
2 Ein kohlpechrabenschwarzer M…[1].
3 Die Sonne schien ihm aufs Gehirn,
4 Da nahm er seinen Sonnenschirm.
5 Da kam der Ludwig hergerannt
6 Und trug sein Fähnchen in der Hand.
7 Der Kaspar kam mit schnellem Schritt
8 Und brachte seine Brezel mit;
9 Und auch der Wilhelm war nicht steif
10 Und brachte seinen runden Reif.
11 Die schrie'n und lachten alle drei,
12 Als dort das M… chen ging vorbei,
13 Weil es so schwarz wie Tinte sei!

14 Da kam der große Nikolas
15 Mit seinem großen Tintenfaß.
16 Der sprach: „Ihr Kinder, hört mir zu
17 Und laßt den M…en hübsch in Ruh'!
18 Was kann denn dieser M… dafür,
19 Daß er so weiß nicht ist, wie ihr?"
20 Die Buben aber folgten nicht
21 Und lachten ihm ins Angesicht
22 Und lachten ärger als zuvor
23 Über den armen schwarzen M… .

24 [Sankt Nikolas tunkt die Jungen in schwarze Tinte.]

25 Du siehst sie hier, wie schwarz sie sind,
26 Viel schwärzer als das M…enkind!
27 Der M… voraus im Sonnenschein,
28 Die Tintenbuben hinterdrein;
29 Und hätten sie nicht so gelacht,
30 Hätt' Niklas sie nicht schwarz gemacht.

[1] siehe Kulturbox in LERNEN, 275b

As he had often done before, 1
The woolly-headed black-a-m… 2
One nice fine summer's day went out 3
To see the shops and walk about; 4
And as he found it hot, poor fellow, 5
He took with him his green umbrella. 6
Then Edward, little noisy wag, 7
Ran out and laugh'd, and waved his flag, 8
And William came in jacket trim, 9
And brought his woollen hoop with him; 10
And Caspar, too, snatch'd up his toys 11
And joined the other naughty boys; 12
So one and all set up a roar, 13
And laughed and hooted more and more, 14
And kept on singing,—only think!— 15
"Oh! Blacky, you're as black as ink." 16

Now Saint Nicholas lived close by,— 17
So tall he almost touched the sky; 18
He had a mighty inkstand too, 19
In which a great goose feather grew; 20
He call'd out in an angry tone: 21
"Boys, leave the black-a-m… alone! 22
For if he tries with all his might, 23
He cannot change from black to white." 24
But ah! they did not mind a bit 25
What Saint Nicholas said of it; 26
But went on laughing, as before, 27
And hooting at the black-a-m…. 28

[Saint Nicholas dunks the boys in black ink.] 29

See, there they are, and there they run! 30
The black-a-m… enjoys the fun. 31
They have been made as black as crows, 32
Quite black all over, eyes and nose, 33
And legs, and arms, and heads, and toes. 34
And trowsers, pinafores, and toys,— 35
The silly little inky boys! 36
Because they set up such a roar, 37
And teas'd the harmless black-a-m…. 38

Quelle: Heinrich Hoffmann, „Der Struwwelpeter" (Übersetzung von Mark Twain)

Drei weiße Jungen verspotten (*mock*) die Hautfarbe eines Schwarzen Jungen.

deutscher Text: ☐ Z. 1–3 ☒ Z. 11–13 ☐ Z. 21–23

englischer Text: ☐ Z. 3–4 ☒ Z. 13–14 ☐ Z. 23–24

Das Schwärzen (= Schwarzmachen) der Haut ist hier eine Strafe.

deutscher Text: ☐ Z. 14 ☐ Z. 18 ☐ Z. 24

englischer Text: ☐ Z. 17 ☐ Z. 24 ☐ Z. 29

Der Text beschreibt den Schwarzen Jungen als M...en, ein rassistisches Wort (siehe Kulturbox in LERNEN, 275b).

erste Erwähnung im deutschen Text:	Z. 1	Z. 2	Z. 7
Entsprechung im englischen Text:	Z. 2	Z. 5	Z. 16

Nikolas sagt, dass der Schwarze Junge sich seine Hautfarbe nicht auswählen konnte. Er impliziert, dass weiße Menschen diesen Jungen für seine Hautfarbe bemitleiden (*pity*) sollten.

deutscher Text:	Z. 16–17	Z. 18–19	Z. 25–26
englischer Text:	Z. 23–24	Z. 31–32	Z. 37–38

277c **Gibt es in Ihrem Heimatland ähnliche rassistische Darstellungen, z.B. in Büchern, Filmen oder in den Nachrichten, wie in der Geschichte, die Sie in Aktivität 277b kennengelernt haben? Berichten Sie.**

____

____

____

____

____

277d **Rassistische Sprache in Büchern. Sollten Verlage rassistische Sprache in älteren literarischen Texten, zum Beispiel in der Kinderliteratur, abändern? Hier sehen Sie sechs Argumente zu dieser Diskussion. Bringen Sie die Wörter in die richtige Reihenfolge und entscheiden Sie, ob das Argument für (pro) oder gegen (contra) solch eine Veränderung ist.**

Aussage: Rassistische Sprache in älteren literarischen Texten sollte geändert werden.

Argumente:

können / alleine / Kinder / erkennen , gut oder böse / ob / ist / ein Wort / .

Kinder können alleine erkennen, ob ein Wort gut oder böse ist. (pro | contra)

dagegen / Ich / bin , Verlage / verändern / solche historischen Zeugnisse / dass / .

______________________________ (pro | contra)

Kinder / denken / könnten , rassistische Wörter / dass / sind / normal / .

______________________________ (pro | contra)

verletzend/ Es / für POCs / ist , zu lesen / solche Texte / .

______________________________ (pro | contra)

Wir / nicht / können / durch ein paar Veränderungen / Rassismus / beenden / .

______________________________ (pro | contra)

von gegenseitigem Respekt / ist / Es / ein Zeichen / .

______________________________ (pro | contra)

277e **Pro oder contra? Schreiben Sie vier Sätze über die Themen im Kasten: Sind Sie dafür oder dagegen?**

~~Straßen mit kolonialen Namen werden umbenannt~~
Student*innen bezahlen Studiengebühren
Impfung ist für alle Menschen obligatorisch
das Wahlrecht wird durch eine Wahlpflicht (*obligation to vote*) ersetzt
für ungesunde Lebensmittel soll man höhere Steuern (*taxes*) bezahlen

Ich bin (dafür) | dagegen, dass *Straßen mit kolonialen Namen umbenannt werden.*
Ich bin dafür | dagegen, dass ______
Ich bin dafür | dagegen, dass ______
Ich bin dafür | dagegen, dass ______
Ich bin dafür | dagegen, dass ______

87: Afrodeutscher Aktivismus°

278b **Reflektieren: 2011 entstand die Gruppe Bühnenwatch, um gegen das Phänomen von Blackfacing zu protestieren. Blackfacing ist wie Blackface in den USA und Kanada, wo es das als rassistische, beleidigende (*offensive*) Kunstform seit dem 19. Jahrhundert gibt. Bühnenwatch ist eine Gruppe von Menschen aus Kunst, Wissenschaft und Journalismus, die darauf aufmerksam machen, dass Blackfacing immer wieder auf deutschen Bühnen verwendet wird. Das macht die Gruppe zum Beispiel über die sozialen Medien. Was denken Sie über diese Form von Protest? Wie kann antirassistischer Aktivismus die sozialen Medien nutzen? Kennen Sie noch andere Beispiele, z. B. aus Ihrem eigenen Land, bei denen öffentlich protestiert wird?**

278c **Verstanden? Sie hören einen Text über Sharon Dodua Otoo. Beantworten Sie die R/F-Fragen.**

richtig	falsch	
		Sharon Dodua Otoo ist eine deutschsprachige Schriftstellerin und Aktivistin.
		Sie hat in Berlin Management studiert.
		Otoo hat auch über ihre Eltern eine Beziehung zu Ghana.
		Sie engagiert sich bei der Initiative Schwarze Menschen in Deutschland.
		Sie beschäftigt sich mit politischen Themen wie „Feminismus" und „Weißsein".
		Otoo hat bisher noch keinen großen Literaturpreis gewonnen.

88: Über Erinnerung stolpern

281e **Denkmal oder Mahnmal? Sie wissen nun, was der Unterschied zwischen einem Denkmal und einem Mahnmal ist. Erstellen Sie eine Liste mit vier *monuments* aus den USA oder anderen Ländern. Schreiben Sie hinter jedes *monument*, ob es ein Denkmal oder ein Mahnmal ist und – in Stichworten – woran es erinnert.**

______
______
______
______

282b Verstanden? Sie hören ein paar Meilensteine aus der Biografie von Gunter Demnig, dem Künstler, der das Stolpersteinprojekt begonnen hat. Notieren Sie sich so viele Informationen wie möglich in Stichworten.

____

____

____

____

____

282c Beenden Sie die Sätze. Sie können die Information aus MACHEN benutzen oder Ihre eigenen Ideen verwenden. Achten Sie dabei auf die Konjunktionen.

Erst 1997 wurden die ersten Stolpersteine verlegt, obwohl ______________________

Nicht alle Städte haben Stolpersteine, obwohl ______________________

Nicht alle Städte haben Stolpersteine, weil ______________________

Ich finde die Idee der Stolpersteine __________, weil ______________________

Ich finde die Idee der Stolpersteine __________, aber ______________________

283c Streit um die Stolpersteine in Hellenthal I. Lesen Sie den Text und beantworten Sie die Fragen.

„Kirchenasyl" für die Stolpersteine?

Hellenthal. Die Gemeinde Hellenthal macht Schlagzeilen. Als in der Region einzige (*only*) Kommune hat der Rat der Gemeinde entschieden, Stolpersteine, mit denen an jüdische Opfer des Nationalsozialismus erinnert werden soll, nicht gegen den Willen von Anliegern (*residents*) zu verlegen. Auch dann nicht, wenn diese Mahnmale im öffentlichen Raum, also auf Gehwegen, verlegt werden. Und das, obwohl die Administration selbst keinen einzigen Fall nennen konnte, dass es jemals (*ever*) nach solchen Aktionen zu Krawallen (*riots*) gekommen ist.[1]
Für die Gemeinde ist die Sache mittlerweile peinlich (*embarrassing*) geworden, besonders weil die Initiative Judit.H (Juden im Tal, Hellenthal) schon Nachfahren (*descendants*) der Opfer nach Hellenthal eingeladen hat. „Wir haben Menschen aus Amerika eingeladen, die haben ihre Flugtickets schon gebucht", sagt Karl Reger. Bürgermeister Rudolf Westerburg stellt klar: „Organisatorisch ist das mehr als unglücklich gewesen."
In Blumenthal trafen sich am Donnerstag Vertreter von Judit.H und der Kirchengemeinden Hellenthal und Blumenthal. „Wir haben uns gefragt: Was machen wir mit den sechs Stolpersteinen, die wir nicht verlegen können", berichtet Karl Reger. Pfarrer Oliver Joswig von der evangelischen Kirche hat schon früh den Vorschlag gemacht: „Wir legen die solange in die Hellenthaler Kirche, bis sie verlegt werden können."
Karl Reger kam auf die Idee, dass man den Stolpersteinen ja „Kirchenasyl" geben kann. „Sie sollen gut sichtbar in einer Vitrine mit Infos und Zeitungsartikeln liegen", sagt Reger. Dass auf diese Weise in der Kirche permanent daran erinnert wird, dass ein Anlieger die Verlegung von Stolpersteinen verhinderte, findet Reger in Ordnung.

Quelle: Kölnische Rundschau (gekürzt und vereinfacht)

[1] In Blumenthal wurde Ende Juli 2013 zum zweiten Mal das Mahnmal beschädigt. Es steht dort, wo früher die Synagoge stand, die in der Reichskristallnacht von 1938 zerstört worden war. Die Anlieger*innen, die gegen die Verlegung der Stolpersteine vor ihren Häusern waren, hatten deshalb Angst vor Sachbeschädigung (*damage to property*).

Notice that the author of this text from 2013 uses the generic masculine forms.

richtig	falsch	
		Der Hellenthaler Gemeinderat hat entschieden, Stolpersteine nur zu verlegen, wenn Anlieger*innen einverstanden sind.
		Alle Anlieger*innen haben der Verlegung von Stolpersteinen vor ihren Häusern zugestimmt.
		Einige Anlieger*innen wollen die Stolpersteine nicht, weil sie es nicht wichtig finden, dass die Gemeinde an die jüdischen Opfer des Nationalsozialismus erinnert.
		Zur Verlegung der Stolpersteine reisen Nachfahr*innen von Opferfamilien aus den USA an.
		Die Stolpersteine sollen trotzdem in der Öffentlichkeit zu sehen sein: in einer Vitrine in der Kirche.

283d **Streit um die Stolpersteine in Hellenthal II. Zwei Leser*innen haben auf die Situation in ihrer Gemeinde (Aktivität 283c) mit Briefen reagiert. Lesen Sie die Briefe und beantworten Sie dann die Fragen in 4–5 Sätzen.**

Leserbrief 1:
Es ist wirklich schwer zu verstehen, dass es immer noch Menschen gibt, die gegen diese öffentliche Erinnerung sind. Rat und Anlieger sagen, es geht ihnen um Datenschutz (*protection of privacy*). Aber das ist doch nur ein Vorwand (*pretext*)! Für uns alle muss es Priorität sein, uns an diese schrecklichen Dinge zu erinnern, damit sie nie wieder passieren. Deshalb müssen die Stolpersteine dort verlegt werden, wo sie gut sichtbar sind. Ich habe aber das Gefühl, dass die Entscheidungsträger (*policymakers*) das noch nicht verstanden haben.

Dr. Heribert Schmitz, Kammerwald

Leserbrief 2:
Ich bin wütend, dass der Rat der Gemeinde die Stolpersteine nicht wie geplant verlegen lassen will. Wenn der Grund Angst ist, dann muss man sich fragen, warum und wovor die Menschen Angst haben. Wir dürfen uns nicht von einer Minderheit einschüchtern (*intimidate*) lassen, sondern müssen noch stärker für unsere eigenen Werte eintreten (*stand up for*). Wir müssen „Ja" zur Erinnerung an unsere früheren Nachbarn sagen. Ich appelliere an die Anlieger und unsere gewählten Repräsentanten das aus eigener Überzeugung zu tun.

Elena Berghaus, Miescheid

Notice that the authors of these text from 2013 use the generic masculine forms.

Fragen zu den Leser*innenbriefen: Warum haben die Schreiber*innen (kein) Verständnis für die Entscheidung des Rats? Was denken sie über die Argumente gegen die Stolpersteine? Warum sind sie (nicht) für die Verlegung der Stolpersteine vor den Häusern? Worin sehen sie die Funktion der Stolpersteine?

Und was denken Sie: Wie wichtig finden Sie es, dass Anlieger*innen mit der Verlegung von Stolpersteinen vor ihren Häusern einverstanden sind?

____

____

____

____

____

283e  **Reflektieren: You now know about *Stolpersteine* in Germany. Do you think such an approach could also work in the U.S. to make people aware of places of enslavement or genocide against Native Americans or other traumatic events in U.S. history? Why (not)?**

89: #MeTwo

285c **Verstanden? Sie haben schon viel über #MeTwo gesprochen. Aber wie hat diese Bewegung begonnen? Lernen Sie nun Ali Can kennen, der als erster #MeTwo benutzt hat, um über seine persönliche Erfahrung zu erzählen. Füllen Sie Cans Steckbrief aus.**

Steckbrief Ali Can

Alter: ______________________________

Geburtsdatum: ______________________________

Aufgewachsen in: ______________________________

Studienfächer: ______________________________

Beruf: ______________________________

Ziel seines Vereins Interkultureller Frieden:

____

____

286a **Reflektieren: Was denken Sie? Warum gehen manche Hashtags viral? Sie können über #MeTwo oder andere Bewegungen in den sozialen Medien reflektieren. Schreiben Sie 4–5 Sätze.**

287i **Ergänzen Sie die folgenden Sätze mit „deshalb", „also" oder „trotzdem".**

Mein Laptop ist kaputt,

deshalb/also muss ich mir einen neuen kaufen.

Es regnet schon den ganzen Tag,

____

Von Koffein bekomme ich starkes Herzklopfen (*palpitations*),

____

Meine Katze mag keine anderen Katzen,

____

Viele Menschen haben mehr als einen Job,

____

90: WAS DARF COMEDY?°

288b **Was darf Comedy (nicht)? In MACHEN haben Sie mit einer anderen Person darüber diskutiert, was Comedy darf und wo ihre Grenzen sein sollten. Was waren Ihre Antworten? Beantworten Sie die Fragen und begründen Sie.**

Beispiel: Comedy darf sich nicht über das Aussehen einer Person lustig machen, weil das verletzend (*hurtful*) ist.

Was darf Comedy?

____,

weil ____.

____,

weil ____.

Was darf Comedy nicht?

____,

weil ____.

____,

weil ____.

289c **Der Comedian Teddy Comedy. Verbinden Sie die Sätze, sodass sie am Ende die Biografie von Teddy Comedy erzählen.**

Der deutsche Komiker ist unter dem Namen Teddy Comedy bekannt, ____

Teddy wuchs in Eritrea auf, ____

Weil er in beiden Ländern gelebt hat, ____

Obwohl sein deutscher Dialekt Schwäbisch ist, ____

Teddy spielt nicht nur Gitarre, ____

Nachdem er 2005–2008 die Internationale Schauspielakademie Crearte Stuttgart besucht hatte, ____

Sein wanderndes Bühnenprogramm „Teddy Show – Was labersch du ...?!" führt ihn durch ganz Deutschland; ____

Seit 2011 hat er einen YouTube-Kanal mit vielen Zuschauer*innen ____

a) trotzdem hat er Zeit, um seine eigene Fernsehshow zu filmen.
b) kann Teddy auch Sächsisch sprechen.
c) sondern auch Cajon-Trommel.
d) und sein populärstes Video ist „Umfrage zum Integrationstest (was nicht gesendet wurde)".
e) aber er lebt schon lange in Deutschland.
f) wurde er 2009 als Schauspieler im Fernsehen aktiv.
g) aber sein bürgerlicher Name ist Tedros Teclebrhan.
h) spricht er Tigrinya und Deutsch.

289d **Verstanden? Der Comedian Teddy Comedy hat einen Sketch zum Thema „Integrationstest" gemacht. Hören Sie gut zu und kreuzen Sie die richtigen Antworten an.**

Welche Information über das beliebteste Video von Teddy Comedy ist korrekt?

- [ ] Das Video ist aus dem Jahr 1992.
- [ ] Das Video wurde auf YouTube mehr als 39 Millionen Mal angeschaut.
- [ ] Das Video darf nicht mehr auf YouTube gezeigt werden.

Was macht Teddy im Video „Umfrage zum Integrationstest"?

- [ ] Er antwortet, dass die deutsche Hauptstadt Luxemburg heißt.
- [ ] Er sagt dem Reporter, dass er ein Deutschland-Experte ist.
- [ ] Er nennt den korrekten Namen der Bundeskanzlerin.

Was war Teddys Ziel mit dem Video „Umfrage zum Integrationstest"?

- [ ] Er wollte zeigen, wie gut er die deutsche Geschichte kennt.
- [ ] Er kritisiert rassistische Klischees, wie zum Beispiel das Stereotyp von „dummen Ausländern".
- [ ] Er zeigt, wie einfach man den Integrationstest bestehen kann.

289e **In MACHEN haben Sie einen Clip von Kaya Yanar, Anke Engelke oder Enissa Amani gesehen und Ihre Eindrücke aufgeschrieben. Nehmen Sie Ihre Notizen und schreiben Sie eine Rezension. Achten Sie auf die Teile/Elemente einer Rezension, die Sie in LERNEN Aktivität 289a gesehen haben.**

____

____

____

____

____

____

91: PROJEKT 7 – EINE PETITION°

291a **Erzähl mal: Protest, Widerstand, Mitbestimmung. Was bedeuten diese Begriffe für Sie? Nehmen Sie ein kurzes Video auf (z. B. mit Ihrem Handy oder am Computer) und beantworten Sie die Fragen.**

Erzählen Sie von einem Protest oder einer Bewegung, die Widerstand leistet, bei der Sie mitgemacht haben oder die Sie bewundern. Diese Fragen helfen Ihnen dabei:

Was macht die Bewegung? Wofür engagiert sie sich? Wogegen protestiert sie?

Warum finden Sie diese Bewegung bewundernswert? Haben Sie mitgemacht? Wenn ja, wie?

Welche Resultate und/oder Konsequenzen hatte der Widerstand? Wie haben Sie sich gefühlt?

291b **Self-Assessment**

You now get a chance to reflect on the many things you have learned throughout the chapter. Carefully read through the "Can-Do Statements" below, and ask yourself if you can perform all of these tasks. It might be helpful for each of the statements to actually practice the communicative scenario. Once you are confident that you are able to perform a task, check the respective box on the left side.

- I can have simple conversations about controversial opinions and state whether or not I agree with them.
- I can compose effective communications about a topic I care about.
- I can understand short informational texts about different forms of protest and activism communicated during *Karneval* in Germany.
- I can express and support an opinion about which (future) technologies will have the greatest influence on my life.
- I can give a presentation about the advantages and disadvantages of automation based on statistics and infographics.
- I can connect biographical information about famous resistance fighters into paragraph-length biographies.
- I can read a text about the 1968 student movements in different countries.
- I can write a fictitious letter processing historical information, such as the transnational 1968 movement, through a string of connected sentences.
- I can compose short argumentative texts, such as a proposal for a street art project.
- I can express what challenges societies across the globe in terms of social (in)justice.
- I can understand the main message of social media posts dealing with contentious issues, such as the #MeTwo campaign.
- I can compose short messages that express my viewpoint about a social issue that is important to me.
- I can read a poem and identify its main topics and perspectives.
- I can compose connected sentences comparing different forms of public commemoration of victims of the Holocaust.
- I can connect sentences with *weil*, *da*, and *denn* to give reasons for doing something.
- I can express and elaborate on opinions with *dass*-clauses.
- I can present contrasting information by connecting sentences with *aber* and *sondern*.
- I can express counter-arguments by using *obwohl*-clauses.
- I can write short texts in different argumentative and descriptive genres.

- I can use idiomatic verb-preposition combinations.
- I can use *da*- and *wo*-compounds as a replacement for prepositional phrases.

- I am familiar with the 1968 student movements from a transnational, intercultural perspective.
- I am familiar with Afro-German activists and organizations that do anti-racist work in Germany.
- I am familiar with the *Stolpersteine* project and its transnational importance for remembering the victims of the Holocaust.
- I am familiar with names of places and people related to colonialism.

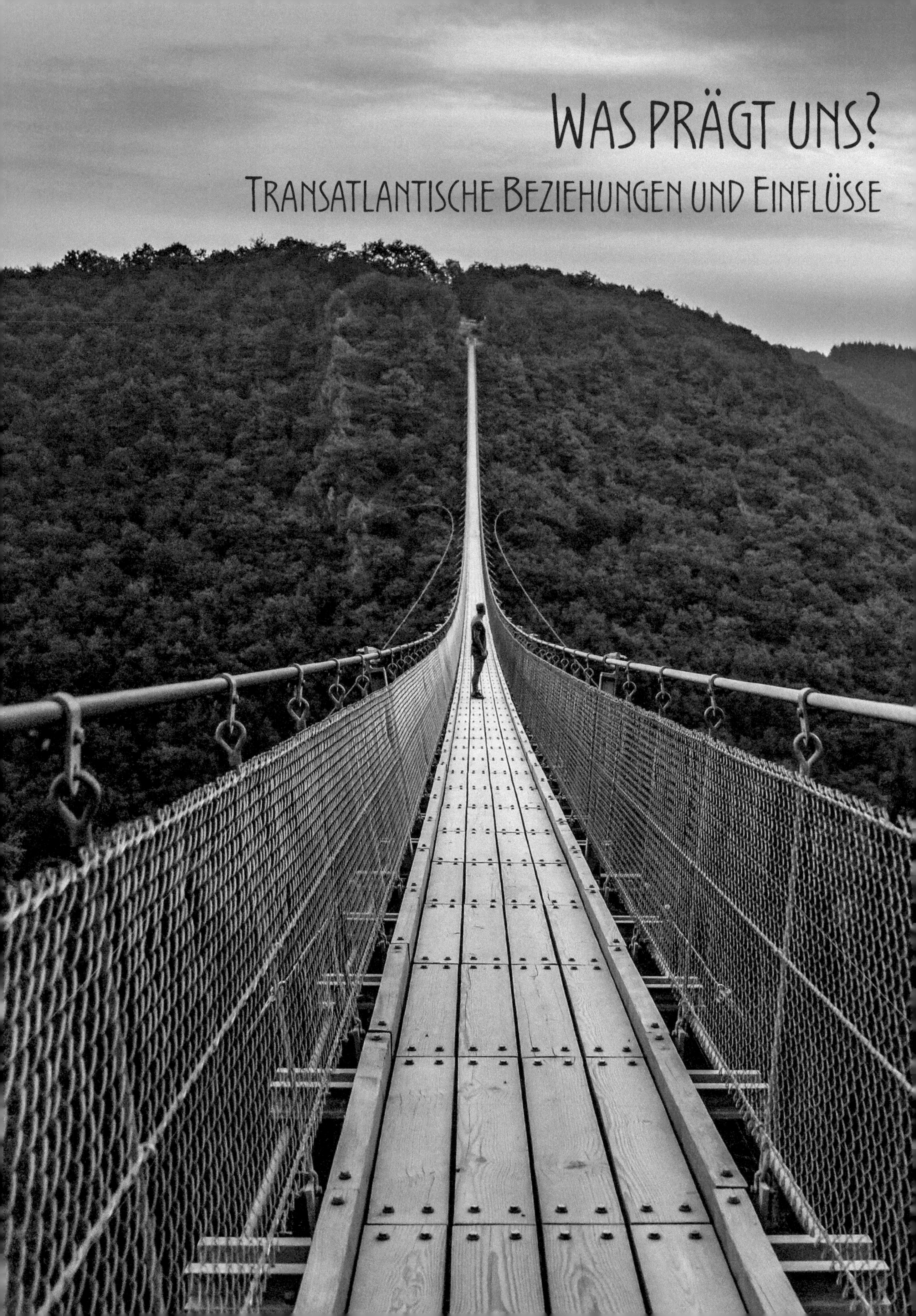
Was prägt uns?
Transatlantische Beziehungen und Einflüsse

92: KULTUR – WAS IST DAS EIGENTLICH?

292e  **Das prägt mich: In MACHEN haben Sie darüber gesprochen, was Kultur ist. Sprechen Sie jetzt darüber, mit welchen kulturellen Gruppen Sie sich identifizieren (z.B. national und regional/lokal, aber auch: Hobbys, Familie, Beruf/Studium etc.). Wählen Sie dabei drei Beispiele, wie verschiedene Gruppen Sie prägen.**

Diese Fragen können Ihnen helfen:

- Haben Sie ein bestimmtes Vokabular gemeinsam mit anderen Menschen, die auch studieren?
- Haben Sie bestimmte Traditionen, die es nur in Ihrer Familie gibt?
- Kennen Sie Regeln, die nur die Menschen kennen, die das gleiche Hobby wie Sie haben?
- Haben Sie Dinge (z.B. Kleidung oder Kochutensilien), von denen nur Leute aus Ihrer kulturellen Gruppe wissen, was man damit macht oder was sie symbolisieren?
- Gibt es ein Motto, nach dem die Menschen in Ihrer Region leben und das sich von anderen Regionen unterscheidet? Was machen/denken/fühlen Sie, weil es andere Menschen in Ihrer (großen oder kleinen) kulturellen Gruppe auch so machen/denken/fühlen?

293b  **In MACHEN haben Sie über Ihre Erfahrung mit dem Kulturstandard-Spiel reflektiert. Schreiben Sie einen kurzen Text und reflektieren Sie etwas mehr über die folgenden Fragen: Haben Sie in Ihrem Leben schon einmal eine Situation erlebt, in der Sie einen Kulturstandard missachtet/gebrochen haben, weil er Ihnen nicht klar/bekannt war? Wenn ja, beschreiben Sie die Situation. Wie haben Sie sich gefühlt? Wenn nein, was denken Sie, wie Menschen sich dabei fühlen? Haben Sie in dem Spiel oder in dieser Situation Kulturstandards als etwas Positives oder Negatives erfahren? Warum?**

Oder: Glauben Sie, dass Sie Kulturstandards beachten müssen, wenn Sie in einem Land oder einer Region sind, die kulturell anders ist? Wer sagt Ihnen, wie Sie sich verhalten müssen und was passiert, wenn Sie es nicht tun? Was meinen Sie: Macht es einen Unterschied, ob Sie im Urlaub sind, im Ausland studieren oder ausgewandert sind, das heißt, ob Sie nur kurz, länger oder vielleicht für immer in dem Land / der Region leben?

293c **In MACHEN haben Sie Kulturstandards des Landes Pulmsi kennengelernt. Überlegen Sie nun: Welche Kulturstandards gibt es in Ihrem Land und welche davon würden Menschen aus Pulmsi komisch finden? Benutzen Sie die Struktur, wie im Beispiel.**

Beispiel: *In meinem Land gibt es den Kulturstandard, dass sich die Menschen zur Begrüßung umarmen. Die Menschen aus Pulmsi würden das komisch finden, weil sie sich dort mit Stampfen und Klatschen begrüßen.*

294e  **Bodo Wartkes ironisches Lied „Die Amerikaner" endet mit den Zeilen, die Sie hier sehen. Er schrieb diesen Song kurze Zeit nach einem Amoklauf an einer deutschen Schule. Den Deutschen war also klar, dass das Lied ironisch gemeint ist, und dass es eigentlich eine Kritik an Deutschland und den Deutschen ist. Wartke spielt mit der Idee, dass es einfacher ist, andere Personen und Länder zu kritisieren als sich selbst oder das eigene Land. Kennen Sie solche Beispiele auch aus Ihrem eigenen Leben und/oder aus Ihrem eigenen Land (heute oder historisch)? Was denken Sie, warum Menschen Kritik eher projizieren, als auf sich selbst zu schauen?**

Wenn wir uns all das, was die Amerikaner machen,
Einfach mal vor Augen führen,
Kann ich nur sagen: Gut, dass solche Sachen
Bei uns in Deutschland nicht passieren,
Bei uns in Deutschland nie passieren.
Denn sonst könnten wir die Amerikaner
Ja nicht so einfach kritisieren.

Quelle: „Die Amerikaner", Musik & Text: Bodo Wartke

294f Verstanden? In Bodo Wartkes Lied „Die Amerikaner" gibt es viele Stereotype. Sie hören jetzt ein Gespräch zwischen zwei Freund*innen über Stereotype. Kreuzen Sie die richtigen Antworten an.

Warum findet Niklas kulturelle Stereotype nicht problematisch?

- Er findet, dass Stereotype helfen können, eine Kultur besser zu verstehen.
- Er findet, dass Stereotype immer auf der Wirklichkeit basieren und diese nur etwas übertreiben.
- Er findet, dass Stereotype zu einem Dialog zwischen Kulturen führen können.

Warum ist Nele nicht der gleichen Meinung wie Niklas?

- Sie denkt, dass kulturelle Stereotype verallgemeinern und oft sehr oberflächlich sind.
- Sie findet Stereotype problematisch, weil sie Menschen verletzen.
- Sie denkt, dass alle Stereotype vermeiden müssen, um die Nuancen einer Kultur kennenzulernen.

Worauf einigen sich Nele und Niklas am Ende?

- Sie einigen sich darauf, dass kulturelle Stereotype in Ordnung sind, wenn sie niemanden verletzen.
- Sie einigen sich darauf, dass Kulturstandards eine interessantere Kategorie sind.
- Sie einigen sich darauf, nicht mehr über dieses Thema zu sprechen.

294g Kulturelle Unterschiede. Ergänzen Sie die folgenden Fragen jeweils mit der richtigen Komparativ- oder Superlativform. Beantworten Sie dann alle Fragen in Stichworten.

Die Deutschen machen am ______________ (gern) Urlaub im eigenen Land. Wo machen Sie ______________ (gern) Urlaub: in Ihrem Land oder im Ausland?

Es ist vielleicht ein Stereotyp, aber oft auch wahr: Für die ______________ (viel) Deutschen ist Pünktlichkeit immer noch eine Tugend (*virtue*). Ist Pünktlichkeit in Ihrer Kultur genauso oder ______________ (wenig) wichtig?

Menschen in nordeuropäischen Kulturen, darunter auch die Deutschen, fühlen sich ______________ (wohl), wenn sie nicht nur zu Fremden, sondern auch zu Freund*innen eine „Komfort-Distanz" einhalten. Mit welcher Distanz fühlen Sie sich beim Kontakt mit anderen Menschen am ______________ (wohl)?

Die Deutschen haben keinen Humor? Haben sie doch! Man muss vielleicht nur ein bisschen ______________ (lang) danach suchen … Denken Sie, dass Ihre Kultur humorvoll ist?

____

____

93: AUF NACH NORDAMERIKA

295e **Berühmtheiten aus den deutschsprachigen Ländern in den USA. Suchen Sie sich aus jeder Spalte eine Person aus und recherchieren Sie die Gründe und/oder Ziele ihrer Flucht/Auswanderung. Schreiben Sie 1–2 Sätze pro Person.**

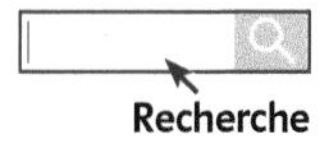
Recherche

Nach dem Zweiten Weltkrieg	1933–1945	1933–1945	In den 1920er Jahren	Frühe Ausgewanderte
Q'orianka Kilcher *1990	Hannah Arendt 1906–1975	Albert Einstein 1879–1955	Max Steiner 1888–1971	Adolphus Busch 1839–1913
Diane Kruger *1976	Raul Hilberg 1926–2007	Amalie/Emmy Noether 1882–1935	Ernst Lubitsch 1892–1947	Löb Strauß / Levi Strauss 1829–1902
Heidi Klum *1973	Billy Wilder 1906–2002	Hilda Geiringer 1893–1973	Hedy Lamarr 1914–2000	Karl Pfizer 1824–1906
Wolfgang Puck *1949	Bertolt Brecht 1898–1956	Gerty Cori 1896–1957		Eberhard Anheuser 1806–1880
Arnold Schwarzenegger *1947	Erich Maria Remarque 1898–1970	James Franck 1882–1964		Heinrich Steinweg / Henry Steinway 1797–1871
Hans J. Massaquoi 1926–2013		Ruth Hubbard 1924–2016		

Person 1:

Person 2:

Person 3:

Person 4:

Person 5:

295f Reflektieren: In LERNEN haben Sie Schub- und Sogfaktoren verglichen. Beantworten Sie ein paar dieser Fragen:

- Aus welchen aktuellen oder hypothetischen Gründen würden Sie aus dem Land auswandern, in dem Sie jetzt leben?
- Wohin würden Sie auswandern und warum?
- Was macht eine Auswanderung/Einwanderung leichter (Fähigkeiten, Kenntnisse, Kontakte ...)?
- Gibt es Menschengruppen in Ihrem Land, die für eine Auswanderung ganz andere Gründe als Sie haben könnten? Warum?

296i Verstanden? Sie hören Informationen über die vier großen Auswanderungsphasen aus Österreich in die USA. Hören Sie gut zu und tragen Sie in die Tabelle ein, welche Gruppen wann und warum ausgewandert sind.

Wann?	Wer? (Gruppen)	Warum? (Gründe)

296j Deutsche Einwanderung in die USA: Ergänzen Sie die Adjektivendungen.

Nach der gescheitert_____ Revolution von 1848 sind enttäuscht_____ Revolutionär*innen oft in die demokratischer_____ USA ausgewandert, weil sie sich dort größer_____ politisch_____ Freiheit erhofften. Zur gleich_____ Zeit ist aber auch die arm_____ bäuerlich_____ Bevölkerung in die USA ausgewandert, weil weiße Europäer*innen dort „frei_____" Land bekommen konnten und sie nicht nur ein klein_____ Stück Boden bebauen mussten. Weil es wenig religiös_____ Toleranz im monarchistisch_____ Deutschland gab, sind religiös_____ Minderheiten auch oft ausgewandert.
Im zwanzigst_____ Jahrhundert sind die deutsch_____ Auswanderer*innen auch aus viel_____ verschieden_____ Gründen ausgewandert: Manche wollten dem groß_____ Chaos in der Weimarer Republik (1919–1933) entkommen. Davor hatte die schnell_____ Industrialisierung zu einem rasant_____ Anstieg der Bevölkerungszahlen in groß_____ Städten geführt, wodurch es dort viele arm_____ und auch krank_____ Menschen gab. Aus Angst vor der brutal_____ Verfolgung durch die Nazis sind mehrer_____ Gruppen von Menschen ausgewandert, zum Beispiel jüdisch_____ Menschen, bekannt_____ Künstler*innen, queer_____ Menschen und Mitglieder kommunistisch_____ Parteien wie der KPD.
Nach dem Zweit_____ Weltkrieg zog der amerikanisch_____ „Post-War-Boom" viele hochqualifiziert_____ Menschen an. Es gab auch familiär_____ Gründe für die Einwanderung in die USA, wenn z. B. ein amerikanisch_____ Soldat eine deutsch_____ Frau geheiratet hatte.

297b **Schmelztiegel oder Salatschüssel. In MACHEN haben Sie über kulturelle Vielfalt im Kontext von Migration gesprochen. Schauen Sie noch einmal auf Ihre Notizen von Aktivität 297 und beantworten Sie die folgenden Fragen in 1–2 Sätzen.**

Was bedeutet das Wort „Schmelztiegel" im Kontext von Migration?

____

____

Was bedeutet im Kontrast dazu das Wort „Salatschüssel"?

____

____

____

Welches Konzept finden Sie positiver: den Schmelztiegel oder die Salatschüssel? Warum?

____

____

____

"Hold on a second: What is the difference between …

… U.S. and German Christian denominations?" German migrants to the U.S. didn't just bring pretzels and Christmas traditions (the tree, but definitely not the pickle)—they also brought religious beliefs. In areas with lots of German settlers, you can still see a predominance of German Lutheran churches, in Minnesota and Wisconsin, for instance. But not all descendants of Germans in the U.S. today are Lutheran, nor are all Germans in Germany. In fact, Germans who identify as Christian are pretty evenly split between *katholisch* (Catholic) and *evangelisch* (which in German just means Protestant, but with the many Protestant denominations in the U.S. complicating this designation, it is most similar to Lutheran here, and shouldn't be confused with evangelical). Here are statistics from 2018, where percentages are based on the total number of Germans:

Catholic:	27.7%	Other Christian communities[1]:	1.1%
Protestant:	25.5%	Religious Jew:	0.1%
konfessionslos (unaffiliated with any religion):	37.8%	Buddhist:	0.2%
Muslim:	5.1%	Hindu:	0.1%
Orthodox:	1.9%		

In the U.S., self-identified Christians make up 70.6% of the population; 1.9% of Americans identify as religiously Jewish, 0.9% Muslim, 0.7% each Buddhist and Hindu, and 22.8% are unaffiliated. Catholics, who were mostly Irish and Italian immigrants, used to be a minority in the U.S., whereas evangelical Christians comprise the main Protestant group. They make up the majority of Christian Americans and are the most influential group in the U.S. Today, the numbers are a bit more even with evangelical Christians at 25.4% and Catholics at 20.8%, due to the growth of the (mostly Catholic) Latinx diaspora.

These numbers, however, only show part of the picture. In the German statistics, only those who participated in a community of worship were counted, whereas those who culturally identify with Islam, Christianity, or Judaism are not represented in these numbers. Twenty-nine percent of German Muslims say they never engage in religious practices but identify as Muslim because of traditions and lifestyle. Estimates say that around 50% of German Jews are involved in a *Gemeinde*, which is a religious but also cultural community. For Christians, a study defined a person as a "practicing Christian" if they went to church at least once a month. In Germany, only 13.4% of all people do that. All others go at most for big holidays (such as Christmas) and celebrations (baptism, wedding). Within Catholicism, there are more "church-goers" with 18%, compared to 12.2% of Protestants. The numbers are declining, and older people are more likely to go to church regularly, so they will continue to decrease. This is different in the U.S., where people overall attend church more and the ratio between Catholics and Evangelicals is reversed: 58% of evangelical Protestants and 39% of Catholics in the U.S. attend church at least once a week.

Beyond the practice of religion, how much are society and faith intertwined in the two countries? In Germany (and it's very similar in Austria and Switzerland), you become a member of one of the two "state" churches (*katholisch* or *evangelisch*) through baptism. In schools, there is religious education; Christian students are split into groups according to their church affiliation. These lessons are not Bible study but rather cover all kinds of topics, such as the history of the specific group and of world religions, as well as topics such as friendship and values. Once a person who was baptized begins to work, church tax is withheld from their salary, unless they leave the church officially (8-9% of anyone's income tax). Despite there being a legal church tax in Germany, religion plays a significantly smaller role in Germany and most of Europe than in the U.S. In a research study from 2011, half of all Americans said that religion is very important, whereas only 21% of Germans said the same; 53% of Americans agreed that it is necessary to believe in God to be a moral person, whereas only a third of all Germans agreed with that statement. Some may think this is a contradiction, but let's look a little closer. In Germany, one of the large parties carries "Christian" in its name (CDU means Christian Democratic Union) but otherwise hardly ever mentions religion. Some of the CDU's political positions of course reflect "Christian" values, such as an emphasis on traditional families. On the other hand, religion in the U.S. is very much part of politics despite the fact that church and state are separated financially. God and faith play a role in arguments for different political positions, are present on money and in pledges, and politicians try to appeal to specific religious groups when campaigning. The financial separation in the U.S. also means that churches need to recruit paying members to pay for upkeep whereas the historical German churches are covered by the church tax.

[1] Among those are *Freikirchen*, Christian denominations other than Catholic and Protestant that include Mennonites, Baptists, Jehovah's Witnesses, and many others.

297c **Reflektieren: Answer the following questions about the text.**

- Did any of this information surprise you? What surprised you, and how?
- How would you explain the role religion plays in the U.S.? How do you experience religion in your own life, in school, and in your own environment?
- What is missing from the conversation about religion by looking at statistics?

94: Auf nach Europa

299c **Ergänzen Sie die Sätze mit dem Partizip I des angegebenen Verbs. Vergessen Sie nicht, die richtigen Adjektivendungen hinzuzufügen.**

Viele Neuankömmlinge (*newcomers*) in den Deutsch ____________________ Ländern wollen zuerst ihre Sprachkenntnisse verbessern. (sprechen)

Wenn eine eingewanderte Person einen Arbeitsplatz gefunden hat, gehört er*sie zur ____________________ Bevölkerung. (arbeiten)

Wenn sie noch keine Stelle haben, zählt das Arbeitsamt sie zur Arbeit ____________________ Personengruppe. (suchen)

Oft kommen junge Leute als ____________________ Personen in die D-A-CH-L-Länder. (studieren)

Andere junge Menschen aus dem Ausland streben eine berufliche Ausbildung an. Manche ____________________ Firmen suchen auch außerhalb der D-A-CH-L-Länder nach Nachwuchstalenten. (ausbilden)

299d **Wer ist ein*e Migrant*in? In der letzten Einheit haben wir über die Salatschüssel und den Schmelztiegel gesprochen und festgestellt, dass nicht alle Zuwander*innen Elemente ihrer Kultur in die neue Kultur einbringen können. Lesen Sie jetzt einen Text über die Wahrnehmung von Migrant*innen in den deutschsprachigen Ländern und kreuzen Sie unten an, ob die Aussagen richtig oder falsch sind.**

In den deutschsprachigen Ländern werden Migrant*innen verschieden wahrgenommen, oft nach ihrer Herkunftsregion oder ihrer Religion. In deutschen Statistiken werden „Menschen mit Migrationshintergrund" aufgeführt. Das können auch Menschen sein, die in Deutschland geboren wurden, deren Eltern aber nach Deutschland eingewandert sind. Das Wort „Migrationshintergrund" impliziert, dass diese Menschen wegen einer Migrationsgeschichte keine Deutschen sind und auch nicht werden können. Migrantisch wahrgenommen werden vor allem Menschen, die aus der Türkei, dem Nahen Osten und Nordafrika kommen. Die meisten Menschen in dieser Gruppe sind Muslim*innen. Auch Schwarze Deutsche werden von der weißen Mehrheitsgesellschaft zuerst als Besucher*innen oder Migrant*innen gedacht. Das Label „migrantisch" hat also mit dem Aussehen zu tun. Ganz im Gegenteil dazu ist die Positionierung von weißen Migrant*innen aus Nordwesteuropa und Zuwander*innen aus den USA. Diese Menschen nennen sich selbst oft Expats. Sobald man einen „coolen" Akzent hört, der verrät, dass die Person aus den USA kommt, werden auch Schwarze Amerikaner*innen in die Kategorie Expat eingeschlossen. Auch wenn Expat, genau wie Migrant*in, heißt, dass eine Person außerhalb des Herkunftslandes lebt, gibt es einen großen symbolischen Unterschied. Expats sind privilegierte Migrant*innen – ihnen wird selten vorgeworfen, dass sie sich nicht integrieren, viele sprechen ganz selbstverständlich Englisch mit ihnen und sie treffen auf wenig Vorurteile.

richtig	falsch	
		Migrant*innen in deutschsprachigen Ländern werden unterschiedlich wahrgenommen.
		Alle Menschen mit Migrationshintergrund sind selbst nach Deutschland immigriert.
		People of Color werden als migrantisch oder Besucher*innen wahrgenommen.
		US-amerikanische Migrant*innen heißen auch Expats.
		US-amerikanische Migrant*innen müssen Deutsch lernen und sich integrieren.
		Weiße Migrant*innen haben mit wenigen Vorurteilen zu kämpfen.

299e **Reflektieren: Kommen Ihnen diese Unterschiede auch aus Ihrem oder einem anderen Land, das Sie gut kennen, bekannt vor? Welche Zuwander*innen werden wie wahrgenommen und warum? Wer soll sich „integrieren" und wessen Herkunftskultur erscheint im Gegensatz dazu als „interessant" oder „cool"? Welche Gruppen von Zuwander*innen sind Vorurteilen ausgesetzt und warum?**

300b **In MACHEN haben Sie einige Orte in Berlin kennengelernt, die wichtig für Audre Lorde waren. Wählen Sie einen Ort und erzählen Sie zwei Minuten lang, warum dieser Ort für Lorde wichtig war. Erwähnen Sie so viele Details wie möglich. Sprechen Sie frei; es muss nicht fehlerfrei sein.**

301a **Verstanden? Tina Turner ist Ihnen vielleicht als erfolgreiche Sängerin bekannt mit Hits wie „The Best" oder „Proud Mary". Aber Turners Biografie ist auch deshalb interessant, weil sie schon jahrelang in der Schweiz lebt und 2013 sogar ihre amerikanische Staatsbürgerschaft aufgegeben hat. Kreuzen Sie die richtigen Aussagen an.**

Anna Mae Bullock ist

- eine unter dem Namen Tina Turner bekannte
- eine in New York City aufgewachsene
- eine mit ihren Geschwistern singende
- eine von Ike Turner geschiedene
- eine in der Rock and Roll Hall of Fame gefeierte

Sängerin und Schauspielerin.

301b Verstanden? Sie hören weitere Informationen über Tina Turners Biografie. Notieren Sie sich dann so viele Informationen wie möglich.

____

____

____

____

302d Was sagen die Personen, die Sie in MACHEN Aktivität 299 kennengelernt haben? Ergänzen Sie die Sätze mit dem Partizip II des angegebenen Verbs und fügen Sie dabei die richtigen Adjektivendungen hinzu.

„Als die Zürich Grasshoppers mich kontaktierten, bin ich sofort mit dem ______________ Angebot (*offer*) zu meinen College-Fußballtrainer*innen gelaufen und habe ihnen die E-Mail gezeigt!" (erhalten)

„Ich hatte nicht genug ______________ Geld, um die hohen Studiengebühren in den USA zu bezahlen. (ersparen) Dank des Stipendiums der Technischen Universität München kann ich jetzt studieren, ohne mir Sorgen um Geld zu machen. Ich hoffe, später nach Wien zu ziehen. Ich möchte nach meinem Studium am Institut für Molekulare Biotechnologie arbeiten. Seit längerer Zeit arbeite ich mit Professor Zeiler an einem fast ______________ Projekt." (abschließen)

„Ich habe am Ende meiner Militärzeit lange Jahre in Wiesbaden gelebt und gearbeitet. Mit meiner deutschen Frau habe ich dann einen alten Bauernhof gekauft. In dem ______________ Haus betreiben wir jetzt eine kleine Pension, vor allem für US-Soldat*innen." (renovieren)

„Meine Frau und ich haben zuerst in Berlin gelebt. Aber nach drei Jahren hat sie eine neue Stelle in Wien bekommen. Zu so einer gut ______________ Arbeit konnten wir nicht nein sagen. Wir leben jetzt schon seit fast zehn Jahren in Österreich." (bezahlen)

302e Das prägt mich: In MACHEN haben Sie Geschichten von Menschen kennengelernt, die von Nordamerika in deutschsprachige Länder ausgewandert sind. Für all diese Menschen gab es unterschiedliche Faktoren (wirtschaftlich, familiär etc.), die zu dieser großen Entscheidung beigetragen (*contributed*) haben. Welche großen Entscheidungen mussten Sie in Ihrem Leben schon treffen? Welche Faktoren waren für diese Entscheidungen wichtig? Erzählen Sie darüber.

302f Ergänzen Sie die folgenden Sätze mit der korrekten Form des Partizip I oder II.

Aus ihrem Heimatland ______________ Menschen müssen viele Dinge vor ihrer Ausreise organisieren. (auswandern; Partizip I) Aus ihrem Heimatland ______________ Menschen können dir Tipps für eine erfolgreiche Emigration geben. (auswandern; Partizip II) Über Schengen-Länder ______________ EU-Bürger*innen müssen an den Grenzen keinen Pass vorzeigen. (einreisen; Partizip I) Nach Deutschland ______________ Auswander*innen müssen sich beim Meldeamt für Einwohner*innen (*registration office*) ihrer Stadt melden. (einreisen; Partizip II) Die die neue Sprache ______________ Auswander*innen können sich leichter in die Gesellschaft integrieren. (sprechen; Partizip I) Wenn du die im neuen Land ______________ Sprache nicht lernst, wirst du es im Alltag schwer haben. (sprechen; Partizip II) Es ist sehr hilfreich, einen für gute Berufe ______________ Schulabschluss zu haben. (qualifizieren; Partizip I) Viele Länder in Europa suchen dringend nach ______________ Mitarbeiter*innen. (qualifizieren; Partizip II)

302g **Übersetzen Sie die ersten beiden Sätze (Aus Ihrem Heimatland ...) aus Aktivität 302f ins Englische, um den Unterschied zwischen der Partizip I- und der Partizip II-Version klarzumachen.**

____

____

____

95: Die Faszinationen mit dem „Wilden Westen"°

305c **Verstanden? Zwei Freund*innen unterhalten sich über den Film „Der Schuh des Manitu". Hören Sie gut zu und wählen Sie die richtigen Antworten aus.**

Warum findet Dirk den Film „Der Schuh des Manitu" nicht gut?

- Er mag den Film nicht, weil es der Lieblingsfilm seines Vaters ist.
- Er mag den Film nicht, weil er Westernfilme nicht gut findet.
- Er mag den Film nicht, weil der Film sich über die Winnetou-Filme lustig macht.

Wieso ist Nele ein Fan von „Der Schuh des Manitu"?

- Sie mag den Film, weil sie ihn früher immer mit ihrer Oma angeschaut hat.
- Sie mag den FIlm, weil er eine gute Parodie der Winnetou-Filme ist.
- Sie mag den Film, weil er ein traditioneller Western ist.

Was parodiert und kritisiert „Der Schuh des Manitu" laut Nele?

- Der Film parodiert und kritisiert, dass andere Western die Beziehung von Weißen und Amerikanischen Ureinwohner*innen romantisiert.
- Der Film parodiert und kritisiert romantische Beziehungen zwischen Weißen und Amerikanischen Ureinwohner*innen.
- Der Film parodiert und kritisiert, dass Karl May in seinen Geschichten zu wenig Humor benutzt.

305d **Karl May und der glorifizierte „Wilde Westen". In MACHEN haben Sie über den Schriftsteller Karl May und seine Winnetou-Geschichten diskutiert. Schauen Sie sich noch einmal Ihre Notizen von Aktivität 305 an und beantworten Sie die folgenden Fragen.**

Welches Bild von dem „Wilden Westen" und den Amerikanischen Ureinwohner*innen erschaffen die Bücher und auch der Film von 2016? Was denken Sie darüber?

____

____

____

Warum ist die Darstellung von Old Shatterhand als „edler Weißer" (*noble white man*) problematisch?

____

____

Schauen Sie sich (auf Englisch) die Trailer der Dokumentarfilme „Searching for Winnetou" und „Forget Winnetou" an. Beschreiben Sie, was Sie sehen und die Reaktionen der indigenen Sprecher*innen in den Filmen. Inwiefern hilft Ihnen diese Perspektive, die Geschichte(n), die über Indigene erzählt wird/werden, besser zu verstehen?

____

____

____

305e **What was your first reaction upon learning about Karl May, his Winnetou stories, and their popularity in Germany? What effects, positive and negative, do you think such a romanticized portrayal of the relationship between Native Americans and European settlers has on German audiences? Think, for example, about the fact that dressing up as cowboys and Native Americans is still common in Germany: What do these kinds of clothes actually represent? When and where do Native Americans wear such attire (today)? In contrast to that, in what ways are the German "costumes" stuck in the past without considering cultural appropriation and/or the lived presence of Native Americans today?**

OR

Tommy Orange's novel *There There* has recently been translated into German (*Dort Dort*). As you have seen when searching for children's literature, German literature about Native Americans is mostly about the past. This novel may not be the first indigenous perspective that Germans get, but it is one that moves narratives about Native Americans from a glorified past into the present time. If you don't know the novel, look up an interview with Tommy Orange or a review of the book online. Then reflect on the ways in which this novel (or similar ones like it that you may know) differs from the Winnetou stories and other Westerns. Is it important to hear a voice like Tommy Orange's? And what is the significance of thinking about Native Americans today rather than in the past?

305f **„The Frontier" – Trennlinie zwischen Wildnis und Zivilisation? Der typische Western arbeitet mit Gegensätzen, so zum Beispiel „Wildnis im Westen" vs. „Zivilisation im Osten" (der USA oder in Europa). Hier sind weitere Kontraste:**

offenes Land – Privatland
Erfahrung – Bildung
Gesetz der Natur – Gesetzbücher
Instinkt – Wissen
Praxis – Theorie
Freiheit – Einschränkungen
Gemeinschaft – Individualismus
Gleichheit – Hierarchien

Beide Seiten sind nicht objektiv besser oder schlechter, aber wer über eine andere Kultur schreibt, will entweder die eigene überlegen (*superior*) zeigen oder die andere Seite als ideal (und die eigene als korrupt) darstellen. Wenn Sie das nötige Hintergrundwissen haben, wählen Sie eine Seite und schreiben Sie einen kurzen Reisebericht über Ihre Reise westlich der „Frontier". Wenn Sie das lieber nicht machen möchten, erklären Sie, warum nicht.

Beispiel: Die amerikanischen Ureinwohner*innen kennen keinen Privatbesitz. Für sie ist das Land nur eine Leihgabe (*loan*), die sie an die nächste Generation weitergeben.

____

____

____

____

305g **Ost-Western: DEFAs Konstruktion der Amerikanischen Ureinwohner*innen als eine Art von Kommunist*innen. Die DDR war ein kleines Land umgeben von „mächtigen Feinden" (= den kapitalistischen Ländern). „Indianer*in sein" hieß, allein gegen den Rest der Welt zu kämpfen und eine ideale Form von Kommunismus zu praktizieren. Lesen Sie hier die Beschreibung eines Ost-Western-Films: „Apachen" von 1973.**

Der Film basiert auf Dokumenten des Mexikanisch-Amerikanischen Kriegs (1846–1848). Der junge Krieger Ulzana sucht Rache für die Ausrottung (*extermination*) seines Volkes: 1822 kommen die Apachen zu einer Einigung mit einer mexikanischen Bergbau-Firma. Sie geben alle Rohstoffrechte auf und garantieren der Stadt Santa Rita Sicherheit. Dafür garantiert die Firma den Indigenen Essen, weil ihre Jagdgründe verloren sind. Aber amerikanische Firmen sind auch an den Rohstoffen (Edelmetallen) interessiert. Unter dem Geologen und Ingenieur Johnson versuchen sie, die Apachen zu vertreiben. Als die Apachen ihre jährlichen Essensrationen in Santa Rita bekommen sollen, initiiert Johnson ein Massaker an den Indigenen. Ulzana sucht die Hilfe eines befreundeten Volkes und sie schwören, das Verbrechen zu rächen (*avenge*). Es kommt zu einem letzten Kampf zwischen Ulzana und Johnson – Ulzana gewinnt. Aber er weiß, dass das nur ein kleiner Aufschub (*delay*) war.

Wer sind die verschiedenen Akteur*innen im Film? Schreiben Sie in Stichworten auf, was Sie wissen (z. B. Wer ist das? Gut oder böse? Pläne/Motivation/Ziele?)

Ulzana: ______________________________

Mexikanische Bergbau-Firma: ______________________________

Johnson: ______________________________

Schauen Sie sich die Gegensätze in Aktivität 305f noch einmal an. Welche Seite zeigt der Film als positiver? Wie passt das in das Bild der DDR, das Sie haben?

____

____

____

306a **Das prägt mich: Erzählen Sie, welche Filme Sie gerne sehen und welche Rolle Filme und Fernsehen in Ihrem Leben spielen. Können Sie sich an Filme erinnern, an die Sie gute Erinnerungen haben (vielleicht weil Sie sie als Kind gesehen haben), die Sie heute aber problematisch finden? Beeinflusst Sie das? Und wie fühlen Sie sich, wenn Sie darüber nachdenken?**

96: Musikalische Einflüsse aus Nordamerika

307b **Das prägt mich: Erzählen Sie, welche Musik Sie gerne hören und welche Rolle Musik in Ihrem Leben spielt. Inwiefern bringt Musik Sie mit anderen Gruppen zusammen? Welche Symbole, Praktiken oder Perspektiven gibt es vielleicht in einer Gruppe, die die gleiche Musik hört oder mag? Gehören Sie zu solch einer Gruppe? Welchen Einfluss hat diese Gruppe auf Ihre kulturelle Identität und Ihr Leben?**

308a **Verstanden? Sie hören nun Informationen über den Jazzsänger Roger Cicero, dessen Musik stark von amerikanischer Jazz- und Swingmusik beeinflusst wurde. Beantworten Sie die Fragen.**

Frage	Antwort
Wann wurde Roger Cicero geboren?	
Was war das erste große Orchester, mit dem er gespielt hat?	
Wie ist das Orchester entstanden, mit dem Cicero mit 16 Jahren gespielt hat? Gibt es dieses heute noch?	
Wo und was hat Cicero studiert?	
Was waren die größten Einflüsse auf seine Musik?	
Wie hat er sich gesellschaftlich engagiert?	
Wann und woran ist Cicero gestorben?	

309d **Deutsche Musikhits in den USA. Hier lernen Sie fünf Lieder von Musiker*innen aus der D-A-CH-L-Region kennen, die in den USA sehr beliebt waren. Ergänzen Sie die fehlenden Genitivendungen, wo nötig.**

Ein großer, internationaler Hit d_____ 80er_____ war „Forever Young" von der deutschen Pop-Band Alphaville.

Die englische Version d_____ Song_____ „99 Luftballons" wurde 1984 zu einem weltweiten Hit. Der Inhalt d_____ englischen Liedtext_____ unterscheidet sich allerdings von der deutschen Originalversion.

Das erfolgreichste Lied d_____ Sänger_____ Falco, mit bürgerlichem Namen Johann Hölzel, war „Rock Me Amadeus" aus dem Jahr 1985. Der Tod Falco_____ 1998 war ein großer Schock für seine Fans.

Mit „Girl You Know It's True" landete die Discopop-Gruppe Milli Vanilli 1989 auf dem ersten Platz d_____ amerikanischen Billboard Charts. Ein Jahr später kam das Ende d_____ Band_____, als bekannt wurde, dass die beiden Sänger keines ihr_____ Lieder_____ selbst gesungen hatten.

Das Lied „Wind of Change" von der Rockgruppe Scorpions aus dem Jahr 1991 wurde auch „Hymne d_____ Wende_____" genannt.

310d **Geschichte des AFN-Senders in Europa. Lesen Sie den Text und unterstreichen Sie zwei präpositionale Attribute, die Sie im Text finden. Beantworten Sie dann die Fragen.**

Als die Kämpfe 1945 in Deutschland zu Ende gingen, folgte ein militärischer Radiosender den amerikanischen G.I.s, wo immer sie sich aufhielten (*to be located*). Die Geschichte von diesem Sender, dem American Forces Network (AFN), ist einer der größten Erfolge des US-Militärs in Europa nach dem Zweiten Weltkrieg trotz der Tatsache, dass sein Erfolg völlig überraschend war. Die Hauptaufgabe des Senders war es, amerikanische Streitkräfte zu unterhalten. Die deutsche Bevölkerung hatte in den ersten Jahren nach dem Krieg kaum Zeit für Unterhaltungsmusik, aber was sie im Radio hörte kam zum größten Teil von militärischen Radiotrupps der USA und Großbritannien, die spontan neue Wort- und Musikprogramme einführten. Die Nationalsozialist*innen hatten bekanntlich amerikanische Musik als „entartet" verboten, nun spielte sie tagtäglich in vielen Regionen Deutschlands. Amerikanische Soldaten mischten sich zunächst selten mit der deutschen Bevölkerung, zum Teil wegen militärischer Vorschriften und zum Teil, weil nur wenige G.I.s Deutsch sprechen konnten. Aber die deutsche Bevölkerung lernte ihre Musik trotzdem durch AFN kennen – und diese Musik, und darüber hinaus die G.I.s, wurden von den Zuhörer*innen sehr positiv aufgenommen. Viele Deutsche wollten Jazz-, Blues-, Country- und Rockmusik hören, die nicht von staatlichen Radiosendern in Deutschland gesendet wurde. AFN hatte zwar nie beabsichtigt oder versucht, mit seinem Programm die Deutschen zu beeinflussen, aber mit der Musik kam auch ein positives Bild von dem „American Way" und der amerikanischen Kultur nach Deutschland.

richtig	falsch	
☐	☐	Deutsche durften nach dem Krieg keine englischsprachige Musik hören.
☐	☐	Amerikanische Soldaten hatten viel Kontakt mit der deutschen Bevölkerung.
☐	☐	Amerikanische Musik wurde nach dem Krieg nicht auf deutschen Radiosendern gespielt.
☐	☐	Nach Kriegsende wurde amerikanische Musik als „entartet" verboten.

310e **Besuchen Sie die Webseite von AFN und schauen Sie, welche Musik AFN heutzutage spielt. Unter „Schedules" finden Sie auch Informationen über die sogenannten „Artist Specials". Wie hat sich der Musikstil seit den Anfängen von AFN verändert? Was wird heute gespielt? Welche anderen Informationen bietet die Webseite noch außer Musik- und TV-Sendeplänen?**

Recherche

____

____

____

____

310f **Klassik in Neu-England: Der sinfonische Chor The Hartford Chorale aus Hartford in Connecticut widmet sich dem klassischen Repertoire für Chormusik. Hier ist das Chorprogramm 2017–2018.**

Recherche

Komponist	Stück	Sprache
______ van Beethoven, aufgewachsen in ______	Symphony No. 9 in D Minor, Op. 125 „Choral"	______
______ Händel, aufgewachsen in ______	„Messiah"	______
______ Rutter, aufgewachsen in ______	The Music of John Rutter: „Prayer of St. Francis", „Requiem", „Te Deum and Gloria"	______
______ Orff, aufgewachsen in ______	„Carmina Burana"	______
______ Brahms, aufgewachsen in ______	„Ein Deutsches Requiem", Op. 45	______

Ergänzen Sie die Vornamen, die Städte, in denen die Komponisten aufgewachsen sind, und die Sprache der Stücke. Recherchieren Sie dann, was das Orchester in Ihrer Stadt oder der nächstgrößeren in der letzten Saison gespielt hat. Woher kamen die Komponist*innen?

______

______

______

Wer sind die „Three Bs" in der klassischen Musik? Was wissen Sie über sie?

______

______

______

97: Sprachliche Einflüsse aus D-A-CH-L

311a **Kreative Definitionen! Sie haben in Aktivität 311 in MACHEN deutsche Wörter kennengelernt, die auch in der englischen Sprache benutzt werden. Hier sind die korrekten und einige augenzwinkernde (*tongue in cheek; literally: eye-winking*) Definitionen. Ordnen Sie diese den Begriffen zu.**

der Weltschmerz: ______ die Wanderlust: ______

der Doppelgänger: ______ der Kindergarten: ______

der Poltergeist: ______ der Rucksack: ______

a) ein Dämon, der laut in einem Haus spukt
b) eine Person, die fast genauso aussieht wie eine andere Person
c) ein Stück Natur, in dem kleine Kinder wie Karotten oder Tomaten wachsen
d) eine Person, die jeden Weg zweimal geht
e) die Kopfschmerzen, die unser Planet manchmal bekommt
f) ein Beutel (*bag*), den eine Person auf ihrem Rücken (*back*) trägt
g) ein positives Gefühl, das sehr gerne um die Welt reist
h) ein melancholischer Kummer (*anguish*) über die Imperfektion unserer Existenz
i) eine Einrichtung (*facility*), in der kleine Kinder betreut (*look after*) werden

Kulturpunkt: Deutsches Englisch

"Hold on a second: Why do Germans …

… have all these great words that we don't?" You already see in the question that this will be a tongue-in-cheek *Kulturpunkt*, the last one in *Impuls Deutsch*. But we are also serious: the German language is creative and descriptive and has some really ingenious words that we think should totally be part of the English vocabulary. It's of course nothing new to integrate words from foreign languages into another language's vocabulary, and Germans have contributed words such as *Schadenfreude* and *Kindergarten* already. But there are so many more!

The first category consists of sentiments expressed in a single word in German that would, in English, require a whole phrase (such as *Schadenfreude*). There are lots of social media comments out there that describe a state of being or a mood and then ask: is there a German word for that? And often there is. So, here are a few that would be great to import: *verschlimmbessern* is derived from *verbessern*, which means to improve. But the addition of *schlimm*, meaning bad, makes this word express the action of wanting to improve something but ending up making it worse than it was before. Convenient to have for sure. You may have already heard of and you have definitely experienced *fremdschämen*, which means to be embarrassed for somebody else's actions. You most often experience this when watching somebody make a fool of themselves on screen. When you feel like you can't watch, you know it's going to go badly, and you just want to get out of this embarrassing situation, you engage in *fremdschämen*.

The second category consists of words that you have in English but underutilize. One of these words is *genau*. *Genau* means exactly, and Germans use it all the time to confirm what somebody else said. "Exactly" just doesn't have the same ring to it; it doesn't roll of the tongue as easily, so let's just replace it with *genau* and use it all the time. Germans are already doing it, and we just can't help ourselves; it doesn't even matter which language we are speaking.

And the last category consists of words that don't exist in English but that are not descriptive words that have to be invented to express some complicated process; they are just regular, small words. *Jein* and *doch* are great examples here. How beautiful is it to not have to say yes or no but to be able to express that it is something in between? It isn't "maybe" either; it is in fact *jein*. Let's give an example for that: if somebody asks, did you like the movie? The answer could be *jein*, and then the person could say, "I liked the characters, so yes, but I really didn't like the plot, so no." Much more accurate than deciding on one or the other or going with a complicated "well, yes and no"-answer. *Doch* is also very handy and not just for toddlers who want to contradict anything you say. *Doch* allows you to negate a negative statement. So, when somebody says, "You can't do that," or, "It isn't like that," the person can counter with *doch* and just with this one word say: "You sure can," or: "Of course it is like that." Super practical, isn't it?

Now, let's make this happen! Use these words all the time and they will become part of the English language!

311b Reflektieren: The German language has also borrowed many words from English. Most of them are tech-related. Germans not only borrow them, but they make them their own, which means they add the appropriate verb ending and conjugate them (*googeln, ich googele, du hast gegoogelt, sie wird googeln*), or they assign an article and use adjectives accordingly (*der Computer, das Internet*). Which other words should be introduced into the German language and why?

311c Der Verein Deutsche Sprache, gegründet 1997, hat sich die Wahrung (*preservation*) der deutschen Sprache zum Ziel gesetzt. Seine Mitglieder kritisieren vor allem die zunehmende „Anglisierung und Amerikanisierung" der deutschen Sprache. Für sie ist diese Entwicklung ein Kultur- und Identitätsverlust. Deshalb hat der Verein einen Anglizismenindex auf seiner Webseite, der helfen soll, Anglizismen zu verstehen und beim Schreiben zu vermeiden (*avoid*). Wegen ihres Kampfes gegen Fremdwörter werden die Mitglieder des Vereins oft als Sprachpurist*innen mit nationalistischer Tendenz kritisiert. Was denken Sie? Ist die generelle Ablehnung (*rejection*) von Anglizismen sinnvoll? Oder können Sie verstehen, dass andere diesen Verein dafür kritisieren? Warum (nicht)?

312c **Aktuelle deutschsprachige Zeitungen in den USA. Die Nordamerikanische Wochenpost und Das Fenster sind zwei Publikationen, die auch heute noch für Deutschsprechende in den USA herausgegeben werden. Besuchen Sie die Webseiten dieser Publikationen und ergänzen Sie die folgende Tabelle in Stichworten.**

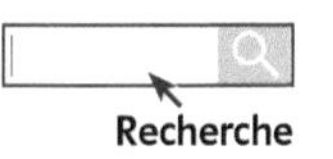

	Die Nordamerikanische Wochenpost	**Das Fenster**
Publikationsort		
Publikationsart		
Gibt es seit …		
Rubriken/Themen		
Layout/Stil		

Welche Publikation finden Sie interessanter? Warum?

____

____

____

____

____

312d **Verstanden? Deutsch in den USA als offizielle Sprache? Sie hören jetzt Informationen über die sogenannte Muhlenberg-Legende. Hören Sie gut zu und wählen Sie die richtigen Antworten aus.**

Worum geht es in der Muhlenberg-Legende?

- Sie beschreibt den Versuch von Frederick Muhlenberg, Deutsch als offizielle Sprache in den USA zu etablieren.
- Sie beschreibt eine Gesetzesvorlage (*bill*), die Deutsch als offizielle Amtssprache etabliert hätte.
- Sie beschreibt den Versuch der Stadt Muhlenberg in Pennsylvania, Deutsch zu verbieten.

Wer hat die Petition für die Gesetzesvorlage geschrieben und warum?

- Frederick Muhlenberg hat sie geschrieben. Er wollte mehr wirtschaftliche Geschäfte mit Deutschen machen.
- Deutsche Einwander*innen haben sie geschrieben. Sie wollten Gesetze besser verstehen können.
- Es ist nicht klar, wer die Gesetzesvorlage geschrieben hat, aber es war wahrscheinlich ein Repräsentant aus Virginia.

Wie war das Ergebnis der Abstimmung für dieses Gesetz?

- Die Gesetzesvorlage wurde im Repräsentant*innenhaus sofort abgelehnt.
- Die Gesetzesvorlage ist an nur einer Stimme gescheitert, weil Muhlenberg dagegen gestimmt hat.
- Die Gesetzesvorlage war erfolgreich und Deutsch wurde in Pennsylvania zur offiziellen Sprache.

313i **Das prägt mich: Welche Rolle haben Sprachen in Ihrem Leben? Sprachen werden manchmal Fenster zur Welt genannt. Das heißt, dass eine andere Sprache uns neue Perspektiven geben kann. Gibt es Wörter oder Konzepte, die Sie auf Deutsch oder in einer anderen Sprache gelernt haben, die es aber so in Ihrer Muttersprache nicht gibt? Haben diese Wörter oder die Sprachen allgemein Einfluss darauf, wie Sie die Welt wahrnehmen?**

313j **Braucherei: Die Volksmagie der Pennsylvania Dutch. Lesen Sie den Text und beantworten Sie die Fragen in Stichworten.**

Braucherei ist der Name für die christliche Volksmagie der Pennsylvania Dutch. Ihre Praktiken sollen Gesundheit, Schutz und Segen[1] herbeiführen. Diese Tradition lehrt zahlreiche Methoden, um Krankheiten und Verletzungen bei Menschen und Tieren zu heilen. Es gibt aber auch Anweisungen/Rezepte, um zum Beispiel Metalle im Boden zu finden, sich vor Dieb*innen zu schützen oder besonderes Glück zu haben.

Um den gewünschten Effekt zu erzielen, werden oft verschiedene Dinge aus dem alltäglichen Leben benutzt: Pflanzen, Stoffstücke[2] oder Papier, ein Glas, Alkohol, Münzen[3] usw. Das Wichtigste ist jedoch, dass sich die Person, die Braucherei praktiziert, auf den christlichen Gott oder seinen Sohn Jesus beruft und um ihre Hilfe bittet. Oft werden Stellen aus der Bibel zitiert. So legitimiert sich Braucherei als christliche Praxis und schützt sich vor dem Vorwurf[4] der Magie oder Hexerei[5] (obwohl praktisch kein Unterschied besteht).

Eines der bekanntesten Werke der Braucherei ist „Der lange verborgene[6] Freund" (1820) von Johann Georg Hohman. Darin gibt es viele Anleitungen zum Heilen von Krankheiten, zum Beispiel „Zauber"[7] zum Schutz vor Hexen und dem Teufelswerk, Hilfe, um gestohlene Sachen wiederzubekommen, oder auch Rezepte für gutes Bier.

Braucherei hat den Beinamen „Pow-Wow", und auch heute gibt es noch den Begriff „powwowing". Dieser Begriff sollte allerdings differenziert gesehen werden, da er der Sprache der Algonquin entnommen wurde.

[1] der Segen – *blessing*
[2] das Stoffstück – *piece of fabric*
[3] die Münze – *coin*
[4] der Vorwurf – *accusation*
[5] die Hexerei – *witchcraft*
[6] verborgen – *hidden, disguised*
[7] der Zauber – *spell*

Woher kommt Braucherei?

____

Warum oder in welchen Situationen wird Braucherei benutzt?

____

Welche religiösen Aspekte hat sie?

____

Was ist Pow-Wow bei den Pennsylvania Dutch? Wissen Sie, was es für amerikanische Ureinwohner*innen bedeutet?

____

____

Gibt es in Ihrer Familie Bräuche (*customs*), die Sie an Braucherei erinnern?

____

____

98: Politik im Vergleich°

315f **Wandeln Sie die Phrasen mit Partizip I-Adjektiven in Relativsätze um, wie im Beispiel.**

die regierende Partei = *die Partei, die regiert*

die kandidierende Senatorin = ________________

der die Affäre leugnende (*to deny*) Abgeordnete = ________________

die koalierenden Parteien = ________________

die in Hamburg regierende Bürgermeisterin = ________________

die die CDU leitende Politikerin = ________________

315g **Verstanden? Sie hören jetzt Informationen über die Fünf-Prozent-Hürde in Deutschland. Hören Sie gut zu und beantworten Sie die Fragen.**

Was ist Ziel und Zweck der Fünf-Prozent-Hürde?

- Sie existiert als Anreiz (*incentive*) für die Gründung kleiner Parteien.
- Sie soll stabile Koalitionen ermöglichen und eine Zersplitterung im Bundestag vermeiden.
- Sie existiert, um eine Balance zwischen großen und kleinen Parteien zu schaffen.

Gibt es Ausnahmen bei der Fünf-Prozent-Hürde?

- Nein, Parteien brauchen immer 5 % für den Einzug ins Parlament.
- Ja, bei neuen Parteien gilt die Fünf-Prozent-Hürde bei der ersten Wahl nicht.
- Ja, Parteien nationaler Minderheiten in Deutschland sind frei von dieser Regel.

Welche Argumente gibt es gegen die Fünf-Prozent-Hürde? (2 richtige Antworten)

- Sie ist ein sehr altes Konzept, das in der heutigen Zeit nicht mehr notwendig ist.
- Es ist undemokratisch, weil nicht alle Stimmen repräsentiert sind.
- Andere europäische Länder haben keine Fünf-Prozent-Hürde. Deutschland braucht sie auch nicht.

315h **Reflektieren: In Deutschland leben 22,5 % Menschen mit Migrationshintergrund, aber im Bundestag sind nur 8,2 % migrantische Parlamentarier*innen. Wie ist das in Ihrem Land? Welche Minderheiten werden in Ihrem Land (nicht) repräsentiert? In welchen Bereichen außerhalb der Politik gibt es diese Ungleichheit der Repräsentation?**

316a **Das prägt mich: Welche Rolle hat Politik in Ihrem Leben? Sind Sie Mitglied einer Partei und/oder engagieren Sie sich politisch? Wie beeinflusst Ihre (un)politische Haltung Ihr Leben? Fühlen Sie sich als Teil einer Gruppe wegen Ihrer Einstellung zu Politik? Wie fühlen Sie sich deshalb?**

99: Sport im Vergleich

317f **Zusammen Sport treiben. Ergänzen Sie die folgenden Sätze mit den passenden Appositionen.**

also in einem Team | draußen oder drinnen | in vielen Gesellschaften immer noch prävalent | oft auf sich allein gestellt | also der neuen Kultur | egal ob im Verein oder in der Nachbarschaft

Bei Freizeitaktivitäten, ______________________________,
lernen wir andere Menschen kennen.

Für Geflüchtete, ______________________________,
ist es besonders wichtig, Kontakte in der neuen Heimat zu knüpfen.

Sport, ______________________________, ist hierfür
besonders gut geeignet, vor allem, wenn ganz verschiedene Menschen
aufeinandertreffen.

Beim Gruppensport arbeiten wir als Mannschaft, ______________________________, zusammen.

Die Begegnung mit Menschen aus anderen Kulturen hilft dabei, Vorurteile, ______________________________
______________________________, abzubauen.

Geflüchteten hilft Sport dabei, in der neuen Gesellschaft, ______________________________,
anzukommen und sie besser zu verstehen.

317g  **Verstanden? Sie hören Informationen über das Konzept des Vereins und wie der Sport in Deutschland oft in Vereinen organisiert ist. Beantworten Sie die Fragen.**

Wer ist in einem Verein?

- In einem Verein sind Menschen, die an der gleichen Universität studieren.
- In einem Verein sind Menschen, die ein gemeinsames Interesse teilen.
- In einem Verein sind Menschen, die gemeinsam Geld verdienen wollen.

Wie sind Vereine organisiert?

- Jeder Verein hat einen Vorstand, der alle Entscheidungen trifft.
- Vereine haben nur Mitglieder und werden von externen Expert*innen geleitet.
- In einem Verein treffen der Vorstand und alle Mitglieder die Entscheidungen gemeinsam.

Was sind positive Aspekte der Vereinskultur? (2 richtige Antworten)

- Alle Mitglieder haben Mitspracherecht und Entscheidungen werden demokratisch getroffen.
- Vereine sind eine gute Möglichkeit für kleine Orte, um Geld zu verdienen.
- Vereine sind oft eng mit der lokalen Gemeinschaft verbunden.

317h  **Reflektieren: In Deutschland findet Sport hauptsächlich in Vereinen statt, aber in den USA spielt Sport an den Universitäten und Colleges eine größere Rolle. Reflektieren Sie, welche Rolle Sport an Ihrer Universität spielt. Welcher Sport ist am beliebtesten? Wer kommt zu den großen Sportveranstaltungen (Studierende, Alumni etc.)? Finden Sie es richtig, dass *Student Athletes* kein Geld verdienen? Warum (nicht)?**

317i  **Das prägt mich: Was hat Sport mit Ihrer Identität zu tun? Treiben Sie aktiv Sport? Welchen Sport können Sie (nicht) machen und warum? Hat das einen Einfluss auf Ihre Perspektive von Sport allgemein oder diesen Sportarten? Ist „sportlich sein" wichtig für Sie und/oder Ihr Umfeld und die Gesellschaft, in der Sie leben? Wie prägen Sie die Erwartungen und Ihre eigenen Wünsche, die mit Sport zu tun haben? Falls Sie gerne Sport sehen (live oder im Fernsehen): Fühlen Sie sich als Teil einer Gemeinschaft, wenn Sie Sport sehen? Wenn ja, welche Art von Gemeinschaft (z.B. national oder von Ihrer Uni)? Welche Produkte, Praktiken und Perspektiven teilen Sie mit diesen Menschen?**

318b   **Reflektieren: Hier sehen Sie eine Liste von in Deutschland Fußball spielenden US-Amerikaner*innen und Kanadier*innen und eine Liste von Deutschen, die in den USA professionell Basketball spielen. In ihren Heimatländern gehören diese Athlet*innen zu den besten in ihrer Sportart. Was denken Sie, warum diese Sportler*innen sich entschieden haben, ihre Karriere in Deutschland / in den USA zu machen? Welche Gründe könnte es für Sportler*innen geben, in einer ausländischen Liga zu spielen?**

Deutsche Basketballspieler*innen in der NBA und WNBA (2020)	Nordamerikanische Fußball-spieler*innen in der 1. Bundesliga (2020)
Isaac Bonga	Tyler Adams
Leonie Fiebich	John Anthony Brooks
Luisa Geiselsöder	Timothy Chandler
Isaiah Hartenstein	Bryane Heaberlin
Maxi Kleber	Julie Karn
Satou Sabally	Noëlle Maritz
Dennis Schröder	Weston McKennie
Daniel Theis	Alfredo Morales
Moe Wagner	Giovanni Reyna
	Brady Scott

319a **Profil einer Parasportlerin. In diesem Text lernen Sie die Leichtathletin Irmgard Bensusan kennen. Ergänzen Sie zuerst die richtigen Adjektivendungen. Setzen Sie dann die Appositionen aus der Liste in die richtige Lücke.**

Irmgard Bensusan wurde 1991 geboren und wuchs in Pretoria, ______________________________, auf. Die erfolgreich____ Sportlerin ist schon als Kind gern gerannt. Als Jugendliche gewann sie die national____ Meisterschaft im Hürdensprint. Mit 18 Jahren aber verletzte sich Bensusan während eines Rennens, als sie mit dem recht____ Fuß an einer Hürde hängen blieb und stürzte. Die Diagnose lautete „Drop Foot", ______________________________ ______________________________, wegen einer permanenten Schädigung (*damage*) der Nerven. Aufhören wollte Bensusan, ______________________________, mit dem Rennen aber nicht. Nach langer Rekonvaleszenz fing die jung____ Sportlerin wieder mit dem Trainieren an. Um ihren rechten Fuß, ______________________________, zu stützen, trägt sie seitdem eine Schiene (*brace*). 2016 zog sie nach Deutschland. Bald darauf gab es den ersten groß____ Erfolg: Weltmeisterin über 400 Meter bei der Para-WM in London. Sechs Rekorde, ______________________________, hat Bensusan schon aufgestellt. 2019 wurde sie zur Parasportlerin des Jahres gewählt.

ein Kontrollverlust des Fußes und eine partielle Paralyse des Unterschenkels
ambitioniert und willensstark
der Hauptstadt von Südafrika
drei in der Halle und drei draußen
von Bensusan scherzhaft „Schluffi" (*slacker*) genannt

100: Bildung im Vergleich

321d **Das prägt mich: Wie hat Ihr eigener Bildungslebenslauf Ihr Leben geprägt? Was haben Sie selbst entschieden? Was haben andere für Sie entschieden? Welche Auswirkungen hatten diese Entscheidungen? Welche Hürden sind Ihnen begegnet und wie haben diese Hürden Ihren Bildungslebenslauf beeinflusst? (Optional: Was hätte anders sein können? Und wie hätte Sie dieser Unterschied anders geprägt? Wer wären Sie heute?)**

322b **Verstanden? Max ist Senior in einer High School in Michigan. Er spricht in einem Videoanruf mit Tino, der in Deutschland in die 13. Klasse im Gymnasium geht. Die beiden kennen sich von einem Austauschprogramm. Hören Sie gut zu und beantworten Sie die Fragen.**

Für wie viele Unis hat Max schon eine Zusage erhalten?

- Max hat bisher von seinen drei Favoriten eine Zusage erhalten.
- Max hat bisher nur Zusagen erhalten und hat sich für seinen Favoriten entschieden.
- Max hat bisher nur Absagen erhalten, aber wartet noch auf weitere Antworten.

Was wird Tino nach dem Abitur machen?

- Er wird an der Fachhochschule Elektrotechnik studieren.
- Er wird eine Ausbildung zum Mechatroniker machen.
- Er hat sich noch nicht entscheiden, ob er studiert oder eine Ausbildung macht.

Welche Alternativen hat Max zum Unistudium?

- Wenn er keinen Studienplatz bekommt, macht er eine Ausbildung in Deutschland, weil er gut Deutsch spricht.
- Wenn er keinen Studienplatz bekommt, dann macht er eine Ausbildung im IT-Bereich in den USA.
- Wenn er keinen Studienplatz bekommt, sucht er einen Job oder macht ein Praktikum.

322c **Marion und Rocco recherchieren für eine Präsentation über internationale Schulsysteme. Lesen Sie die Notizen von den beiden und ergänzen Sie die fehlenden Adjektive. Welche Form passt: Positiv, Komparativ oder Superlativ? Achten Sie dabei auf Kasus und Endungen.**

Es gibt 194 Länder auf dieser Welt und fast so viele ____________ Bildungssysteme. (verschieden) In den ____________ Ländern sind die Bildungssysteme an die gesellschaftlichen Erwartungen gebunden. (viel) Wenn Kinder mehr Wissen für ____________ Berufe brauchen, hat ein Land oft weniger Universitäten und mehr Lehrwerkstätten. (praktisch)
Finnland und Japan haben die ____________ Schulsysteme der Welt, aber sie unterscheiden sich sehr. (gut)
Finnland ist ein ____________ Land als Japan und die gesamte Bildung kostet nichts. (egalitär)
Dagegen ist Japan ein ____________ Land und die Kinder müssen oft nach der Schule weiter büffeln (*cram*), um sich als Superlerner*innen zu qualifizieren. (hierarchisch)
Japanische Kinder gehen auch ein Jahr ____________ in die Schule als finnische: mit sechs Jahren. (früh) In Deutschland ist es nochmal anders: Man bezahlt hier nur sehr ____________ Gebühren für die Bildung; in Deutschland gehen aber auch schon ____________ Kinder in die Schule. (gering; sechsjährig)

101: Grenzüberschreitender Wissenschaftsaustausch°

325a **Transatlantischer Wissenschaftsaustausch. Lesen Sie den kurzen Text zum wissenschaftlichen Austausch zwischen Deutschland und den USA. Beantworten Sie dann die R/F-Fragen.**

Es gibt schon seit Jahren einen intensiven wissenschaftlichen Austausch zwischen den USA und Deutschland, besonders in der Forschung mit einem Fokus auf den STEM-Bereich. Aber auch in anderen Feldern, wie den Geisteswissenschaften, gibt es intensive Kooperationen. Gefördert wird dieser durch unterschiedliche Mittlerorganisationen. Es gibt zum Beispiel den Deutschen Akademischen Austauschdienst (DAAD). Der DAAD vergibt Stipendien für Studierende und Forscher*innen zum wissenschaftlichen Austausch. Unterstützt werden Forschungsprojekte auch direkt durch Forschungsgelder. Im Bereich Künstliche Intelligenz gibt es das Deutsche Forschungszentrum für Künstliche Intelligenz in Kaiserslautern. Sie haben ein Austauschprogramm für junge Forscher*innen mit der UC Berkeley. Aber auch auf der amerikanischen Seite gibt es Programme, die den Austausch fördern. So gibt es zum Beispiel die Fulbright Commission, die jährlich amerikanische Studierende und Forscher*innen in die ganze Welt, auch nach Deutschland, zur Forschung und Lehre schickt. All diese Programme wollen in der Forschung transatlantische Synergien erzielen und damit auch den interkulturellen Austausch fördern.

richtig	falsch	
		Wissenschaftlichen Austausch gibt es nur in den STEM-Feldern zwischen den USA und Deutschland.
		Der DAAD ist eine Mittlerorganisation, die wissenschaftlichen Austausch durch Stipendien unterstützt.
		Forschung im Bereich Künstliche Intelligenz gibt es nur an amerikanischen Unis wie z. B. UC Berkeley.
		Wissenschaftlicher Austausch wird nur durch deutsche Organisationen gefördert.
		Fulbright erlaubt amerikanischen Studierenden, in Deutschland zu forschen oder dort zu unterrichten (*to teach*).

325b **Das prägt mich: Ist für Sie Kooperation oder Konkurrenz wichtiger? Wie prägt das Ihr Leben und auch Ihr Studium? Können Sie sich an Projekte erinnern, in denen Sie mit anderen Menschen zusammengearbeitet haben? Wie hat die Zusammenarbeit funktioniert? Gab es Probleme? Reden Sie darüber.**

102: Impulse für Ihr Leben

328a **In MACHEN haben Sie über Ihre Erfahrung als Deutschlernende*r reflektiert und was Sie über die deutsche Sprache und Kultur sowie über sich selbst gelernt haben. Die Autor*innen von „Impuls Deutsch" würden sehr gerne von Ihnen und Ihrer Erfahrung hören. Wenn Sie möchten, schreiben Sie eine E-Mail an die Autor*innen und erzählen Sie ihnen von Ihrer Erfahrung mit „Impuls Deutsch". Sie können über alles schreiben, was Sie den Autor*innen mitteilen möchten: Das können positive und negative Dinge sein. Schicken Sie Ihre E-Mail an ImpulsDeutsch@gmail.com.**

328b **Das prägt mich: Wie hat Sie das Deutschlernen bisher geprägt? Was haben Sie gelernt, das Sie für Ihr weiteres Leben mitnehmen werden? Was können Sie schon und womit haben Sie noch Schwierigkeiten? Wie haben Sie sich verändert?**

329a **Im Kurs haben Sie darüber präsentiert, wie es mit dem Deutschlernen ab jetzt weitergeht. Schreiben Sie jetzt Ihre spezifischen Pläne und die konkreten *action steps* auf: Falls Sie einen weiteren Deutschkurs belegen, schreiben Sie, wie Sie bis zum nächsten Kurs (z.B. falls Sie Ferien haben) Ihr Deutsch weiter üben und nicht vergessen. Falls Sie keinen weiteren Kurs belegen, schreiben Sie, wie Sie auch ohne Kurs Ihr Deutsch weiterhin verbessern können/ möchten.**

103: Projekt 8 – Ein Forschungsprojekt°

330a **Self-Assessment**

You now get a chance to reflect on the many things you have learned throughout the chapter. Carefully read through the "Can-Do Statements" below, and ask yourself if you can perform all of these tasks. It might be helpful for each of the statements to actually practice the communicative scenario. Once you are confident that you are able to perform a task, check the respective box on the left side.

- ☐ I can ask and answer questions about people from German-speaking countries who immigrated to the United States and Americans who emigrated to German-speaking countries.
- ☐ I can have a simple conversation about why people might immigrate to a different country.
- ☐ I can use my language to talk about what products, practices, and perspectives shape my understanding of my own culture.
- ☐ I can talk about the use of German words in the English language.
- ☐ I can make speculative statements about the stigmatization of the German language in the U.S.
- ☐ I can give a presentation about important cultural locations, like "Audre Lorde's Berlin."
- ☐ I can reflect on cultural stereotypes about Germany and the U.S. and how they get reinforced through popular culture.
- ☐ I can understand information about American influences on German music.
- ☐ I can have a simple conversation about the role of nationalism and patriotism in sports.
- ☐ I can write about the differences between the German and American educational systems.
- ☐ I can speak and write about my educational experiences thus far.
- ☐ I can exchange information about different German political parties and their agendas.
- ☐ I can reflect on differences between the German and American electoral systems.
- ☐ I can reflect on the way my experience of learning German has thus far shaped me personally.

- I can distinguish between causal and final sentences and use them in appropriate contexts.
- I can use common predicative adjectives and adverbs in their positive, comparative, and superlative forms.
- I can modify and decorate noun phrases with attributive adjectives in all cases.
- I can modify and decorate noun phrases with genitive modifiers.
- I can modify and decorate noun phrases with appositions.
- I can understand basic rules of suffixation in order to transform nouns and verbs into adjectives.

- I am familiar with important dates of German migration movements to the United States.
- I am familiar with projects and organizations that foster transatlantic exchange in scientific research.
- I am familiar with different theoretical models of "culture."
- I am familiar with the history of German newspapers in the United States.
- I am familiar with basic linguistic features of Pennsylvania Dutch and Texas German.
- I am familiar with the German political system and how it compares to the American system.

Picture Credits

LERNEN

Cover.1 (Suzanne Tucker); **Cover.2** (Bokica); (c)_EOTO_2018 **247; Online**; 123RF.com, Nidderau: **97.6** (gbuglok); **102.1** (Fedor Selivanov); adornix [CC BY-SA 3.0 (https://creativecommons.org/licenses/by-sa/3.0)] **16.1**; Adrian Michael [CC BY-SA 3.0 (https://creativecommons.org/licenses/by-sa/3.0)] **102.2**; aus Ulrike Rylance: Penny Pepper Alarm auf der Achterbahn";, Seiten 5, 139 und 140 von dtv junior, München 2015 mit freundlicher Genehmigung von dtv Verlagsgesellschaft mbH &Co. KG **13.1**; BAMF, Quelle: MARiS **161.1**; Bundesarchiv, Bild 183-U1109-022 / Foto: Gabriele Senft **18.1**; CERN, Geneva: **75.1** (© CERN); Dr. Dagmar Schultz, Berlin: **248.1**; Fotograf: Erwin Raupp, gemeinfrei **272.2**; Getty Images, München: **xx.1** (Linka A Odom); **1.1** (fotokon); **5.1** (Smith Collection); **5.2** (Jupiterimages); **6.1** (eurotravel); **B, Online** (Robert_Ford); **8.1** (GreenTana); **11.1** (chieferu); **11.2** (Hung_Chung_Chih); **11.3** (george tsartsianidis); **11.4** (Visions of America/UIG); **11.5** (Andrew Chittock/Stocktrek Images); **11.8** (grandriver); **iii.1** (Nadasaki); **Online** (10';000 Hours); **Online** (484867446); **Online** (8213erika); **Online, 90.1, 90.4** (Ariel Skelley); **Online** (Bernhard Lang); **Online** (CASEZY); **Online** (ChamilleWhite); **11.9** (Joel Carillet); **12.1** (Gutzemberg); **15.1** (Cineberg); **15.1** (Tara Moore); **15.1, Online** (pablohart); **15.2** (AntonioGuillem); **17.1** (GeorgiosArt); **19.1** (Jan_Kowalski); **21.1, 51.3, 62.8, 92.1, 97.2, 286.1** (Image Source); **21.1** (Inok); **22.5, 22.10** (bubaone); **22.4, 22.9** (-VICTOR-); **22.3, 22.8** (petovarga); **22.1, 22.6** (the_guitar_mann); **22.2, 22.7** (setory); **24.1** (Portra); **24.2** (Terry Vine); **24.3** (Bambu Productions); **27.9** (fmajor); **27.10** (GrigoriosMoraitis); **28.1, 72.1, 119.4, 238.12, 238.13, Online** (John M Lund Photography Inc); **29.1** (caracterdesign); **30.1** (ULRO); **31.1** (YinYang); **31.1** (amriphoto); **31.1, 85.2** (clu); **32.1** (John Lund); **32.1** (Jonathan Kitchen); **32.1** (NatalyaLucia); **36.1** (Radovanovic96); **38.1** (francescoch); **45.1** (Maica); **45.2** (HowardOates); **45.3** (Delmaine Donson); **45.4** (RunPhoto); **46.1, 93.1** (FooTToo); **46.2** (Nikada); **46.3** (Pollyana Ventura); **47.1** (larik_malasha); **47.2** (Milosz_G); **47.3** (Ceneri); **47.4** (rclassenlayouts); **47.5** (Pannonia); **47.6** (esemelwe); **47.7** (heckepics); **47.8** (Riou); **47.9** (hsvrs); **48.2, 57.1** (Jacob Ammentorp Lund); **51.1** (SeanT313); **51.2** (Wavebreakmedia); **54.1** (powerofforever); **59.1, 87.1, 87.1, 190.1** (Luis Alvarez); **60.1** (Georgethefourth); **61.1, 191.2** (Chris Tobin); **61.2** (Jacobs Stock Photography Ltd); **62.3** (pitr134); **62.9** (tzahiV); **62.10** (AWelshLad); **62.11** (Soldt); **62.12** (Claudiad); **64.1** (ZargonDesign); **64.2** (Andersen Ross Photography Inc); **67.2** (gremlin); **69.1** (MediaProduction); **69.2** (Dean Mitchell); **71.1** (FroggyFrogg); **73.1** (Evgen_Prozhyrko); **74.1, 74.2** (Tolga TEZCAN); **79.1** (JaCZhou); **79.1, 79.2** (DenPotisev); **79.4, 160.1** (ii-graphics); **81.1** (Bim); **81.2** (Wysiati); **84.1** (xenotar); **85.1** (popovaphoto); **85.3** (RapidEye); **86.1** (FluxFactory); **90.2** (Thurtell); **90.3** (AaronAmat); **91.1** (ThomasVogel); **92.2** (gaffera); **92.3** (cometary); **93.2** (SteveAllenPhoto); **93.3** (mactrunk); **95.1** (Uwe Moser); **95.2** (yuelan); **97.3** (Diamond Sky Images); **97.4** (Davel5957); **97.5** (AngiePhotos); **97.7** (schulzie); **97.8** (imaginima); **97.9** (D3Damon); **103.1** (Bartosz Hadyniak); **103.2, xx.2** (FG Trade); **103.3** (RyersonClark); **104.1** (Guido Mieth); **104.2** (ifish); **105.1** (Pom669); **112.1, 197.1, 226.1, 252.2, Online** (Oliver Rossi); **113.1, Online** (urbazon); **114.1** (Mmdi); **115.1** (PIER); **115.2** (borchee); **115.3** (Naga Film); **115.4, 190.2** (Buena Vista Images); **117.1, 119.2, 225.1, Online** (Tom Werner); **119.1, 238.9** (fotografixx); **119.1, Online** (skynesher); **119.3** (crossbrain66); **123.1, 123.5** (LOVE_LIFE); **123.2** (Creative Crop); **123.3** (fcafotodigital); **123.4** (xxmmxx); **123.6** (AlasdairJames); **123.7** (mariusFM77); **123.8** (Viktor_Kitaykin); **128.1** (Igor Alecsander); **129.1** (narvikk); **130.1** (Drazen_); **130.2** (Andrew_Rybalko); **131.1, 238.10** (Hiroshi Watanabe); **134.1** (Yuri_Arcurs); **136.1** (kowalska-art); **137.1** (VectorFun); **137.2** (chang); **143.1, Online.1** (Willie B. Thomas); **147.1** (LarisaBlinova); **147.2, Online** (vgajic); **149.1** (Hemera Technologies); **151.1** (3bugsmom); **154.1, Online** (Teka77); **156.1, 156.2** (Isono); **159.1** (LucynaKoch); **163.1** (opico); **167.1** (Lehman); **167.2** (Nikolay_Donetsk); **167.3** (didyk); **167.4** (LukaTDB); **168.1** (ac_bnphotos); **170.1, 263.1** (mediaphotos); **171.1** (Rowan Jordan); **176.1** (Tetra Images); **178.1** (John Coletti); **179.1, 88, Online.1** (izusek); **180.1** (mixetto); **181.1** (Martin Keiler); **188.1** (VioletaStoimenova); **192.1, Online** (Klaus Vedfelt); **198.1** (Alistair Berg); **207.1** (Franz-Marc Frei); **208.1** (Justin Case); **208.2** (Sally Anscombe); **208.3** (LeoPatrizi); **208.4** (RUNSTUDIO); **208.5** (Brooke Fasani Auchincloss); **208.6, 208.8, Online.4** (MoMo Productions); **208.7** (katleho Seisa); **210.1, 283.3, Online** (Thomas Barwick); **210.2** (Jose Luis Pelaez Inc); **210.3** (Flashpop); **211.1** (Colin Hawkins); **212.1** (Betsie Van der Meer); **212.1** (Turnervisual); **212.3** (IlexImage); **212.4** (sharply_done); **212.5** (CostinT); **212.6** (Lalocracio); **212.8** (Sinan Kocaslan); **212.1**; 212.7; 212.9 **(alphacat)**; **215.1** (praetorianphoto); **219.1** (S M Nazmul Haque); **221.1** (Vesnaandjic); **226.2** (Ridofranz); **226.3** (Morsa Images); **226.4** (bymuratdeniz); **230.1, Online** (chris-mueller); **231.1** (Horst Gerlach); **234.1** (mifaimoltosorridere); **236.1** (Fox Photos); **238.1, Online** (Jon Feingersh Photography Inc); **238.2** (andreynikolajew); **238.3, Online** (SIphotography); **238.4** (sefa ozel); **238.5** (metamorworks); **238.6** (kevinjeon00); **238.7** (Plume Creative); **238.8, Online** (Viaframe); **238.11** (D-Keine); **239.1** (Martin Ruegner); **239.2** (maumapho); **240.1** (Thossaphol); **240.2** (JIRAROJ PRADITCHAROENKUL); **240.3** (miriam-doerr); **241.1** (Rawpixel); **242.1** (Wachiwit); **245.1** (Meinzahn); **247.1** (Bruce Yuanyue Bi); **248.1** (Zoonar RF); **248.2** (Animaflora); **248.2, Online** (bluejayphoto); **248.3** (Hans-Peter Merten); **249.1** (chrisdorney); **251.1** (Anna_Hirna); **252.1** (Thomas Jackson); **255.1** (ljubaphoto); **258.1** (Delpixart); **262.1** (sivarock); **264.1** (lisegagne); **271.1** (FangXiaNuo); **272.2** (SDI Productions); **272.3** (Juanmonino); **273.1** (SunChan); **274.2** (Hill Street Studios); **275.1** (goodynewshoes); **279.1** (kycstudio); **281.1** (bizoo_n); **282.1, Online** (Hinterhaus Productions); **283.1** (Rebecca Nelson); **283.2, Online** (JW LTD); **284.1** (Thomas-Soellner); **285.1** (romrodinka); **287.1** (spxChrome); **Online** (Denys); **Online** (Dougal Waters); **Online** (Dylan Ellis); **Online** (Elenarts); **Online** (Eva-Katalin); **Online** (FamVeld); **Online** (FatCamera); **Online** (Firn); **Online** (Frank Günther); **Online** (JANIFEST); **Online** (Jens Domschky); **Online** (JoenStock); **Online** (Jorg Greuel); **Online** (Jules_Kitano); **Online** (Kritchanut); **Online** (Lazy_Bear); **Online** (Lightstar59); **Online** (Lya_Cattel); **Online** (Medioimages/Photodisc); **Online** (NUMAX3D); **Online** (Nadezhda1906); **Online** (Oleh_Slobodeniuk); **Online** (Risto0); **Online** (Trifonov_Evgeniy); **Online** (Walter Bibikow); **Online** (Xantana); **Online** (ZU_09); **Online** (Zhenikeyev); **Online** (bukki88); **Online** (damedeeso); **Online** (energyy); **Online** (eugeniek); **Online** (frankpeters); **Online** (fstop123); **Online** (funky-data); **Online** (gaspr13); **Online** (gregobagel); **Online** (jgroup); **Online** (kali9); **Online** (monkeybusinessimages); **Online** (nadia_bormotova); **Online** (piratedub); **Online** (sorincolac); **Online** (sturti); **Online** (suteracher); **Online** (swissmediavision); **Online** (tolgart); **Online** (whitemay); **Online** (yacobchuk); **Online.1** (Digital Vision.); **Online.1** (ilbusca); **Online.2** (Cristalov); **Online.3** (Jamie Garbutt); Heinrich-Böll-Stiftung [CC BY-SA (https://creativecommons.org/licenses/by-sa/2.0)] **33.1**; Iain Masterton / Alamy Stock Foto **152.2**; Martin Weinhold, Berlin: **245.3** (Martin Weinhold Menschenfotograf); NS-Dokumentationszentrum der Stadt Köln **233.1**; picture-alliance, Frankfurt: **267.1** (empics); Privabesitz/Gedenkstätte Deutscher Widerstand **235.1**; Privatarchiv Tahir Della **245.2**; Ravensburger Spieleland **49.1**; RD Gastro / Lars May **168.1**; Shutterstock, New York: **11.6** (mimmikhail); **11.7** (AlejandroCarnicero); **18.2** (da-vooda); **48.1** (Palau); **96.2, 96.4, 96.7, 96.8, 96.9, 96.12, 96.13, 96.14.2** (attaphong); **96.1, 96.3, 96.5, 96.6, 96.10, 96.11, 96.15** (MicroOne); **97.1** (Cienpies Design); **150.1** (Markus Wissmann); **155.1** (catwalker); **164.1** (Denis Makarenko); **165.1** (Matthias Wehnert); **170.2** (Bjoern Deutschmann); **251.1** (ph.FAB); **xx.3** (Jose Luis Pelaez Inc); **Online** (Andreas Mann); Stiftung Denkmal für die ermordeten Juden Europas, Berlin: **220.1, 220.2, 220.3, 220.4** (Marko Priske); Wikimedia Commons, San Francisco: **7.1** (Andreas Schwarzkopf); **236.2** (Public Domain); © D. Schoppen **39.1, 62.1, 62.2, 62.4, 62.5, 62.6, 62.7, 62.13, 62.14**; © dpa **66.1**; © EDEKA **101.1**; © Sabine Reinecke **157.1**; © Statista 2020 **162.1**

ZEIGEN

Cover.1 (Suzanne Tucker); **Cover.2** (Bokica);123RF.com, Nidderau: **49.2** (Roman Babakin); **50.1** (Leonid Andronov); AlliiertenMuseum, Berlin: **168.1** (Quelle: AlliiertenMuseum/U.S. Army; Copyright: Public Domain); aus Ulrike Rylance: Penny Pepper „;Alarm auf der Achterbahn";, Seiten 5, 139 und 140 von dtv junior, München 2015 mit freundlicher Genehmigung von dtv Verlagsgesellschaft mbH &Co. KG **29.1, 29.2**; Carlos Fernandez Laser **105.1**; Getty Images, München: **1.1** (fotokon); **3.1** (Sladic); **3.2** (raclro); **4.1** (da-vooda); **5.1, 16.1** (grebeshkovmaxim); **5.1, 16.2** (mehmetbuma); **5.5** (GreenTana); **8.1** (luminis); **8.2** (Hemera Technologies); **13.1, Online** (Thomas Barwick); **13.2** (Jetta Productions Inc); **13.3, Online** (Hill Street Studios); **14.4** (fcafotodigital); **15.3** (Thomas Tolstrup); **22.2** (blackred); **24.1, 164.2** (Nikada); **25.1** (simonkr); **25.2** (Imgorthand); **31.2** (Heath Korvola); **33.1** (Wolfgang Deuter); **33.1** (zizar2002); **34.1** (Leonid Andronov); **35.1** (ericsphotography); **40.1, 135.1** (Flashpop); **48.1** (TARIK KIZILKAYA); **49.1** (Jordan Siemens); **51.1** (Rostislavv); **51.2** (Alexander Hastov); **54.1** (izusek); **54.2** (ER Productions Limited); **54.3** (SelectStock); **54.4** (skynesher); **54.5** (Fertnig); **55.1** (Moyo Studio); **57.1, 70.1** (James O';Neil); **58.1** (PytyCzech); **59.1** (Orbon Alija); **59.2** (PredragImages); **59.3, Online** (Jose Luis Pelaez Inc); **59.4** (Alain Intraina); **60.1** (GrigoriosMoraitis); **62.1, Online** (Buena Vista Images); **64.1** (Pom669); **65.1, Online** (SolStock); **65.2** (georgeclerk); **65.3** (Tom Werner); **66.1** (Colin Anderson Productions pty ltd); **67.3; 67.4; 67.5; 67.6; 67.7; 67.8; 67.9; 67.10.3** (Omadbek Nabiev); **67.1, 67.11, 171.1, 173.1, Online,** (Hinterhaus Productions); **67.2** (David Trood); **67.14; 67.16, 67.12; 67.15; 67.19, 67.17, 86.1, 164.4** (Willie B. Thomas); **67.13; 67.18.6** (James Silver); **70.1** (Stanislaw Pytel); **70.1** (iamnoonmai); **70.2** (Micha Pawlitzki); **73.2** (PopsaArts); **74.1; Online** (jotily); **79.1** (Marilyn Nieves); **79.2** (Noel Hendrickson); **79.3** (Zero Creatives); **79.4** (MoMo Productions); **80.1** (Klaus Vedfelt); **80.2** (Walker and Walker); **80.3** (drbimages); **80.4** (marcogarrincha); **81.1** (FrozenShutter); **82.1, 83.1, Online,** (SDI Productions); **91.1, 164.5** (Morsa Images); **94.1** (Roy Morsch); **96.1** (JLGutierrez); **100.1** (AntonChalakov); **104.1, 111.2** (TommL); **108.1** (Rowan Jordan); **109.1** (fotyma); **110.1, Online** (Tara Moore); **111.1** (mixetto); **116.1, 116.2** (suteishi); **117.1** (timnewman); **126.1** (Nick David); **126.1** (Rakdee); **133.1** (Vesnaandjic); **137.1** (clu); **138.1** (Sora-Tobi); **140.2** (Bettmann); **142.1** (amriphoto); **144.1, Online** (peepo); **144.2** (Blaine Harrington III); **144.3, Online** (WIN-Initiative); **145.1** (Thomas_EyeDesign); **146.1** (Spauln); **156.1** (ljubaphoto); **158.1** (kokouu); **158.2, Online** (fizkes); **162.1; Online** (EMS-FORSTER-PRODUCTIONS); **163.1** (GreenPimp); **164.3, Online** (martin-dm); **169.2** (Ariel Skelley); **172.1** (Shana Novak); **Online, 161.1** (Dimitri Otis); **Online** (AJ_Watt); **Online** (AndreyPopov); **Online** (AnnaNahabed); **Online** (AntonioGuillem); **Online** (Arctic-Images); **Online** (Bennett); **Online** (Chalffy); **Online** (David Malan); **Online** (DisobeyArt); **Online** (DjelicS); **Online** (DragonImages); **Online** (ELizabethHoffmann); **Online** (Eike Leppert); **Online** (Eugenio Marongiu); **Online** (EvgeniyShkolenko); **Online** (Ezra Bailey); **Online** (FilippoBacci); **Online** (Guido Cozzi/Atlantide Phototravel); **Online** (Jekaterina Nikitina); **Online** (John Banagan); **Online** (Leonard Mc Lane); **Online** (LightFieldStudios); **Online** (Luis Alvarez); **Online** (Michael Duva); **Online** (Owen Franken); **Online** (PeopleImages); **Online** (Peter Cade); **Online** (Poike); **Online** (Richard Drury); **Online** (RomoloTavani); **Online** (SIphotography); **Online** (Sekundemal); **Online** (Siegfried Layda); **Online** (Sisoje); **Online** (Stadtratte); **Online** (Steve Mason); **Online** (Stockbyte); **Online** (VisionsofAmerica/Joe Sohm); **Online** (Wavebreakmedia Ltd); **Online** (Worawee Meepian); **Online** (champc); **Online** (cobalt); **Online** (dk_photos); **Online** (eclipse_images); **Online** (fergregory); **Online** (golero); **Online** (gong hangxu); **Online** (gpointstudio); **Online** (hsyncoban); **Online** (jhorrocks); **Online** (kajakiki); **Online** (kali9); **Online** (kontrast-fotodesign); **Online** (manfredxy); **Online** (mbbirdy); **Online** (mgkaya); **Online** (miodrag ignjatovic); **Online** (mmpile); **Online** (rarrarorro); **Online** (recep-bg); **Online** (smiltena); **Online** (spreephoto.de); **Online** (stock-eye); **Online** (sturti); **Online** (style-photography); **Online** (track5); **Online** (vgabusi); **Online** (vgajic); **Online** (vm); **Online** (volkansengor); **Online.1** (FatCamera); **Online.1** (RelaxFoto.de); Heinrich Hoffmann / Public domain **Online, 147; Online.1**; Klett-Archiv, Stuttgart: **6.1, 6.2** (Friedemann Weidauer); kraftfoto / Alamy Stock Foto **99.1**; Maria Reger **22.1**; Mit freundlicher Genehmigung des Hartford Chorale **Online, 169.1**; picture alliance/BREUEL-BILD **97.1**; picture alliance/nordphoto nph/Kurth **175.2**; picture alliance/REUTERS **Online**; picture-alliance, Frankfurt: **Online** (Geisler-Fotopress); Ravensburger Verlag **71.1**; Sabrina Richmann Fotografie **149.1**; Shutterstock, New York: **2.1** (Palau); **92.1** (Fabrizio Andrea Bertani); **Online** (lev radin); **Online** (photocrew1); Susanne Böhme Fallschirmsport, Karlsruhe: **39.1, 38, Online.1**; Swatch Drive-Thru Store in Biel, Schweiz **Online**; Wikimedia Commons (Benutzer: Krummbein123; https://creativecommons.org/licenses/by-sa/3.0/) **31.2**; www.franknuernberger.de **90.1**; © Barbara Sigg **53.1**; © BFS 2019 **50.1**; © Bundesministerium für Familie, Senioren, Frauen und Jugend; aus: „;25 Jahre Deutsche Einheit - Gleichstellung und Geschlechtergerechtigkeit in Ostdeutschland und Westdeutschland"; **16.1**; © CERN **45.1**; © D. Schoppen **21.1**; © dpa - Fotoreport **95.1**; © dpa - Report **140.1**; © Edith Held **101.1**; © Statista 2020 **77.1**

Alle Bilder, die mit „**Online**" gekennzeichnet sind, erscheinen nur in der digitalen Ausgabe des Arbeitsbuchs (Blink Learning).

Authentic Texts and Copyrights

LERNEN

S. 19, 20: Katja Hildebrand: „Zwischen uns die Mauer" © 2006 Thienemann in der Thienemann-Esslinger Verlag GmbH, Stuttgart
S. 25 aus „Natürliches Maß", Seite 40f. © DER SPIEGEL 34/1969
S. 33: Textauszug aus „Das neue „Wir" ohne uns" auf www.deutschlandfunkkultur.de © Azadê Peşmen
S. 66: „TÜV (Technischer Überwachungsverein)", Erstveröffentlichung auf www.hanisauland.de, Autorin: Christiane Toyka-Seid, Herausgeber: Bundeszentrale für politische Bildung/bpb

ZEIGEN

S. 10: Auszug aus der Rangliste „Die 200 Idole der Deutschen" auf www.stern de, basierend auf einer forsa-Umfrage im Auftrag des STERN
S. 11: Katja Hildebrand: „Zwischen uns die Mauer", S 92 © 2006 Thienemann in der Thienemann-Esslinger Verlag GmbH, Stuttgart
S. 14: Zitate aus Artikel „Ich bin nicht männerfeindlich" von Helena Ott vom 13.03.2018 auf www.sz.de © Süddeutsche Zeitung
S. 17: Hörtext erstellt unter Zuhilfenahme von Ergebnissen aus dem „Sozialreport 2014" des SFZ e.V. (Sozialwissenschaftliches Forschungszentrum Berlin-Brandenburg)
S. 17: aus Gedicht „grenzenlos und unverschämt. ein gedicht gegen die deutsche sch-einheit" von May Ayim aus „weitergehen" © Orlanda Verlag, Berlin 2018, S. 65
S. 24: Hörtext basiert auf Zahlen und Fakten von www.oktoberfest-besuch.de von Edition Sportiva
S. 29: Seitenauszug aus Ulrike Rylance: „Penny Pepper Alarm auf der Achterbahn", Seiten 139 und 140 von dtv junior, München 2015 mit freundlicher Genehmigung von dtv Verlagsgesellschaft mbH &Co. KG
S. 35: vereinfachter Textauszug aus „Achterbahn" auf https://klexikon.zum.de/wiki/Achterbahn unter der Lizenz https://creativecommons.org/licenses/by-sa/3.0/de/
S. 38: Auszug aus „Wir sind nicht alle Draufgänger" (FAZ.NET vom 27.12.2016 von Sebastian Eder) © Alle Rechte vorbehalten. Frankfurter Allgemeine Zeitung GmbH, Frankfurt. Zur Verfügung gestellt vom Frankfurter Allgemeine Archiv.
S. 41: aus Beitrag „Vom Manager zum Obdachlosen" des Deutschlandfunks Kultur, Moderation: Susanne Führer
S. 42: Daten und Fakten aus dem Medscape „Global Physicians' Burnout and Lifestyle Comparisons" auf https://www.medscape.com © Tim Locke, UK Editor, Medscape / WebMD LLC
S. 71: aus „Die Wolke" von Gudrun Pausewang © Ravensburger Verlag GmbH, Ravensburg; vereinfachte Form aus der Serie „Easy Readers" (Seiten 21,23)© Alinea Verlag, Dänemark
S. 97: Statistiken auf Grundlage von Daten der Bundesanstalt Statistik Österreich © STATISTIK AUSTRIA
S. 102: www.kaleidos.de - Deutsch lernen mit kurzen Postings für Lehrende und Lernende aller Niveaustufen. Lehrmaterial, Sprechanlässe und Impulse zum alltäglichen Leben im deutschsprachigen Raum.
S. 147: Heinrich Hoffmann, „Der Struwwelpeter" (Übersetzung von Mark Twain)
S. 150: Auszug aus „„Kirchenasyl" für die Stolpersteine?" von Klaus Pesch vom 27.09.13 auf www.rundschau-online.de / Lokalredaktion Euskirchen © DuMont Mediengruppe GmbH & Co. KG
S. 158: Auszug aus DIE AMERIKANER, Musik & Text: Bodo Wartke; © Reimkultur GmbH & Co. KG, Hamburg / Alle Rechte vorbehalten!; www.bodowartke.de

Audio Material

Aufnahmeleitung: Katharina Theml, Büro Z, Wiesbaden
Produktion: Andreas Nesic, custom music, Stuttgart
Sprecher: Robert Atzlinger, Dorothea Baltzer, Irene Baumann, Marit Beyer, Chantal Busse, Dominik Eisele, Anuschka Herbst, Alistair Mehne, Maximilian Mehne, Lola Moos, Stephan Moos, Mario Pitz, Lotta Rojas, Corinne Steudler, Elisa Taggert

Zugehört-Interviews: Nicole Coleman, Stine Eckert

Video Material

Konzept und Aufnahmeleitung: Niko Tracksdorf
Produktion: Ernst Klett Sprachen GmbH
Redaktion & Regie: Niko Tracksdorf
Postproduktion: Ernst Klett Sprachen GmbH
Musik: Marcel Schechter
Mitwirkende: Mahdi Ghalandari, Marie Kieß, Jana Murosová, Li Peng, Charlotte Pfeil, Lorenz Pfeil, Jan Stein, Nardos Tecle

NOTES

NOTES

NOTES